3ºº

D1361748

HERO

AN ORAL HISTORY OF THE OKLAHOMA HEALTH CENTER

Bob Hardy

HERO

an oral history of the
Oklahoma Health Center

by Robert C. Hardy

BY ROBERT HARDY

SICK: How People Feel About Being Sick and What They Think of Those Who Care For Them. 1978.
FREEWOMAN. (A novella). 1984.
HERO: An Oral History of the Oklahoma Health Center, 1964-1984. 1985.

Copyright © 1985
Robert C. Hardy

All rights reserved. No part of this book may be reproduced or utilized in any form or by any means, electronic or mechanical, including photocopying and recording, or by any informational storage and retrieval system, without permission from the author.

Manufactured in the United States of America.
ISBN: 0-86546-067-1

For Jim Dennis

"The right man
  at the right time."

ACKNOWLEDGEMENTS

Having been engaged in the planning and development of the Oklahoma Health Center for eighteen and a half of the twenty years this history covers, I identified closely with the events which took place. But it was my wife Ann who suggested that I talk with the people who were involved to learn their attitudes and reactions to these events. Perhaps this story explains some of the motivations for the way the health campus was built. I am grateful for Ann's idea and her encouragement during the three years this project required.

Without the gracious cooperation of the 154 people who are quoted, this story would not have been possible. Others who proved valuable insights but were not specifically mentioned include Roy Allen, Ed.D., William Bross, Janis Edwards, Dan Lane, M.D., Ph.D., Charles McDermott, Bob Nichols, Raymond Parr, Esther Pahlka, Vivian Smith, Ph.D., and Charles Smith, M.D.

I appreciate the guidance and editing talents of Dr. Kenny A. Franks, Editor-in-Chief, Oklahoma Heritage Association, who taught me about the way histories are written.

Historian Paul Sharp, Ph.D., president emeritus of the University of Oklahoma, read the manuscript and gave me valuable assistance.

Barbara James Tuttle, executive secretary of the University of Oklahoma Board of Regents, kindly reviewed portions of this material against University records.

I also thank two officers of the Oklahoma Health Sciences Foundation: Dean A. McGee, Chairman of the Executive Committee, who authorized this project, and Vice President Stanton L. Young for his recognition of its possible value.

Robert C. Hardy
June, 1985

CONTENTS

AN ORAL HISTORY OF THE OKLAHOMA HEALTH CENTER

INTRODUCTION

This is the story of the Oklahoma Health Center, a cluster of medical institutions located on a single campus in Oklahoma City. It may be, as Rainey Williams, M.D., described it in 1983, "the best kept secret in Oklahoma."[1]

In medical circles, the Oklahoma Health Center would be identified as an "academic, tertiary health care center." In plain language, that is a group of hospitals and other health organizations surrounding a university medical school and other educational programs in the health sciences. That is the reason for the term "academic." "Tertiary" means that many people treated in such a center have unusual or complicated health problems which require a high level of medical expertise. "Tertiary" is the third level of a somewhat arbitrary and theoretical system of health services. Primary health care refers to general or family medical services for the routine, everyday health problems such as cuts and bruises, the flu and "red ears" (otitis) from which children often suffer. Secondary health services involve the estimated 15 percent of cases which family practitioners refer to specialists in particular fields because the patient's problem requires more expert management. These specialists are the general surgeons, orthopedists, ophthalmologists, gynecologists, pediatricians and so on.

On the next level, tertiary health care is provided by those esoteric disciplines involving satellite or super specialties like pediatric orthopedics, retinal ophthalmology and neuropsychiatry. In academic, tertiary health care centers, medical research results move from the laboratory bench to the bedside, new treatments are developed and the science of medicine moves forward. Procedures like open heart surgery, kidney dialysis and organ transplants were developed in university medical centers. The Oklahoma Health Center has three broad responsibilities: the education of health professionals—physicians, dentists, nurses, pharmacists and other members of the health team; the care of sick people with more complicated medical problems; and the search for new knowledge through basic and clinical medical research. In addition, as William L. Parry, M.D., head of the department of urology in the O.U. College of Medicine pointed out, academic medical centers must constantly look to the future. They have the responsibility for the development of medical leaders and for the continuing education of health professionals. They are obligated to alleviate health problems affecting their community and to communicate with the public about medical matters.[2]

There are several reasons the Oklahoma Health Center is not well known. Although the University of Oklahoma Medical School has existed since 1910 and "Old Main," the University Hospital built in 1919, has come and gone, the second surge of construction and growth which resulted in the Oklahoma Health Center began only 17 years ago, in 1968. In the life cycle of academic, tertiary health care centers, the Oklahoma Health Center is a mere youngster.[3]

Second, the Oklahoma Health Center is located on the "wrong" side of town. It is on the near, northeast side which has long since ceased to be the preferred residential area. Through the 1920s and 1930s, the northeast quadrant of Oklahoma City claimed the residence of many of the capital city's leaders. Since World War II, though, the movement of money and influence has been toward the northwest and the Santa Fe Railroad tracks have become a north-south Mason-Dixon line, separating the black community from the rest of the city. This line is slowly blurring as civil rights legislation and changing attitudes permit integration of formerly all-white neighborhoods and urban renewal efforts stimulate relocation.

But tradition dies deliberately. Many people who work in downtown Oklahoma City, commuting daily from outlying residential areas, travel the Broadway Extension southward and cross 13th Street, but never venture the half mile east to the Oklahoma Health Center. They may have some vague notion that "the medical center's over there somewhere" but have no occasion to visit. Dr. Williams, the chairman of the department of surgery at the College of Medicine, lives in Nichols Hills which is on the northwest side of the city and he knows the extent of Oklahoma Health Center unawareness among his friends and neighbors. This is a problem in Oklahoma City; it is a significantly greater problem in Tulsa, Ardmore, Beaver, Gotebo and Idabel.

Perhaps this history will help people of Oklahoma understand where much of their tax money has gone

Dr. William Parry makes a point about the many responsibilities of medical educators. (University of Oklahoma)

and where it goes each year. Hopefully, it also will give them a better appreciation of the Oklahoma Health Center, thus making them aware of its importance to the health future of every person in the state.

The name Oklahoma Health Center is not a household word. In fact, a third reason for the relative obscurity of the health campus is the confusion surrounding the name. For years, when the only health institution located on Northeast 13th Street was the university, its several buildings were known as the University of Oklahoma Medical Center. In the 1940s and 1950s, when the Oklahoma Medical Research

Foundation and the Veterans Administration Hospital put their footings down along the same street, the trend toward a multi-institutional health campus was begun, portending the Oklahoma Health Center. But the area was still called "the Med. Center".

In 1965, the Articles of Incorporation of the Oklahoma Health Sciences Foundation, formed to assist the development of the proposed multi-institutional health campus, described the project and named it the Oklahoma Health Center. The name of the University Medical Center remained the same. There was some confusion, of course, having a medical center within a health center, but the university was seen as the nucleus of the total cell called the Oklahoma Health Center and it was assumed the public would understand.

In 1972, this modest confusion of names became total confusion, a state which has remained ever since. Leonard P. Eliel, M.D., executive vice president and director of the O.U. Medical Center, decided it would better reflect the intent and activities of the university if the medical center were renamed the O.U. Health Sciences Center. He also believed this title would enhance the grant applications then being submitted to the U. S. Department of Health, Education and Welfare for capital funds under the Health Professions Educational Assistance Program. After all, nursing and dentistry and public health and allied health professions were involved along with medicine, and Dr. Eliel thought the new title would more accurately indicate the scope of the university's program in the health sciences.

The new title did not enhance public understanding of the emerging Oklahoma Health Center, however. Even the press did not understand the difference between the "health center" and the "health sciences

center." Reporters still use the terms interchangeably. When Donald B. Halverstadt, M.D., became interim provost of the University of Oklahoma Health Sciences Center on November 1, 1979, he did not comprehend the difference, asking "where that Oklahoma Health Center name came from." As late as 1983, C.G. Gunn, M.D., professor of internal medicine and a member of the faculty since 1956, asked who came up with the name Oklahoma Health Center. He observed that it was too much like the official name of the University of Oklahoma at Oklahoma City, the O.U. Health Sciences Center. And of course, he was right. Also in 1983, a classified advertisement for an EKG (electrocardiograph) supervisor, placed in the *Sunday Oklahoman* by the Oklahoma City Clinic, noted that the clinic is "in the Health Science Center." The word "science" should not be used at all to refer to the entire Oklahoma Health Center campus and if it is used to refer to the University of Oklahoma's part of the campus, the plural form of the word should be used.[4]

To add to the confusion of names, the Veterans Administration Hospital became the Veterans Administration Medical Center on September 6, 1978. This new policy originated in Washington, D.C., so the local director could not have resisted the change just because it added to the confusion in Oklahoma City. Also, three separate buildings on campus house the university's Speech and Hearing Center and the Department of Human Services' Child Study Center and the Pauline Mayer Children's Center. Tucked around in various campus buildings are five other centers: Breast Cancer Screening Center, Cystic Fibrosis Center, Oklahoma Cancer Center, Poison Control Center and the Sleep Disorders Center.

Nobody can decide what to do about this confusion

Sign at the Byers Exit from I-40 directs motorists to the Oklahoma Health Center. (OHSF Collection)

of names. In 1979, representatives of several Oklahoma Health Center institutions spent six months trying to devise a more descriptive and distinctive way to identify this cluster of health organizations. They failed.

The graphics on Interstates 35 and 40 at Oklahoma City direct travelers to the Oklahoma Health Center. The signs at the campus use the official and proper term. It is the people who get confused, particularly the people who work on the campus and have been through many of the name changes..., the people who have been there the longest.

Unlike most histories, many of the principal characters in this story were available to relate their personal experiences and their reaction to the events of the past two decades. To a great extent, *Hero* is an oral history and therefore departs somewhat from the traditional format. Quotations are used extensively to convey the attitudes and feelings of the people who influenced and were influenced by the growth of the Oklahoma Health Center. History is more compre-

hensible when the reader learns the mindset, motivations and the pressures besetting the people who made the events happen. A wide spectrum of opinion is presented in this story; the truth lies somewhere between these differing points of view.

This story covers 20 years, from 1964 when James L. Dennis, M.D., was appointed dean of the medical school and Director of the O.U. Medical Center. It traces the development of the Oklahoma Health Center from the time there were 3 institutions, 3 schools, 900 students and 8 buildings on 24 acres until the present, when there are 12 institutions, 7 colleges, more than 3,000 students and 34 buildings on 200 acres. But the physical growth of the campus and the expansion of the student body are only part of the story. The real story is the effort and experience of the many people who helped put the Oklahoma Health Center together and who once served or still serve the health needs of the people of Oklahoma. While the title *Hero* is an acronym for "Health and Education for a Richer Oklahoma" and identifies a 1968 state bond issue, in many ways the tale which follows is a saga of heroic deeds.

PART ONE

THE OLD DAYS: 1964-1965

CHAPTER 1
SEARCH FOR A LEADER: 1964

The ladies of the Child Welfare Committee of the American Legion invited him. The Ponca City, Oklahoma group wanted a specialist to speak to them so they chose a professor of pediatrics at the University of Arkansas College of Medicine in Little Rock. In addition to being a child specialist, he was also associate dean for clinical services…an authority. They liked that.

James L. "Jim" Dennis, M.D., looked the part. He had just turned 50 and had the quiet, kindly manner which inspired immediate confidence in mothers who were worried about their babies. His gentleness with kids kept them from becoming frightened. His once-dark hair was graying and his small, well-trimmed moustache was almost white. He smoked a pipe. Although he was not an extremely large man, he had sufficient girth to give him a fatherly appearance, a look he came by naturally, having three teen-agers of his own at home. The friendly, solicitous tone of his voice and the warmth of his manner convinced those about him that Jim Dennis was a caring and competent healer. He described that meeting in Ponca City:

> The committee was mostly women and they were supportive of children's programs. I was hoping to get something for our department at the medical school. There was a lady there who perked up when she heard I was a graduate of Oklahoma. Afterward, she told me they had been looking for a dean for the medical school for a long time and she said, "You're an associate dean; have you applied?" I said, "No, you don't apply to become dean in an academic situation. They have to invite you." I found out since a lot of people *do* apply but I don't think that's appropriate. She said she was a good friend of Dr. Malcom E. Phelps and she knew he was important in the state medical association and probably had something to do with the search committee. "I'm going to see him," she said.[1]

Dr. Phelps was in private practice in El Reno, Oklahoma and, although he was not on the search committee, he and his colleagues were concerned about the philosophy of the University of Oklahoma Medical School. It was producing mostly specialists and researchers when the critical need was for family practitioners in the smaller communities throughout the state. As the doctor recalled, he and his fellow

James L. Dennis…pediatrician, visionary, planner, leader.
(University of Oklahoma)

practitioners "felt as welcome in the halls of the medical school as they would if they had been wandering in the vaults of the First National Bank." As it turned out, Dr. Phelps had known Jim Dennis for a number of years.[2]

The relationship between the university's full-time faculty and the practicing physicians in the area was indeed strained. Allergist Robert S. Ellis, M.D., worked closely with the university and thus he could see both points of view:

> A lot of doctors in Oklahoma City had the feeling the Medical Center shouldn't expand because they looked at it as a source of real competition. I remember very clearly in the late 1950s the tremendous animosity which developed between a lot of the practicing physicians and the new full-time heads of departments like Dr. Stewart Wolf and Dr. John Schilling. They viewed them, and

particularly Dr. Jim Merrill, as threats to their practice. They felt the full-time men had an unfair advantage in that their offices and staff were paid for by public funds and they were able to see private patients. Many strong people like Stewart Wolf and Pete Riley and Jim Merrill just made enemies because they were so positive, so action-oriented. They could make people mad even if they didn't want to![3]

Filling the position of dean of a college of medicine is quite an involved process. With the appointment of a search committee consisting primarily of faculty members, there begins an intricate series of steps, a kind of academic ritual, which usually takes months and not infrequently requires more than a year, depending on the marketplace. If private enterprise took as long to appoint new leadership, there would undoubtedly be more business failures than there are, but in academia, the selection process is highly democratic and thus quite time consuming.

The members of the search committee solicit names of candidates for the deanship from their colleagues. Curricula vitae are collected from eligible and interested persons. These are studied and discussed at length. The list is narrowed to a manageable number of front-runners sufficiently qualified and attractive to be invited to the campus for a visit. Each of these finalists then goes through a rigorous round of appointments, interviews and conferences. This takes days. Every department head and administrative person who might be affected by the new leadership and who is sufficiently important to be asked for an opinion is listed on the candidate's interview schedule. Tours of the campus and the city are conducted to explain the advantages of the area and show off the academic environment. There are breakfast meetings, luncheons, receptions and dinners, even meetings on into the night. The president of the university, who must make the final decision, is usually the last stop in this marathon course. The search committee may rank the candidates, make an outright recommendation or may submit the names of the top candidates without selection.

The campus visit is quite an exercise for a healthy person. When Dennis received an invitation to come to Oklahoma City for interviews, he had been out of the hospital only a week following gall bladder surgery and, as he put it, "I was feeling pretty shaky." Dr. Leonard Eliel, then president of the Oklahoma Medical Research Foundation (OMRF), was chairman of the search committee. Dr. Dennis described his visit:

When I got there, they had a four-day schedule for me, beginning at seven o'clock in the morning and going through dinner, something every hour. It was fascinating. The faculty members were interested in my attitude toward fundamental academic concerns. I understood those and apparently answered their questions satisfactorily. At the tail end of the visit, Mark Johnson [an internist and a member of the O. U. Board of Regents] picked us up and drove us to George Cross's Hall Park suburban home in Norman [Oklahoma]. Virginia [Mrs. James Dennis] was with us as was Mark's lovely wife.[1]

As George L. Cross, Ph.D., president of the University of Oklahoma, explained, no cocktails were served in the president's home in the mid 1960s. When he had guests who would enjoy a cocktail, he entertained them out there so there would be no embarrassment to the university.[5]

The president plied me with liquor, a little food and a lot of questions. We had a good time. Dr. Cross asked, "If you were running the medical school, what would you do?" I told him I was concerned about the quality of medical education which I felt was more and more becoming dependent on public support and I didn't think we were going to get public support unless we were responsive to public needs. I said there was a great opportunity here, the kind I would like to have.

I felt we needed to get involved with some of the community hospitals and we needed to pay attention to primary care.... We called it general medicine then. And certainly, we *had* to have some modern facilities. One of the things that shocked me when I went through the University Hospital on that visit was that it hadn't improved since I was a student there, 25 or 30 years before. It had deteriorated! There were wards for 27 men, mostly elderly patients, and only one latrine. The urinal was a hole in the floor with a tin drain. It smelled of ammonia.... The odors which pervaded the place were terrible.

I told Dr. Cross, "Oklahoma is my home and O.U. is my alma mater and before I die, I'd like to see that it is good enough that we can brag about it." It was very exciting as we sat and talked about it. I got the feeling Mark and Dr. Cross thought these were worthy goals and that they were important enough that we could get the financial support to achieve them.

I sensed very quickly that George Cross was a winning man and a great guy to work with. I had not known him before. He asked me right on the spot if I'd take the job. I said I thought I probably would take it but first I'd have to go back and talk with President David Mullins and Dean Win Shorey because I'd promised them I wouldn't do anything until I talked with them.

The O.U. Medical Center as it appeared in 1964 when Jim Dennis visited the campus of his alma mater. (University of Oklahoma)

I thought Dr. Cross understood. The next morning, Virginia and I were driving back to Arkansas. About noon, as we were approaching Fort Smith, we heard a newscast that Dr. Cross had given a commencement address and announced that at last O.U. had a new dean for the school of medicine. He gave my name![6]

As Dr. Dennis told this story, he laughed and shook his head. "Oh, boy! George was a good salesman." The search committee had recommended Dr. Dennis for the deanship but, as President Cross said:

I was so enthusiastically in favor of him, I would probably have hung in there for him had they recommended someone else. He was so obviously competent and exactly what we needed. As a matter of fact, he delayed my retirement for quite a while. I sensed a certain nervousness about the position on Jim's part because a number of physicians in the city had signed a petition asking that Dr. Newt Stone be named the dean. He was a very popular physician, active in medical school affairs. Dr. Dennis might have been additionally concerned with a change in the administration of the University on the Norman campus. I had planned to retire about the time Jim got here but stayed on for four years, until June 30, 1968. I got so interested in Jim's plans to develop the medical center, I stuck around to try to help.[7]

Mark R. Johnson, M.D., as chairman of the Medical Center Committee, was proxy for the O.U. Board

George L. Cross, Ph.D., was president of the University of Oklahoma for a quarter of a century. (University of Oklahoma)

Dr. Mark Johnson (center), the only physician on the O. U. Board of Regents, had a special interest in getting the right man as dean and director of the Medical Center. (University of Oklahoma)

Popular Samuel Newton "Newt" Stone, clinical professor of surgery, was a front-running candidate for the deanship. (University of Oklahoma)

of Regents in negotiating with Dr. Dennis and discussing the appointment with President Cross. He recalled the circumstances this way:

I felt an urgency based on our desire to terminate a mounting campaign to name Dr. Stone as dean. There were some unpleasant characteristics of that campaign which were generating ill will and accomplishing nothing. Jim was a real dark-horse until, ironically, the anti-Dennis campaigners began to bring him more and more to my attention. Here was a native Oklahoman who had acquired some prestige in academia and was also familiar with the private practice of medicine. He was a beautiful combination of the talents we needed, although I wasn't really impressed with his administrative accomplishments. He was the most promising of an original list of 16 candidates which was reduced to 10 or 11 when those who would not consider the position were screened out.

From the appointment of the search committee to that evening with Jim in Dr. Cross's home was maybe a little over a year. The pressure was incredible and I was losing patience with Len Eliel, but I couldn't tell him what I was experiencing because I didn't want to manipulate any of the search committee's activities. I couldn't go to him and say, "Hey, Len, these guys are giving me the hot-foot every day and, man, you've got to do something!" That meeting with Jim Dennis was like an answer to a prayer.[8]

Because Oklahoma had not had to recruit a director of the medical center for a long time, salary was a problem. Governor Henry Bellmon was paid $25 thousand a year, which was the same as the salary of President George Cross, but the average of medical school deans and directors around the country was $40 thousand. Apparently the ceiling for state employees in Oklahoma was well established. As Dennis recalled:

They finally gave me $25 thousand a year my first year there, which was the same thing I was making in Arkansas as professor of pediatrics and associate dean. I believe Dr. Everett was on the payroll for $17 or $18 thousand, in that range, so they had to make a $7 or $8 thousand increase. Come the second year, when they felt they needed to reward what was developing and give me a raise, it would have put my salary above the president's. George Cross quickly found that every time I got a raise, he got one, too.[9]

But Governor Bellmon's salary did not go up when Dr. Dennis got a raise. The legislature set the governor's salary at $25 thousand, effective in 1961, and it was not raised again (to $35 thousand) until David Hall became chief executive in 1971.

Dr. Dennis was correct. There was great opportunity in his home state. Born and raised in Britton, Oklahoma, now a suburb of Oklahoma City, he had an intuitive understanding of the people and their pressing need for health services. Because he had spent many years in private practice and was then in academic medicine, he was sensitive to the requirements of each. It was quite apparent to Jim Dennis that Oklahomans could get the health care they needed and deserved only if there were a lot more doctors, nurses, dentists, technicians and other health professionals in the state. In the mid-1960s, shortages were everywhere. The federal government estimated the nationwide shortage of physicians at 50,000. The demand for nurses had exceeded the supply since the beginning of World War II. In every category of health manpower, there was serious understaffing.[10]

The central mission of the University of Oklahoma Medical Center was to improve the health of the people in the state. As Dr. Dennis pointed out, "Health care is trained people at work," so the way to carry out that mission was to increase the supply of health manpower, and womanpower, in the state. The idea was to educate health professionals on an expanded, multi-institutional health campus in Oklahoma City and encourage them to go to every corner of Oklahoma to take care of people when they got sick.

The four days of interrogation, touring and entertainment may have seemed long to Dr. Dennis but it was a woefully inadequate period in which to learn the politics and perversities of that complex medical center. Had he been completely aware of the problems he would face, the nervousness Dr. Cross sensed in him might have been more apparent. And he might have declined the challenge.

The small medical faculty and the deterioration of the University Hospitals strongly signalled chronic underfunding. Other elements of the situation were not so obvious. The relationship between the medical center and the State Regents for Higher Education was, to put it kindly, strained. The medical school departments were so decentralized, they were sometimes referred to as independent fiefdoms. In the effort to build a better medical school by developing full-time faculty, town physicians like Dr. Phelps had become estranged from the academic doctors. Federal officials who held the key to capital financing of new educational buildings were quite contemptuous of Oklahoma's ability to qualify for assistance.

CHAPTER 2
TRANSITION: 1952-1964

E.T. Dunlap, Ed.D., became chancellor of the Oklahoma State Regents for Higher Education on July 1, 1961, 20 years after the Oklahoma system of higher education had been created by an amendment to the state constitution. Originally, Governor Leon C. "Red" Phillips had forced this amendment through the legislature in an effort to coordinate higher education and stabilize personnel in the state's colleges and universities. The solons and succeeding governors, however, did not like it because it limited their influence on appointments at these institutions. And not just presidents but faculty and janitors, clerks and yardmen. They still wanted to apply some subjective judgment as to the needs of "their institution," the one in their particular district. During the dust bowl days of the 1930s, Dr. Dunlap recalled, "A job was a job and people had to hustle...do anything to make a buck to put food on the table for their family." Thus, political patronage was extremely important to the legislators who could make jobs available and to the people who needed work. The practice extended into the 1940s.

The system of higher education was adopted in March, 1941, but it was July two years later before a chancellor was hired. A. M. Nash, LL.D., the president of Oklahoma College for Women at Chickasha (now the University of Science and Arts of Oklahoma), was elected to this position. As a group, the legislature seemed to want this office to function, but individual legislators certainly did not want it to affect the power they traditionally had enjoyed. Dr. Nash had a mammoth assignment—almost humanly impossible. A very able person, he recognized that his first priority was to hold the system together against considerable opposition in the legislature, which constantly attempted to abolish the Oklahoma system of higher education and repeal Article 13A of the Oklahoma Constitution.[1]

Dr. Dunlap, who was president of Eastern Oklahoma A and M College during the 1950s, remembered Dr. Nash's admonition:

[He told us,] "You presidents stay home, teach school, run your college and let this lay board represent you as a unit before the legislature!" The Board of Regents for Higher Education had broad responsibilities. It had to determine the functions and responsibilities of each in-

Chancellor E.T. Dunlap foresaw the dramatic challenge to higher education brought about by the launching of Sputnik I and the post-World War II baby boom. (University of Oklahoma)

stitution in the system, set educational standards and grant the degrees conferred by the colleges and universities. Its job was to recommend to the legislature the financial needs of the system. Then, under the constitution, the legislature was required to make a two-year appropriation of funds for higher education in consolidated form to the State Regents who in turn allocated the money to the various institutions according to their needs and functions.

The launching of Sputnik I by the Russians on October 15, 1957, dramatically influenced higher education in the United States. This first satellite was looked on by the people of the Western world as an indication the Russians had outstripped us in education, especially in science and technology. It created vigorous demand for change in American education. The National Defense Education Act was passed the very next year, in 1958, and was the first federal aid to education. In this bill were provisions to explore the objectives of education across the board. Of course, everyone had his notion about what was wrong with Western education and what should be done about it. A lot of money was appropriated for research by universities in the fields of science, mathematics and technologies.[2]

Dr. Nash was almost 70 years old when he retired in 1961. During his 18 years as chancellor, he had indeed held the system together and slowly the opposition to it had subsided. A generation of legislators and governors had to pass before there could be full acceptance of a coordinated system of higher education, a system which could achieve maximum effectiveness. Before the first Sputnik, only one third of Oklahoma's high school graduates went to college and only one third of those persisted to graduation. In mid-1961, there were 44,551 students enrolled in public colleges and universities and another 5,000 in Oklahoma's private schools, less than 50,000 in all. But that situation was soon to change. The percentage of high school graduates entering college had stepped up to 48 percent and soon the first youngsters born in the post-World War II baby boom would be knocking on the doors of Oklahoma's colleges and universities. As Dr. Dunlap remembered, "Looming out there was a drove, a deluge of applicants for higher education."[3]

At first, E. T. Dunlap turned down the job of chancellor, but Governor J. Howard Edmondson persuaded him to reconsider. Dr. Dunlap explained to the chief executive what should be done. "We need to study and plan. We not only must accommodate what is destined to be a doubling of the number of students in the decade of the sixties, but we must plan for significant changes in the educational programs we offer."

The legislature was still in session when the new chancellor assumed office. Dr. Dunlap's first job was to work with the legislators to get the appropriation for the biennium which had already begun. He requested and got an extra $150 thousand to create a research staff with which to begin planning. At that time, the total budget for all Oklahoma higher education was $42 million a year, of which $30 million was appropriated by the legislature. The following month, on August 17, 1961, the chancellor called all of Oklahoma's college and university presidents together:

> Here's what we've got, fellows. We're going to double enrollments in the 10 years ahead and we're going to be challenged to change what we do to the kids when we get them on the campus. They're not going to be happy with this old, staid curriculum we have today. By the mid sixties, with the infusion of great sums of money for research at universities, new knowledge will be brought forth which will affect our college programs. We are going to have to harness that new knowledge in remodeling our educational programs.

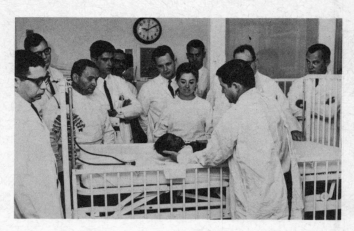

Pediatric residents surround Dr. Harris D. "Pete" Riley as he discusses a tiny patient in Children's Memorial Hospital. (University of Oklahoma)

So we assembled a research team of three and began our studies. First of all, we concluded that we Oklahomans were going to do these studies ourselves. Up to that point, the procedure had been to hire an expert to come in, make a study and tell you what to do. Then, whoever arranged for the study would put the report on the shelf and be done with it. Instead, we decided to bring specialists in from outside the state, pick their brains, pay them an honorarium and their expenses and send them back home!

We wrote a study plan which was published in the little blue book. It called for eight different studies. The first one was on admission standards, student enrollments and trends, projected to 1975. The next one was on faculty and faculty needs, also to 1975. The third had to do with facilities. We made an inventory of all buildings on all campuses and classified them as to need for remodeling, repair or demolition. We determined what we needed then and what we would need through 1975.

Our study on curriculum showed we were actually offering over 3,500 educational programs. We boiled those down so that today, with four times the enrollment we had then, we have fewer than 1,800 programs and they are really functioning. And we developed a system by which we keep them pertinent, relevant. Functions and goals for Oklahoma higher education made up another area of study. Governance and its improvement was also considered.

Then there was a special study. Because of the great demand and the evidence of great changes in medical science which would affect medical education, we decided we ought to do a special self-study on medical education in Oklahoma. By early 1964, we had completed four of the eight studies and we began the study on medical education.[1]

As Dr. Dennis came onto the Oklahoma scene in

September, 1964, preliminary planning for medical and other health science education was well under way. By contrast, planning for community health services was only beginning to take place and had not yet reached Oklahoma. The Hill-Burton program, which provided federal money for the construction of hospitals and health centers involved only institutional planning when local communities initiated non-profit projects in response to the need for additional hospital beds or clinic services in the area. This program had been operational since 1947 and in Oklahoma was under the direction of Paul Snelson of the Oklahoma State Department of Health. But to say there was real community health planning in Oklahoma in 1964 would be an exaggeration.

There was concern, though. Kirk Mosley, M.D., the Oklahoma Commissioner of Health in 1964, also was the head of the Organization of State and Territorial Health Officers. This group was worried about the future of public health efforts and recognized the need for broader health planning. About that time, there was some work going on by the National Commission on Community Health Services, a private corporation sponsored by the American Public Health Association and the National Health Council. Lee Holder, Ph.D., now dean of the College of Allied Health at the University of Oklahoma, was on the commission staff as director of the Community Action Studies Project. The commission's objective was to take a systematic look at all health care services from the community perspective. It was "deeply concerned with health and the urgency of closing the gap between what we know in the health sciences and what we do about preventing health hazards which threaten the life of modern man." The staff studied 21 communities from Massachusetts to California, including Enid, Oklahoma. One aim of this work was to get more attention on preventive health care and to help people understand that there are environmental conditions which cause illness. The now familiar environmental movement was just beginning.

In 1964, the commission was about midway through this four year study which resulted in a book, published in 1966 by the Harvard University Press, entitled *Health Is A Community Affair*. The awareness, however, of the need for community-based health planning was just beginning to seep into the consciousness of Oklahoma health professionals. The fact that James L. Dennis was an innovator and a conceptualizer, according to Dr. Cross, equipped him for the challenges ahead. As Jack Boyd, director of the Okla-

Mark R. Everett and Chief of Orthopedics Don H. O'Donoghue enjoy themselves at a faculty party honoring the dean in 1963. (University of Oklahoma)

homa Health Planning Commission, observed in 1983, "Doctor Dennis was the right man at the right time!"[5]

The medical school was in a period of marked transition. Like other state schools, particularly in the middle of the country, O.U. was converting to a full time clinical faculty. As Dr. Mark Johnson recalled:

Dr. Robert H. Bayley was the very first full-time, salaried chairman of the department of medicine. I remember the first lecture he gave us.... I was a junior medical student at the time...in 1945. The lecture he gave was absolutely brilliant! In fact, I still remember many of the things he actually said. As a cardiologist, Dr. Bayley's specialty was the diagnosis of myocardial eschemia and his approach was to cover first the non-cardiac causes of chest pain. Our entire class was stimulated by this brilliant, articulate presentation. Naturally, this created a lot of enthusiasm to develop the full-time professor concept.[6]

Louis Jolyon "Jolly" West, M.D., the first full-time professor of psychiatry at O.U., credits Mark R. Everett, Ph.D., the dean of the medical school preceding Dr. Dennis, with advancing the full-time faculty concept.

Mark Everett was a remarkable man. He had extraordinary vision and a very sound background in academic, high quality, Harvard-style values. He realized in the early fifties that if the University of Oklahoma School of Medicine was going to keep up with what was happening at all of the other good universities, and going back to 1912 at places like Hopkins and Harvard, there would have to be full-time faculty, full-time leadership in the clinical departments as well as the basic science departments. With his advisors, he laid out a timetable, department by department, for the changeover from the old, part-time model where the practitioners in the city ran the departments to the Hopkins-style full time clinical departments. Minnesota, where I had gone to medical school, had done it long before. Oklahoma was really one of the last to bite the bullet, so to speak. Mark Everett knew it had to come.

How he did this I am not sure, but he attracted one of the most brilliant and academically creative physicians to be chairman of medicine, Stewart Wolf. Stewart brought a number of "crackerjacks" with him. The dean decided that psychiatry would be next, then surgery and pediatrics and then Ob-Gyn...something like that. After three prominent psychiatrists had turned them down, the search committee decided maybe they ought to look for somebody younger because they weren't getting any of these well-established leaders. They jumped to somebody very young, namely myself. I was 29....This was in 1954.[7]

Stewart George Wolf, M.D., recalled his first impression of Oklahoma when he flew in from New York City:

In 1948, I was invited to give a talk at the American College of Physicians meeting being held in San Francisco. At that time, airplanes flew only halfway across the country, had to stop and refuel. My wife Virginia was with me and the plane stopped in Tulsa. In those days, you were allowed to get out of the plane and walk around on the tarmac. We got out and looked around. It was windy, flatter than a pancake and it looked like the middle of nowhere! We laughed and said, "Well, there are people who live out here, but I can't imagine anybody *wanting* to live here." Four years later, I was there! I went out in the fall of 1951. Dr. Everett picked me up at the door [of the Skirvin Hotel] and I was immediately taken by him, his enthusiasm, his intelligence and his vision. I had a wonderful visit. The search committee was an outstanding group of people, especially Bill Rucks [W.W. Rucks, M.D.]. They had in mind beefing up the educational program, bringing sort of a one-man show there. I explained that couldn't be done in the modern era and they'd have to develop a core of full-time people in medicine. It would have been impossible for one man to do the job. They were slow in absorbing that so when they offered me the post, I turned

The acknowledged leader of the emerging full time medical faculty at Oklahoma was Stewart G. Wolf, M.D. (University of Oklahoma)

it down. Then I got a telephone call from Dr. Everett saying they'd arranged for a second person to come on. Dr. Everett had a budget of only $725,000 for the entire medical school but what appealed to me at Oklahoma was that it was "wet clay."

I invited Bob Bird [Robert M. Bird, M.D.] who was also at New York Hospital, Cornell University, to have a sandwich and a martini at our apartment. I offered him the job at Oklahoma and he accepted it. He came out two weeks after I did. [Dr. Wolf arrived at the university on April 15, 1952.] In the early days, the two of us did everything. We actually put the old type of "partner's desk" in the office, facing each other, so we both knew exactly what was happening. The third person we brought on was John Colmore and Bill Schottstaedt was the next one.[8]

It was quite true that Dr. Everett did not have much money with which to operate a medical school. Lloyd E. Rader, the director of the Department of Public Welfare, learned this when he visited Children's Hospital at the dean's invitation:

When I found out that he didn't have the money to buy a typewriter, I loaned him one. I called Mr. Singleton in, my attorney for the department, and said, "I don't have time to research this but that med school down there...that dean, pardon my French, he hasn't got enough money to 'finance a sick whore for breakfast' and he's trying to run a medical school! Seems to me, while I may be hazy, somewhere in the law back there,

there's a provision for one department to loan another department equipment or even sell it to them at a reduced price." Mr. Singleton said, "Yeah, you're right, Lloyd." So we became very close friends [the dean and I]. I started out to be a doctor [once] so I've always had sympathy for medical education.[9]

Mark Johnson talked about the transition of the medical school:

To say the full-time faculty concept was an improvement is possibly an understatement but it also is an invitation to overstatement. The practicing physician who served as a professor in the clinical years brought a certain quality to his instruction and supervision which the full-time academician simply did not have. But it was a beautiful mix between the voluntary, practicing physician and the full-time faculty. Of course, the arrival of Stewart Wolf in 1952 polished the image of the full-time professor and brightened the future, convincing each of us we really needed to move quickly toward full-time clinical chairmen. But one of the pitfalls later recognized involved the many federal grants and funds coming from a variety of sources that could be assigned to "principal investigators." Those research funds went with the individual and began to distract and dilute the loyalties of some faculty members. I'm certainly not assigning this concern to Stewart Wolf because I had no anxieties about his allegiance to the mother institution.

Individuals with large grants would be sought after by other medical schools, not necessarily because of their skills as a researcher or a teacher…certainly not from the standpoint of their position as a role model…but because they would be dragging with them, say, a $3.5 million grant! Some of them became very independent, almost derogatory of the local setting. They went where they wanted to, when they wanted to; they virtually set their own schedule. They were almost like a one man institute. Because of their ability to win grants, the academicians who engaged in research were the ruling class; they were the sophisticated possessors of prestige. Classroom teaching and the skills associated with leading students to gain knowledge were simply, by a matter of relativity, being deprecated. All of the kudos, all of the honors, all of the media exposure…these were garnered by the research members of the clinical faculty.

By the early sixties, I was concerned this was going to cause some serious dislocations of effort and interest. My great worry was, because we were becoming a family of academicians, we were losing contact and visibility in the community of practicing physicians. We were beginning to have the isolation which is the basis of the notorious "town-gown syndrome."[10]

As the full-time faculty of the medical school grew,

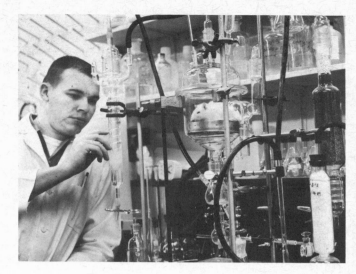

Biochemical research in the 1960s. Research Professor Marvin Shetlar's laboratory. (University of Oklahoma)

more and more operating funds were required but support from the legislature did not keep pace. As John Schilling, M.D., the third full-time department chairman and first one of surgery, remembered:

Our budget in 1956 for the whole department, including salaries for me and six others, was $35,000! We had to earn every damn cent above that. Essentially, the university provided only facilities and opportunity. I often wondered why people joined the department under those circumstances, except Mark Everett and all of us had great academic dreams. Each one of the individuals we had was like a one-man department of surgery, developing technical people and labs and so on.[11]

Dr. Parry learned about the medical school's financial constraints when he was interviewed in 1962 for the position of chief of urology:

Dr. Everett said he knew my department would generate a certain amount of money for [professional] services rendered but he did not want to know the details of that money. As the dean of the medical school, he had to appear before the legislature every year and petition for the budget and he did not want to go out there [to the state capitol] with any knowledge about finances relative to private practice. On the other hand, he said, "The School of Medicine doesn't have very much money and from time to time, I may need to come to you about borrowing money to get over an emergency."[12]

Mark Allen Everett, M.D., the son of the dean, recalled those early, full-time faculty leaders. "Wolf and West and Schilling were three young, idealistic, slightly maverick physicians who shared a great dream. Their

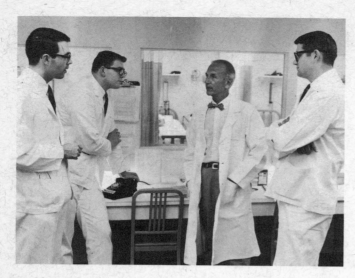

Chairman of Surgery John Schilling discusses a case with his residents in University Hospital, 1969. (University of Oklahoma)

enthusiasm was infectious and my father's response to that was very supportive. It was a fantastic group of people."[13]

The necessity to spend so much time treating private patients whose fee payments supported the department bred a feeling of financial independence among these full-time chairmen. They earned the money and they believed it belonged to the department. Although they deposited these funds in a departmental trust fund which was administered by the medical center, it was rumored that surgery had seven different bank accounts in the Oklahoma City area and nobody but the chairman knew where all the money was. The department chairmen did control the money deposited to their account in the trust fund and used it as they saw fit. Dr. Schilling continued:

We didn't have much money, but what we did have went into our academic enterprises. We didn't use it wrongly. I think sometimes we were able to accomplish more that way than with larger budgeted funds over which bureaucratic checks and balances keep you from doing anything with it. Mark was quite honest in this regard. Everything was done on faith and what you generated was yours. It was assumed you would use it honestly, the best you could.[14]

This situation frustrated Dr. E.T. Dunlap because he could not be sure what was going on in the medical school; he could not obtain the financial information to which he thought the State Regents for Higher Education were entitled. "We couldn't get any information from the medical center that had any validity. The data Raymond Crews [the Medical Center business administrator] gave us just wasn't believable."[15]

But from Raymond Crews viewpoint, it was a matter of Medical Center policy:

The basic conflict was over research grants from the National Institutes of Health and other sources. The [Medical Center] administrative attitude was that those research and training grants were made to the individual grantee to carry on his research and his program. The State Regents wanted that [money] included in the general budget of the institution so they could allocate it just as they allocated state appropriated funds but the university never agreed to that approach.

Another part of the problem: we never knew from month to month how much the Crippled Children's Commission or the Welfare Department was going to pay us. On three different occasions in late May or early June, Mr. Rader determined they were going to have substantial funds available and requested we bill for services we had provided. We'd get great big chunks of money—anywhere from $300 thousand to $600 thousand, which was a big sum in those days. This came in after we'd turned in our budget and the allocation had been made. Then, when we requested authority to spend it, the chancellor would want to know why we'd hid it and all of that.

We had absolutely no control over Mr. Rader and his money but we damn sure didn't turn any of it down! Lloyd Rader was the one member of the Crippled Children's Commission who was most supportive. He had a soft spot in his heart for Children's Hospital from the very beginning. As far as the help I got from him while I was running those hospitals, I have absolutely no complaint.[16]

While the chancellor was suspicious that departmental funds were not being used properly, this lack of trust seemed to be reciprocal. Dr. Schilling said, "None of us thought very highly of the government and the higher education thing there. Some of the things we stood for were in opposition to the Higher Regents."[17]

CHAPTER 3

OLD MAIN: 1964

When Dr. Dennis agreed to return to his alma mater as dean of the medical school and director of the O.U. Medical Center, he left a new University Hospital at Arkansas to assume responsibility for one which was 45 years old. In 1917, the Oklahoma Legislature made an important decision, choosing between the public ego and the public health. Instead of authorizing the construction of a dome on the capitol building, thus completing the original design, the members elected to establish a hospital for the University of Oklahoma School of Medicine. The legislature appropriated $200,000, added $76,000 in 1919, and the construction of what later became known as "Old Main," a 176 bed teaching hospital, was completed in 1919. The Oklahoma State Capitol still has no dome.[1]

The art of hospital design had not advanced very far in 1919. Currently common amenities such as televison, air-conditioning and electrically-adjusted hospital beds were unknown. Penicillin was still more than two decades away. Drug therapy, by comparison with modern medication, was rudimentary and medical laboratory science was in its infancy. In the 1920s, a hospital was essentially a place in which to collect sick people, provide what few efficacious procedures existed, perform simple surgery, administer copious quantities of TLC (tender loving care) and pray that the vast restorative powers of the human body would respond to the largely empirical management of the case by the physician.

As a consequence, hospitals were fairly simple structures. Nursing units at University Hospital were 27 bed wards; beds arranged in non-military fashion in large rooms. Although the hospital was designed with 25 private rooms, perhaps they had been put to other uses because, as E. W. Young, M.D., now dean of students of the College of Medicine, commented:

It wasn't until the late fifties that there were any private rooms in University Hospital and then only a few. And some of the wards were in the basement, where we had to duck overhead pipes. And Children's Hospital [built in 1928] wasn't much better. The biggest thing that frustrated me was the lack of privacy. When we made rounds, everything about the patient was discussed with students at the bedside. You had to. And it was within earshot of the patient in the next bed or across the open

The University of Arkansas Medical Center at Little Rock. (OHSF Collection)

The tree-shaded entrance to "Old Main," the University of Oklahoma adult hospital. (University of Oklahoma)

A typical ward in Children's Memorial Hospital, reflecting the state of the art of hospital design in the 1920s. This picture was taken in 1963. (University of Oklahoma)

ward. Physical examinations were done under the same circumstances. Admittedly, we could draw [cubicle] curtains around the bed but this didn't assure privacy.

There never seemed to be enough money in the budget to provide adequate maintenance, let alone remodel the building and replace systems and equipment to keep up with improvements as they were introduced into the field of hospital services. The legislature did not appear concerned. As Dr. Young further recalled, "We were accustomed to the medical school and University Hospital being *chronically* underfunded. It was an annual procedure, almost, for either the school of medicine or the hospital to go to the legislature for a supplementary appropriation because they had been inadequately funded in the first place. It was almost a begging relationship."[2]

Both the adult and children's hospitals had a cluttered, run-down, crowded appearance. Paint was peeling from the walls and the crisp, light, sanitary image of clean, quiet competence most people have when they think of a hospital was not the impression the university facilities gave. Legislators were aware of conditions at the University Hospitals in the mid-1960s but because most of the patients treated there were poor and powerless, there was little impetus to increase the operating budget. After touring the adult hospital, one lawmaker was said to have summed up his attitude this way, "That's good enough for those bums."

The State Regents for Higher Education were the University Hospitals' representative at the legislature and their primary interest was education, not patient care. There was no organized constituency lobbying for the sick poor in the halls of the state capitol, so when Dr. Dennis went through the University Hospital a quarter of a century after he graduated from medical school in 1940, he saw the result of years of financial strangulation.

Despite the handicap of inadequate hospital facilities, many competent people were being recruited to the faculty at that time. James A. Merrill, M.D., who came on as chief of gynecology-obstetrics in 1961, gave two reasons for the success of this effort:

One was the fact that Stewart Wolf was here and was a superb recruiter, a very attractive, academically-oriented person. The other reason was the obvious cooperative spirit which existed in this relatively small faculty. Maybe a third reason was the fact the dean was supportive but left the running of the medical school to his clinical departments. Dr. Everett was not a physician so he depended on his clinical faculty. There was a hospital administrator [Raymond Crews] but he really was subject to the decisions made by the faculty which functioned as a hospital board for University and Children's which were run as one.

This situation gave young people the feeling of freedom. They could come with an idea and try to make it fly. If it didn't work, it wasn't because the bureaucracy got in their road because essentially there *was* no bureaucracy. Doctor Everett's administrative style was laissez-faire…with a giggle.[3]

Jenell Hubbard, R.N., who started as a staff nurse at Children's Hospital in 1946 and rose to director of nursing of the hospitals in 1955, a position she held for 17 years, remembered hospital life in the mid-1960s:

As far as physical facilities were concerned, conditions were very, very bad. What we knew then as proper technique in infection control was hard to carry out. There were no convenient hand-washing facilities, so many times we had to leave the ward to wash our hands between patients. We didn't have air-conditioning and the wards were cooled with huge blower fans. They were four-foot square, boxed fans in the middle of the corridors. This made infection control almost impossible. Our doctors were good at diagnosing infectious diseases pretty quickly and isolating these patients in the few private rooms we had. It was amazing to me we had no more nosocomial [hospital-acquired] infections than we did.

Most of the patients we had were indigents. Some were patients from the mental hospital in Norman who needed special surgical or medical intervention. Also, if a private patient needed a particular procedure that was available only at University Hospital, we had those patients, too. Mostly, they went into the few private rooms we had, if available. We were pretty well fully integrated. I would estimate at least half of the patients were black and we had a fair number of Indians. Most of our patients were from the general Oklahoma City area. There were many accusations from other sections of the state that we were serving as the "county hospital." This presented some funding problems for us.[1]

To this day, that situation has not changed. Tulsa hospitals, in particular, believe they are not receiving their fair share of state support for the indigent patients they admit. Neither of the two largest cities in Oklahoma has a municipal hospital. Mrs. Hubbard continued:

We never had enough nursing staff. We survived by using student nurses but by the mid-sixties, that was beginning to change. Half of our people were nurse aides and we had about 30 percent LPNs [licensed practical nurses] and 20 percent RNs [registered nurses]. The shortage of nurses was so great, we gave crash courses to medical students and used them as nursing assistants. But that didn't last too long....The med students didn't like it! Surprisingly enough, they didn't like the way the doctors treated them when things didn't go right—when lab reports were slow or something. We didn't have much of the technique available then in information systems.

University Hospital was the first in the state to train nurse aides in an organized fashion. We had federal MDTA [Manpower Development Training Assistance] funds through vo-tech [vocational technical education] and ran a three to four month program. It soon became apparent we were a training center for the whole community. After they finished their course with us, out they went! Our salaries were always lower than anybody else's. We never caught up. There was a year or two years' drag behind the other hospitals. A person *had* to be interested in a teaching institution to work at University.

Nurses had to "double over" [work two consecutive shifts] and pull extra hours all the time, but for straight pay; we didn't have time and a half for overtime. There was a lack of adequate supplies to care for patients. The nursing staff literally did things like bring their own towels from home and tear them up to make wash cloths. We never had enough linen.

We were trying to move from that old common can of alcohol sponges to individual sponges for each patient. We brought baby food jars from home and sterilized them to make each patient an individual supply of whatever kind of sponges they needed—Zephrin, alcohol, whatever we were using at the time. We re-autoclaved [re-sterilized] everything. I can't recall exactly

Jenell Hubbard had been director of nursing three years in 1958. (University of Oklahoma)

when disposables came in but we were late in moving to them. Disposables cost more.

I always felt we didn't get a fair share of the medical center budget. In those days, we were sort of a lab for the university [teaching program] and it was hard to divide those dollars. The hospital got second priority. Every time the legislature met, we went through this business of nursing staff and medical faculty anxiety. We had the gamut of rumors: "The hospital is going to be closed. Funding will be reduced further." People in nursing would get anxious and go to another hospital to work. This happened every two years and was one of the most demoralizing things to have to live through. And the medical school faculty [members] were afraid something would happen to further negatively impact their "lab".

We really did live pretty close. We borrowed instruments between the adult and children's hospitals and yet we ran surgery every day. We had to schedule so that on no day did we have to have the same instruments for the same type of procedures in both hospitals because we had only one set. The V.A. Hospital was our backup....Sometimes Saint Anthony [Hospital] was. If a bone drill broke, we held that patient while somebody ran and got a bone drill from the V.A. or "Saints."

A lot of things we needed were purchased by volunteers. We had an active group of mostly physicians' wives. They set up a gift shop and had other activities which brought in money. They bought us wheel chairs, pillows, carts, carriers, examination tables for the emer-

Raymond Crews was the hospital superintendent and the business manager for the entire Medical Center. (OHSF Collection)

gency room…basic equipment we couldn't buy out of the budget.

We budgeted in rather great detail for each patient unit…staffing requirements and supplies needed for gynecology or obstetrics or urology. But the funding never met our needs. Our budget would often be reduced to a 70 percent occupancy or at most an 80 percent occupancy rate when in fact many of those units ran close to 100 percent occupancy. We filled up because we couldn't refuse to admit patients as long as there was an empty bed. So we had to stretch!

In spite of all these difficulties, the *esprit de corps* was good. There was a camaraderie. The morale and attitude among the staff was really commendable.[5]

The hospital superintendent, Raymond Crews, said:

At that time, the legislature was meeting only every two years so we had to prepare our budget 30 to 36 months ahead. With inflation coming along, that was an absolute impossibility. The big problem, of course, was the conflict between teaching and charity. There was never real acceptance on the part of the State Regents that the teaching hospitals were an educational expense; [in their minds] it was charity so we were always at odds. The hospitals were never adequately funded. We were the major training center for practically all the medical and paramedical people in the state. For this reason, the Joint Commission on Accreditation of Hospitals

[JCAH] allowed us to continue to operate although we were never in full compliance.

We had a helluva time keeping [surgical] instruments. In the first place, we couldn't buy very many and in the second place, it seemed like most of the young physicians who went into practice after training in our hospitals equipped their offices with them. It seemed like we were always and forever short of instruments.

But the *esprit de corps* was never better. The volunteer staff contributed hours and hours of their time and when the full time faculty came in, conditions improved markedly in that we had young clinical department heads who were ambitious and hard-working. And 90 percent of the people [employees] who worked for the University Hospitals, in department head or supervisory situations, felt like they were a part of something very worthwhile.[6]

While there was sincere dedication to and concern for the individual patient on the part of the doctors and nurses, the clients of the University Hospital and Clinics were thought of as "clinical material." Of course, this was a point of view common to most teaching centers. The first obligation of a medical school is to teach students about the human body and the ills which befall it. Thus, the patients were indeed clinical material and represented a reservoir of pathology which faculty and students studied in their laboratories, clinics and hospitals. The convenience and economics of the people who made up the patient group received second consideration if indeed they were given any thought at all. As William W. Schottstaedt, M.D., dean of the College of Health between 1967 and 1974, observed:

Morning clinic patients were scheduled to arrive at seven o'clock. After they were checked in and sent to the right area, they had to wait until the medical students could see them. This was about nine o'clock, after the students had been to their first class. The last patients to be seen in the morning waited more than four hours.[7]

At noon, the afternoon patients arrived and the long hours of waiting began for another group. Of course, for the teaching program, this schedule was quite efficient. In the event one patient failed to show, the next patient was on hand and waiting, so neither the students nor the faculty had to waste any of their time. As Dr. Schottstaedt pointed out, the faculty attitude was: the patients have no money; they can pay for their care in time. However, those clinic patients who had a job could least afford a full day away from work, so they paid in lost wages as well as time. For the working poor, who never had enough money to cover

The "clinical material": people waiting to see a doctor. (University of Oklahoma)

all of the necessities, health care was usually on the bottom of their list. Patients who thought they could not afford time away from their job would put off going to the clinic, neglecting their health until the problem became too painful or debilitating to ignore. Prenatal care for the wife or medical check-ups for the kids would be neglected or postponed because there was no money to buy gasoline to get there or buy prescription drugs after they were seen at the clinic. Also, the working poor had less ready access to help from the Welfare Department than those who were "on welfare." This is not to imply that the school of medicine could assume responsibility for the financial plight of every clinic patient, but the clinic system was designed primarily for the benefit of the teaching program, not the consumer of health services.

As Dr. Dennis moved from Little Rock, Arkansas, to take up his new position on September 1, 1964, he was not fully aware of the magnitude of the problems which awaited him. Search committees looking for a leader invariably act their hospitable best, glossing over the sticky situations and emphasizing the opportunity. But Dennis could sense the climate of his home state and his alma mater. He was realistic enough to know it would not be easy to expand the O.U. Medical Center into a health campus of which he and all Oklahomans could be proud. He was experienced enough to know the average tenure of deans of medical schools and directors of academic health care centers is remarkably short. Later, Dr. Dennis paraphased the observation of George Harrell, M.D., former director of the University of Florida Medical Center at Gainesville and subsequently dean of the Pennsylvania State University Hershey School of Medicine. "Deans don't stay very long. When they accept the position and bring a lot of new ideas and proposed changes, they are up against an entrenched group of department heads who like things the way they are and see the new man as a threat to their power. Then, after a few years, when the new dean has managed to make some of the changes he visualized and improvements have been achieved, there is always a group in the school ready to take the credit and take over!" As John Schilling said, "The higher up you are, the more people go after you just because you are fair game."[8]

Dale Groom, M.D., the cardiologist who directed the Regional Medical Program at O.U. from 1968 to the fall of 1971, quoted the average tenure of deans of medical schools as 2.7 years. While Dr. Dennis was at the medical center, he was dean and director until he appointed Dr. Robert Bird dean of the school of medicine in 1970. In the 20 years this history covers, the medical center directors [later called provost] at the University of Oklahoma have surpassed that average tenure by the impressive period of 57 days to reach 2.85 years.[9]

CHAPTER 4
NEW BEGINNING: 1964

The University of Oklahoma School of Medicine building was a yellow brick, limestone-trimmed structure built in 1928 on the corner of Phillips and 13th Street, across from the adult University Hospital. On September 1, 1964, when the new dean began his first day of work, there was nothing in his first floor office except a big mahogany desk and an executive chair. Dr. Dennis recalled the tension:

> The staff had been there many years and they were just as uneasy as I was about what was going to happen. There were two associate deans; Joe White for clinical affairs and Phil Smith for student affairs, but they were part-time. My secretary was Lora Johnson, a very bright girl who was totally loyal and of whom I became very fond. I asked her to write a request to [the] Physical Plant [department] to build me some bookcases or bring me some. I needed my reference books near my desk.
>
> I got a reply back from the controller's office, "Sorry, we have to refuse this. There is no money available for the dean's office." Well, that teed me off so I put a note on the bottom of the reply: "The hell there isn't!" and told Lora to send it back.

Dr. Dennis laughed as he thought about the episode and said he did not know where the money came from but Raymond Crews saw to it that some bookcases were put in his office. "I knew then we had financial problems!" he said and continued:

> That same week, Joe White told me that a site visit was imminent. A $7 million dollar bond issue had been voted the year before to build a new University Hospital. The designs had been done and the university was counting on a two-to-one match with federal money so they could build a 600 bed, $21 million teaching hospital.
>
> Henry Clark, Jr., the dean of the school of public health at the University of North Carolina, was the chairman of the site visit team and they were due in just a day or two. When the group arrived, Henry Clark was very unhappy with us. The first application looked to me like it was about two sheets of paper and, in essence, it said, "We have $7 million and we need $21 million to build a hospital. Give us 14 million dollars. We deserve it."[1]

This was the second site team to review the university's application for hospital funding. Joseph M. White, M.D., head of the department of anesthesiology and associate dean of the school of medicine, took

The old medical school building has since been remodeled for the Colleges of Public Health and Allied Health. (University of Oklahoma)

over as acting dean and director of the medical center when Dr. Everett resigned and departed. This was in June, 1964, and shortly thereafter, the first review team arrived. Dr. White had not been involved in putting the application together so he was not familiar with it. "I found it in the file," he said. Dr. Everett and Raymond Crews had submitted it.

The visitors were appalled that any university would submit such an incomplete request. Apparently, neither Everett nor Crews was aware of the specifications of an acceptable grant application and the extent of detailed information which the federal government required. The next day, Dr. White telephoned

Genial Joe White was chief of anesthesiology as well as associate dean of the medical school. (University of Oklahoma)

Teaching space in the medical school was crowded, as this 1967 picture of the microbiology laboratory attests. (University of Oklahoma)

Robert M. Bird, M.D., associate professor of medicine, who was in the first week of what he thought would be a month-long fishing vacation in the Colorado Rockies. "Get back here right away! We've got to write a grant application for the hospital." So Dr. Bird cut short his holiday and flew back to Oklahoma City.

Because Dean A. McGee was a member of the national commission which reviewed applications under the Health Professions Educational Assistance Program, he made available to Bird and White an application from another university for use as a model. It was a single-spaced, typewritten document perhaps two and a half or three inches thick, detailing every aspect of the proposed project. With this introduction to the emerging craft of grantsmanship, the dean and Dr. Bird, joined by Dr. Bill Schottstaedt, spent the summer of 1964 compiling an application which federal officials would accept.[2]

In September, a new site team was dispatched to Oklahoma City. Dr. Dennis continued his account of that second visit:

> Clark said it was embarrassing in Washington even to acknowledge the first application. I was embarrassed and had no ready answer. I could see how it could have happened but, knowing the feds, I sometimes think they make grant awards on the basis of how many pages are in the application and how much it weighs.
>
> We got a good dressing-down from the site visitors

and obviously we had a relationship problem with the granting agencies for a while. But we showed Dr. Clark around and he conceded our needs were very great. I told him I had just gotten there and I'd like to have time to assess the situation. My thought was to develop a master plan if we could and after we knew what we had and what we wanted and what was reasonable, we would submit a plan and a new application.

> It seemed to me we had the cart before the horse. What we needed first was educational facilities. The pressure was on us to take more medical students and I pointed out that we had those students for two years prior to the time they went into the hospital for clinical training. We had students actually sitting in the aisles of the old lecture hall. I took pictures of this overcrowding to convince site visitors we needed basic science educational facilities first.
>
> Another complication I learned about almost immediately was that Benham, Blair and Affiliates, the hospital architects, had been paid $225 thousand for their services out of the $7 million bond issue. Dr. E. T. Dunlap, whom I met very shortly, was very unhappy with that. The attorney general ruled it was illegal to pay the architects from that source and the money had to be replaced somehow. So what it amounted to, I had to dig up $225,000 from the general [medical center] budget which was already in shambles. This was one of the biggest problems I had because that was about 10

percent of our medical education budget, as I recall. Not many people knew how we sweated that one out! This was a political resolution of the problem, one I never understood. They solved the legal problem, all right, but it created a tremendous financial one for me. But we tightened our belts and did what we had to do.[3]

Bill J. Blair, A.I.A., one of the principals of Benham, Blair and Affiliates, recounted the events which led to the $225 thousand set of design drawings for a teaching hospital which was never built. Planning began in 1962:

The university had a maximum of $5 thousand to spend on a study which would ascertain whether or not a hospital could be built in the medical center. The designated site was on the south side of 13th Street between the out-patient clinic building and Children's Hospital. We undertook that study, signed a contract with the university. There was a planning group in the center headed by Bob Bird and Monty DuVal [Merlin K. "Monty" DuVal, Jr., M.D., Professor of Surgery] along with other physicians, department heads in the medical school. Ray Crews, who was the hospital administrator, and I set out to visit teaching hospitals all over the country. We went to the University of Washington up in Seattle and hospitals in San Francisco, Florida, West Virginia. We traveled everywhere. We probably spent the $5 thousand fee on one trip!

When we came back with all this information about what was really required in a teaching hospital, we sat down with the building committee to develop a rationale for such a facility on this campus. I remember we recommended to Dr. Mark Everett that we not put the hospital on the location he had indicated for it. We didn't have enough site. Oh, we could have put it there but it was going to be so jammed up. I never will forget what Dr. Everett said to us. I don't remember his exact words but the message was, "You weren't hired to say if this site is the right one. We want to know if a hospital can be put there."[4]

Raymond Crews said that without authorization to buy additional land, it was the only place they had to put a new hospital:

The decision was to build a teaching hospital between the two existing hospitals, using the outpatient clinics, which were opened in 1952, as a tie-in arrangement. It was decided to use the old hospitals for basic science labs and offices and clinical sciences support areas. The voluntary faculty had their offices downtown and did not need space in the medical center but the full time clinical faculty wanted offices for themselves and their support groups and laboratory space to carry on their research. The medical school building wasn't adequate

for the needs of the basic science departments, let alone the clinical departments, so in the hospitals there was always conflict, push and shove for space.[5]

Bill Blair continued:

We worked up our feasibility study which said, yes, a hospital could be put in that area. We indicated what the building should consist of, the various departments it should have and so on. We had visited 12 or 14 hospitals around the country and our study contained a lot of information gathered from those places. Beside Crews, our own people went with us; in fact, we were using our own plane. After we made our presentation of the feasibility study, next thing we knew, the university was so pleased with the report we had made and the intensity of the study we had accomplished, they asked us to proceed with the project. We signed another contract and began working on the design of the hospital. We were to be paid a percentage, maybe five and a half or six percent of the construction cost. Back in those days, I was very naive and it didn't dawn on me that something might happen to keep the hospital from being built. We designed that hospital working hand in hand with the building committee. Joe White and Bill Schottstaedt were on it, and maybe John Schilling. We completed the design development phase of the project [the step between schematic drawings and final working drawings] before we were pulled off of it.

I hated to see the project go down the drain. We had worked very closely with the hospital to develop what we thought they wanted. We did it together...the building committee and us. We got paid for our work but it got taken away from us! I don't know all the politics behind that but they said we had an illegal contract. We had to pay the money back. We were pretty upset. I had spent a year and a half or two years of my life working on that hospital. I lived it, slept it, ate it....That was my life. Then to have that pulled out from under us...it hurt me. I felt we had made a real contribution.

According to David Benham, the other principal in the architectural firm, they did give back one check but got another one in its place from the University of Oklahoma Regents, so the designers were compensated for their work. A teaching hospital was built later but a different architect was appointed and the original plans were never used. Raymond Crews explained that "Benham, Blair was hired under a Democratic governor and then we elected a Republican governor and that's why the architects were changed."[6]

Dr. Dennis was also surprised by other unanticipated expenses affecting the Medical Center:

One morning I had a telegram from Dun and Bradstreet [requesting] $3,500 to pay for one dead ele-

The new University Hospital was going to be jammed between Old Main and Children's. See aerial photo of the campus in Chapter 1. (University of Oklahoma)

phant! In 1962, apparently Jolly West and his colleagues had the idea that LSD [lysergic acid diethylamide], which was then a new psychotropic drug, caused behavior you might expect in an elephant "on musth" [a form of madness which occurs almost exclusively in mature male elephants once or twice a year. For about two weeks, the elephant, normally cooperative and tamable, runs berserk during which time he may attack or attempt to destroy anything in his path]. Jolly found out that one of the circuses in Dallas had an [available] elephant and he arranged to have it shipped up to the Lincoln Park Zoo [in Oklahoma City].

Then he went out and gave this big [6,500-7,000 pound, Asiatic] elephant [named Tusko] a massive dose of LSD, based on weight. The elephant promptly fell over dead! [Actually, it took an hour and 40 minutes.] The pathologist who did the autopsy, Bill Jaques [William E. Jaques, M.D., head of the department of pathology] said, "You know, I got inside that thoracic cage and it was like walking around in a room."

Dr. Dennis laughed and continued:

The dosage probably should have been calculated on body surface area but I can understand how it happened. [Proportionately much larger doses of LSD have been required to obtain results in lower animals comparable to reactions to the drug observed in man.]

Dr. Louis Jolyon "Jolly" West headed the Department of Psychiatry, Neurology and Behavioral Sciences for 15 years. (University of Oklahoma)

27

Anyway, the circus had billed Jolly and he didn't have any money to pay for it. A year had transpired [in fact, more than two years had gone by] and they had gotten upset. While I was trying to keep the Medical Center afloat, here comes this bill, addressed to me, for $3,500. I told Jolly, "We've got to find a way to take care of this."

And he did…dug it up out of professional fees, borrowed it or something. We got it paid.

There was an *esprit de corps* in the faculty that was really exciting. Stewart Wolf and Jolly West emphasized their own positive, happy outlook on things and lifted the faculty up with them. They were great![7]

CHAPTER 5
THE DENNIS DREAM: 1964

Tiburon, California, consultant Lester Gorsline helped Jim Dennis and his colleagues organize planning for the future of the Medical Center. (OHSF Collection)

It was not many weeks after Dennis arrived to face the financial problems and planning challenges at Oklahoma that, somewhat by happenstance, he met the person who was to become a major facilitator in the development of a plan for the medical center's expansion. About the last week in September, 1964, the Association of American Medical Colleges (AAMC) held its annual meeting. Dr. Dennis described his first conversation with Lester "Les" Gorsline, a medical facilities planner based in Belvedere-Tiburon, California:

> The AAMC had a workshop on planning and I was impressed by Lester Gorsline's presentation. At one of the intermissions, I visited with him, told him we were certainly in need of some direction in planning but I had no funds and I didn't know how I would get any funds for that purpose. He was immediately interested in our concept of sharing costs, facilities, space and services in a unified community center rather than just the classical hospital and the typical medical school. I was interested in multi-discipline education buildings....We knew we had to do that, too.
>
> I pointed out we had only $7 million to do all of this

and I didn't know when we would get any more but we had to get started. Les very quickly said, "I would like to visit Oklahoma and see what's there. We won't charge you anything for the first visit." He did visit us and brought his associate, Roger Bennett, and an architect/campus planner from San Francisco, California, Lawrence Lackey.[1]

The dean appointed a planning committee and named Robert Bird chairman. Joe White, Vernon Scott, Sc.D. and Robert Patnode, Ph.D., both microbiologists, and Leonard Eliel were on it. The director of the Veterans Administration Hospital, Oren Skouge, M.D., and Raymond Crews, administrator of the University Hospitals, were members along with a number of others from the medical school faculty. The committee met with the consultants and, as Dr. Dennis said, "got a dialogue going which stimulated a lot of thought." He commented further about the chairman:

> Bob Bird was a man everyone liked. Stewart Wolf, the head of the department of medicine, was gone a lot and Bob was really the "resident chief," if you want to put it that way. He was easy to talk with, receptive to new ideas and knew how to get to and along with the faculty. This gave me a communication system with faculty which I would not have had time for otherwise. It was a very fortuitous choice and, with the planning committee in place, we had some good brains going.[2]

Lester Gorsline was neither a scientist nor an educator, but he was a pragmatist whose ideas were quite similar to Dr. Dennis's way of thinking. In describing his work as a planning consultant, he recalled:

> What I tried to do in Oklahoma was to find ways to implement a plan that would be a realistic response to the [health] needs of the people. That's a populist idea, I'm sure, but we pay taxes and all of us want something back. Our job was to help the planning committee establish their basic, educational philosophy. Architects who design buildings in which educational programs are conducted have trouble hearing what is required. They *listen* but they don't *hear*. And the physicians and educators don't know how to tell them what they are supposed to be listening to. So these are two languages and neither understands the other, like swahili and urdu! What I did was try to work in the middle between them so they

The planning committee included L. Vernon Scott, Stewart Wolf, Ernst Lachman, Robert M. Bird, William Campbell, the university architect, and Henry Mayfield. Edward N. Brandt and W.W. Schottstaedt were also members. (University of Oklahoma)

understood each other. Then the feds and the state government could understand what the health professionals were up to and could provide money in a realistic fashion. Afterward, they could be sure the money was spent properly. We developed a program....That's all it was.[3]

Dr. Mark Johnson, chairman of the University Regents Medical Center Committee, remembered that "much of the very preliminary deliberation in developing the master plan for what was to become the Oklahoma Health Center was concentrated on the question 'Where should it be?' "Those universities in which the medical school and other health sciences programs are an integral part of the main campus, like Duke University, Vanderbilt University and the University of Chicago, enjoy a synergism not possible at the medical centers of Alabama, Arkansas, Tennessee, California and Oklahoma, which are some distance removed from their parent university. Even the short separation of 20 miles between Norman and Oklahoma City inhibited communication to the extent the two campuses were almost like two different

worlds. William "Bill" Campbell, A.I.A., the campus architect at Norman, said, "My recollection is that the medical center could have been on the other side of the state as far as the people on the Norman campus were concerned."[4]

Of course, the university administration and the regents wanted to bring the two units closer together because much of the pre-health sciences preparation was provided in undergraduate programs in Norman. In addition, other scientific disciplines, such as engineering, physics and mathematics, were germane to medical education and research. According to Dr. Johnson:

We would have liked to move the medical center to Norman but we knew there would not be enough patients in the area to provide clinical experience for students in the health sciences. We actually explored the feasibility of putting the medical center in Moore, Oklahoma [a small community midway between Oklahoma City and Norman], but we came to realize the land cost there would be absolutely prohibitive. We also recognized that it was the metropolitan population that made

30

Architect Lawrence Lackey and Dr. Bob Bird share a pleasant interlude between planning sessions. (OHSF Collection)

the medical center feasible. As in Norman, we would not have sufficient patients in Moore to support the teaching mission. Besides, it did not make sense to move away from the V.A. Hospital and the Oklahoma Medical Research Foundation with which the medical school was so closely affiliated.

When we concluded we could not move the medical center, we wanted the students in Oklahoma City to be enriched by the same kind of truly collegiate activities that were available to the students on the Norman campus. We wanted to establish free bus service between the two campuses. We wanted a student union, intramural sports and a physical education program on the medical center campus.[5]

Roger Bennett, Lester Gorsline's associate, looked back at the beginning of the planning process in the fall of 1964:

At the first meeting of the [planning] committee, Jim Dennis introduced me. I didn't realize that the former dean's son was sitting there and I was quite critical about the approach that had been made to the feds to fund the construction of the hospital. I said, "You will not get anywhere by doing it that way. We have to decide on a proper, logical base for a program." Dr. Mark Allen Everett did ask some questions and evidently he and a number of the faculty realized that things hadn't been done very well.[6]

In the early 1960s, the federal government declared there was a shortage of 50,000 physicians in the United States and this realization stimulated the Congress to enact a program of federal aid to schools for medical, dental and other health personnel and to medical, dental and osteopathy students. Known as the Health Professions Educational Assistance Act of 1963, the legislation was signed into law on September 24 of that year. It was a multi-million dollar program from which much of the financing for educational facilities at the O.U. Medical Center was expected to come. Bennett continued:

In order to get funding for new buildings, medical schools had to increase their enrollment by 20 percent. At that time, Oklahoma was admitting about a hundred students in its entering medical school classes. It was decided the teaching [basic science education] building could be funded best because that's what this new act was mainly about. The feds would provide two-thirds of the money to build it if you increased enrollment at least 20 percent.[7]

Thus, the first step in the development of the Oklahoma Health Center was taken. Essentially all of the necessary elements were already accessible or quickly had fallen into place: a concensus of the faculty to begin with educational facilities, a newly-reorganized planning committee, a group of nationally-recognized planning consultants, agreement by the federal site committee that the need for basic science education space at O.U. was critical, a mandate by the national government to expand medical schools, excellent prospects that federal funding would be forthcoming, local matching funds in the form of the 1963, $7 million bond issue originally intended for the hospital, and a site on property already owned by the university. The missing ingredient was the approval, indeed the blessings of the State Regents for Higher Education.

The State Regents, appointed by the governor, were a seemingly ethereal, anonymous group which met periodically but maintained an extremely low profile. The chancellor, on the other hand, who "walked point" for the regents when encountering a sometimes hostile legislature or who issued commands from battalion headquarters to the troops in the companies of Oklahoma universities and colleges, was an ever-present, highly visible and oft-quoted force. Relations between the chancellor and the medical center had been strained for years. Jim Dennis came to Oklahoma with a different attitude:

I thought I could get along with E. T. Dunlap. I recognized his responsibility and I really didn't have any

The head of the planning committee consults the dean.

trouble with the chancellor. I think I understood why he didn't trust the medical center after seeing some of the reports he received. Most universities I've been associated with learn to play budget games. They show what they want to show and cover up what they don't want to be too prominent unless, of course, they *have* to bring it out. They're not dishonest; they're just playing the game every other university and college is playing. We had some pretty sharp people out there and E. T. had been burned a few times. He didn't know whether to believe them or not, so he didn't believe! Finally, after a few days of watching and listening, I just went to him and said, "Look, Dr. Dunlap, I'm more confused than you are and I *have* to know what's going on. I give you my word that I'm going to tell you what I *think* is correct and do my best to give you the right figures. I don't want to play games and that may be dangerous. I'm going to put myself at your mercy. We'll try and show you what we've got and what we need. You'll have to trust me and I'll have to trust you." And I tried to do that.[8]

At the time Dr. Dennis arrived, the self-study of medical education in Oklahoma being conducted by the researchers in Chancellor Dunlap's office had been in progress about eight months. As Dr. Dennis said:

Much of this had been done before I got there but after I visited with Dr. Dunlap, he agreed that we needed to go over the whole thing together. I spent a number of days, all day long, with him and his staff. Joe White went with me on several occasions. The more I got into the situation, the more I realized we had to get a basis of fact for the plan. It had to be more than a plan for the medical center; it had to be a plan that addressed the concern for the health needs of the entire state. I really got a good, warm feedback when I expressed this sentiment to E.T. Dunlap because he immediately sensed, "You can sell that to the legislature." That's what their concern was. When the legislators went home, they heard what "that damn University Hospital did.... They didn't admit our people!" Or they listened to their constituents complain that "The university didn't take my son into medical school." Or they again received that most frequent complaint, "They aren't producing any more doctors up there and we can't get a doctor to come to our town." The legislators had a totally negative feeling toward doing anything for the medical center because it didn't seem to be doing much for the people.

I felt that if we really found out what the needs out there were and really addressed them with a plan that had professional support, it would be very difficult for the legislature to turn us down. And once we had the legislative backing, E. T. would back us.[9]

CHAPTER 6
SELF-STUDY OF MEDICAL EDUCATION: 1965

Report Six of the Self-Study of Higher Education in Oklahoma was released in June, 1965. It was the only one of the eight reports which covered a particular discipline, Medical Education in Oklahoma. The State Regents for Higher Education recognized that "if the citizens of Oklahoma are to be provided access to the full range of available preventive and therapeutic measures, there will need to be planning and coordination along the entire spectrum of programs for the education of physicians and other health care personnel."

The State Regents put together a "blue ribbon" committee to advise them on the study of the medical center. This group of 17 was headed by an attorney from Tulsa, John Rogers, who was then serving as president of the Oklahoma Medical Research Foundation. The vice chairman was Dean A. McGee, chairman of Kerr-McGee Oil Industries, Inc., of Oklahoma City. Governor Henry Bellmon, Dr. George Cross, Raymond Crews, Dr. Leonard Eliel and Dr. Mark Johnson were members, along with the Speaker of the Oklahoma House of Representatives, J.D. McCarty, and the President Pro Tempore of the Senate, Clem McSpadden. Dr. Dennis joined the group in the fall of 1964. Seven other citizens and health professionals made up the balance of the committee. In addition, there were seven smaller committees, composed primarily of leaders in the medical school, which had the responsibility to examine functions and goals, medical education opportunities and needs, enrollments, faculty, operating costs and needs, control and administration and physical facilities. Counting three outside consultants and three research staff men, 50 people were involved in this study, a process which required 18 months.

The chancellor had identified a matter of great concern to the people of Oklahoma. He recognized that "the health of its citizens is basic to the strength of the state" and that an adequate supply of health manpower was necessary "to serve an expanding population whose health problems grow more complex with each passing year." Many studies published throughout the country in the early 1960s had stressed a growing shortage of health manpower.[1]

Dr. Joe White, the associate dean of the medical school, recalled the situation when the study was started in January, 1964.

Early on, there was a lot of distrust between Dr. Dunlap and Dean Everett, who was inclined to be secretive. He didn't want the chancellor and his people nosing around the medical center. It turned out that Dr. Dunlap brought a young man into the administration of the higher regents named John L. Coffelt. Coffelt and I began to relate very well....We played golf together...and our relationship allowed them [the State Regents] to get a much better picture of the medical center than they were prepared to get.

I think quite naturally someone coming into the [chancellor's] job with Dr. Dunlap's background would suppose the medical center operated like any other higher education institution, that is, students came there and there were lectures and laboratories. What was difficult for them to understand was the relationship of the hospital to all this...the fact that the clinical faculty, which was a large segment of the medical school faculty, actually took care of patients. There was a fee system involved for some of those patients and this money was placed in departmental funds and used to enhance residency programs and other functions. We worked primarily toward getting Dr. Coffelt to understand how this worked and that it worked to the benefit of the medical center. The money was not taken out of the system and used frivilously nor were faculty physicians getting wealthy from it. I spent *hours* with John Coffelt trying to make him aware of the details of medical center functions. I believe the self-study is as fair a representation of the situation in 1964 and 1965 as we could get.[2]

Dr. Dennis spoke about the self-study process as it looked to him when he came to Oklahoma:

Much of the preliminary work with the faculty had been done by the time I got there. There was not an awful lot of change but there were some absolutely key revisions insofar as what was to evolve later. I insisted on including more about what we now call primary care and the need to develop working relationships with most private and public institutions which were involved in health care for the state. Outreach programs were suggested for the first time. It seemed to me we should form a partnership between the university and the state in addressing health needs.[3]

Health care problems in Oklahoma, as elsewhere, stemmed from several phenomena. The population of the state was rising, people were demanding better health care, there were significant advances in medical knowledge and the patterns of health service were changing. The American population in 1963 was 188 million and was expected to reach 230 million by 1975. The age distribution of that population was changing, too, with the number of people more than 65 and less than 11 years old growing faster than the group in the middle. Of course, it is the old and the young who use the health care system most frequently.

As the level of affluence and education in the United States rose, the demand for better health care increased. Another factor buoying demand was that more people were getting medical and hospitalization insurance as a fringe benefit from their employer. So concern for the cost of medical care declined. The consumer was beginning to regard health care almost as an endowed right. It was something of value and if someone else would pay for it—the employer or the government—why not take advantage of it?

As Dr. Dunlap pointed out to Governor J. Howard Edmondson, the money then being made available for medical research was producing new information at an ever-increasing rate which was "a major factor in raising the standard of medical care to the present high level." This also had another effect; it increased specialization. By the mid-1960s, four in 10 doctors were full-time specialists who had taken three to six years post-doctoral training. This trend toward specialization was accelerating for another reason; that was where the prestige and the money were. Because medical school faculty were almost all specialists, medical students had a built-in role model. As a result, fewer graduates went into general practice and retiring family doctors, particularly in the smaller communities, were not being replaced.[4]

The general practitioner became less and less available and medical practice became more institutionalized. People who did not have a family doctor went to the hospital emergency room or clinic for care. Groups of specialists, such as the Oklahoma City Clinic, grew as medical care became increasingly sophisticated. Fewer than 10 percent of the physicians' visits were in the home and these were destined to disappear rapidly. Because Oklahoma was, in the main, a rural state, these changing patterns of health care delivery had a profound effect on many people. They were of particular concern to leaders like Dr. Dennis who could see current trends needed to be changed

or things would only get worse. Medical education had to be expanded and restructured to accommodate needed improvements in the delivery of health services.

Thus the purpose of this study was to identify the need for medical education. In this sense, the term "medical" was used broadly to include all of the health sciences and professions. The study also was designed to analyze the current resources and figure out what additional resources would be required to educate the professionals who could deliver the health services Oklahomans needed. Dr. Dennis had pledged to the chancellor he would try to show him "what we've got and what we need." The study of the medical center did just that.[5]

The health of the American people had improved remarkably in the 64 years since the turn of the century. Life expectancy had increased more than 72 percent from 40 to almost 70 years. But the population was exploding and the production of doctors and other health professionals had not kept up with the growing numbers of people and their increasing propensity to use medical services. The United States population was expected to be up by 42 million in the next dozen years.

Traditionally, the supply of physicians has been tallied in terms of the ratio of doctors to 100,000 population. In 1964, this ratio was 151. Just to maintain this level of service to the people meant the output of American medical schools had to be increased from 7,500 to 11,000 graduates a year.

In Oklahoma, the basic goal was to see that people received the best possible medical care. To do that, there had to be a sufficient number of physicians and other health workers to take care of people when they got sick. In 1964, the ratio of doctors to people was 115 per 100,000, so Oklahoma had a considerable shortfall when compared to the nationwide average of 151. Oklahoma had 2,823 M.D. (allopathic) and D.O. (osteopathic) physicians in 1964. There was much catching up to do as well as preparation for a rapidly expanding population. Also, migration to the "sunbelt," as the southern and southwestern United States was called, was in progress, and Oklahoma's population was growing faster than the nation as a whole.

Curiously, the medical center study did not attempt to measure the need for physicians or other health personnel in Oklahoma. The committee concluded: "The lack of meaningful information regarding health science manpower needs and student demand in Oklahoma has prevented accurate en-

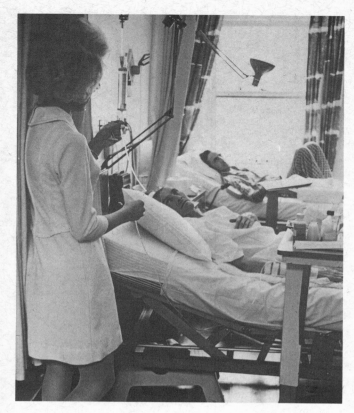

Two patients in Old Main watch their nurse adjust an I.V. (University of Oklahoma)

rollment projections. Rather, enrollment projections for the Medical Center are based on current and anticipated resources which may be available to accommodate existing programs." Thus, the projections included in the study were not related to the market for the health professionals to be produced. However, the committee, noting the absence of hard data, "recommended that the Medical Center be encouraged to study the health science personnel needs of the state."[6]

Although the committee did not know how many and what kind of health professionals were needed, it listed among the goals of the people, "To produce enough physicians and other health related personnel to meet the needs of Oklahoma and to assist in meeting the health needs of the Nation in those medical and allied fields where Oklahoma is or can become pre-eminent." It also emphasized the quality of health professionals, high standards of service, care within reach, geographically and economically, of all Oklahomans, educational opportunities in the health sciences for young people seeking careers, improved medical research and, finally, "to promote awareness of good health care." This last goal, coupled with the

expressed notion of "providing access to the full range of preventive...measures," foreshadowed the rather significant change in the public's attitude about health, shifting the emphasis from sickness to wellness and the responsibility for health from the doctor to the individual.

In the mid-1960s, the University of Oklahoma Medical Center was the state's principal facility for the education of health professionals and therefore was a natural focal point for coordinating all health agencies and educational programs in Oklahoma. This is the role the State Regents believed the medical center should fulfill, as well as provide leadership toward these goals: To provide opportunities for medical and other health science education, achieve excellence in these educational programs, pursue research and disseminate the new information and practices which result from it, provide continuing education and produce physicians and other health workers responsive to the needs of the people. In addition, the medical center was expected to take the lead in solving health care problems brought on by the changing times. It was a difficult task.[7]

In 1964, the medical center operated a school of medicine and a baccalaureate level school of nursing. Post doctoral internships, residencies and research fellowships were offered, as well as programs in the basic medical sciences, preventive medicine and public health. Ten allied health programs at the bachelors level or less completed the list of 37 educational opportunities for students.

One of the authorized basic functions of the medical center was "to maintain and operate hospitals for the purpose of providing clinical material essential to the instruction of students." Also, it was to "provide hospitalization for the indigent poor, emergency cases, obstetrical patients that are public charges and students in state colleges and universities." The Children's Hospital was operated as "a service institution for the physically handicapped and as a teaching hospital." Some of the older physicians and hospital employees still think of it as the "Crippled Children's Hospital."

Having these official patient care responsibilities over 45 years, it was not surprising the university institutions were viewed as "charity" hospitals. And the dual obligation of teaching and indigent care created problems. As Jenell Hubbard explained, they filled up the beds whether or not there was enough money to operate them properly. At times, this unrestricted admission policy serving the sick poor inhibited care-

A 1960 photograph of Children's Memorial Hospital displaying its new name, changed from "Crippled Children's Hospital." (University of Oklahoma)

Clinic patients spent long hours just sitting. (University of Oklahoma)

ful selection of "varied patient material needed for teaching and demonstration." The near-maximum load of patients also occupied the time and energy of the medical staff/faculty so the educational process received less attention. The State Regents, however, gave first priority to teaching and wanted people to "be made aware of the true concept of the primary function of the Medical Center—the education of competent physicians and other health related personnel." But the public, particularly county officials and doctors in outlying areas of the state, looked to the medical center for hospital care of indigent patients.[8]

The use of the term "clinical material" to describe the patients who attended the clinics and filled the hospitals of the university reflected the wide social gap between these patients and the faculty physicians who treated them. This was and still remains a common pattern in many American medical schools and teaching hospitals. The charity hospital has not disappeared despite the many government programs which pay at least a portion of the cost of medical care for the poor and theoretically give them access to private hospitals. "Two tier medicine," one level for the poor and another for the people who can pay, is still with us. This does not necessarily mean that the care which the poor receive is inferior; indeed, some of the best care available is provided in teaching hospitals. But it can be quite different.

Medical research is the third basic activity of medical schools in addition to teaching and patient care. In the 1963-1964 budget period, 74.6 percent of the total current operating income of the school of medicine was from research and training grants. While the State Regents were apparently pleased that O.U. had federal and philanthropic funds to support research, they were fearful medical research would soon become the dominant activity of the school. They cautioned those in authority not to lose sight of the fact that the major mission of a medical school is education. This paralleled Regent Mark Johnson's concern about the dominance and independence of faculty members who controlled large research grants.[9]

The 1965 Study of the Medical Center recognized that "the current emphasis being given to medical research presages even greater changes in the foreseeable future—changes that stagger the imagination." It went on to forecast organ transplants, physiochemical control of mental disorders and work in recombinant DNA—gene splicing—although the latter had not acquired the labels we know today. This new knowledge coming out of the medical research laboratory not only expanded the curriculum of the medical school but also spawned a "host of specialized professional services and auxiliary personnel—psychologists, social scientists, occupational and physical therapists and a variety of paramedical technologies." The regents also gave credit to modern methods of delivering medical care and massive population shifts for causing the general practitioner to give way to the specialist. Nursing, occupational therapy and physical therapy educational requirements were being lengthened to the baccalaureate level. The report said "the concept of a medical school has been broadened into that of a University Center for the Health Sciences." This was an accurate analysis. Seven years later, the name of the medical center was changed to better reflect what was happening there; it became the O.U. Health Sciences Center.

In 1964, the medical school was admitting 104 students to the freshman class. Applicants had to be between the ages of 19 and 35 and have maintained a C+ average for the three years (90 semester hours) of pre-medical college work. At least 80 percent of the freshmen were selected from Oklahoma residents. Applicants from out of state had to have a B average in their college work.

As now, medical students spent their first two years in the study of the basic medical sciences: anatomy, biochemistry, physiology, pharmacology, pathology and microbiology. During their last two years, they learned the art of clinical medicine in the wards of the two university hospitals and in the clinics.

The first year of post doctoral work in medicine was then called the internship during which the young graduate was the lowest member of a hospital "house staff." Under the supervision of resident and clinical staff doctors, he learned to assume increasing responsibility for the care of sick people. The 749 hospitals which then had approved internship programs offered more than 12,000 internships for less than 8,000 medical graduates. As a result, there was a lot of competition in the recruitment of interns who "assumed an important share of the patient care responsibility." Unfortunately, the O.U. Medical Center did not fare well in this nationwide recruitment contest. In 1963, it filled only 14 of 24 approved internship positions and the next year the first year group had dwindled to seven.

One of the problems was money. Interns at University Hospital received $175 a month, exactly half of the top stipend paid in other Oklahoma hospitals, which also provided better fringe benefits, including meals for the intern's family, living quarters for him and his family and malpractice and health insurance. The average intern stipend nationwide was $250 a month. There was a serious morale problem at University Hospital and low pay was only one part of it. The regents recommended that the medical school faculty face this issue and make an objective study of the situation.

When it came to resident recruitment, the medical center did considerably better. Medical residencies, in which physicians learned one of 17 specialties dur-

The strenuous routine of pediatric resident Jim Turner also had its moments of delight. Children's Hospital—1963. (University of Oklahoma)

ing three or more years after their internship, also were in surplus over the nation. In 1963, there were 37,610 approved residencies, all of which were not filled. That same year, the medical center's resident staff numbered 153 of 204 approved positions, or 75 percent, which was about the nationwide average.

In nursing, the shortage of qualified people was even more acute than in medicine. Hospital admissions had risen from 60 per year for every thousand people in the nation in 1937 to 147 admissions per thousand population in 1957. The output of nurse training programs in hospitals could not keep up with the demand for the services of these health professionals. A 1965 study by the Oklahoma Employment Security Commission reported 5,548 registered nurses in the state and projected the need for 11,238 in 1975, just 10 years away, a 103 percent increase. The percentage need for more licensed practical nurses over the next decade was almost as great. From a level of 3,719 in 1965, the study indicated that Oklahoma would need 7,300 LPNs in 1975, up 96 percent.

To meet these needs would require new nursing education programs throughout the state. The University of Oklahoma was expected to educate the fac-

The newest building on campus was razed to make space for the Basic Science Education Building. Nurse students lived and learned in this structure. The "petunia bed" is in the foreground. (University of Oklahoma)

ulty for these new schools of nursing as well as supply supervisors and directors in hospitals. At that time, the university had the only four-year program leading to a Bachelor of Science in Nursing in the state. Only 48 students were enrolled in the first year of the degree program in the 1963-1964 academic year, so the need to expand the student body was obvious.

In 1965, the study estimated "there were approximately four paramedical workers for each practicing physician" and looked ahead to a ratio of 8 or 10 to one in 1975. Although there were no Oklahoma studies to quantify the need for allied health personnel, the national trends were clear. Not only would enrollment in existing programs have to be expanded but education in newly emerging allied health disciplines would no doubt be required. At that time, the medical center offered programs for students in administration, cytotechnology, surgical technical assistance, practical nursing, x-ray technolgy, oxygen therapy, physical therapy, medical technology, public health service nursing and nursing home administration.

As Mark Johnson pointed out, there was a growing amount of "soft" or grant money flowing to the medical school faculty members for research. From 1940, when federal expenditures for medical research were a mere $3 million, the tax-generated support grew to $1 billion in 1963. On top of that, another $700 million was available from private philanthropic sources. The University of Oklahoma had its share of accomplished grantsmen who tapped these sources for $5 million in 1964, which amounted to 40 percent of the annual operating expenses of the entire medical center.[10]

These non-state monies buttressed the medical center program but, the State Regents noted, also produced some "pernicious side effects." They observed that "money exerts influence and unfortunately, some of these influences do not always parallel the basic goals or welfare of a particular institution...." The regents were apprehensive about the "subtle shift in emphasis from teaching medical students to that of research and research training and the diversion of faculty interest away from the care of patients." They saw this preoccupation of the faculty with medical science rather than the patient as "a serious threat to the proper balance among programs of teaching, research and medical care." To meet this threat, the regents called for a "knowledgeable, courageous and skillful brand of medical school administration" which could adhere to a carefully-conceived statement of overall objectives regardless of the source and availability of the money.

The maldistribution of physicians in Oklahoma also worried the regents. With more doctors going into government service, public health, specialty practice, full time teaching and research, only 36 percent were left in the general or family practice of medicine. This change, coupled with the population explosion and the shift of that population from rural to urban centers threatened an acute shortage of family doctors. The exodus of doctors from the small towns of Oklahoma was already quite apparent. Towns of 5,000 people or fewer had suffered a net loss of 135 doctors over the previous ten years, leaving only 288 physicians where 435 had been in 1956. Many small towns lost the only doctor they had.[11]

The self-study indicated what the medical center might do to alleviate the shortage of health manpower in Oklahoma. It made a two part, 10 year projection of student enrollment in the health sciences. The first projection showed the increase in students if no additional facilities or resources were available. Even then, the total enrollment was expected to rise by 130 students in 10 years, a 13 percent increase. The study committee was sufficiently realistic to know that without more state dollars, little could be done to increase the supply of health manpower. The second projection assumed the legislature *would* provide more resources for the medical center, in which event the student body could more than double, totaling 2,026 by 1975.

To repeat, these were "supply side" projections, es-

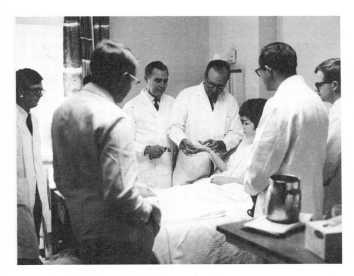

Dr. Stewart Wolf and others look on while Dr. Jim Hammarsten examines a patient on the medicine service in University Hospital. (University of Oklahoma)

timating the number of students that could be enrolled if the medical center got the money to expand. The need or demand for health personnel in Oklahoma had not been accurately measured. This supply-side basis for the development and expansion of educational programs in the health sciences was used repeatedly as time went on, even when data about health manpower requirements became available. Such decisions were later to create controversy and problems.[12]

Traditionally, physicians have been independent professionals. In early times, medicine was a "cottage industry" and to the extent doctors are still individual entreprenuers providing a one-to-one service, the label still applies. Teaching, as the self-study pointed out, is similar. "Perhaps no profession leaves so much determination of self effort in the hands of the individual as does teaching." Thus, the doctor-teacher makes most of the decisions which determine his effectiveness in each role. The study report described the situation succinctly:

> Because the teacher-doctor is a practitioner of scholarship as well as medicine, because his ability as a teacher or researcher cannot be ordered by a dean or president, because his loyalty is primarily to his profession and specifically to his discipline or field of specialization, he does not view himself as an employee of the medical school but rather as a member of the medical profession associated with the institution in order to engage in medical research and teaching. Similarly, non-physician medical scientists engaged in medical school

teaching and research identify more closely with their discipline than with the institution.

It is little wonder the tenure of deans of medical schools is so short. From the faculty point of view, the dean is expected to generate public support for the school, get sufficient money to operate it properly, insulate the faculty from outside pressure in areas the doctors think they should control and be the front man, "representing the faculty to outside groups." Undoubtedly, the key to Dr. Everett's long and successful deanship was his laissez-faire style of administration. He trusted his department chairmen and let them operate independently.

In medical school organization, the department, as an administrative subgroup, is very strong. "Ordinarily, it is the department which collectively decides who shall be invited to join the group, who will be recommended for promotion and increase in salary, and what the general scope and level of subject matter will be." As the State Regents for Higher Education had experienced over many years, "the department tends to resist supervisory authority or the imposition of centralized control, and institutional efforts to ascertain information about faculty work load or the nature of the faculty members' professional activities are viewed with apprehension." For these reasons, Dr. Dennis had some difficulty acquiring adequate information to understand what was happening in the medical center because little detailed data previously had been collected by the dean's office.

The study committee wrestled with recommendations of the Association of American Medical Colleges (AAMC) and the United States Public Health Service (USPHS) as to the number of full-time faculty needed to operate a school of medicine. The variables which had to be considered were the size of the student body, how many volunteer and part-time faculty were available, the emphasis on medical research, the curriculum and methods of teaching and the scope of graduate and paramedical programs. For the 1962-1963 academic year, Oklahoma had 106 full-time faculty compared with the 154 the AAMC recommended the medical center should have. Using USPHS standards, the medical center appeared to be understaffed somewhere between 15 and 34 full-time faculty members. Furthermore, Oklahoma ranked number 8 of 12 medical schools in full-time faculty when compared with Arkansas, Colorado, Kansas,

Iowa, Louisiana, Missouri, Nebraska, Oregon, Wisconsin and two medical schools in Texas. The State Regents concluded that the medical center was understaffed but the committee could not judge what optimal faculty requirements were because neither medical center records nor national standards were adequate.

They easily could see, however, that faculty salaries at the medical center lagged behind the averages in the region and the nation. For example: the average salary for a geographic full-time professor in clinical medicine at Oklahoma in 1963-1964 was $17,539, well below the regional average of $19,721 and the national average of $20,591. The additional income from private patients and consultation that year averaged $3,697 for Oklahoma medical school professors.

In addition to volunteer and part-time medical faculty, there are two types of full-time teachers. Geographic full-time faculty can have some private practice with which to supplement their income. At Oklahoma, this extra income could equal the amount of their salary from the university. Strict full-time faculty, however, receive all of their income in the form of salary from the medical school. The State Regents believed it desirable "to work toward the development and adequate support of a strict full-time faculty." They were aware this would require a substantial increase in state support.

Fringe benefits such as group hospitalization insurance, major medical coverage, accident insurance and a retirement program, were minimal at the medical center. Faculty received only the latter two, although they were eligible for the entire program which was provided elsewhere in the state system of higher education. The medical center administration believed it did not have the money to give all of these benefits to the faculty members.[13]

Financing an expanding medical center could not be accomplished without "the financial information that tells the whole story." This point was made unequivocally to the faculty in view of the trouble the regents had previously experienced. The committee set about to get accurate data about the medical center and comparable data from other medical schools and teaching hospitals. But it was not easy. There were then 90 active medical schools in the United States and no two were identical. Because medical schools are a part of and related to their parent university and because they also relate to facilities such as hospitals, clinics and research laboratories which may be privately or publicly supported, the process of comparison becomes more than a little complicated.

In the decade between 1955 and 1964, the operating income of the medical center went up from $4 million to $13 million, including the cost of operating the two hospitals. In 1955, grant funds from "sponsored programs," i.e., soft money not provided by the state, was half a million dollars, or 14 percent of the total income. By 1964, grants had reached $5.4 million or 41 percent of the entire medical center income. Compared with the state appropriation to the medical school for educational and general purposes, revenues such as student fees and miscellaneous sales plus the soft money totaled almost five times the amount of the hard money. The faculty competed for this soft money with researchers in other medical schools from sources such as the National Institutes of Health and the National Science Foundation. The supply of this kind of money was rising and the State Regents had "every reason to believe it would continue to expand in the foreseeable future."

The self-study noted that, contrary to rumored misuse of departmental funds, professional fees for care of private and welfare patients were placed in a departmental trust fund which was centrally administered at the medical center. However, there was still a difference of opinion as to just how these funds should be handled...whether they should go direct to the medical school department or be placed in the revolving fund of the state treasury. This question was not to be answered completely for another seven years.

When compared with 10 other medical schools in the southwest region, Oklahoma ranked tenth, next to the bottom, when money for sponsored programs was excluded and only state support was tallied. Also, O.U. had the highest ratio, 72 percent, of soft money to the total spent for education and research. It had reached, indeed surpassed the "danger point" of 50 percent soft money expressed by Dr. Ward Darley, director of the AAMC. This situation indicated two problems: too much emphasis was being placed on research and state support for the educational program was inadequate. Further comparisons showed Oklahoma close to or at the very bottom of a list of 12 medical schools in respect to educational expenditures. The State Regents estimated Oklahoma's annual budget shortfall at $1.5 to $2 million.

In national rankings, Oklahoma was seventh from the bottom among 84 medical schools in the amount of money spent for educational and general purposes. There was not much question the University of Oklahoma School of Medicine was poor in the early 1960s. It spent less than $1.5 million of hard money annually when the median expenditure in other medical schools throughout the country was more than double that amount, $3.5 million.

The 1964 USPHS planning guide for new medical schools showed the budget of a school of medicine the size of Oklahoma, which admitted 96 students in the entering class, should be $4.112 million. An advisory committee on finance for the medical center came up with a recommended budget of $5.325 million but that was based on an entering class of 105 students. The State Regents recommended that "Oklahoma should move as rapidly as possible toward a more adequate financing...of the School of Medicine."

In its financial review, the study committee also compared the cost of the two University hospitals with six other teaching institutions in the region and found that, once again, O.U. was next to the bottom. Expenditures in 1962-1963 were $10,241 for each of the 463 beds in operation. In another comparison, O.U. spent $3,192 per bed less than the average of 32 teaching hospitals in the nation. To come up to average, the medical center would have had to increase its $5.2 million hospital budget by another $2.1 million. The University Hospitals' budget included the school of nursing (third and fourth years) and teaching programs in physical therapy, medical technology and other allied health professions. Again,

operational variables make comparisons difficult and the money spent was only one measurement. The self-study concluded, however, that O.U.'s teaching hospitals were "inadequately financed." The State Regents could take only meager comfort in the recognition that the hospitals were not as bad off as the medical school.

The medical education study pointed out that the formula used to evaluate budget requests of the other schools in the state system just did not apply to the medical center. "A major problem that has long plagued the State Regents in their efforts to appraise the budget needs of the Medical Center has been that of obtaining normative data with which to compare and evaluate its financial needs." The State Regents determined to "continue to compile normative data" so they could better understand the financial requirements of a modern medical education program.[14]

The study report carefully detailed the legal position of the medical center, making clear that the school of medicine and university hospitals were "constituent agencies of the State System of Higher Education." The State Regents for Higher Education further identified itself as the "coordinating board of control" and specified its powers to prescribe standards, determine functions and courses of study in each institution, grant degrees, recommend to the state legislature the budget allocation to each institution as well as recommend to the Legislature proposed fees. There was not much legal question who was in charge

State Regents for Higher Education in 1966 were Harry P. Conroy, John J. Vater Jr., R.L. Crowder, Jr., Bob F. Allee, Clyde A. Wheeler, Mrs. F.S. Ditmars, chairman, Dr. E.T. Dunlap, chancellor, Donald S. Kennedy, W.T. Payne, G. Ellis Gable and T.G. Sexton, administrative assistant. (University of Oklahoma)

although some medical center faculty members, especially those with independent income sources such as patient fees and research grants, did not always acknowledge the sovereignty of the State Regents.

Yet another board, the University of Oklahoma Board of Regents, was charged by the state constitution with the government of the university, which gave the seven members appointed by the governor the power "to prescribe rules and regulations for the operation of the School of Medicine and the University Hospitals." This is the reason Dr. Mark Johnson and the University of Oklahoma Regents in 1964 were so interested in selecting the right person as dean and director to head the medical center.

For years, the University Hospitals and the School of Medicine were two separate budget agencies. The study committee could readily see the basic functions of these two units were "so intertwined that they cannot be separated." The State Regents had the authority to combine these budgets and so recommended a single budget for the medical center. Ironically, less than a decade later, this inability to distinguish teaching costs from patient care expense was to become the principal reason for a dramatic change in the governance and financing of the hospitals.

The study committee identified the flaws in the organizational structure of the medical center. Three weaknesses were "immediately apparent" in the July, 1963, organizational chart. Of primary concern was the fact that the business manager reported direct to the vice president for finance on the Norman campus. Similarly, the associate dean of the graduate college ultimately answered to the vice president for academic affairs, also on the main campus. There were, of course, contacts with the director of the medical center because both of these officials were responsible for vital functions on the Oklahoma City campus. Organizationally, however, they could by-pass the medical center director who, in the language of the self-study, lacked "unity of command." This organizational ambiguity could "limit the effectiveness of administrative performance," the report said.

Also, because Dr. Dennis filled the position of medical center director as well as dean of the medical school, the organizational chart showed 31 people reporting to him. Actually, the number was closer to 35 or 40, at least five times the number organizational experts thought any administrator could effectively supervise. Therefore, the dean/director's "span of control" was stretched well beyond practical limits.

In addition, his title was wrong. On the chart, the

Bob Terrill was aware of the challenge of University Hospital before he became administrator in June, 1965. (OHSF Collection)

director of the medical center shared the same level as three vice presidents who also reported to President George Cross and was one of only four people with direct access to the president. The study committee concluded the position of medical center director "should carry a title parallel to that of the vice presidents." This recommendation was destined to arise as a crucial issue just five years in the future.

The committee noted that Raymond Crews also filled two positions. He was superintendent of University Hospitals as well as business administrator of the medical center. One of the first recommendations he made to Dr. Dennis in September, 1964, was that he remain as business administrator but a new superintendent be appointed for the hospitals. The new director of the medical center agreed.[15]

By the time the study report was published, a new hospital administrator was on the job and Crews had been instrumental in recruiting his own replacement. He told Gerhardt Hartmann, Ph.D., superintendent of the University of Iowa Hospitals, that Oklahoma was looking for an administrator. Dr. Hartmann contacted one of his former graduate students, Robert C. "Bob" Terrill, then administrator of the Mary Fletcher Hospital in Burlington, Vermont, who called Dr. Dennis. Because Terrill's roots were in Oklahoma City, he had reason to be interested:

I think in part that was the answer. I was interested

because I wanted a teaching hospital, had always been in them and there of course were not many teaching hospitals in the country, still are not many. When I got out there, I was very attracted to Jim Dennis's concept of the center.

Of course, I was fully aware of what I was getting into because a couple of years earlier one of my closest friends died in University Hospital. During one vacation, I was there morning, noon and night for most of the month he was ill. When I was there for the interview in January, 1965, I kept saying to Jim Dennis that I would like to have a tour of the hospital and see more of it. He kept finding other things for me to see! Eventually, I got across the street to see it. It was an enormous challenge.

Bob Terrill took up this challenge on June 15, 1965. He talked about his relationship with Crews, whom he replaced:

Raymond sensed that I was nervous about the role of administrator and afraid he wouldn't turn loose. As I look back, I have to say that Raymond did what I couldn't have done—he really *did* take his hands off the reins. [Even though Crews was the business manager of the Medical Center, Terrill reported hospital financial matters direct to Dr. Dennis.] I don't know that he ever became involved in anything in the hospital again. That was my business, so to speak. He was a gentleman in every way, very courteous, helpful. I was the nervous one of the two and I probably caused more problems because of my nervousness.[16]

Because future plans for the medical center were yet to be formulated, the study committee reviewed the need for physical facilities on the basis of the educational, patient care and research programs then in operation. Interestingly, the medical center buildings had been studied periodically for the previous 20 years and each report turned up major deficiencies. The governor had appointed a special hospital study committee in 1952 and, two years later, the president of the university organized a committee on future plans for the medical center. These committees preceded the 1963, $7 million bond issue for a new teaching hospital by about a decade.

Each of the in-state groups listed in detail the shortcomings of the medical center's physical plant and called for replacement and expansion. The Joint Commission on Accreditation of Hospitals, a national group, made similar observations in 1959, 1960 and 1963 about the "inadequate and outmoded facilities of the two hospital plants," noting particularly the overcrowding of beds, insufficient plumbing, the poor

system for serving food to patients and inadequate emergency exits should patients have to be evacuated from the buildings. All of these reports enumerated in detail the inadequacies Dennis saw at a glance as he walked through his alma mater in June of 1964.

Even the land on which the buildings were located was inadequate. The term "medical center" also was used at times to include the affiliated non-university institutions, namely the V.A. Hospital and OMRF. These eight buildings occupied less than 24 acres; recommended minimal land area for a medical center of comparable size was 50 acres. The optimal amount of space was 150 acres. In 1965, the Oklahoma City Urban Renewal program visualized expansion of the O.U. Medical Center south to 10th Street and east to Stonewall which would bring the land area to 53 acres.

Most of the medical center buildings were old; 88 percent were at least 10 years old, 44 percent were 40 years old and Old Main had been in service for 46 years. The advisory committee on physical plant needs looked at the space inventory and developed quality ratings of the academic and service buildings then in use. Aided by consultants from Kansas State University and Pennsylvania State University, the committee concluded that nearly half of the 616,630 gross square feet of space was substandard and about a third of the assignable space was "badly overcrowded." In the medical school building, half the space was overcrowded. "It has been a matter of including too much for the space and money available," the report stated flatly, and recommended the university "should carefully program its total medical needs, and then should establish master plans and a schedule of the proposed construction in a system of priorities." The university also was advised to seek the help of professional hospital and planning consultants and employ architects who specialize in hospital construction.

Dr. George T. Harrell, from the Hershey School of Medicine at Pennsylvania State University, one of the consultants, observed that most of the medical center buidings were very poorly designed for their purpose and recommended they be replaced rather than remodeled. He said, "An immediate need is apparent for an overall long range plan." The O.U. Medical Center had 412,000 net assignable square feet of space compared with 625,000 square feet recommended by the 1964 U.S. Public Health Service guide for planning new medical schools and teaching hospitals.[17]

The study committee made the point that "despite certain financial limitations, organizational weak-

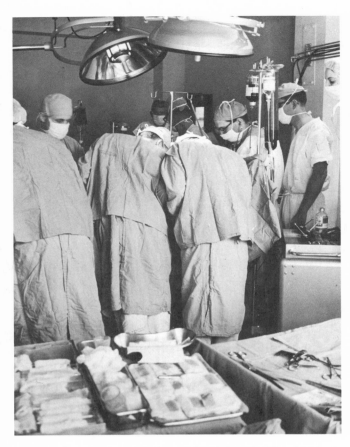

Open heart surgery performed in University Hospital in 1961. (University of Oklahoma)

The first director of the Oklahoma Health Planning Agency was Jack V. Boyd, shown here in 1969. (Oklahoma Publishing Company)

nesses and lack of comprehensive planning, the activities of the medical center are essentially sound and of high quality." It gave much of the credit to the growing, full time faculty which had engineered much of the expansion and improvement in the educational programs during the previous 10 years. The State Regents were faulted for never having clearly defined the medical center's functions or programs and early attention to the "development of such a policy document" was strongly recommended. The report warned that "the high quality of the current [educational] effort" could not be maintained without more money, which was needed right away. The committee also cautioned against further dependence on "soft" research money and said the State of Oklahoma needed "to provide a more stable source of money for its medical center."

The State Regents echoed the consultant's call for improved long range planning. Already, Dr. Dennis had begun compiling a "work program" toward that end with the aid of Lester Gorsline and Associates. The study committee realized that a long range plan would have to be completed in order "to obtain the

financing that will be necessary for its implementation." Other conclusions dealt with the need to change the organizational structure and the need for a single medical center budget.

Briefly, the 13 specific recommendations of the Self-Study of Medical Education in Oklahoma were:

1. Raise the level of income of the medical center.

2. Develop a written policy statement setting forth the functions and programs of the medical center.

3. Develop a statement of overall medical center objectives and plan to implement the basic functions...teaching, research and service...with appropriate balance.

4. Expand the medical center into a comprehensive educational center for the health sciences, including schools of public health, dentistry and allied health sciences.

5. Complete a master plan for long range campus development and a capital budget as quickly as possible.

6. Revise the organizational structure of the medical center.

7. State Regents define operational and capital budget needs in a single unit for the medical center and allocate funds accordingly in the 1965-1967 biennium.

8. Clarify the policy for identifying and handling welfare and private patient income.

9. Move toward a strict full-time faculty plan and make salaries competitive with other medical schools in the region.

10. Study faculty workload and performance.

11. Extend to the medical center faculty the same staff benefit programs available to the faculty of the University at Norman.

12. Medical Center study (a) health manpower needs of the state, (b) ways to increase the number of family

physicians and (c) the best way to deliver health care to both urban and rural communities.

13. Restructure fiscal budgeting and accounting procedures.

The study clearly defined the task which Dr. Dennis and the medical center faced. The value of this 18-month exercise was that it legitimized the need for major improvements because the study originated with the State Regents. It also gave them an instrument with which to present the needs of the medical center to the Oklahoma legislature. In addition, it gave Dean Dennis the authority to proceed with the concept of a truly modern, academic, tertiary health care center—a concept which was taking form in his brain.

Some people live in the past, others in the "now." A few, the inventors, the conceptualizers, the planners, live in the future. James L. Dennis was a futurist and again quoting Jack Boyd, he was "the right man at the right time!"[18]

PART TWO

THE DENNIS YEARS:
1965-1970

THE POWER STRUCTURE: 1965-1966

Robert S. Kerr, the senior United States Senator from Oklahoma, working with Congressman Wilbur Mills of Arkansas, the Chairman of the House Ways and Means Committee, developed the Kerr-Mills legislation which was the forerunner of Medicaid, federal support of medical care for the indigent. The physicians in Senator Kerr's conservative home state were not enthralled with this program because to them it smacked of socialized medicine, an idea to which they were unalterably opposed. According to Dr. Joe White:

The senator was a little bit concerned about his chances of getting reelected and had always felt the medical profession had opposed him because of Kerr-Mills. So he wanted to mend his fences and a couple of Kerr's lieutenants came to see me and asked if we wouldn't do something to enhance the senator's image with the medical community in Oklahoma.

So we had him to lunch one day in 1962. Sitting around the table we had DuVal, Rainey Williams, Jim Merrill, Stewart Wolf, Eliel; we had some reasonably bright people there. As we carried on the conversation, it just occurred to me there wasn't any question that the smartest guy at that table was Senator Kerr. In spite of that, he had on his red galluses and [there was] this down home, country thing he turned on. But he was a *sharp* guy and we had trotted out our biggest brains to be with him.

Then we had a big, open house reception for him and invited the whole town [doctors] to come to the Faculty House. And he was *so* charming that night. People would come up and he'd hold their hand, put his hand on their shoulder and talk to them all, the physicians and their wives. I think every physician in Oklahoma City who came that night went away deciding to vote for Senator Kerr![1]

One of the most important decisions Kerr made was in 1937 when he persuaded geologist Dean A. McGee to join him in business. By 1964, McGee had risen to chairman of Kerr-McGee Oil Industries, Inc. McGee also was interested in medical affairs and was to become the leader of community forces instrumental in the development of the Oklahoma Health Center.[2]

Dr. Dennis recalled his first contact with Dean A. McGee:

There was a special meeting of the [Oklahoma City]

Oklahoma's highly influential Senator Robert S. Kerr and founder of firm that became Kerr-McGee. (OKC Chamber of Commerce)

Dean A. McGee worked as a geologist for Phillips Petroleum before he joined Robert S. Kerr. (OKC Chamber of Commerce)

Chamber of Commerce that Stanley Draper [executive vice president of the chamber] set up. This happened early in 1965. I presented a concept of a health center in which public, private and university services would pull together. That was the essence of it. Stanley Draper got excited about the idea and there were some other forces.

Within a matter of a few weeks, there were two or three other meetings that Stanley Draper set up and turned over to William Morgan "Bill" Cain [head of Cain's Coffee Company of Oklahoma City and chairman of the board of trustees of the Presbyterian Hospital]. This was fortuitous because I had not been aware Presbyterian had been thinking of a move. Bill Cain was interested in this kind of a move although he was uneasy about whether or not the medical staff would accept it at that time.

I think that Stanley Draper probably talked with Dean McGee and also Bill Payne [William T. Payne, president of Big Chief Drilling Company] and to E. K. Gaylord [president of the Oklahoma Publishing Company] and John Kirkpatrick [president of Kirkpatrick Oil Company]. I had luncheon with those people and suggested that a prototype for this kind of development would be the Texas Medical Center in Houston, although ours would not be on that scale. I had some basic material on the organization of that center and read it to them. Bill Payne offered his company plane to visit the Texas Medical Center. There was a good crew of power brokers who flew down there and I was privileged to be among them.[3]

Paul Strasbaugh, Stanley Draper's assistant who later succeeded him as executive vice president of the chamber, recalled:

It was a jointly sponsored trip of the Urban Action Foundation and the Oklahoma City Chamber of Commerce. The reason the Urban Action Foundation was involved was because it was organized to foster and encourage urban renewal in certain areas of the city. It was the precursor of the Oklahoma City Urban Renewal Authority. It organized, employed and paid the urban renewal staff in the early days and financed the early planning. The Urban Action Foundation was an arm of the Chamber of Commerce, really, because the chamber was raising funds to support the foundation, which was housed inside the chamber.

So the trip to Texas was to show our community leaders what could be done with the establishment of a major medical center like the one in Houston. Guy Keith, who was then the general manager of the Urban Action Foundation, and I went to Houston two days in advance to set up the tour with the M.D. Anderson Foundation, the umbrella agency for the Texas Medical Center which financed the studies and coordinated the devel-

Stanley Draper was the moving force behind the Oklahoma City Chamber of Commerce. He is shown with his assistant, Paul Strasbaugh, who later became the executive vice president of this dynamic organization. This picture was taken in 1968. (Oklahoma Heritage Association)

opment of the center....The group flew down on the morning of May 12, 1965 [which just happened to be National Hospital Day]. Keith and I met the airplanes and took the people directly to the medical center where they were briefed. There were 25 of our leaders present and we had a luncheon with a number of Houston leaders. My personal impression was the Texas Medical Center was a very imaginative approach to the establishment of broad gauge health care capability, one that I thought was really outstanding. It did the unique job of bringing together community and state resources to provide a major medical center in the City of Houston.

Our group came away with a tremendous amount of enthusiasm and determination to move ahead with a project here. And there was an historical connection. The Anderson family got their start in Oklahoma City. Hugo Anderson and his brother Leland, who was president of the Texas Medical Center, had grown up here and a lot of men who went on that trip, like C.A. Vose, Harvey Everest and Stanley Draper, knew them. The Oklahoma City people had a lot of respect for the Anderson family. That was one ingredient which made the Texas trip so successful.

I had always viewed the expansion of the medical center as an extension of a long-standing project of the Oklahoma City Chamber of Commerce. For instance, in the early days, the chamber took the lead in establishing and financing the Medical Research Foundation

49

in the late forties. The record will show that, concurrently, the chamber was very active in the location and acquiring the site for the Veterans Administration Hospital on 13th Street. Although we did not have a plan, we knew we wanted to do certain things with health care in this city. So it was a natural step when Jim Dennis came along with the idea of expanding the medical center. Dr. Dennis was given a great deal of encouragement by Stanley Draper and the chamber.[1]

Gloria Bremkamp, then the director of public relations of the Lowe Runkle Company, an advertising agency in Oklahoma City, was the one woman among 26 men who went on that trip to the Texas Medical Center. She was

…particularly interested in the signage (graphics) on the campus. At that point in time, they did not have a central communications effort. Each entity was responsible for its own. One of the things they stressed in that first meeting was the sense of cooperation among all the institutions that were involved in the Texas Medical Center. From my view, if there was one really important point that was emphasized, it was that. I had no way of judging whether that was just talk for us visitors or if

they really had that sense of cooperation. I would say, from my experience later on, if they *did* have that kind of cooperation, it would have been a rarity![5]

According to Dennis, during the flight home, "You could almost feel the adrenalin flowing! I think," he recalled, "they all felt it was a concept that was not just pie in the sky. However, there was a big job to be done, but fortunately, when Stanley Draper saw something that needed to be done, he pulled people together and kept pushing."[6]

In February of 1965, there was an evening meeting of some members of the state medical association and other physicians in family practice. Governor Henry Bellmon was their guest. At the suggestion of some of the doctors, Dennis talked with the governor about the problem of getting adequate medical care in rural areas and the need to produce more physicians. Dennis continued:

Also that month, I gave a talk to a meeting of the Oklahoma Academy of Family Practice in which I presented the concept of a rural health unit. I called the program "Operation Responsibility." My challenge to the physi-

The Texas Medical Center as the visitors from Oklahoma saw it in 1965. (Texas Medical Center - Houston)

50

Gloria Bremkamp was the only woman on the trip to Houston on National Hospital Day, 1965. (Lowe Runkle Company)

cians was to join with us and meet the responsibility to address the health needs of the people of Oklahoma. The university medical center would be the core and this would be an outreach program, a cooperative, collaborative effort all the way through. I got a very enthusiastic response to that idea, which gave me a base of support with the physicians. It opened many invitations to state and county medical meetings where I ran into people with whom I had gone to college and to medical school. That was a wonderful thing, to come back after 25 years and renew friendships.

After the trip to Houston in May, 1965, the pace of progress quickened. According to Dennis:

Things were beginning to come together amazingly quickly in terms of acceptance of a concept. I think everyone had been fighting, were sick and tired of it and didn't know the way out. Suddenly, here were some plans that included everyone, practicing physicians and the faculty. Dean McGee emerged and it was he who went out to the capitol to visit with Governor Henry Bellmon to enlist his support. Of course, the doctors alone couldn't do it and the university alone couldn't do it but when you got Henry Bellmon and Dean McGee and E. K. Gaylord and some others to break bread and agree on an issue, it's going to go! And E.T. Dunlap. I think E.T. willingly, gladly, even enthusiastically embraced the concept. He was glad to see a good program developed. After I met E.T., I never thought he was an enemy of the medical center. But he was very sensitve

and if he thought he was being tricked, he was just like an elephant....He never forgot it.[7]

Dean McGee had a personal interest in medicine because one of his daughters graduated from the O.U. College of Medicine and the other daughter married a physician. McGee recalled:

I was on a [federal] commission to increase the output of medical graduates in the United States. The Surgeon General called and asked me to serve on a committee which was required to have two people from industry. I really wasn't interested but the President [Lyndon Johnson] had been "X"ing the ones who had been submitted for membership. They couldn't meet without complying with the law so they asked me at least to come so they could have a meeting. This was the Surgeon General but I knew the president quite well. About this t'me, the plan for the medical school was under discussion and that interested me so I stayed on.

Of course, I did not vote when Oklahoma's applications [under the Health Professions Educational Assistance program] came up, but I think it helped from the standpoint we learned how to submit an application. It was a pretty tough commission which did not respond to pressure.

Dean Dennis and I went to see Governor Bellmon and sold him on supporting the plan to expand the medical center.[8]

Henry Bellmon was secretly ambivalent about it. According to the governor:

Dean and Dr. Dennis came in together and showed the artist's rendering as to what the center would ultimately look like and talked about what they had in mind about the scope of services the center would provide. At that time, it seemed like an impossible dream, to tell you the truth. They wanted me to be a party to inviting people in from all over the state; they didn't want this to be just an Oklahoma City undertaking. They wanted a broadly representative group. I agreed to do this and Dean, then, hosted a luncheon for this group.

I like to work with people who think big and dream big dreams but *that* one, at that time, seemed completely out of reach financially. The medical center was terribly underfunded and being threatened, as I remember, with loss of its accreditation. The notion that you'd suddenly find the resources, financial and human, to superimpose the health sciences center on that kind of a foundation didn't seem to make any sense. I could see the possibilities, the need to bring together state activities, the dental school, department of health, school of nursing, but that was only a small part of what they were striving for.

When it was observed he did not appear to have

Henry Bellmon was Oklahoma's first Republican governor. He and Dean McGee were the leaders of the community power structure backing Dr. Dennis's plan. (University of Oklahoma)

any doubts, Governor Bellmon laughed and said, "In the business I was in, you've *got* to be supportive and I was. In fact, I thought it was a great idea but, as a realist, it didn't seem to me it was doable in the time frame they had in mind."[9]

Dennis's next move was to involve Dr. George Cross with the Oklahoma City supporters:

> Cross is a smart man and became a fine leader and supporter of our program. Dr. Cross never, ever told me how to run the medical school. I went to Norman to see him, usually once a week or so. I tried to let him know ahead of time what we were doing....I believe he thought we were going awfully fast but he was never negative.[10]

Cross admitted that he "enjoyed working with Jim immensely. He was a great innovator...conceptualizer. He could plan and he could inspire his associates. We met frequently and kept track of things but certainly, there were no restraints imposed from the Norman campus." The president was enthusiastic about Dennis's ideas because for years he had listened to complaints about the medical school producing doctors who would not practice in small towns. According to Cross, "The people who were paying for the medical school wondered why they couldn't have a better result."[11]

The concept of a multi-institutional health campus which would permit expansion of the university's ed-

ucational programs in the health sciences and provide clinical experience in related hospitals and health organizations seemed to be gaining acceptance. The idea was that the health manpower produced on this campus would then move out into the state to take care of sick people where they live. It was not an effort to centralize health services for the state or even the Oklahoma City community.

The doctors, both on and off the campus, the state political leadership in the personage of the governor and the local community power structure all were in favor of Dr. Dennis's proposal. To consolidate this support among Oklahoma's leaders, Dennis submitted his idea of a non-profit "umbrella" foundation similar to the M.D. Anderson Foundation in Houston. After drafting a statement, a definition of the proposed foundation, he went to Dean McGee, who called in his attorney, C. D. "Don" Ellison, who put it into formal language, describing the partnership. "I presented this," Dennis recalled, "to the university trustees and the faculty and then Mr. McGee and Don organized a non profit, corporate group. Mr. McGee, from that point on, emerged as the catalyst that made things go. He became the driving force as soon as the Foundation became a reality."[12]

At the first meeting with some of the potential members of the umbrella foundation, Dennis described the concept he had in mind and assured these leaders, "I'm not here to pick your pockets; I want to pick your brains." The proposed foundation for the Oklahoma Health Center was described in July, 1965. It was to be a non-profit corporation known as the Oklahoma Health Sciences Foundation, Inc., registered in Oklahoma for benevolent, charitable, educational and scientific purposes. Its functions were to serve as a land holding trust, attract, encourage and assist institutions dedicated to patient care, health science education and bio-medical research to locate in a "functional geographic relationship" and operate as a cooperative and coordinated multi-institutional center called the Oklahoma Health Center. It also was to aid development of health science programs; maintain continuous planning in conformity with the master plans; work with government and professional associations and agencies toward the development of the center; coordinate efforts of individual institutions in the development of a "unity of diversity" and operate selected services of benefit to the Health Center such as a student union recreational facility, central library, central computer, professional buildings and housing for personnel and a central parking and traffic control system. In addition, it was to receive and administer voluntary contributions, gifts, research and training grants and "non institutional" income from individuals and granting agencies.[13]

The Articles of Incorporation were signed on November 30, 1965. They were more general as to the purposes of the Foundation, particularly regarding the proposed operational and fund-raising functions. The articles, however, did ascribe sufficient powers to the Foundation so it could have performed these functions but this degree of operational involvement was not to be.[14]

Ex officio trustees included the Governor of Oklahoma, the Chancellor of the State Regents for Higher Education, the President of the O.U. Board of Regents, and the presidents of three universities, Oklahoma, Oklahoma State and Oklahoma City. The executive committee listed as *ex officio* members the directors of the three institutions already in the medical center, namely, the university, the V.A. Hospital and the Oklahoma Medical Research Foundation, plus the Commissioner of Public Health for Oklahoma. The purpose of these *ex officio* appointments was to amalgamate the educational and health science leadership with the outstanding community people who comprised the majority of the Foundation membership.[15]

Both McGee and Bellmon were acquainted with many state leaders, including educators, publishers, oil men, bankers, industrialists, utility executives, physicians, ranchers and attorneys, so the list of people they invited to join them as incorporators of the Oklahoma Health Sciences Foundation read like a "who's who" in Oklahoma. They were:

E.T. Dunlap—Chancellor, State Regents for Higher Education, Oklahoma City

Julian Rothbaum—O.U. Board of Regents, Tulsa

George L. Cross—President, University of Oklahoma, Norman

Oliver S. Willham—President, Oklahoma State University, Stillwater

John F. Olson—President, Oklahoma City University, Oklahoma City

William D. Little, Jr, Publisher—*Ada Evening News*, Ada

R. W. Moore—Arkla Gas Company, Altus

Otto Barby—Rancher, Beaver

Harry P. Conroy—Halliburton Oil Company, Duncan

Henry B. Bass—Construction and Real Estate, Enid

Milton Garber—Publisher, Enid

Henry Hitch—Rancher, Guymon

Virgil Jumper—Rancher, Idabel

Exall English—Security Bank and Trust Company, Lawton

John T. Griffin—Grocer, Muskogee

William Morgan Cain—Cain's Coffee Company, Oklahoma City

Stanley C. Draper—Oklahoma City Chamber of Commerce, Oklahoma City

Luther Dulaney—Industrialist, Oklahoma City

Harvey P. Everest, President—Liberty National Bank, Oklahoma City

E.K. Gaylord—Oklahoma Publishing Company, Oklahoma City

E.L. Gaylord—Oklahoma Publishing Company, Oklahoma City

Donald S. Kennedy—Oklahoma Gas and Electric Company, Oklahoma City

John E. Kirkpatrick—Kirkpatrick Oil Company, Oklahoma City

W.W. Rucks, Jr., M.D.—Oklahoma City Clinic, Oklahoma City

C.A. Vose—First National Bank, Oklahoma City

James A. McNeese—Insurance Executive, Ponca City

Ned Stuart—Shattuck National Bank, Shattuck

Davis D. Bovaird—Bovaird Supply Co., Tulsa

H.A. Eddins—Oklahoma Natural Gas Company, Tulsa

W.H. Helmerich—Helmerich and Payne, Tulsa

W.H. Helmerich, III—Helmerich and Payne, Tulsa

Russell Hunt—First National Bank, Tulsa

Richard Lloyd Jones—*Tulsa Tribune*, Tulsa

F.G. McClintock—First National Bank, Tulsa

John Rogers—Attorney, Tulsa

Paul E. Taliaferro—Sunray DX Oil Co., Tulsa

R.F. Walker—North American Aviation, Tulsa

John Dunn—Rancher, Woodward[16]

Thus the Oklahoma City power structure, supported by the Chamber of Commerce and joined by other leaders representing every sector of Oklahoma, forged the connection with the Medical Center which Dr. Dennis believed essential if the Oklahoma Health Center dream were to become reality.

CHAPTER 8
ELEMENTS OF A CONCEPT: 1966

The concept of an academic, tertiary health care center as it might be established in Oklahoma was becoming clear. The University of Oklahoma Regents, the State Regents, the faculty of the medical school, the town doctors and Oklahoma City's community leaders were beginning to grasp in schematic form what appeared to Dr. Dennis in sharp detail. Certainly, the acute need for more health manpower was felt throughout the state although it was not accurately measured. The underfunding of the Medical Center and the outmoded state of its educational buildings and hospitals were obvious. But the idea of clustering more health organizations on a single campus was not yet completely understood. Some suspected it was an effort to centralize health services in Oklahoma City rather than provide a convenient and comprehensive clinical experience for students while they were learning to take care of sick people.

Dr. Dennis was optimistic about the progress of the plan. "Every piece that was essential for a 'critical mass' came together in a manner I'd never seen before," he commented. Now that he had general support for his basic concept, he needed the participation of other health institutions, land to put them on and also for expansion of the university, a plan for the arrangement and relationships of the institutions in the Oklahoma Health Center and a huge amount of money with which to do it all. Later, his consultants estimated the planned campus would cost $185 million. Twenty years later, the cost of building the Dennis dream totaled almost twice that amount.[1]

The two affiliated institutions already in the Medical Center had developed close working relationships with the medical school and many faculty had joint appointments at the V.A. and OMRF depending on their principal interest. The Oklahoma Medical Research Foundation had been created in August, 1946, and "was envisioned as the best possible solution to the problem of enabling the School of Medicine to continue its advancement as a site for training in medicine and the paramedical sciences." The idea was to provide through private means the additional research scientists and laboratories which the medical school needed but the state of Oklahoma could not finance.[2]

The original building, with 50 laboratories, was completed in 1950 and cost $880,000. Hugh G. Payne, Sr., the Foundation manager, organized the project and garnered the money to build it. As Gene White, who came on as assistant manager in 1949, recalled:

Hugh Payne was the idea guy and I was the guy out there trying to do it [the fund raising]. He hit on a system of "fractured efforts," choosing particular groups like bankers, physicians, pharmacists, dentists, even the nurses. OMRF was built on $100 gifts. We asked the doctors to pledge $1,000, payable a hundred dollars a year. We even got farmers to pledge bushels of wheat.

In the 1960s, grants were far more readily available and that's what we used to sustain the research effort. About then, the first Chapman benefit [from Tulsa oilman J. A. Chapman] came along as an anonymous trust which was worth about $150,000 a year. John Rogers was his attorney and Chapman was Rogers' only client. The smartest thing anybody ever did was to get Rogers to be the chairman for the big kick off banquet when the first campaign was held....Mr. Rogers' wife had trouble with diabetes and had been helped as a result of research, so he was personally interested and he spoke to Mr. Chapman. As far as I know, nobody in the Research Foundation ever saw or talked personally with Mr. Chapman. He did the first thing, an anonymous trust, and that's exactly what it was. The provision was if we ever publicized it, brought any attention or his name into it, it would be revoked. We used to invite him carefully by letter and we always received a very polite reply commending us on our work but gracefully declining. He was a very shy, withdrawn man as far as the public was concerned but a rather imposing man, physically. He lived very quietly and most of what he did was not known by Tulsa people. He was happiest on his ranch near Holdenville, a rancher and cattleman. His original investment was $800 in a wildcat well that opened up one of the oil fields in the Tulsa area. He wound up a major stockholder in Humble Oil.

He knew about what we were doing. We complied with his request, we did keep it secret and ran a good operation. When he passed on, there was a trust of $110 million and the Research Foundation received 22 percent of the earnings, somewhere in the vicinity of $4 million a year.

One of the little country campaigns we ran was in Coal County, not an economic strong point of Oklahoma. There was a lady who lived south of town [Coal-

The Oklahoma Medical Research Foundation. In 1950, $800,000 bought a lot of building. (University of Oklahoma)

OMRF's three vice presidents: Reece McGee, Director of Administration, Dr. Leonard P. Eliel, Director of Research and Gene White, Director of Financing and Public Relations. (University of Oklahoma)

gate] who was a prime prospect. We fully expected to get at least a hundred dollars from her. The workers were extremely disappointed; she gave them a dollar! They were crestfallen and I was pretty cut up, myself. She went on the mailing list and we kept sending her stuff....We published a magazine. Maybe 10, maybe 15 years later, we got a letter from Coalgate, an attorney's office, and there wasn't a thing in the world in it but a check for $20,000 from her estate.[3]

Because of such financial support, B. Connor Johnson, Ph.D., a biochemist whose research engaged the molecular level of life, speculated that OMRF performed perhaps three quarters of the basic science research on the OHC campus. However, as he explained:

> By virtue of the fact OMRF has to get its money via "sentiment," research has to be targeted in terms of what people say. Nobody will give you money to study the carboxylation of the glutamyl residue of a polypeptide chain but they will give you money to conquer cancer. You're probably doing the same thing in both cases but you've got to give it a name which has sentimental meaning. So you call it cancer, or arthritis, or atherosclerosis. You give it a disease name and then, if you're lucky, you go ahead and do what needs to be done so that finally, somehow or other, a solution to some disease...probably not the one you're looking for...will fall out.
>
> I don't think there's any other way. If you knew it was there, you'd go do it. But you don't know *at all* what you're looking for....You just look and hope that through looking, something that will apply someplace will fall out.

During a period of 15 years, Dr. Johnson was given more than a million dollars by the military to study food preservation by irradiation. Out of that work came the discovery he could produce Vitamin K deficiency in a rat by pure dietary manipulation. Then he studied what Vitamin K does and determined exactly what it does in making blood-clotting proteins. Dr. Johnson observed, "The army would never have funded that but they were perfectly willing to fund

B. Connor Johnson had a national reputation as a biochemist specializing in nutrition. (Oklahoma Medical Research Foundation)

[research of] irradiated food even though it tastes so horrible and is so miserable nobody would ever eat it."[4]

The other university-affiliated institution in the Medical Center was the Veterans Administration Hospital. During General Omar Bradley's tenure as administrator of the Veterans Administration in 1945, it became national policy that, wherever possible, Veterans Administration hospitals would be affiliated with medical schools and become "dean's committee" hospitals. The purpose was to improve staffing and thus the quality of medical service to veterans. This arrangement was a two-way street because it provided a way to expand medical school faculties and it also increased the availability of "clinical material" for teaching purposes. The first dean's committee was at the University of Minnesota in 1946. Dan Macer, then chief of hospital operations for the Veterans Administration at Minneapolis, Minnesota, worked with Dr. Charles Mayo who was chairman of the advisory committee in the reorganization of the department of medicine and surgery there. Twenty-five years later, Macer became director of the Oklahoma City V.A. Hospital.[5]

As Walter H. Whitcomb, M.D., Director of the V.A.

The Oklahoma City Veterans Administration Hospital, opened in 1953, was a prototype "dean's committee" hospital. (University of Oklahoma)

Hospital since 1981, pointed out, "In the V. A. system, this hospital is one of the prototypes for a very close affiliation. It began almost from the day [September 14, 1953] this building was occupied. It is one of the most closely integrated relationships and has been nurtured ever since."[6]

The four health organizations possibly interested in joining the university in the proposed Oklahoma Health Center were in various stages of planning for new facilities. One was Presbyterian Hospital. Its board of trustees and medical staff recognized their need for a new and expanded facility to replace the old, 190-bed Wesley Hospital at 12th Street and Harvey Avenue, originally founded in 1910, which became Presbyterian Hospital in 1964. In December, 1965, Ted Clemens, Jr., M.D., later the chief of the medical staff at Presbyterian, joined the hospital planning committee, chaired by Robert Lawson, M.D. Other physicians in the group were William Hughes, Edward R. Munnell, James P. Luton and R. Barton Carl. Three were in the Oklahoma City Clinic, a multi-specialty group practice headquartered across 12th Street from the hospital. Before deciding to move to the Oklahoma Health Center, Dr. Clemens recalled that two other sites were considered:

One was at 10th and Harvey, where the Red Cross is. It was a three or four square block site in the same general area. Then Jim Dennis came over and talked to us about his ideas for the health center. At that time, we thought of other areas, one of which was at 50th Street and Lin-

The planning committee for the Presbyterian Hospital was headed by internist Bob Lawson. (OHSF Collection)

Presbyterian Hospital as it looked on a wintry day in 1967. (OHSF Collection)

coln Boulevard, where the Howard Johnson [Motel] is now. That would have put us close. We considered that location because of the extreme, ghetto nature of the [medical center] area. There was great concern [among] some trustees and staff members about the financial future of the hospital if we moved there. We were all concerned about it but I felt it was something that could be overcome.

When it became known we were going to move over there [to the Oklahoma Health Center], I had feedback from some patients…not very many. Some may have left me and gone elsewhere and not said anything. As a general rule, when a physician moves, about 80 percent of his patients will follow him. Usually, patients are dedicated to the physician, not the hospital he goes to.

It took a lot of courage to decide to move to the health center. The board of trustees thought long and hard about this move because of the large financial outlay and because they were not certain the [medical] staff would support it enough so they could make a go of it. I was favorably impressed by the plan Dr. Dennis presented and I wasn't concerned about where the money was going to come from to do all that. I was young enough at that time that I was not involved in money matters. There were senior people involved in that; I was on a different plane. I just figured if the older guys said the money would come, it would come.

Observing "Now that I'm one of the older guys, I've got to worry about the money!" Dr. Clemens laughed heartily.[7]

The Oklahoma State Department of Health also had outgrown its facilities and was casting about for ways to expand. Kirk Mosley, M.D., D.P.H., had been the part-time head of the Department of Preventive Medicine and Public Health at the College of Medicine for eight years and was also associate dean when in 1960 he was appointed Commissioner of Health for Oklahoma. The Health Department was then housed in what had been a Union Civil War soldiers' home located at 3400 North Eastern Avenue in Oklahoma City. This building now houses the administrative offices of the State Department of Corrections. Dr. Mosley recalled that during the mid-1960s:

The most important thing was the relationship between the medical school and the state health department which was so close I really did not know whether I was employed by the health department or the medical school. The health department was paying me but we were so closely interlocked, I felt very comfortable in the dean's office and with the heads of the medical school departments. There was mutual respect, mutual concern about doing the best for the state. That largely accounts for the health department being where it is today…on the campus.

The idea of a new building was there because if you had seen the building we were in….It was old and obviously too small. We had planned to build a new building but it was to be out there [on North Eastern]. We had 30 acres beautifully situated up on a hill…a lovely spot.

As state health commissioner, I was keen to be sure that people on my staff had a role to play in the medical

Kirk Mosley, right, shown with Bill Schottstaedt, was the chairman of the medical school's Department of Preventive Medicine and Public Health in 1955, when this picture was taken. He became Commissioner of Health five years later. (University of Oklahoma)

Building of many uses. The old State Health Department Building was once a Union Civil War soldiers' home. (Oklahoma State Department of Health)

school. I was quite insistent that there be an interlocking of the resources of both institutions for the betterment of Oklahoma. We had many programs together, so it was natural for us to move the health department in when the campus was expanded. And the board of health approved of the move.

Dr. Dennis's idea for a health campus is the kind of dream you have to have as dean of an institution of that sort. You always have to look ahead or you're going to go backwards. I was very strongly in favor of it because you do not stand still. We have a Chinese proverb [Dr. Mosley had been a medical missionary in China] which says, "*Buh pa man zuh pa zan.*" and means, "Don't worry about going slow; get worried when you stop!" You've got to be bold and daring to move ahead. If you worry too much about money, you'll never do anything.

The best thing about Dr. Dennis, he could conceive of the needs and also could conceive how those needs could be answered. Many people can have dreams but don't have the faintest notion how they can be implemented. Jim Dennis had that laid out pretty clearly in his own mind. Without him, we would never have had it.[8]

Dr. Mosley recruited LeRoy Carpenter, M.D., in July, 1966 from the medical school where he was chief of the pulmonary disease service. Dr. Carpenter, who

became state epidemiologist and later commissioner of health, remembered that employees and even some members of the state board of health were opposed to moving into the Oklahoma Health Center. "This was mostly resentment of the old guard," he explained, "which was emotionally tied to that acreage. Thelma Mitchell, who had a lot of political friends, pulled about as many political strings as a woman could, but she could not prevail. She took as many memorabilia as she could out of that building and transported them to the new building...old clocks, things like that."[9]

The third institution considering affiliation with the university was Mercy Hospital. In 1966, the 25 bed original section of the hospital was 49 years old. Located at the corner of 12th Street and Walker Avenue, two blocks west of Presbyterian Hospital, Mercy had expanded numerous times. When it was purchased in 1947 by the St. Louis Province of the Sisters of Mercy, it had a complement of 145 beds and 25 bassinets for newborn babies. Previously the Oklahoma City General Hospital, it was renamed Mercy Hospital-Oklahoma City General. By 1961, it had grown to 225 beds.

Sister Mary Coletta had been a night nursing supervisor at Mercy Hospital in Oklahoma City in the early 1950s and from 1956 to 1962 was administrator. She had just completed her master's degree in nursing in 1955 at Catholic University of America, Washington, D.C., with a major in administration. In August

Sister Mary Coletta wore this traditional habit when she first became interested in the Oklahoma Health Center. (OHSF Collection)

Mercy Hospital was clustered with St. Anthony and Presbyterian on the near northwest side of the city. (OHSF Collection)

of 1962, she was assigned as Director of the School of Nursing at St. Edwards Mercy Hospital in Fort Smith, Arkansas. After four years there, she returned to Oklahoma City and Mercy Hospital, again as administrator.

When Sister Mary Coletta returned and took stock of the situation at Mercy Hospital, she knew she faced major problems. The deteriorating building was located in an aging part of the city. People with money were migrating to the northwest suburbs, "leaving behind those least able to pay for health care and Mercy was but one of only two private hospitals in all of Oklahoma City that would admit any patient regardless of ability to pay." The urban decay around the institution and the financial problems it faced made long range planning imperative.

That planning was just beginning in 1966 when Sister Coletta returned. She found the hospital planned to build a new wing on the northeast corner of its three acre, one city block site and the $500,000 to pay for this expansion had already been raised from private donations. But the east wing of the building no longer met public health standards, the central wing needed complete renovation and by the time all that was done, the west wing would no longer meet standards. In addition, a forecast of the hospital's diminishing income and its rate of occupancy signaled that Mercy would reach a break-even point about 1972

and then begin losing money. Something had to be done.[10]

About that time, Sister Mary Coletta was invited to join other hospitals and health organizations in meetings regarding the development of the Oklahoma Health Center. Boyd Shook, M.D., hematologist and oncologist, was director of medical education at Mercy Hospital and remembered the attitudes among the medical staff members:

As it developed, we were looking for a stronger educational affiliation with the university and I became chairman of the planning committee. The interest in education was pretty limited. There was a small corps of physicians who were very, very active in teaching at the university and had strong emotional support for the educational program. This was a minority of the [medical] staff, but because these people were dedicated and willing to spend their time, it was a rather vocal minority. They attended the meetings, came to all the conferences and committees and consequently gave a little bit erroneous portrayal of the make-up of the staff.

To my knowledge, the idea of closer affiliation with the university and in fact, moving the hospital in that direction, came from Sister Mary Coletta. This was initially opposed by almost everyone on the staff but as the people began thinking about it more, there were more and more physicians who thought, in order to have a first-rate institution, we did need to be heavily involved in education. If so, we needed to be very, very close to the people who were professional educators. So we came to see that the affiliation with the University was really desirable.[11]

Joyce Swingle went to work for Sister Mary Coletta in January, 1957, as director of medical staff services and medical education. When Sister Coletta returned to the hospital in 1966 and began planning for a new institution, Ms. Swingle worked closely with her, becoming both companion and confidante to the administrator. She emphasized that:

> ...Sister was very enthusiastic about Mercy becoming an affiliate of the university. We were always a teaching hospital, having interns and residents. Those [staff physicians] interested in medical education were interested in moving to the health center. Those who were not, were not. I was quite aware of this division of the staff. In the beginning, I would say it was about 50/50.
>
> I really don't believe Sister was aware of this divisiveness in the staff. She was so enthusiastic herself that she more or less had on blinders. She was looking down that road to a big teaching hospital affiliated with the medical center. She was homing in on that and wasn't aware of the vibrations from the staff and of course, the doctors were reluctant to make their feelings known until it came right down to the actual decision.[12]

The fourth institution fighting space problems in 1966 was the Oklahoma City-County Health Department which was scattered in four different buildings. The administrative offices and the environmental services were in the old Center Building on Main Street at Hudson Avenue. The laboratory was on the fifth floor of the Municipal Building, the nursing division was in the Civic Center Music Hall and the public health clinic was at 1229 North Kelley Avenue. The Center Building had been a department store at one time, the Halliburton Building, and was across the alley from the YWCA. Goldie McCall, then a clerk-typist and now personnel manager, said, "I was anxious to move anywhere but where we were. We had such a terrible situation to work in down in that old building, we were excited about going anywhere."[13]

Charlotte DeCair was secretary to three directors during the 21 years she worked at the City-County Health Department beginning in 1955. She commented:

> I don't know anyone who wasn't happy about that idea. We thought it would be excellent. The basement of the Halliburton Building was horrible. It was dangerous, too. They had only voting machines on the fifth floor and no way of knowing whether the building was structurally sound enough to keep those machines from crashing through. We were there for three or four years in the late sixties.[14]

M. L. Peter, M.D., who had been director of the City-County Health Department since October, 1954, had been trying for a dozen years to get a new build-

ing. It was obvious new facilities were needed in which the entire operation could be centralized and the board of health believed the proposed Oklahoma Health Center would be an appropriate location. Dr. LeRoy Carpenter remarked, "We all thought the City-County would join in. There was a gentlemen's agreement the state and the city-county would share laboratory facilities when we were both on the campus."[15]

According to Mrs. DeCair, to get adequate financing for a new building was a major problem. "There was always an effort to get millage. We knew that unless we had millage [a county tax earmarked for the health department], we would never be able to achieve much." Once a millage levy was voted in 1965, much of that money was set aside to finance a new building. "We scrimped!" she recalled. "I even made scratch pads to save money." Spare funds were invested in [U.S.] Treasury bills. In addition, the City-County Health Department expected to get Hill-Burton funds. The chairman of the board appointed a building committee to explore land and get bids from architectural firms.[16]

So there would be easy access from one building to the other, the site chosen in the OHC by the City-County Health Department was west and south of the State Health Department. Although the City-County Health Department was an operation of two political subdivisions, policy making procedures changed in the mid-1960s. Mrs. Decair said, "After we went on the millage, the county took over completely as far as decisions were concerned." It was a county millage so apparently the "golden rule" applied, i.e., he who has the gold makes the rules. Mrs. DeCair went on:

> The board of health was doing the planning. Well, when these ideas were presented to the county commissioners, apparently they said, "We'll pick the architectural firm and we'll pick the site!" I think the commissioners did pick the architect on bid and that was all above board.[17]

In addition to the major, established health institutions which might move to the Medical Center, there was a fifth one which was still only an idea. For two years, Richard A. "Dick" Clay, M.D., had been organizing a group of ophthalmologists and lay people into what in 1965 became the Oklahoma Eye Foundation, with the purpose of developing an eye institute. As he recalled:

> In 1964, we had a dinner party in the home of Guy James, a construction man, to interest a number of the men in town [in this project]. We got preliminary sig-

It was Dr. Richard Clay who pioneered the idea of an eye institute for Oklahoma City. (Richard Clay, M.D.)

natures asking for a [state] charter [as a non-profit, public service foundation]. John Speck, [an attorney and philanthropist] did all of the legal work in applying for the charter free of charge. Finally, in November, 1965, we got the official certificate of incorporation.

The articles of incorporation were signed by 24 ophthalmologists and 18 community leaders, including B.D. Eddie, R.A. Young, Robert S. Kerr Jr., Guy Anthony, Walter Butcher, Morrison Tucker, Winston Eason, Harvey Everest, John Kirkpatrick, Edward Gaylord and Gerald Marshall. Mr. and Mrs. E.K. Gaylord were also interested and attended an organizational dinner the first year. Later, M.G. McCool, of the Little Giant Pump Company, saw a newspaper article about the eye foundation and became its first president. Dr. Clay, the vice president, emphasized that:

> Dr. Bob Lawson played a tremendous part because he got Stanton Young interested in it and, of course, Stanton Young was the one who got Mr. McGee interested. We wanted to set up the eye institute separate from a general hospital...as a free-standing clinic. Bob Lawson saw that picture and thought Presbyterian Hospital would benefit by having an eye institute next to it. All of the surgery would be done in the hospital and the eye institute wouldn't have any beds. Eye surgery constituted 20 percent of Presbyterian's surgical patient load and we showed the hospital we could double their eye surgery if they'd help us build the institute.

Stanton Young originally estimated the institute would cost $600 thousand; Dr. Clay had in mind a $2 million structure, including equipment.[18]

In addition to institutions, other elements were needed to create a multi-institutional health campus. One of the first was land which, fortunately, could be obtained through the Oklahoma City Urban Renewal Authority (OCURA). The authority was created by the City Council of Oklahoma City on November 2, 1961, but little happened until the Urban Action Foundation was organized the following October. This Chamber of Commerce-sponsored community group advanced the money so the authority could begin planning their first project, the Medical Center. Guy Keith, an engineer and later Dowell Naylor administered this "head start" effort of the Chamber.[19]

The authority submitted an application for federal funds on February 1, 1963, and Washington approved the money for planning in May that year. As mentioned briefly in the Self-Study on Medical Education, the Oklahoma City Urban Renewal program visualized expanding the medical center south and east, doubling the land area to 53 acres. James "Jim" Yielding arrived from Cleveland, Ohio and became the first director of the Oklahoma City Urban Renewal Authority (OCURA) on February 18, 1963, but he stayed less than four years. James B. "Jim" White, a local attorney who took over in January, 1967, described the national beginnings and the purposes of this massive federal program:

> In 1949, Senator Robert A. Taft of Ohio introduced the original legislation to create the urban renewal program. This conservative Republican was not in tune with the Marshall Plan to rebuild [war-devastated] foreign cities. He thought many of our own eastern cities had [suffered] deterioration and actual destruction not unlike some cities that were "bombed out." His theme was, "We can't give grants to our [one-time] arch-enemies and not fulfill our duty to our own communities."
>
> Federal urban renewal legislation had three rationalizations. They should reclaim areas [for redevelopment] to reestablish a deteriorated tax base. Remember, under this program you couldn't buy land, clear it and then sell the bare land. Land had to be sold under a redevelopment agreement; something had to go back on it. Our downtown program was designed for this purpose. Several years ago [about 1980], just in the downtown area, Oklahoma County was collecting in excess of $3 million more than had ever been collected before. So we met that criterion. The second criterion was to redevelop, reclaim and to build new housing. The John F. Kennedy project had that thrust. The last

The director of the Oklahoma City Urban Renewal Authority, attorney Jim White, explains the proposed downtown galleria. (Oklahoma City Urban Renewal Authority)

count I had, OCURA had rehabilitated in excess of 1,500 homes, more than had been rehabilitated under this low interest rate loan program in Texas, Arkansas, New Mexico and all of the rest of the cities in Oklahoma combined! And there had been no loan defaults. So we met that criterion, too. In addition, the federal government hoped that urban renewal projects would generate new jobs...not just temporary construction jobs but ongoing employment. This was the objective of the medical center project.

The Oklahoma City Urban Renewal program met all three criteria which would qualify us for grants under the federal program. There was competition for these grants and many communities had very good programs but they were aimed in only one direction. With applications for three to 15 dollars for every available grant dollar, when the federal people had to eliminate even good programs, they would put those which met only one criterion on the back burner. We had a well-rounded program, well-supported and locally well-financed; our success in capturing grants reflected this. The local community leaders, the Oklahoma City Chamber of Commerce and the congressional delegation in turn were able to orchestrate our grant application effort with the Department of Housing and Urban Development and the Department of Commerce.[20]

The federal urban renewal grants had to be matched with Oklahoma City expenditures on a two-thirds federal/one-third local basis. Cash was not required. By financing improvements in or in support of an urban renewal project, the city earned "local non-cash grants-in-aid credits" which were used as the local matching funds. These improvements could be public facilities such as the Myriad Convention Center in downtown Oklahoma City, parking structures in the Oklahoma Health Center, drainage systems and the like. Oklahoma City did not put up any cash to match federal urban renewal grant money.

The Medical Center Urban Renewal Project (R-20) was bounded by 13th Street, Stonewall Avenue, 4th Street and Durland Avenue [which later became Lincoln Boulevard] so Dr. Dennis could see an expanded horizon to the south, the east and the west. In addition, the mechanism, money and planning effort

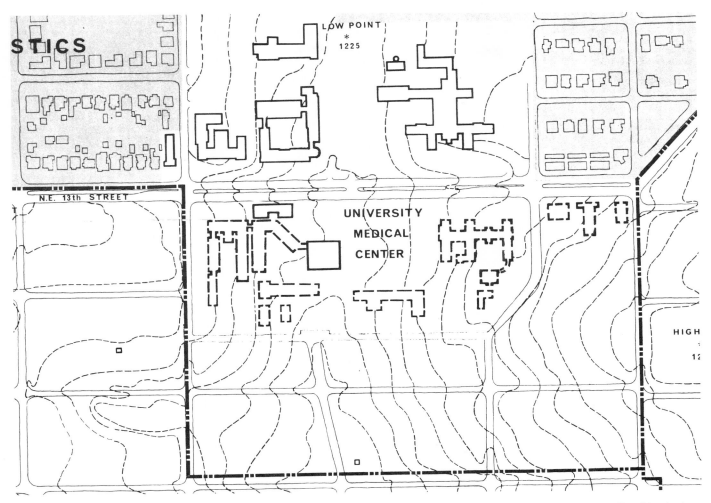

STICS

LOW POINT
* 1225

N.E. 13th STREET

UNIVERSITY
MEDICAL
CENTER

HIGH
12

The land proposed for the Oklahoma Health Center was located in two urban renewal areas. The buildings outlined by dash lines were to be removed. (OHSF Collection)

needed to acquire land for the health campus he had in mind were already in place...land, the first essential for development of the Oklahoma Health Center.

But the people living in the neighborhood who were destined to be displaced by the university's expansion plans were not happy with that idea. In describing their attitude, Dr. Dennis commented:

> Unfortunately, at that same time there were major riots in Jersey City because the university was planning to expand its medical center into the surrounding neighborhood which was predominantly black. I spent some sleepless nights worrying about handling that problem. It was inevitable we were going to run into some resistance and there were some undercover mutterings going on. There were no demonstrations or formal incidents but I had visits in my office from blacks in the neighborhood, telling me they were concerned. They thought if the university kept ignoring the black situation, they

> might have to resist. Their big concern was being evicted from their homes. If you got into the story, many of them moved into Oklahoma City from out over the state because "grandpa" had to have medical care so they moved near University Hospital rather than travel back and forth.[21]

Planning, of course, was the next necessary element. In 1965, Lester Gorsline and his people were busy working with the university planning committee, developing the program and plans for the building for basic science education. Meanwhile, Dr. Dennis, Lester Gorsline and Lawrence Lackey spent hours and hours making "butcher paper sketches" of the expanded center, getting Dennis's concepts converted to diagrams depicting the relationship between the university and the current and proposed affiliating health organizations. Each institution had its own purposes and goals, whether those were inpatient hospital care, public health service, medical research, health service for veterans or something else. These purposes had first priority and yet the reason for affiliation with the university was to support the central mission of the health center—to increase the supply of health manpower for Oklahoma. Thus, a loose consortium of health organizations had to be put together, built along the pattern of the teaching cooperation already established with the Oklahoma Medical Research Foundation and the Veterans Administration Hospital.[22]

By the time the new Oklahoma Health Sciences Foundation had its organizational meeting on March 2, 1966, the elements of a plan were beginning to emerge. Governor Henry Bellmon, who presided at this dinner meeting hosted by Dean McGee in the Kermac Building in Oklahoma City, declared, "The proposed expansion of the University of Oklahoma Medical Center into a comprehensive health sciences complex is an exciting challenge to everyone in the state." The formation of the foundation was considered the first step in long-range planning for developing the medical center into what was then estimated to be a $100 million complex to be called the Oklahoma Health Center.[23]

Most of the 38 trustees attended this initial meeting and heard Dr. Dennis envision at least 34 structures on the expanded campus accommodating hospitals, research institutions, health agency headquarters, administration, student and staff housing and teaching activities. He emphasized the economy which could be gained by centralizing services, such as a single power plant, receiving depot, laundry, and other "behind-the-scenes" operations planned to benefit all participating institutions. At that time, only Presbyterian Hospital and the Oklahoma State Department of Health were committed to move to the campus. Mercy Hospital and the City-County Health Department were considering the idea.

Much of that first meeting of the Oklahoma Health Sciences Foundation centered on hiring "an administrative executive to serve as liaison for all private and public institutions and agencies who plan to become a part of the complex." There again, Dennis helped by suggesting the administrator of the University of Arkansas Medical Center Hospital. Robert C. "Bob" Hardy was then 46 years old, a pharmacist with 20 years of varied experience in the health field. He had an MBA degree from the University of Chicago where he studied hospital administration. For almost 10 years, he was administrator of the City of

Memphis Hospitals, a 712-bed teaching institution associated with the University of Tennessee College of Medicine. He had been administrator of the University Hospital in Little Rock, Arkansas, since 1962. Thinking back on his interest in the Oklahoma project, Hardy commented:

Jim and I were not only associated in the hospital, we were close neighbors in a suburb two miles west of the university. Our teen-age kids were school friends and our wives were very close. I was intrigued by Jim's description of the project he had taken on in Oklahoma City and when he left Little Rock in 1964, I said to him, "If they need an administrator over there, let me know." He invited me to visit in Oklahoma City not long after that because they wanted someone to take over University Hospital and Children's but when I toured them, all I could think was, "These are real firetraps!"

On Easter night, 1960, after a pre-season exhibition baseball game, the wooden stands of Russwood Park burned to the ground. This park, which was the home of the Memphis Chicks, a triple-A minor league baseball club, was adjacent to the maternity wing of the City of Memphis Hospitals. By the time I got there, the window frames of the hospital were on fire. Fortunately, the house staff and the nurses had moved more than a hundred mothers and newborn babies out of danger. No one was hurt, but it was a frightening experience. So, when I looked at the University of Oklahoma Hospitals, I said to myself, "I don't need this!"

The job at Arkansas was comfortable but not very exciting. During my 10 years at Memphis, there was hardly a time we were not remodeling or building or planning to do both. This was what I liked to do but when I arrived in Little Rock in 1962, the hospital was almost new and we had more space than we could staff with nurses. In fact, Arkansas then had fewer nurses per unit of population than any other state. We couldn't even say, "Thank God for Mississippi!" because we were at the very bottom of the list. Consequently, we struggled to keep staffed 315 of the 400 beds we had in the hospital. In the four and a half years I was administrator there, we were able to open only 15 more beds.

Jim had mentioned the idea of an umbrella foundation to coordinate planning of the new center and that looked like a job tailor-made for me. I thought I could handle it and I was ready for a change.

The trustees invited Hardy to visit Oklahoma City and the announcement of his appointment as executive of the Oklahoma Health Sciences Foundation and coordinator of the Oklahoma Health Center was published on March 20, 1966. He got on the job in June.[24]

Another vital element was money. Both the university and the new institutions planning to move to

The executive for the Oklahoma Health Sciences Foundation, Bob Hardy, had been in hospital pharmacy, planning and administration since 1945. (OHSF Collection)

the Oklahoma Health Center had to find sources of capital with which to build new facilities. The university and the state health department looked to the state legislature and the federal government for money. The state of Oklahoma had the option of providing money for construction from current tax income or issuing bonds approved by the voters. The two grant sources then available within the federal government were the Health Professions Educational Assistance program and the Hospital Survey and Construction (Hill Burton) program. The latter also financed health centers and health departments.

E.T. Dunlap, the chancellor of the State Regents for Higher Education, was fully aware of the need to improve teaching facilities at the University of Oklahoma Medical Center so Dr. Dennis had to believe state money to match federal grants would be forthcoming. The availability of capital funds from Washington meant Oklahoma could get a new medical center for about 50 cents on the dollar. Dennis reasoned that few legislators would pass up that kind of bargain.

CHAPTER 9
THE FOUNDATION: 1966

By the middle of 1966, the elements required to advance the Dennis dream were either in place or being implemented. Specific planning for the Oklahoma Health Center could get under way. At a meeting of the Oklahoma Health Sciences Foundation (OHSF) on May 6, 1966, the Executive Committee agreed to appoint an Operations Committee, headed by Dr. Dennis and composed of representatives of Presbyterian Hospital, Mercy Hospital-Oklahoma City General, Oklahoma City-County Health Department, Oklahoma State Department of Health, Oklahoma Medical Research Foundation, Oklahoma City Veterans Administration Hospital, University of Oklahoma School of Medicine, University of Oklahoma Hospitals and two trustees from the Oklahoma Health Sciences Foundation.[1]

The question was raised about who would have title to the land in the expanded area. Dean A. McGee, the chairman of the Executive Committee, suggested this would either rest or pass through in the name of the Oklahoma Health Sciences Foundation with appropriate covenants in the deeds or leases to participating institutions to provide the necessary control. The idea of the covenants was to require appropriate coordination of institutional activities within the OHSF. This concept was unanimously approved but its actual implementation was destined to have an important bearing on the outcome of the campus plan.

The Executive Committee agreed to contract with Lester Gorsline Associates to undertake the master planning of the Oklahoma Health Center. Already, the City-County Health Department and Presbyterian Hospital, as well as the university, had engaged Gorsline Associates to help them develop their individual plans. The chairman estimated the cost of operating the foundation would involve some $100 thousand a year and the members authorized him to appoint a finance committee to figure out how funding could be accomplished. Dowell Naylor of the Urban Action Foundation pointed out that the Medical Center Urban Renewal Plan would have to be amended in order to clear the additional land needed for the health center. Originally the plan was intended only for rehabilitation of this residential area,

meaning there would be only spot clearance of deteriorated houses.

At the same time, the University of Oklahoma Regents were developing an agreement with the Urban Renewal Authority to purchase the 14 city blocks between Stonewall and Lottie avenues, from 13th to 8th Street in the John F. Kennedy Urban Renewal Project. This, too, was a housing rehabilitation program calling only for spot clearance. The university, however, had in mind the development of student and faculty accommodations to create a "community of scholars" convenient to the campus and this would also require total clearance.[2]

Three weeks later, the Operations Committee met for the first time. Oliver Willham, Ph.D., president of Oklahoma State University, and James Petty, M.D., a Guthrie, Oklahoma physician, were the Foundation representatives on this committee. Dean Chrislip, a marketing executive for Kerr-McGee, handled the logistics of foundation meetings until Hardy arrived in Oklahoma City.

The members discussed the objectives of the Oklahoma Health Center, how the land should be controlled and the scope of central services which should be provided by the Oklahoma Health Sciences Foundation. At that time, Dr. Dennis and the trustees of the foundation visualized that the administrators of the participating institutions would determine what facilities and services could be centralized and the foundation would then develop and operate them.[3]

On June 6, 1966, Robert C. Hardy, the newly appointed foundation executive, moved into an office in the Kermac Building, along with Linda Dickinson, his secretary. Operations Committee meetings were scheduled on a regular basis. Lester Gorsline's associate, Lawrence Lackey, the architect and campus planner, flew in from California frequently and the pace of planning for the Oklahoma Health Center accelerated.

Hospitals in America were not then part of the private enterprise system. Very few general hospital beds were in proprietary hospitals which usually were small, doctor-owned facilities, often converted residences. The rest of the general hospital system was either sponsored by cities, counties, the federal Veterans

Administration and the U.S. Public Health Service (which operated Marine hospitals) or by non-profit organizations such as churches. As a rule, states operated the mental institutions.

After World War II, during which there had been virtually no civilian hospital construction, the federal government initiated the Hospital Survey and Construction Act—the Hill-Burton Program—to build hospitals and health centers. The main idea of this federal/state matching program was to improve the distribution of health services by building hospitals and health centers in small towns and rural areas.

Because the need for hospitals was so great and there was a feeling of community ownership and pride in these institutions, there was no need to market their services. Each institution was a world unto itself and drew clients largely from its own community, whether this was a town or a county, a section of a city or friends and members of the sponsoring religious denomination. The patients of the medical staff, who usually influenced where their patients would be admitted, formed a client group for the hospital.

There was little overt competition but there was no particular cooperative spirit, either. In Memphis, Tennessee, for example, the medical staffs of Baptist, Methodist and St. Joseph Hospital were completely separate. If Methodist Hospital had no empty beds, patients of that medical staff waited for admission even though there were ample beds available at Baptist Hospital. In Oklahoma City, physicians often had staff privileges at several hospitals so there was less reason for admission delay but most doctors had one hospital in which they preferred to treat their patients. Among the hospitals, there was a sort of friendly rivalry which at times became not so friendly. Generally, however, the competition was "sub rosa", i.e., below the surface, and thus not apparent to the hospital-using public.

One of the early efforts in Oklahoma City to join hospital hands was the United Hospital Fund, a non-profit corporation formed in 1965 to raise funds for the expansion of St. Anthony, Mercy and South Community. It sponsored a campaign that spring to raise $2.8 million and when Mercy Hospital decided to move to the Oklahoma Health Center, approved the use of its share of the money toward building a new hospital rather than expanding the old one. But it would not be accurate to define this as hospital cooperation. This was the community cooperating to provide money for independent hospitals. Interestingly, all of the trustees of the United Hospital Fund except Stanley Draper

Al Donnell, the new head of the Health and Hospital Planning Committee, had also gained his experience in hospital administration. (Oklahoma Publishing Company)

were incorporators of the Oklahoma Health Sciences Foundation—Dean A. McGee, Donald S. Kennedy, E. K. Gaylord, and Harvey P. Everest.[4]

With the Oklahoma Health Center, a new era opened. Not only were hospitals being invited to sit around the same table and plan their future together as clinical teaching affiliates of the University of Oklahoma Medical School. They also were asked to help create and share centralized facilities and services in an effort to stem the rapidly rising cost of health care.

Coincidentally, on the same Monday morning, June 6, 1966, that Robert Hardy began full time with the OHSF, Albert M. "Al" Donnell, former administrator of the Muskogee (Oklahoma) General Hospital, took up his duties as the director of the Health and Hospital Planning Committee of the Community Council of Greater Oklahoma City. This was the first real effort to look at the need for health services from the viewpoint of the people who had to pay for them. Donnell said, "The thing that attracted me was: here was a voluntary program in a good setting where a lot of the power structure was involved. Some of the needs of the Oklahoma City area could really be resolved if you could get people to cooperate, develop and grow in the right ways. It was a noble thought, much easier said than done!"

The objectives of the Oklahoma Health Center were multiple because it proposed bringing together private, voluntary and public organizations, each of which had its own health purpose. However, the primary goal of this consortium was "to serve mankind in the preservation of health and the alleviation of disease."

Dr. John Chase, director of the VA Hospital, Sister Mary Coletta, Dr. Bob Lawson and Al Donnell go over plans for the Oklahoma Health Center in an Operations Committee meeting in March, 1967. (OHSF Collection)

This central goal was expected to be accomplished by creating an environment of excellence for research, education and service in the health sciences, transmitting new medical knowledge to health workers in the field, promoting exemplary health services, and increasing the production of health manpower. Also, the primary goal was to be met by "coordinated cooperation among health center institutions," by avoiding unnecessary duplication of facilities, by sharing commonly used central facilities, and by providing leadership and assistance in health science education and training and demonstrating new technologies to hospitals and health personnel throughout the state. In addition, the Oklahoma Health Center expected to encourage research and education in the preservation of both individual and community health. Broad consultation, planning and cooperation with government agencies at all levels was anticipated. These goals were to be accomplished in the framework of a master plan, in accord with broad policies of the Oklahoma Health Sciences Foundation and in collaboration with the governing boards of the individual institutions within the Oklahoma Health Center.[5]

Just getting everyone to talk with each other and agree on the goals to be accomplished was an undertaking in itself. The idea of the health campus, however, was captivating and all of the institutions had great needs which partially could be met by coming together. Dr. Dennis's enthusiasm and leadership caused people to rally around and a progressive spirit quickly developed among the members of the Operations Committee.

The people who met with Dennis in Operations

Committee meetings represented either the interested institutions, the Oklahoma Health Sciences Foundation or were consultants to the Oklahoma Health Center project. Dr. Robert Lawson, Jack Shrode, the administrator, and Don Nicholson, a trustee, attended for Presbyterian Hospital. Sister Mary Coletta and R.L. "Bert" Loy, long-time business manager of Mercy Hospital, were there. John Shackleford, M.D., usually attended with or for Dr. Kirk Mosley, the State Commissioner of Health. Robert Terrill represented the University Hospitals. Dr. F. Redding Hood was the chairman of the board of the City-County Health Department. The OMRF president, Dr. Leonard Eliel, came to the meetings and John "Jack" Chase, M.D., director of the Veterans Administration Hospital, represented his institution.

Robert Hardy served as staff for the foundation while Dean Chrislip, Dr. Petty, Dr. Willham and Don Ellison, the attorney, usually attended from the foundation's Executive Committee. On July 13, 1966, Sister Mary Coletta made a motion that Al Donnell be invited to meet with the Operations Committee, which he did numerous times. This tied the Oklahoma Health Center planning process into health planning for the rest of the central Oklahoma community.[6]

Lester Gorsline and Lawrence Lackey had been working with Dr. Dennis on a schematic arrangement of the expanded medical center and produced a "Development Plan Study" which was presented at the first Operations Committee meeting. This served as a way to organize the elements of the proposed academic, tertiary health care center and show the geographic relationships. This plan study provided the starting point for the long process of refining the Oklahoma Health Center Development Plan which was published in 1968. Lawrence Lackey explained the early work on this study:

> Our initial work, collaborating with Lester, was directly for the medical school and during those months we generated some preliminary concepts. One of those was to extend the health center to 4th Street, with a retirement community south of 8th Street. This idea, which came from Gorsline Associates, was that prolonged care and convalescent facilities would be a natural adjunct to a medical center. We wanted these initial concepts to be as comprehensive and ambitious as possible in order to expose the interested parties to the widest variety of options.
>
> In the preliminary layout, only one street, Lindsay, bisected the campus north and south. The object was to prevent the utilization of internal circulation for non-

Planner Lawrence Lackey coordinated the architectural elements of this multi-institutional health campus into the Oklahoma Health Center Development Plan—1968. (OHSF Collection)

medical center traffic. We wanted people to go to, not through, the campus.

We worked with Jim Dennis and Bob Bird at the university on these first studies. The formal, long-range master planning began when the foundation was formed. Over a period of two or three months, we negotiated a contract and developed a work program about a quarter inch thick with Dean McGee and his right-hand man, Dean Chrislip.[7]

Gorsline's associate, Roger Bennett, spent a lot of time working with Dr. Dennis and particularly with Dr. Bird on the functional details of the various buildings. As he recalled:

After we got going, Jim Dennis said to Bob Bird, "You run the planning and I'll take care of the political end." In Oklahoma, they had these "confrontation-type" politics. The way you got things done in Oklahoma was to pick up a mudball and see what happened if you splattered it on the wall of somebody's house. They didn't trust anybody because some of the people on the political scene weren't to be overly trusted.[8]

Gorsline concurred, "I have rarely seen a state so ridden with power politics as Oklahoma, everybody pushing and shoving." "I've never seen it happen anywhere," he continued, "except perhaps Texas." These, of course, were outsiders' impressions, perhaps exaggerated, but they did portend the character of the

struggles which Dennis and those who followed him would experience.[9]

Each administrator considering the move to the Health Center was concerned about how his institution would relate with the university and the other health organizations on the campus. Dr. Robert Lawson, Dean Chrislip and Dr. Dennis recognized the need for "prompt emergence of an image of the Oklahoma Health Center" so the first of many subcommittees was appointed. This group was asked to develop a code for the release of information to the news media and the creation of a favorable public image. With so many organizations involved, the Operations Committee could see how the public might misinterpret the purposes of the center and misunderstand some of the effort to bring it about.[10]

In addition to the arrangement of the campus, a major priority was planning for facilities and services which could be centralized and shared by all of the institutions on the campus. The list initially considered on June 29, 1966, included steam, power and refrigeration; laundry; medical library; computer center; continuing education facility; auditorium; parking facility; purchasing; and stores. Also on the list were high energy radiation therapy and radioisotopes; grounds maintenance; traffic, transportation and security; health and welfare services center; manufacturing pharmacy; post office; print shop; preschool nursery; and a cabinet shop.[11]

Most of the people on the Operations Committee were health professionals but Dean Chrislip was an oil man and was quite dubious about the prospect for success of this project. He recalled:

When I first heard about it, my reaction was, "Why there?" There really wasn't any physical plant, just a rickety old hospital and one building. I didn't grasp the significance of what Dennis was talking about; I thought he was trying to get the Medical Center on its feet rather than being a stepchild of the university down at Norman. I didn't think too much about the connection with the V.A. and OMRF. When I was invited by Jim Dennis and Bob Bird to come out to the Medical Center, it seemed even more ramshackle than I had thought! And there didn't seem to be much of an organization. I had been on a trip to India about that time and it reminded me of the bureaucracy there. I didn't see how they ran anything at all!

I felt it was a depressing environment and they would never be able to bring a university atmosphere into it there. So I had a lot of reservations about whether this project could be swung. At that time, I traveled back and forth to Houston and stayed at the Shamrock Hotel,

Even though Dean Chrislip, of Kerr-McGee, was convinced of the need, he was not at all confident the Oklahoma Health Center plan could ever be financed. (OHSF Collection)

Children's Hospital, 1966, part of "that ramshackle piece of machinery out there." (OHSF Collection)

so I had seen the Texas Medical Center develop over a number of years.

I just did not see where the money would come from. Because I was absolutely uninformed about grantsmanship and the federal money then available, I envisioned it would require tapping some resources here that I couldn't identify. I never thought of Oklahoma City as a wealthy town; I had lived most of my adult life in Tulsa, which *was* a wealthy town. With that ramshackle piece of machinery out there, not identifying any local wealth of the Warren or Chapman type and knowing the competitive feeling between Tulsa and Oklahoma City, Jim Dennis's plan seemed a little far out.

When Lackey and Gorsline put some of the first plans together, it looked like we'd have to have a donor of the Rockefeller category, with endowments of the type Gorsline might have known at Stanford. There, a bunch of dough caused a lot of things to happen. And at Rice, the same thing. But I couldn't see that happening in Oklahoma.[12]

The momentum of the Oklahoma Health Center concept received a tremendous boost when Sister Mary Coletta announced that Mercy Hospital would build a new, $18.3 million, 400 bed plant in the Oklahoma Health Center. She speculated the new hospital might be built in two, 200 bed phases because most of the money to build it would have to be borrowed, although they expected $1 million from the United Hospital Fund and $1.5 million in federal Hill-Burton money. Sister Coletta gave several reasons for the decision to relocate, but invariably, she said, they all focused on a single philosophy: "To give better health service to the community."

Dr. Dennis was delighted by Sister Mary Coletta's announcement which, he said, "reflected much imagination and positive thinking." As an affiliated teaching institution, Mercy Hospital hoped to meet American Medical Association standards for a residency program. Sister Coletta noted that "70 percent of the state's medical students leave Oklahoma for internships and never return."[13] The planning process was gathering speed, propelled by the enthusiasm of the people on the Operations Committee. With the announcement of the Mercy Hospital decison to relocate on the campus, two private hospitals and two public health departments would be moving in to join the three institutions already in the medical center. There was an atmosphere of excitement and forward movement as each group stimulated and, yes, inspired the others. While the casual observer could not yet drive down 13th Street and notice any change, the "critical mass" of people, determination and energy Dennis had worked for two years to assemble had formed and an explosion of change was about to occur.

The Operations Committee moved the planning forward so that by the middle of March, 1967, at a dinner meeting of the Oklahoma Health Sciences Foundation board of trustees at the Oklahoma City Golf and Country Club, Dr. Dennis and Lawrence Lackey could present revised plans for the Oklahoma Health Center. Although the *Daily Oklahoman* headlined an article the following day declaring "Final Plans Unveiled For Medical Complex Costing $185 Million," this scheme had yet to undergo more than six months of refinement. However, the basic concept was well developed and locations for the essential educational and patient care elements had been laid out

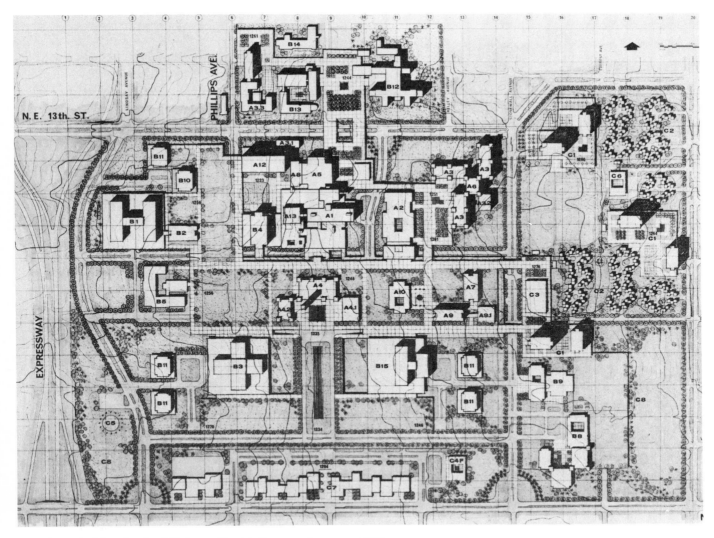

Schematic Plan for the Oklahoma Health Center—January, 1967.

Legend
A1   University Teaching Hospital
A2   Basic Sciences Teaching
A3   Research, Basic Sciences
A3.1 Existing Medical Research
A3.2 Dentistry Research
A3.3 Graduate College
A4   Library, Computer Facilities
A4.1 Auditorium, Continuing Education
A4.2 OHSF Administration, Medical Center
       Administration, Health Education
       Services Center
A5   OPD, Medical
A6   Central Animal Facilities
A7   University School of Nursing
A8   OPD, Dentistry

A9   School of Public Health
A9.1 School of Allied Health Sciences
A10   Student Union
A12   University Mental Health Complex
A13   Rehabilitation and Chronic Disease Wing
B1   Presbyterian Hospital
B2   Presbyterian School of Nursing
B3   Mercy Hospital
B4   Children's Hospital
B5   Community Mental Health Center
B8   State Department of Public Health
B9   Oklahoma City-County Health Department
B10   Oklahoma City Clinic
B11   Other Clinics

B12 Veterans Administration Hospital
B13 Oklahoma Medical Research Foundation
B14 Speech and Hearing Center
B15 Hospital
C1   Student Residence Facilities—High Rise
C2   Student Residence Facilities—Low Rise
C3   Indoor Health and Recreation Facilities
C4   Central Services
C4C Heating Plant
C4F Preschool Nursery
C5   Heliport
C6   University Elementary Laboratory School
C7   Neighborhood Shops
C8   Reserve Area

on the 200 acre site. A preliminary working model, made of scaled cardboard building forms placed on the site map, gave the trustees a notion of the way the various institutions would relate spatially with each other.[14]

Governor Dewey Bartlett and former Governor Bellmon were there and expressed their interest.

Bellmon said, "This is the greatest development taking place in our state right now. We are laying the foundation for one of the leading health centers in the country." In an atmosphere of euphoric expectation, the board unanimously and enthusiastically approved the basic plan for the Oklahoma Health Center.[15]

CHAPTER 10
DELIVERING HEALTH CARE: 1966-1969

During his pre-appointment conference with President Cross and Regent Johnson, Dr. Dennis expressed the idea that the medical center had to become more sensitive and responsive to the health care needs of the people of the state. To be sure, more physicians were needed, but the real challenge was to get the right kind of doctors to the right places in the state—the places where people had no medical service. Dennis concerned himself with the ultimate reason for any educational program in the health sciences—the delivery of health care to people where they live.

Tom Points, M.D., Ph.D., was Dennis's roommate in medical school, University of Oklahoma, Class of 1940. He had submitted Dennis's name to the search committee looking for a replacement for Dr. Mark Everett. When Dr. Dennis returned to Oklahoma City, they renewed their friendship and spent many hours in Points' home discussing the concept of the Oklahoma Health Center.

In February, 1965, Dr. Dennis, in concurrence with Dr. Schottstaedt, offered Dr. Points a full-time appointment to the faculty of the medical school. Dr. Points, an Oklahoma City obstetrician gynecologist whose Ph.D. was in Public Health, started on July 1, 1965, and recalled the responsibilities he was given:

> Jim arranged for me to go out to the medical school for four reasons. The first one was to establish the family medicine program. The second one was to try to change the curriculum to the point of teaching more practicing physicians...especially family medicine. There was the "health intelligence facility" and fourth was the rural health program.[1]

Dennis, in recalling the decision, declared:

> I viewed Tom as liaison to rural Oklahoma G.P.s and to the Oklahoma State Medical Association [OSMA] and he was good at it. I did not envision him as an academic planner. I wanted him to work on altering curriculum, especially residency training, to make room for acceptance of general family medicine training. He set up a program in the Mercy Hospital outpatient department and in obstetrics which did very well at first.[2]

Dr. Points continued:

> What we were doing in the health intelligence facility was trying to list the health professionals in the state of Oklahoma who were licensed or registered, by location, age, job and so forth and keep it up to date with [changes such as] moves, quittings, etc. We hoped to project the need for those various types of health professionals by location and number. Lab technicians were not in it because they were not licensed or registered in the state of Oklahoma.

The health manpower intelligence facility was designed to overcome the lack of hard data about the need for health manpower in Oklahoma so there could be intelligent planning to meet the obvious but unmeasured shortages in the state. Dr. Points had a $60,150, one year contract with the U.S. Public Health Service to develop this information for Oklahoma. It was the first such program in the nation and the Public Health Service expected it to be a prototype for other states.

The census of medical and health personnel was intended to be used to shape future state health planning and predict medical trends. The medical center needed this kind of information to plan the expansion of its educational programs. Dr. Points predicted, "Eventually we will be able to tell how many people we have in 30 health science categories and in what area of the state they are located. The material will be updated and be current." He said that while the Oklahoma State Medical Association, the Oklahoma Nurses Association and other professional groups made periodic studies of their membership, they were not continuously updated and did not become part of a central file. One of the proposed byproducts of the health intelligence facility was to provide civil defense with the names and phone numbers of medical personnel in a disaster area.[3]

The second practical idea for the improvement of health services for people throughout the state was the outgrowth of Dr. Dennis's talk to the Oklahoma Academy of Family Practice in February, 1965. There he introduced the program he called "Operation Responsibility," which involved the concept of a rural health unit, and challenged the family doctors to help. It was proposed as an outreach program, a university assisted demonstration of how medical services could be brought to the small, rural communities of the state.

Thinking back, Dr. Dennis mused about the problems which faced him when he arrived in Oklahoma:

I felt I had to establish rapport with the physicians in organized medicine because every legislator has a family physician…someone he calls…and we had to identify these doctors in order to accomplish [our] goals. Problem number one was: how do you establish the relationships that will permit the development of support essential to be responsive to the obvious health needs of the people of the state, particularly those outside the Oklahoma City and Tulsa areas? There was a great resentment of the medical school faculty by physicians, legislators and other people in rural areas who felt the faculty was irresponsible because they were not producing the kinds and numbers of physicians which were needed.

The problem of financing the development of the health center was one which obviously I could not accomplish without the help of the power structure, the men who *really* influenced both the university and the legislature. Of course, I wanted the support of the faculty but I knew if I went to them first, they would feel we were regressing to paganism in medical education. After the support of the state as a community was developed, I could go back to the faculty and point out that in order to get the resources they needed desperately, we had to demonstrate to the people of Oklahoma that they, the faculty, were responsive to [the people's] needs. And I used these words: "I can see no incompatibility between academic excellence and social responsibility." That was the concept I had to sell all over the state because it works both ways.

As for Operation Responsibility, Dennis recalled:

We had instituted a survey of health manpower [prior to the development of the Health Manpower Intelligence Facility] primarily for the purpose of deciding where we would put an experimental, rural family medicine clinic or two. This was presented at a meeting of the AMA [American Medical Association] in Washington [D.C.]. Afterward, a young man by the name of Hoover came up to me and Dr. Points and said he was in the Division of Statistics of the [U.S.] Public Health Service. He said that the program sounded good enough that they'd like to help fund it. We invited him down. He came and Tom got the first grant of this nature [for the Health Manpower Intelligence Facility] in this country. It was just a fortuitous circumstance, being there first with an idea whose time had come.[1]

The university was considering seven communities for the rural, family medicine clinic demonstration project, including Medford in the north and Valiant in the southeast. When the project became public

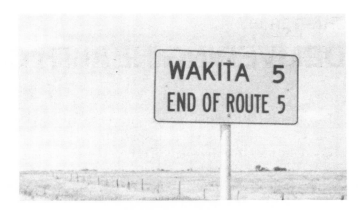

By the time you reach Wakita, you are truly at the end of the road. (OHSF Collection)

knowledge in early February of 1965, John Day Williams, president of the Citizens Bank of Wakita, Oklahoma, was the first to respond. A town of 500 people in Grant County, Wakita was isolated in the broad, flat, wheat and cattle country very close to the Kansas state line. Local interest was high, as Williams remembered:

We were interested in some kind of health care facility for our community. Dr. Dennis told us they were looking at a good many communities…I think a dozen or more. At that time, we met Dr. Points, the coordinator of the project. They promised us they'd visit Wakita and they did.

I don't remember how many months later it was they showed quite a bit of interest in this community. We got down to talking about, if they selected Wakita, whether or not the community could build the facility…and we talked about the financial end of it. They were very emphatic they wanted the project to be private enterprise. We indicated we felt like we could finance the construction of the health center.…

We raised money numerous ways…formed an industrial foundation and a charitable foundation. Then we formed an operating corporation. The community raised a total of $300,000 to put into the project. Liberty Bank bought the first mortgage revenue bonds, supported only by the revenue from the health center.[5]

Groundbreaking ceremonies for this facility, planned as a combination 40-bed nursing home, 7-bed hospital, emergency room, outpatient clinic and pharmacy, were held on September 17, 1966, during Wakita's annual Cherokee Strip Celebration. Governor Henry Bellmon was the featured speaker and praised the effort to bring health services to this rural community. However, it still remained for the university to recruit three physicians to staff the facility.[6]

Simultaneously, Dean Dennis was working to es-

Governor Bellmon addresses the crowd at the ground-breaking ceremony in Wakita. Immediately behind him are Dr. Riley Strong, Bob Hardy and John Day Williams. (University of Oklahoma)

tablish family medicine as a part of the medical school curriculum. Roger Lienke, M.D., a pediatrician, came to the University of Oklahoma School of Medicine on July 1, 1966 to head that new teaching program. Although his selection was not unanimous, Dr. Lienke was recommended by a search committee. Tom Points, who had initially devised the curriculum and established the family medicine program, was particularly disturbed. "They hired Roger without ever checking with me. After he arrived on campus, I quit anything to do with the family medicine clinic. They paid no attention to me."[7]

Dr. Lienke explained the connection between pediatrics and family medicine. He recalled that in the 1950s:

There was a term, "the disgruntled pediatrician," and much was written in the journals about him. It had to do with pediatricians being trained to do hospital care of severely ill patients and then, when he goes out into practice, what he sees is so much different from what he was trained to treat. He mostly sees "red ears" and the croup. The pediatrician as a consulting specialist was not very prominent. The only ones who were becoming prominent were those going into the subspecialties, such as pediatric surgery, orthopedics, neurology or urology. I realized that pediatrics was really just a section of family care. I felt I could better do the bulk of my work in a family setting so I just expanded and declared myself a family physician. Overnight!

At that time, the general practitioner or family doc-

tor was dying out. People were getting distressed, there were no general practitioners and nobody was going into it. So who was going to take care of the people? Internists and pediatricians weren't being turned out fast enough.[8]

But as Lester Gorsline observed:

Every [medical] educator I ever met has always wanted to be certain his tracks were filled by superb scientists, superb clinicians—the top of the heap. Nobody wants to educate a general practitioner to go out to "Boontown"—nobody. The clinicians are interested in the very top aspects of the medical sciences, not in the broad, general health problems of the country.[9]

Therefore, the reception Roger Lienke got in the University of Oklahoma Medical Center was not surprising. Lienke recalled that when he arrived at O.U.:

The apathy, lack of knowledge and no response was greater than any resistance. There was less than a handful of people in the state who had any knowledge of what I was up to or were enthusiastic about my coming—Jim Dennis, Bill Schottstaedt and Jolly West, that was about it. At that time, ours was literally one of the first four active [family practice residency] programs in the country. One was in a private hospital in Wichita [Kansas] and there were programs at the University of Rochester in New York and at the University of Miami in Florida. The unusual thing was that these programs were beginning to take form before there was any recognized specialty of family medicine. I came here with plans for training people in family medicine and the setting in which to do it before the reports came out indicating how it should be done; how to prepare a family doctor and give him dignified, advanced training similar to any other doctor. The famous John Millis report—*The Graduate Education of Physicians*—came out in the fall of 1966. Then the A.M.A.'s *ad hoc* Committee on Education for Family Practice report, sometimes called the *Willard Report*, also came out in the fall of 1966. Our plans antedated both of these. Somehow or other, the principles of the specialty in terms of practice and how the education for practice should be carried out seemed to be self evident.

Dr. Lienke laughed and added, "Otherwise, they wouldn't have been that clear to me."[10]

Thus, Dr. Dennis's effort to measure the need for physicians, educate the kind of specialist who would take care of families and encourage them to practice where their services were most needed was under way. The Wakita project was designed to demonstrate a way in which health care could be taken to rural Okla-

Pediatrician Roger Lienke came from Minnesota in 1966 to pioneer the family medicine program at Oklahoma. (Roger Lienke)

Governor and Mrs. Bartlett, Dr. Points, Lynn Thornhill and Dean Dennis lead the delegation at the opening of the new center at Wakita.

homa. The family medicine program would educate the physicians who would make the delivery.

By late summer, 1968, construction of the Community Health Center in Wakita was nearing completion. Williams, the banker who spearheaded the project, worried about getting doctors to practice there:

> The university's commitment was to staff the facility with three, full-time physicians. The community's responsibility was to provide the facility. That was one of the ironic things about it. We kept asking Dr. Points how he was getting along with their commitment for staff and he would comment, "Well, you all get the building built and we'll worry about that.[11]

The shortage of physicians was not the only problem Points faced. One of the biggest difficulties getting doctors interested in Wakita was their wives. As he pointed out, "They didn't want to be stuck out there at the end of the route." "And, of course," Points continued, "there weren't any young, family practitioners coming out of training who wanted to go to a rural area. Those who had just finished an internship…went to where things were established and going rather than trying to build something." Doctors did not like solo practice in an isolated community because they were forced to work long hours with little relief and infrequent opportunities to get away. Also,

they lacked the stimulating contact with other members of the medical profession.[12]

The Wakita Community Health Center was not quite finished when the Diamond Jubilee of the opening of the Cherokee Strip was celebrated on September 14, 1968, but the occasion was used to dedicate the new facility. The president of the American Medical Association, Dr. Dwight W. Wilbur, was the principal speaker. Unfortunately, within a week after the ceremony, Dr. Points, who had worked so hard on the project, had a coronary. "I'd go up there in the mornings and work with the construction details and all of that and drive 120 miles home to Oklahoma City that night." "I did that three days a week," he continued. "I always thought I might have a heart attack practicing medicine but I've never had any trouble doing that. It was the stress of the Wakita job that caused it."[13]

The Wakita project was expected to bring health services to a rural community of about 500 people which had not had a doctor for four years. The closest hospital was in Enid, 35 miles away, with some of those miles over dirt roads. Money had not been the problem. With its fertile farmlands and its producing oil and gas wells, Grant County was one of the richest areas in the state. The problem was the lack of trained health personnel—the same problem which caused 24 small-community hospitals in Oklahoma to close during the previous two years.

Although the Wakita project was opened by December, 1968, it was necessary for the university to improvise the professional staffing. This was certainly not the outcome Dr. Dennis had planned but it

Construction of the sprawling Wakita Community Health Center was nearing completion when the building was dedicated in September, 1968. (University of Oklahoma)

Dr. Dwight W. Wilbur was the principal speaker at the ceremonies. He, Tom Points and Jim Dennis inspect the new facilities. (University of Oklahoma)

pointed up just how difficult the problem of doctor distribution had become and supported the medical school's program to develop family medicine. The Medical Center expected to utilize Wakita as a teaching facility but not the way it turned out. With Project Responsibility ready for launch, Dennis had no choice but to use medical school faculty and resident physicians to provide services in Wakita. Thomas N. "Tom" Lynn, Jr., M.D., then head of the Department of Community Medicine, inherited the job of staffing the Wakita Community Health Center. In his opinion:

Jim Dennis viewed Wakita as something to attract attention. It *was* an experiment to see if, in fact, a state medical school could step out and influence the distribution of health services favorably in the small com-

Dr. Tom Lynn inherited the responsibility for medical services at Wakita. (OHSF Collection)

munities of the state. If it were successful, then Wakita could be used as a model. There was many a slip between the cup and the lip, so to speak!

When no physician became readily available, Jim Dennis, I think, twisted Tom Points' arm to serve as the physician for Wakita. He was an obstetrician/gynecologist but he'd had experience in general practice. Tom was going to do that but when he had his heart attack, he couldn't go up there. All of a sudden, I got a call from Jim's office indicating the staffing of Wakita was going to become the responsibility of Community Health. When this happened, I went up there in December, 1968, and opened the facility. I was their physician for one weekend until I could mobilize residents from the department.

Eventually, Dr. Larry Magnuson, Dr. Sara DePersio and Dr. Barry Eschen were the residents, but Dr. Lynn and the faculty did their share of the duty. Larry Magnuson carried the principal burden.[14]

John Day Williams reported the community's point of view:

The university did provide temporary staffing on a rotation basis. Of course, the general public was not going to change to the Wakita Health Center if they saw a different physician each time. It provided some coverage but nobody was trying to establish a practice, so the operating company which initially operated the center just lasted six months. We had a hundred thousand dollars capital. Because of the lack of permanent staff and other things, we were strapped. The same operating com-

Banker John Day Williams struggled with the financial problems of Wakita's Community Health Center. (OHSF Collection)

pany developed that 12 or 13 acre housing subdivision south of the center, so we had some money invested in that. About July of 1969, we appealed to the university to take over the operation because we were without funds and they had not been able to keep their staffing commitment. The university regents approved that.[15]

Finally, in October, 1969, Donald Graves, M. D., came to practice in Wakita but not as a result of university recruitment. The project had received quite a bit of publicity and Dr. Graves, who was in Kentucky, became aware of Wakita and was interested in this type of medical setting. The Wakita experiment was stabilized for the time being but serious financial difficulties awaited it in the future.

Wakita was only one of many communities which faced the problem of getting adequate health services. In Oklahoma in 1969, 70 percent of the state's doctors were clustered around Tulsa and Oklahoma City, leaving 30 percent of the physician supply for the other 75 counties. Other communities decided it was a good idea to build and equip a small clinic and doctor's office and offer it rent-free to prospective physicians. Some went to the medical school with full scholarships for any freshman medical student who would sign a contract to serve their community for two to five years after graduation. They hoped that after a few years, the doctor would become such a part of the community he would decide to stay. Still others established first aid stations staffed by nurses and/or a 24-hour ambulance service operated through a volunteer fire department or the sheriff's office. These were desperation efforts as the number of M.D.s in Oklahoma towns of 5,000 population or less declined from 423 to 274 between 1956 and 1969.[16]

The Wakita project put an extra burden on the Medical Center, one it could ill afford at that time. As Bob Terrill, administrator of the University Hospitals, recalled, "My first real clue that we had problems was Wakita, when Dennis asked me to look at Wakita and make some recommendations." "I suggested," Terrill continued, "it probably wasn't going to make it except as a nursing home. It became clear there was nothing to do except for the hospital to take it over."

Terrill was concerned that money which was being spent to operate the Wakita facility was being cloaked as an expenditure of the University Hospital. In one sense, the Wakita budget was merged right into the hospital budget. For example: the administrator, Jim Feist, was paid from monies appropriated to the University Hospital. Terrill thought the basic idea of Wakita was very good, but the arrangement of the facility created many operational problems. He added, "A physician's office with a nursing home and a built-in transportation system to Enid was ideal and that part worked. It also demonstrated to the state that the medical school really cared and was concerned about the [health care] problems of the people.[17]

CHAPTER 11
THE NEIGHBORHOOD: 1967-1968

The year 1967 did not start well. Late Thursday night, January 12, a 20-year-old female medical student was found murdered in her garage apartment at 15th Street and Lindsay Drive, less than three blocks from the medical school. Her nude body, smeared with blood, was lying face down on the floor of her bedroom, and it was later confirmed that she had been sexually assaulted. She died of three bullet wounds near her heart.

Police identified the victim as Jeanette Morrone of Westerly, Rhode Island, a first-year student and one of seven women in the freshman class. Detectives said an aluminum storm screen was pried loose and an unlocked window forced upward. A neighbor heard her yell "Help" once and then heard moaning and groaning. He called police and by the time he got outside, they had arrived. The garage apartment was in the rear of a home owned by Frank Rubane, an Oklahoma City physician who rented apartments on the second floor of the house to medical students and nurses.[1]

Miss Morrone had entered the O.U. School of Medicine because her mother, a physician and native Oklahoman, was an alumnus of the school and wanted her daughter to attend "her school." Naturally, the girl's parents were inconsolable, and this painful tragedy caused much soul searching among the O.U. Regents about the responsibility of the university for the safety of its students. Nancy Davies of Enid, Oklahoma, the third woman in the history of the University of Oklahoma to be appointed to the board of regents, remembered their reaction. "We had always given high priority to student housing because the area surrounding the Medical Center had not developed and security of the students was an important consideration. Student housing was included early in the planning for expansion of the Medical Center."

Philip Smith, Sc.D., the dean of students, said the faculty and students were shocked. While there had been break-ins and things like stereos had been stolen from the places students lived in the neighborhood, there had been no previous muggings or rapes, with one exception. Dr. Smith recounted that incident. "A couple of years before, another female student, Carol Tillotson, who lived on 13th Street about where Der-

Freshman medical student Jeanette Morrone, victim of rape and murder. (University of Oklahoma)

matology is now, was beaten so severely she dropped out of medical school. She, too, was in her house when an attacker broke in and beat her up...may have tried to rape her...I don't know. After the Morrone murder, we learned it was the same man!" Howard Gaddis, a young black man, was apprehended, convicted and sentenced to life imprisonment. As it turned out, he had just been released from the penitentiary where he had been serving time for rape.[2]

This regrettable calamity occurred not long after the medical school in New Jersey had experienced neighborhood riots as it attempted to expand into a predominently black residential area. Many of the Oklahoma City people being relocated by urban renewal because the O.U. Medical Center needed room to expand were not at all sympathetic with the Oklahoma Health Center project. Dr. Dennis could feel the tension in the community, gauged by the telephone calls and visits to his office, but by this time, the university was too far committed to consider changing the OHC plan. The only course was to continue to push the neighborhood back, buy houses in Lincoln Terrace as needed and help rehabilitate the surrounding area wherever possible.[3]

Dr. Philip Smith was Dean of Students in 1967. (University of Oklahoma)

Dentist Frank Cox grew up in the Medical Center neighborhood. (Harrison-Walnut Redevelopment Corporation)

One of the measures the dean took to ease the strain between O.U. and its neighbors was to establish an information office so the two groups could communicate. The university employed McKinley Brown, a retired military man, to keep the residents in the area informed about Urban Renewal progress and Medical Center plans. The office was in a house in the neighborhood. But Frank Cox, D.D.S., a black dentist who grew up at 1226 Northeast 9th Street, west of Lottie, was not impressed:

> After I came back from the service, we bought a place at 1119 Park Place, east of Stonewall. We were never dispossessed by Urban Renewal but my mother died anticipating their home would be acquired. That was really a big problem for them. They had heard they were going to be taken over and things were being torn down around them. Initially, they did not want to leave but after things started being torn down, they *wanted* to leave. Momma died first...had a heart attack. In fact, Dad's house was acquired by Urban Renewal and he moved out. Then he got sick and he didn't last much longer after that.
>
> My parents had two distinct thoughts: the first was a very "anti" feeling about Urban Renewal. The second had to do with the greed of the Health Sciences Center. Originally, it was supposed to come down to 10th Street; that's what we were told. If that had been true, my par-

ents would not have been affected. Of course, they had a lot of friends who were very upset because they were going to lose their homes. So when the rumor started and they found out it was going to get *them*, they were mad at the world! Momma was a very sensitive person and very concerned. I'll bet she asked me three times a week, "When are they going to take us?" First she asked because she didn't want to go but in her later years she asked because she *did* want to go. Momma died in 1967. People sorta felt like urban renewal was a bad deal because they didn't have any power against it. People simply did not like the idea their property was going to be confiscated.

> McKinley Brown is a neighbor of mine, a nice guy and I like him very much, but he was really not the kind of person who was able to do the dynamic things that were really needed at that time. He was not a social worker and that was really what was needed. McKinley Brown probably suffered as a result of accepting that kind of a job. People thought he was an "Uncle Tom."[1]

Meanwhile, a group of governmental agencies in central Oklahoma had engaged consultants to develop a plan to upgrade streets and highways in Oklahoma, Canadian and Cleveland counties. Known as the Oklahoma City Area Regional Transportation Study (OCARTS), it looked ahead 20 years to meet the traffic circulation requirements of the growing metropolitan district. The Capitol Expressway was an element of this plan. Scheduled for development between 1971 and 1975, it proposed splitting Lincoln

In 1966, 11th between Stonewall and Everest was a pleasant, tree-shaded street of 1920s style bungalows. (OHSF Collection)

OCARTS, designed in 1968, was the plan for traffic circulation in the Oklahoma City area in 1985. (The Oklahoman)

Boulevard at 27th Street to go around the Capitol along Stiles to the west and Lindsay on the east, rejoining at 13th Street. It would then proceed southward along the west boundary of the Oklahoma Health Center, curving southeastward at 8th Street to connect with I-40 and I-35 east of Byers.

This vitally important improvement would link the proposed health campus to the interstate expressway system. It also would tie into U.S. 66 (Business) which connected the Northeast Expressway (I-44) using Lincoln Boulevard. In 1967, Lincoln Boulevard stopped at 13th Street, bottlenecking into Durland Avenue, a narrow, neighborhood street. There was no easy access to the OHC from the east or south. With the programming of the Capitol Expressway, the end of the long isolation of the Medical Center was in sight. Frank Lyons, then director of the Oklahoma State Highway Department, observed, "It had long been in people's minds to have a "corridor" along Lincoln. For funding reasons, to get the 90/10 money [90 percent federal/10 percent state], we hoped to get the Capitol Expressway as part of the interstate system."[5]

However, Monty C. Murphy, Assistant Director of Planning and Research for the Oklahoma Department of Transportation, then called the Highway Department, pointed out, "In the 1969 public hearings on the OCARTS plan, there was concern about what a big interchange, a freeway to freeway interchange immediately south of the capitol complex, would do to the south approach to the capitol building." While these plans were by no means final, they were included in the OCARTS program and that meant better access to the Oklahoma Health Center, a very encouraging sign.[7]

For more than two years, the Oklahoma City and Oklahoma County governments discussed the problem of how to get southbound traffic from the Broadway Extension and 36th Street into downtown Oklahoma City. The OCARTS plan called for an expressway connecting this point with the I 40/I-35 interchange east of Byers Avenue. In 1967, this portion of the expressway system was proposed as a toll road. Others thought the toll road route should "lie as closely as economically feasible to the Santa Fe railroad tracks" from the Broadway Extension to the central business district.

Finally, on July 15, 1968, the City Council decided to ask the State Turnpike Authority to build a toll road along the latter route. As a result, the State Highway Department announced eight days later it had dropped plans for an expressway in the vicinity of the state capitol and the Medical Center. Assuming the toll road would be built, the highway department approved the idea of a lower-type facility, possibly a boulevard instead of a limited-access highway. Under this plan, through traffic would be routed several blocks west of the Medical Center yet drivers who wanted to get to the campus could travel an improved Lincoln Boulevard which would bound the Oklahoma Health Center on the west.[8]

This was precisely what Senator Bryce Baggett

Senator Bryce Baggett championed the Dennis plan for development of an academic, tertiary health care center in Oklahoma City. (University of Oklahoma)

wanted. He had raised opposition to the idea of building a major expressway down the alignment of Lincoln Boulevard when it was first proposed in 1961:

I opposed and fought that vigorously! Lincoln was always intended to be a great thoroughfare but accessible, with cross streets and intersections. I felt it should be built as a great boulevard rather than a limited-access interstate highway. My constituents, particularly those who lived in Lincoln Terrace, didn't want any part of a super expressway. Actually, I had many battles with the director of the highway department and many of the powers-that-be, the chamber of commerce and Mr. [E.K.] Gaylord who wanted a high-speed, super expressway. In the long run, my views were adopted.[9]

Despite the security problems in the neighborhood and the unrest among the people who lived in the Medical Center Urban Renewal Project area, the Oklahoma Health Center plan continued to move forward. In January, 1967, when the first federal grant application for construction of the Basic Science Education Building was approved and funded in the amount of $2,175,383, Dennis knew his dream was rooted in reality. He knew the university could qualify for federal money and his insistence that educational facilities be planned first had proved to be the right strategy. This encouraged Dr. Robert Bird and the medical school planning committee; it also set the stage for support in the Oklahoma legislature.

CHAPTER 12

EDUCATION FOR HEALTH MANPOWER: 1967-1970

An event in the middle of the planning process slammed the brakes on the accelerating momentum of Oklahoma Health Center development. Since World War II, the burgeoning demand for nurses consistently had outrun the supply. In the late 1960s, Dr. Roger Egeberg, the Assistant Secretary of HEW, estimated the United States needed 200,000 more nurses. Therefore, there was significant alarm when on July 25, 1967, Mercy Hospital announced it had decided to shut down its 40-year-old school of nursing. Because the avowed mission of the OHC was to increase the supply of health manpower and Mercy was to be an affiliated teaching hospital within the Center, this action looked like a giant step in the wrong direction.[1]

There were good reasons. Sister Mary Coletta pointed out that, "We are finding it impossible to attract highly qualified faculty members, some with masters degrees, to a small, diploma school when there are so many opportunites open to them in collegiate programs." Beside that, Mercy was having difficulty recruiting students because three-year diploma schools were phasing out as four-year baccalaureate level education in nursing gained popularity. Mercy graduated 32 nurses in 1967 but the next freshman class would have numbered only 20 or 25. While they decided to admit no new classes, they announced the school would continue to educate the students in the two remaining classes. Eighteen nurses graduated in the final class in June, 1969. Two other diploma schools of nursing in Oklahoma closed in 1967.

Moreover, the hospital pointed to the economic factors which had influenced the decision to close the nursing school. The net cost of operating the program had increased 50 percent in the past two years. Sister Coletta said the closing was more regretful because nurse power in the state was at a critical stage. Unfortunately, Oklahoma had no master's degree program in nursing so potential teachers of the profession had to be recruited from outside Oklahoma.[2]

Frances I. Waddle, R.N., then the executive director of the Oklahoma Board of Nurse Registration and

Frances Waddle, R.N., was influential in getting the associate degree program in nursing started at Oklahoma State University Technical Institute in Oklahoma City. (Oklahoma Nurses' Association)

Nursing Education, pointed out that nursing education was undergoing important changes at that time. Two year, associate degree (A.D.) programs to prepare registered nurses were being established in junior colleges. The American Nurses Association (ANA) was reinforcing its position in support of baccalaureate education for nurses, in contrast to three-year hospital based programs, and associate degree training for technical nurses who assist the leader nurses. It was an emotional issue and one reason for the declining number of applicants to the Mercy Hospital program. Another reason was money. As Ms. Waddle explained:

Pay for nurses was low. Nurses thought they had a good salary if they were making $300 a month. By 1966, the first nurse strike had occurred in New York; they struck for money and working conditions. After that, the ANA adopted their minimum salary goal which was $7,500 a year. Most nurses could not even envision they would ever make $7,500.[3]

The A.D. program was started in this old elementary school building on N.W. 10th Street. (OHSF Collection)

Dr. Phillip P. Chandler, E.K. Gaylord and Sister Mary Coletta attended the first capping ceremony for student nurses in the new associate degree program at OSUTI in January, 1970. (The Oklahoman)

Today the OSUTI associate degree program in nursing is housed in this handsome, modern building on the campus at 900 N. Portland. (OHSF Collection)

The closing of the Mercy Hospital School of Nursing was perceived as a crisis in Oklahoma City because that left St. Anthony Hospital with the only diploma school in the area. Al Donnell and Bob Hardy visited with Ms. Waddell to see what might be done to make up this impending loss of nurse production. It became apparent that the establishment of an associate degree program was the best alternative and the only possibility for such a program in Oklahoma City was the Oklahoma State University Technical Institute (OSUTI), which was then in an old public school building on Northwest 10th Street. A few days later, on October 31, 1967, the three of them went to Stillwater to talk with Robert Kamm, Ph.D., president of Oklahoma State University. A week after that they met with Phillip P. Chandler, Ph.D., director of OSUTI.

Both President Kamm and Dr. Chandler were highly receptive to the idea of starting the second A.D. program in nursing in the state. The first one had been established at Bacone College in Muskogee several years previously. As Dr. Chandler reflected:

The Institute had always been engineering-oriented and this provided new opportunities. We were elated. And it was all quite serendipitous. The move was initiated by the community to meet a need; we did not know we would be going in this direction.

Without the nursing program, we would not have made the rapid progress we did. We were later able to get a grant from the NIH [National Institutes of Health] to finance the nursing building, the first one on the campus at 10th and Portland. That was in 1974. Now we admit 100 students a year and 90 percent or more graduate and become registered nurses.

With the OSUTI program in the planning stage, the area-wide health planners and the people involved with the Oklahoma Health Center could breathe a sigh of relief. At least it appeared the nurse shortage in central Oklahoma would not get any worse.[4]

In her position as executive director of the Board of Nurse Registration and Nursing Education, Ms. Waddle had frequent contact with state legislators. She recognized Bryce Baggett as perhaps the legislature's best communicator during the 14 years he was in the House and the Senate. He had the ability to get to the core of a problem or situation and restate it in simple language. He also was fond of making suggestions, giving friendly advice to the people around him. Frances Waddle recalled:

The thing about Bryce Baggett was that he was a prob-

The Oklahoma Council for Health Careers was a cooperative student recruitment program headed by Ken Hager. (Daily Oklahoman)

As a veteran clinical instructor in oral surgery at the Medical Center, Dr. Robert Hirschi believed Oklahoma needed a school of dentistry. (University of Oklahoma)

lem-solver. He was not just out to improve his own political fortunes. Back then, there was a clamor to start new [nursing] schools and the Board of Nursing was coming under fire and Bryce was helpful when we got the board members together.

He told me one time that one of our problems was we didn't have a man on our staff walking the halls of the capitol. He said we were at a disadvantage because a lot of the decisions [up there] got made in the men's room![5]

In order to increase the supply of health manpower, high school graduates and college students had to become interested in pursuing a career in the health field. In October, 1967, the Oklahoma Council for Health Careers opened an office on Northeast 15th Street near the Medical Center. This joint venture of the university, professional associations and the hospitals which needed physicians and personnel was headed by Kenneth Hager, formerly associate director of the Oklahoma Hospital Association. The program had instant appeal. During 1968, the council answered 10,567 inquiries about 21 major health careers. It appeared there was ample interest in the health professions and any new and expanded educational programs at the Medical Center would be oversubscribed.[6]

One of those new health sciences programs was dentistry. In August, 1969, William E. Brown, D.D.S., the newly appointed dean, arrived from the University of Michigan to begin detailed planning of the proposed O.U. School of Dentistry. Robert G. Hirschi, D.D.S., who, as a volunteer faculty member, had

taught dental surgery at the university for years, had been one of the leaders in promoting dental education. However, he and his like-minded colleagues faced stiff opposition. Hirschi noted that, "One of the chief proponents of the idea of a dental school in Oklahoma was Dr. Francis J. Reichmann, chairman of the dental service at the University Hospitals." "Many people had spoken for a school for years," he continued, "so the official position of Oklahoma dentistry was in favor of a school. There was a lot of opposition to it, though; a feeling we didn't need a dental school." Others in the profession opposed it for economic reasons; they thought it would cost too much to build.

Dr. Hirschi believed that because Dr. Dennis spoke to the issue, everybody started coming around, accepting the idea a dental school could be built in the complex. It gained momentum from that point. But there was other opposition. Frosty Troy, editor of the *Oklahoma Observer*, said the dental school was "a mistake, a serious mistake." "It was one of those burdens we didn't have to take on," Troy continued. "My theory was: don't do anything you don't have to do."[7]

Dr. Brown accepted the deanship with mixed feelings. "I was well informed that the state money [to build the dental school] was available. I can't say I liked what I saw in terms of what was here at that time; it was messy—in fact, it was very depressing. [But] this looked like an exciting adventure and it ap-

Dr. Bill Brown from the University of Michigan took on the important challenge of building a dental college from scratch. (University of Oklahoma)

Education in human ecology was unique when John Bruhn headed this program in the School of Health. (University of Texas)

peared to me that since dental education had never really done anything here, the opportunities were essentially unlimited and we could do something our way."[8]

Another educational opportunity at the Medical Center was the country's only graduate study program in human ecology. The recognition that the environment was deteriorating and something needed to be done about it was just seeping into the public consciousness. The first Earth Day was observed in America on April 22, 1970, and was a nationally celebrated, bench-mark event. Many people claimed that the earth's fragile eco-system had been violated in numerous ways, resulting in air and water pollution and other health hazards. However, it became apparent that ecological problems were much more complicated than cleaning up the creeks and putting a catalytic converter on the family station wagon.

John Bruhn, Ph.D., a professor in the School of Health, directed the human ecology program. He observed that "In this science of interrelationships, the heart of the problem is man!" "Human ecology," he went on, "involves man's relationship to nature and to other men. Some scientists say we can 'farm the sea' and learn to support ourselves on products from it. But where are we dumping our nuclear wastes? What about oil leakage problems?" This is the reason the

program in human ecology was begun at the University of Oklahoma.[9]

Unfortunately, the family medicine program did not share the rapid growth which most of the other educational programs in the health sciences at the University of Oklahoma were enjoying at this time. It was beset with problems and its progress was painfully slow. This, of course, was particularly handicapping in view of the acute need for family practitioners throughout Oklahoma. As Dr. Lienke explained:

The very first resident came in May of 1968; we had three that first year. It was a two-year program after the internship then; now it is a coordinated, three year program. The biggest thing we accomplished was to bring the program here but it was premature. Looking back, it probably could have gone faster if it had started later. To bring that kind of program to Oklahoma, by a person from the North, an outsider, at a time when there was no understanding and no money meant that it got off to a slower start than it would have if we had waited until some other people had done it and the pressures had come from the outside. This way, the pressure came from Jim Dennis, who, being very perceptive, said, "We're going to do this for the people." We did it the hard way.

This was a drastic understatement because Dr.

Lienke's tribulations were not confined to the academic program. Dr. Lienke's children made the headlines because their ideas and lifestyle in the rapidly changing late 1960s did not conform to the mores and the folkways of conservative Oklahoma. As a result, Lienke said, "Jim Dennis's office was beseiged [with people] requesting my dismissal." "We were just outsiders," he concluded, "and in retrospect, the family medicine program in Oklahoma should have been started by somebody from the area."[10]

CHAPTER 13

OKLAHOMA HEALTH CENTER DEVELOPMENT PLAN: 1968

Lawrence Lackey discusses the Oklahoma Health Center site plan at one of the many OHSF Operations Committee meetings. (OHSF Collection)

The faculty of the medical school certainly understood the purposes of Dr. Dennis's expansion plans and there seemed to be no opposition from them. While there were reservations about the chances for success because of the meager support which state government had provided in the past and some of the campus veterans could not believe that would ever change, almost everybody thought the concept of a multi-institutional health campus was the best answer to increasing the supply of health professionals for the state. One dissenter, however, was Dr. Stewart Wolf. As the first and acknowledged leader of the full-time clinical faculty, he personified the medical school as it operated in the 1950s and the first half of the 1960s. He explained his position:

> I was against it because I think that's a will-o'-the-wisp. I don't know of any campus, including Houston, where these institutions work together, so why have them together? It's a self-deceptive, wishful thinking type of thing. It makes everything more expensive and, because it is big, it becomes impersonal. One of the greatest charms we had at Oklahoma was the personal aspect of it. Once you get a multi institutional campus, with a layered bureaucracy, it gets to be impersonal.
>
> The V.A., OMRF and the university made up a coherent group. Bringing in a school of dentistry, or a school

of public health or the other units of the so-called health sciences—what they do is dilute the science, the science really being *medical* science. The other is a euphemism.

Stewart Wolf was in favor of bringing a private hospital in because "the University Hospital was an antiquated, poorly-designed place for taking care of private patients. You didn't have to be a genius to know that the trend was going to be much more private, third-party [insured] patients." He continued:

> The business of staying small, I think, has enormous advantages. The biggest advantage is financial. The place [OHC] will never be out of trouble financially. The second thing is bureaucracy. When you get something big, you get a lot of pencil-pushers and impersonal bureaucrats who don't know what the hell's going on.
>
> I fought Mark Everett about increasing the size of the medical class. So many of these things are so obvious. I said at that time—and you know I'm no genius—if we go doing that, we'll wind up with too many doctors. And it still doesn't solve the problem of [health care for] people in the ghetto or out in the country. The more sophisticated medicine gets, the fewer doctors are going to locate themselves out in the prairies with no surrounding help. It's got to be organized differently.
>
> It was obvious at the time it was the wrong thing to do. I think it was "Houston neurosis." Expansion carries with it debt, and bureaucracy and a lack of understanding on a personal level of the people—the products of the institution. I can tell you there are a good many nationally prominent physicians and medical scientists scattered around the country who were students at Oklahoma. For example, Walter Stark is one of the top ophthalmologists in the country. I could mention a great many. But the punch line is: these were all before 1964. Why is that? Is it because we had better students then? No. It was the difference in what I call education which is really *inspiration*. Bob Bird and I knew every student, not just by name. We knew them as people and we were interested in their progress. Ed Brandt, who is now Assistant Secretary for Health [U.S. Department of Health and Human Services], was one of those students.
>
> If I could have talked effectively to Dean McGee, to Mr. Gaylord, to Bill Payne and a half dozen others. They were all my friends. I felt that I ought to have been able to do a better job as far as communicating the real sub-

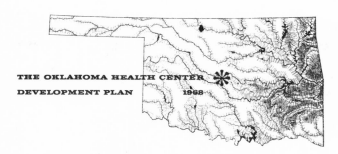

THE OKLAHOMA HEALTH CENTER
DEVELOPMENT PLAN 1968

The central location of the Oklahoma Health Center was ideal for the state's academic, tertiary health care campus. (OHSF Collection)

stance of what the medical school could have been and what its possibilities were at that time.[1]

When Dr. Dennis was asked if he had been aware of Dr. Wolf's attitude toward the Oklahoma Health Center plan, he said, "Stewart didn't say anything to me about it."[2]

The formal plan for the Oklahoma Health Center, published in early 1968, was specific about the institutions, their functional relationships and where they would be located. The planning details, from accommodations for 10,600 parked automobiles to the helipad in the southeast corner of the campus, were so exquisitely coordinated they seemed to answer all of the questions of what, where and how for each institution and how the group would operate together. As the plan stated:

> Of great importance is the strengthening of teaching affiliations between the participating institutions and the educational programs of the University Medical Center. It is from these that the source of additional health manpower will spring, and through which a broader scope of effective educational opportunities can be made available. All participating institutions will remain autonomous. Each will retain its own identity. Each will function with its own board of trustees and its own administration. Matters concerning the entire complex will be coordinated through the Oklahoma Health Sciences Foundation. It is responsible for master planning, site planning and locations, some land acquisition, over-all architectural appearance and campus landscaping, and initial operation of shared central services and facilities.[3]

Thus, the several institutions were woven into a functioning whole, with the expectation the Oklahoma Health Center would emerge as a cohesive unit, in operation as well as name.

The neighborhood surrounding the Oklahoma Health Center was predominantly single-family res-

idential. While there had been numerous misgivings about remaining on the near northeast side of Oklahoma City, the location had the advantage of providing excellent access once the proposed expressway and city street system was completed. As a result of the urban renewal process, probably no other central city location had the expansion potential this area possessed.

Topographically, the site had an interesting roll, with a difference of 65 feet between the low point at Laird Avenue and 8th Street and the high point at 11th Street and Stonewall Avenue. The central swale, which became familiarly known as "DuVal's Ditch" when a 100-year storm in the early 1960s flooded the radiation therapy addition to the outpatient clinics, drained a wide area as far north as the state capitol. The north-south ridge on the west side of the site, along Lindsay Avenue, was more than 50 feet above the central swale. The vantage points of these two ridges offered a dramatic view of the Oklahoma City skyline.

Initially, 14 institutions were to be involved, plus a residential development for 1,000 students in medicine, dentistry, nursing and health-related professions. There were to be about 35 new buildings, excluding the residence area, totaling an estimated 5.7 million square feet. The land area required to accommodate these buildings, in accord with the established development criteria, was 135 acres. The projected daily total population in the Center, excluding the residence area and hospital inpatients, was 5,700 visitors, 6,000 out-patients, 1,150 doctors, 700 faculty, 2,700 students and 12,000 staff, or a total of approximately 28,000 persons per day. This daily population was expected to generate a peak parking need for 10,600 auto spaces which, if planned as surface parking areas, would have required more than 70 acres of land. Approximately 45 acres were required for the student resident facilities which included 750 units in high-rise apartment buildings, parking facilities, 250 low-rise town-house units, and adequate play space.[4]

Access and parking were major considerations. In spread-out Oklahoma City, where the automobile was essential, there was no expectation that mass transportation would soon replace the personal car. About 25 percent of those driving to the OHC were expected to be "short-term parkers," such as doctors on hospital rounds, visitors and people bringing in patients. The remaining 75 percent were "long-term parkers": staff, students and faculty. One side effect of the proposed housing on campus was the reduc-

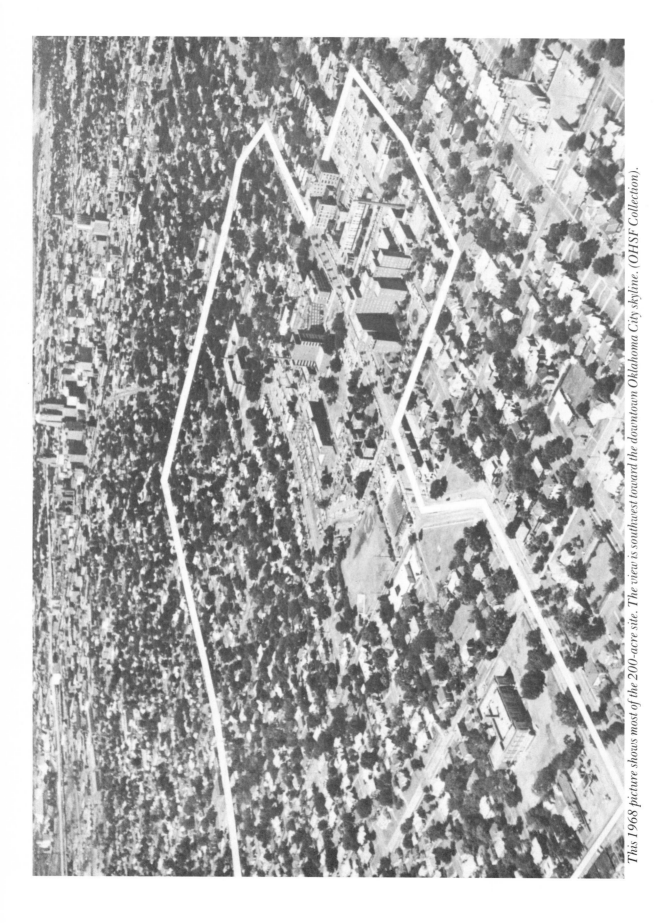

This 1968 picture shows most of the 200-acre site. The view is southwest toward the downtown Oklahoma City skyline. (OHSF Collection).

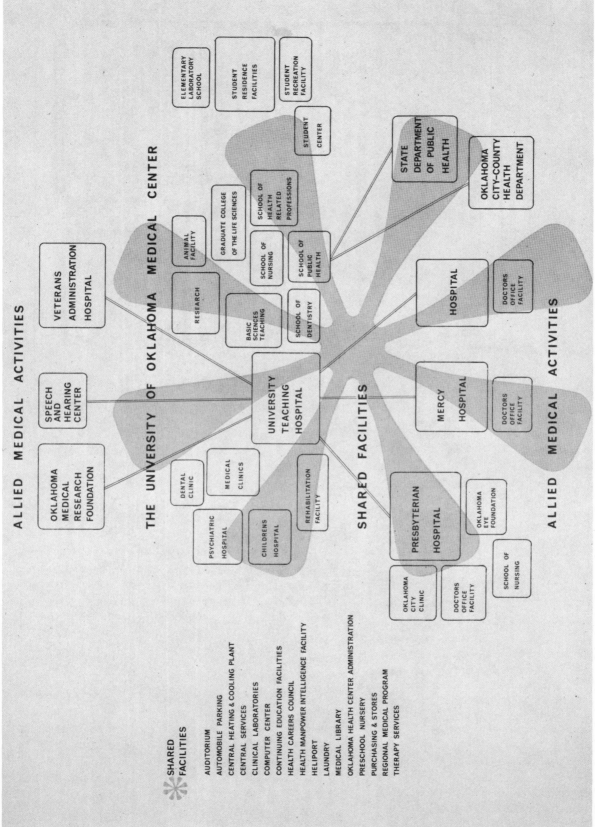

The functional relationships of the institutions and proposed central facilities were depicted in this diagram.

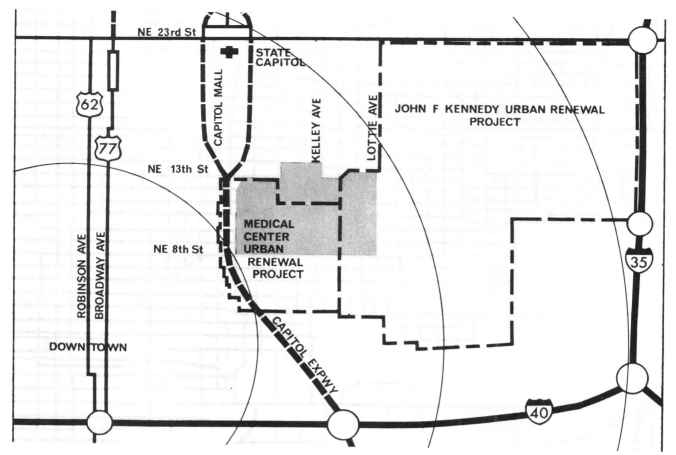

The emerging expressway system made the Oklahoma Health Center increasingly accessible to people from every corner of the state. (OHSF Collection)

tion of parking needed close to the hospitals and educational buildings because staff and students simply could walk across Stonewall.

Arthur Tuttle, who arrived at the Medical Center two years later to assist the implementation of the OHC plan, was intrigued by Lawrence Lackey's work:

> As I got into the development plan, I realized it was a remarkably foresighted document. It combined a lot of ideas, some of which were being tested then, such as interstitial space and the concept of megastructures. What the Lackey plan really did was treat all the parking structures as a kind of megastructure. The health sciences center was designed as a whole series of buildings interconnected by the parking structure.
>
> The biggest problem I saw was getting the parking structures funded. The plan hung very largely on being able to build part of the podium at the same time you were building the space for dentistry and the space for medicine. I was aware the federal government was not putting money into parking facilities.[5]

Others were dubious about the basic concept of the parking blanket; Dr. C.G. Gunn for one. "I thought the plan was untenable in terms of the 'greensward' [atop the parking structures] and building a whole new terra firma which wasn't very 'terra' and was not at all 'firma.' I didn't think we could afford the parking blanket so obviously it wasn't a good idea. I thought the planners were very unrealistic."[6]

In spite of these reservations, the parking plan appeared to be the best way to prevent the Oklahoma Health Center from becoming one vast, continuous used car lot. This "parking podium" linked the hospitals and educational buildings, accommodating drivers on the first two levels and pedestrians on the landscaped deck above. Service activities, such as the central heating plant, laundry, purchasing and storage, were located under and in the parking podium. The podium was above ground, although many who looked at the plan got the impression it was below grade, and was designed to flow with the contour of the land. This allowed the parking to be placed in the

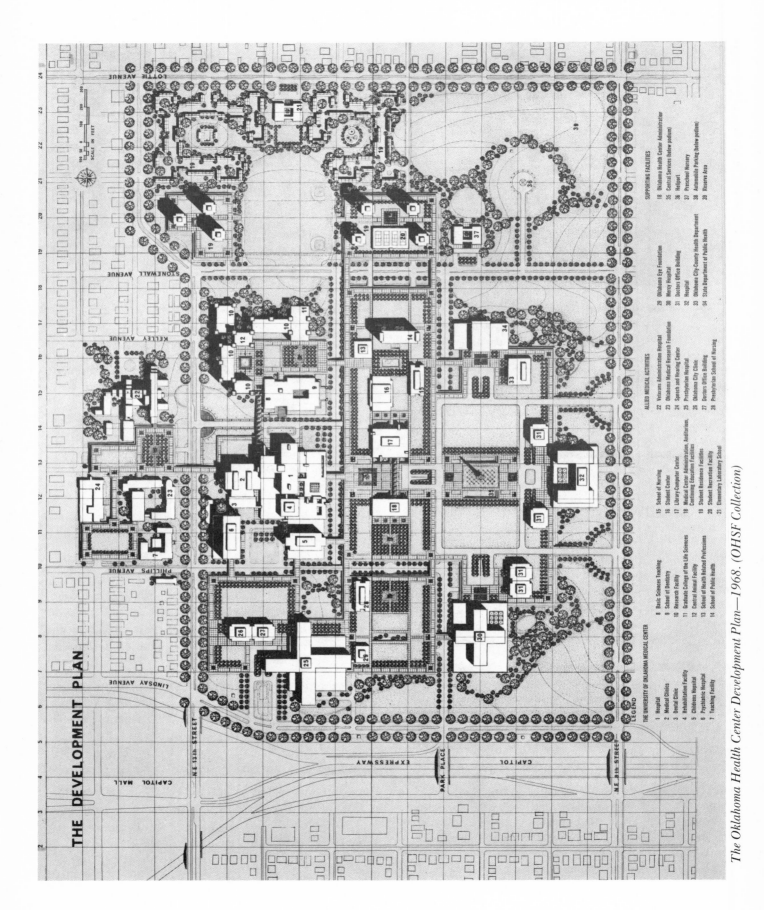

THE DEVELOPMENT PLAN

THE UNIVERSITY OF OKLAHOMA MEDICAL CENTER

1 Hospital
2 Medical Clinics
3 Dental Clinic
4 Rehabilitation Facility
5 Childrens Hospital
6 Psychiatric Hospital
7 Teaching Facility

8 Basic Sciences Teaching
9 School of Dentistry
10 Research Facility
11 Graduate College of the Life Sciences
12 Central Animal Facility
13 School of Health Related Professions
14 School of Public Health

15 School of Nursing
16 Student Center
17 Library-Computer Center
18 Medical Center Administration, Auditorium, Continuing Education Facilities
19 Student Residence Facilities
20 Student Recreation Facility
21 Elementary Laboratory School

ALLIED MEDICAL ACTIVITIES

22 Veterans Administration Hospital
23 Oklahoma Medical Research Foundation
24 Speech and Hearing Center
25 Presbyterian Hospital
26 Oklahoma City Clinic
27 Doctors Office Building
28 Presbyterian School of Nursing

29 Oklahoma Eye Foundation
30 Mercy Hospital
31 Doctors Office Building
32 Hospital
33 Oklahoma City-County Health Department
34 State Department of Public Health

SUPPORTING FACILITIES

18 Oklahoma Health Center Administration
35 Central Services (below podium)
36 Heliport
37 Preschool Nursery
38 Automobile Parking (below podium)
39 Reserve Area

The Oklahoma Health Center Development Plan—1968. (OHSF Collection)

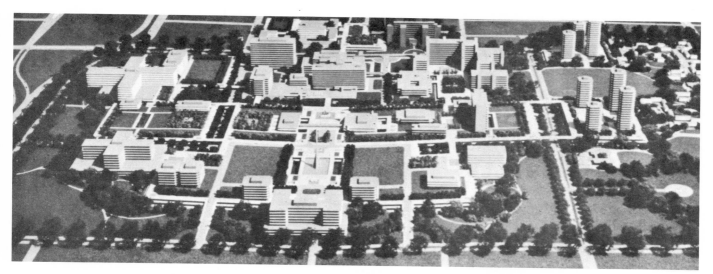

A model of the Oklahoma Health Center helped people visualize its scale and amenities. (OHSF Collection).

View of the model from the north. (OHSF Collection).

View of the model from the southeast. (OHSF Collection).

Not everyone agreed with every aspect of the plan. Dr. C.G. Gunn was a part of the loyal opposition. (University of Oklahoma)

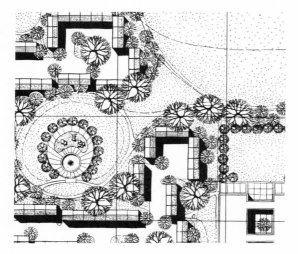

Detail of housing area east of Stonewall. (OHSF Collection)

heart of the complex close to the institutions it would serve. It also allowed the multiple use of the precious land at the core of the complex with several buildings planned to rise above the podium. The landscaped top deck retained the open space and amenities that would otherwise be have been lost had the land area been devoted to surface parking. Bridges across streets at the podium deck level were planned so pedestrians could circulate safely from one building to another.

A basic principle of the OHC plan was achievement of a pleasant environment and a "sense of place":

1 Boulevard

Tree-lined boulevards for traffic circulation within the campus. (OHSF Collection)

Man needs clean air, sunshine, grass, trees, sky; he needs quiet, pleasant, garden retreats where he may seek brief respite from the pressures, tensions and abrasions of intense activity among people. We are trying to restore these amenities in rebuilding our cities. Certainly the health care center should be among the first to achieve them. It should have a clearly perceptible identity, yet it should be compatible in its peripheral relationships with the adjacent residential areas.[7]

The plan also called for harmony and order on the campus in relation to scale, materials, color and detail of buildings, using textured rather than smooth surfaces and integral rather than applied finishes. Browns, terracottas and other natural earth tones were recommended, colors that would harmonize well with the landscape and provide warmth and interest.

The development plan was structured around the location of shared facilities in the center of the site with the several institutions clustered in close proximity to them. The library/computer center, the auditorium, continuing education, university and OHC administrative facilities were located in the heart of the campus.

Two ramps from 8th Street formed the main vehicular entrance to the Oklahoma Health Center. Visitors could drive their automobile to the top level, deposit passengers at the administration and library buildings in the center of the campus and then ramp down into parking levels below. Other buildings were accessible from Lindsay, 13th Street and Stonewall and from 10th Street and 11th Street which trisected the campus east and west.

For numerous reasons, medical centers tend to develop in two general ways: as a campus with separate buildings and ample grounds or as a massive, monolithic structure. Some centers start out as campuses but, as needs expand over the years, become increasingly dense and experience all of the problems this kind of growth brings. Lawrence Lackey, the campus planner/consultant, wanted to assure the Oklahoma

Health Center would retain the characteristics and amenities of the campus and planned accordingly. In keeping with this concept, Lackey's building criteria required that buildings would not cover more than 25 percent of the ground area; this was called the ground coverage ratio (GCR). The gross floor area ratio (GFAR) maximum of 1.0 required that there be one square foot of site area for each gross square foot of floor space in the buildings. A system of development credits was designed so that each institution could make full use of its site without violating the concept of the total campus by exceeding the density limits.

Finally, the plan outlined the stages of growth, expecting virtual completion of the campus by 1974. A third hospital, several doctors' office buildings, certain of the housing facilities and such services as the day care center and the laboratory school for children who lived in university housing were planned as later additions. The cost of the ultimate development was estimated to be $185 million during a period of 10 to 12 years.[8]

As detailed as the Oklahoma Health Center Development Plan appeared, it did not assure unified design throughout the campus. Each institution had its own architects; indeed, the university employed a different firm for almost every project and architects have a penchant for "making a statement" in the buildings they design. The Oklahoma Health Sciences Foundation commissioned the consultants to develop a "design digest" to "amplify the intent and objectives of the 1968 Development Plan as regards the physical environment implied by the plan." Lawrence Lackey and Associates worked two years preparing a digest that contained both general criteria and descriptions of the nature of the desired environment as a reference source for the individual project architects. The idea was not to inhibit the creativity of the architects but have them strive toward "harmony and order in relation to the whole complex." This involved not only the details of colors, textures and building materials but elements common to the total campus, such as signs and graphics, street furniture, plant materials and lighting systems.

It was intended that these elements would "unify the diversity" of the OHC institutions and create a sense of place readily perceived by people as they stepped onto the campus. It did not mean a series of look-alike buildings rigidly following a particular architectural style.

The degree of attention to detail in the plan was not apparent at first glance. For example: the low-rise student and staff housing units were clustered around hard-surface public courts used for automobile access to parking stalls below the units. To the designers, nothing was quite as ugly as a sea of parked cars so, even in the residential section of the campus, the cars were tucked away, out of sight. These courts on which the apartments faced were "by design (small scale, dead ended and of varying size and configuration) [so that] car traffic would move slowly through what are essentially people-oriented spaces." The opposite exposure of the dwelling units looked out to a common, landscaped, pedestrian greenway which connected to the large recreational areas for softball and other games, play yards and swimming pools. This arrangement allowed children to roam freely through these grassy areas and walk to and from the lab school without getting run down by a speeding automobile.[9]

As architect Bill Campbell observed, "The meticulous thought invested in planning the Oklahoma Health Center resulted in an outstanding design." "If the Oklahoma Health Center had accomplished that scheme," he continued, "it would have made every [architectural] journal, every trade paper and would have been published 25 times." Unfortunately, it was not fully appreciated by some of the decision makers who were to follow.[10]

In the interim, planning for the new Presbyterian Hospital and the new Mercy Hospital moved along. Some architects believe, with the possible exception of marine architecture (ship design), the modern, teaching hospital presents the most complicated design challenge the profession faces. Certainly the firms which specialize in hospital design, and acquire a reputation for these skills, agree. Advanced and changing technology, infection control, safety considerations,

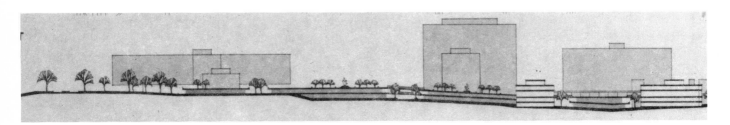

2 Interior Street

A typical interior street spanned by a pedestrian bridge. (OHSF Collection)

3 Parking Structure Edge

The edges of the parking structures were designed to protect people from the weather. (OHSF Collection)

Light Court

A court to provide light and air within the parking blanket. (OHSF Collection)

utility systems, cleanliness standards and automation require the hospital to meet "high-tech" specifications.

One of the basic problems with designing any medical facility is that it is impossible to predict the long-term future use of the space due to rapidly-changing technology in the health field. Not only does the architect have to make the building function usefully the day it is occupied but it must also accommodate all the changes in the state of the healing art which neither he nor the health professionals who will oc-cupy the building in the future can foresee. This is a unique design challenge to the consultant as well as the architect, as Lester Gorsline explained:

> At any moment, they [the faculty or other health professionals] are dealing in the present, with specificity, as I call it; that is, "this happens there and it is always going to happen there." Not true! Everything is transitory. I finally caught on to one of the solutions of the indefinite use of space—nobody knows who's going to be doing what next. It is a *stage*, with props, screens and things you move around as you need. You set it up and you take it down. It's indefinite—no particular walls with all of the utilities in them—no specifics as to occupancy.
>
> We have developed this now into what is known as "interstitial space," separating the activity or stage floor from all of the props and scenery and machinery that goes on—the 57 varieties of utilities, et cetera. This way you can clear an entire floor and start over with something else if you wish to.[11]

This ideal approach had been the focus of discussion among hospital designers but there were constraints which limited its feasibility. The patient room changes more slowly than support functions like computerized information systems and specialized activities such as operating rooms, laboratories, burn units, radiation therapy, cardiac intensive care and the like. Also, if interstitial space is built and radical change does not occur, the extra money it costs is lost. But there is no doubt the high-tech characteristics of the modern hospital demand maximum flexibility in the use of space.

Although Benham, Blair and Affiliates did not get to continue the work they began on the University Hospital, they were chosen by Presbyterian Hospital in late 1965 and named by Mercy Hospital on Febuary 3, 1968, to design their new facilities. Both of the replacement hospitals were to have 400 beds and each was scheduled to start construction in 1969. Presbyterian was expected to cost $16 million and the price tag for Mercy was $18 million.

Another important common characteristic was all private rooms. The state of the art of hospital design had finally caught up with the Sheraton Hotel, the

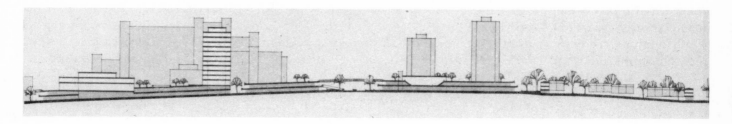

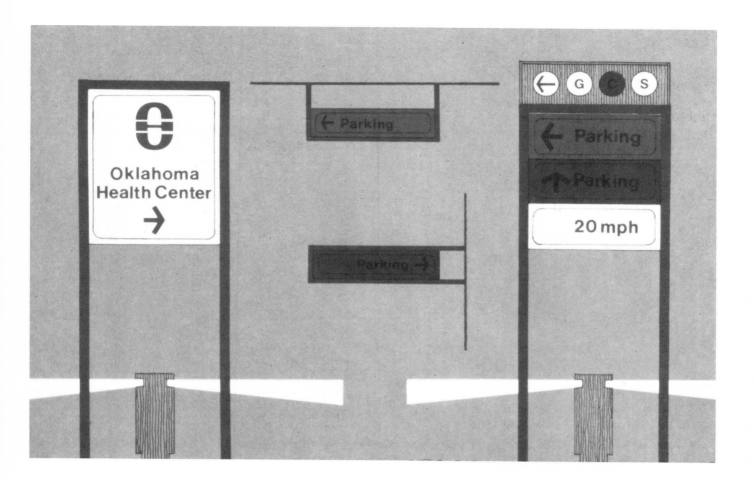

Holiday Inn and the Best Western Motel. That sick people also needed privacy had at last been recognized. This design was not solely for the benefit of the patient, however. Hospitals had discovered that the improved flexibility and increased occupancy possible with all private rooms made up for the increase in construction cost. The need to match patients in multi-bed rooms by sex, age, illness, condition and, yes, compatibility, was eliminated. The similarity of program, size, design, and construction schedule testified to the unspoken competition between Presbyterian and Mercy Hospital. Although both would be in the Oklahoma Health Center and were dedicated to the same educational mission, each seemed to be determined the other would not get ahead.[12]

By the end of 1968, preliminary plans for the Oklahoma City-County Health Department's new headquarters were completed. Presbyterian Hospital also got through its preliminary drawing stage of design and made application for federal funds as a teaching institution. Mercy Hospital had appointed Gordon Freisen, an internationally-known hospital consultant based in Washington, D.C., and was busily work-

ing on schematic designs. The State Health Department also completed its preliminary design drawings and expected to start construction by mid 1969. In addition, a schematic plan for the architectural module of the Oklahoma Health Center parking blanket was developed.

The Oklahoma Medical Research Foundation also worked on expansion plans during 1968 but the beginning of construction was still a year and a half away. Specific planning for a school of public health was moving ahead under Dr. Schottstaedt's supervision. At that point, it looked as though the beginning of construction on a building to house this new school was only 15 months away, in the first quarter of 1970.

Meanwhile, subcommittees of the Oklahoma Health Sciences Foundation Operations Committee continued to plan shared services. They focused on centralizing clinical laboratories, emergency services, cardiovascular care, laundry, linen, and a host of other services. The goal was to reduce the capital investment and achieve economy of scale for every institution on the campus. Bits and pieces of the overall plan were coming together.

CHAPTER 14
HERO: 1967-1968

On March 20, 1967, the State Regents for Higher Education called for immediate state financing of more than $40 million in expansion and improvements at the Medical Center. This was half the projected cost of a long range campus plan for educational facilities which the State Regents had approved in January. They estimated about $37 million would come from federal funds and another $4 million could be raised from private sources.[1]

Senator Bryce Baggett, who represented District 41 in Oklahoma City which included the Medical Center, introduced resolutions calling for a $47 million bond issue for the Medical Center and the new State Health Department building. These general obligation bonds were to be financed by adding another penny tax to each pack of cigarettes but at that point, these measures had not cleared his governmental affairs committee. According to Baggett:

> One of the things Jim Dennis did was persuade the legislators we couldn't build a big, big hospital in every small town in Oklahoma and that the real way of getting service there was to connect all of the small hospitals in some way with the great central hospital and to provide personnel and support services to where they could have fine services in the small, local hospital which they [the community] couldn't sustain on their own. That concept really was sold by Jim Dennis and he developed a receptive mood on the part of the legislators to recognize that the large, central facility operated by the University of Oklahoma was critical to their home town interest.
>
> I hadn't been in the legislature very long before I realized we could find the money for anything we really *wanted* to do. We seem to always answer crises in the legislature. I discovered very early as a young legislator that if I wanted to do something and if a crisis didn't exist, I had to *manufacture* a crisis. So we began talking about the crisis in health care in Oklahoma, the crisis in dental care, the shortage of facilities. Since everybody feels they don't get enough health care, it wasn't hard to get a responsive attitude, everybody beginning to believe we had a genuine crisis.
>
> So I always believed we'd find the money if we were persuasive in explaining what we were trying to do. Late in his career, Senator Robert S. Kerr and Lloyd Rader had been very active in writing federal legislation for Social Security and Department of Welfare-type inter-

A second Republican governor, Dewey F. Bartlett, followed Henry Bellmon. (University of Oklahoma)

> ests, very beneficial to Oklahoma, particularly medical care. The Department of Welfare, under Lloyd Rader's leadership, was always interested in the Medical Center. Much of the funding we had for various programs we had there came because of Department of Welfare research. Then the faculty members were so imaginative in coming up with various research and grant program proposals that were highly acceptable at the Institutes of Health (NIH). I just felt we'd find the money. I knew we couldn't do it all through bond issues or appropriations but through a combination of various sources, I felt we could embark on this giant plan and bring it about.[2]

About two weeks later, on April 6, 1967, Governor Bartlett stopped all movement toward a bond issue during the current legislative session. Chancellor Dunlap talked about the decision:

> Out of our study of medical education, we had arrived at the amount of money we thought we'd need to build the facilities over there [in the Medical Center], taking into consideration certain matching funds from the federal government. Dewey Bartlett had become governor in January and we talked to him about a bond issue. Dewey said, "I don't want to get into that my first session here. I know we've got needs but wait and let

"Out of the Ashes." (The Oklahoman)

"But What If He Quits Smoking?" (The Oklahoman)

me get my feet on the ground. We'll set up a committee this summer."

He did name a committee, headed by Bryce Baggett, which worked with the governor's citizen committee of which Dean McGee was the chairman. We worked together. We at the State Regents' office presented the needs of the Medical Center to both of these committees so they could be united in their recommendations to the governor.[3]

The 18-member "expenditure advisory council," as the citizen committee was known, included three additional trustees of the Oklahoma Health Sciences Foundation. They were Stanton Young of Oklahoma City, John Rogers of Tulsa and William D. Little of Ada. Bryce Baggett said he would not push his ideas over objections of the governor, so the problem of funding the university and State Health Department portion of the Oklahoma Health Center was postponed until the next session.[4]

On April 10, 1968, the Oklahoma legislature approved the large bond issue which Governor Bartlett's study committee had recommended. The date set for this $92.2 million general obligation bond issue for capital construction was December 10. As Baggett had first suggested, the bonds would be retired from revenue produced by an increase in the cigarette tax, which in the process had been upped five cents per pack and had already gone into effect 10 days earlier. Because a large portion of this issue was earmarked for health purposes, this chioce of funding was exquisitely appropriate. Earlier in the decade, the U.S. Public Health Service had published

Smoking and Health, a landmark series of research findings incriminating tobacco as a major contributor to the incidence of lung cancer, emphysema and cardiovascular disease. Because nicotine narrows the blood vessels (a vasoconstrictor), it probably causes wrinkles as well! Hence, it seemed only fair to assess smokers a little extra to build hospitals to take care of them when they got sick. Dr. E. T. Dunlap pointed out that, "The politics of the situation required that it be kept under $100 million, so we had a $99.8 million bond issue. The Medical Center was to receive $26,870,000." In addition, the Oklahoma State Department of Health was included in the bond issue for $4,516,000 to build its new headquarters on the campus. Thus, the state money proposed for new construction in the Oklahoma Health Center totaled more than $31 million. The intent of the legislature was before the public and if the people voted to tax themselves for these new facilities, the Oklahoma Health Center would be able to leap ahead.[5]

In the meantime, Dr. Bob Bird and the members of the planning committee, helped by their consultants Lester Gorsline and Roger Bennett, had been honing their skills in the preparation of construction grant applications ever since the 1964 fiasco. Their work again paid off in the form of the second construction grant, this one to build the first 200 bed phase of the new University Hospital. On Monday, July 31, 1967, United States Senators Mike Monroney and Fred R. Harris and Congressman John Jarman announced a $4,961,769 award from the Department

The planning committee hard at work. Audrey Clonce, Dr. Bird's secretary, Joe White, Bill Schottstaedt, Bob Bird and Ernst Lachman review plans for the Oklahoma Health Center. (University of Oklahoma)

of Health, Education and Welfare. Matched by state money from the 1963 bond issue, the new facility was expected to cost close to $10 million.[6]

Significant as that step was, getting State Question Number 463 approved by the legislature for submission to the voters on December 10, 1968, was only the first one. Passing the $99.8 million bond issue was the real challenge. Even though it would require no new taxes and the burden of repayment would fall on the smokers, the voters had to understand what the issue was all about and grant their approval at the polls. According to Chancellor Dunlap, "Dean McGee and Gene Swearingen [Eugene Swearingen, Ph.D., former president of the University of Tulsa] headed up the committee which was set up to put the thing over. Lowe Runkle's bunch was hired to do the P.R. work and I was designated by the committee to work with that end of it."

In 1965, Dunlap introduced the notion of "pre-vitalization" of bond issues. In the joint resolution signed by the governor, which had the same effect of law as a bill and which submitted the question to the voters, there was a section that previtalized the bond issue. If the people approved it, the money would be immediately available; it would not be necessary for the legislature to appropriate the money to the State Regents. This had the advantage of giving the program almost a year's head start. The planning was done and thus federal funds could be obtained quicker. This meant the state could get more for its money during

inflationary times by starting construction as soon as possible.

Dr. Dunlap continued. "The idea of naming the bond issue was born in the conference room of the State Regents at a meeting with Bryce Baggett, Gloria Bremkamp and Howard Neumann of [the] Lowe Runkle [Company] and myself. I was chairman of the promotion committee. We were groping for a catchy acronym and came up with HERO, Health and Education for a Richer Oklahoma." According to Gloria Bremkamp, this title was created by Bruce Palmer, a Lowe Runkle executive. She outlined a total information program for supporters of the bond issue. It was to be a media blitz, with two-thirds of the $75 thousand budget allocated to newspaper, billboard, radio and television advertising. McGee and Swearingen had the job of raising the money and mobilizing the people in the organizations which were to benefit by passage of the bond issue. In addition, Dunlap could call on them to assist in the publicity campaign. A fund raising goal of $125 thousand was established. Higher education and the communities in which colleges and universities were located were asked to collect $30 thousand. The Tulsa and Oklahoma City Chambers of Commerce, the medical and dental professions, architects and contractors also were solicitied.[7]

The HERO bond issue had something for everyone and because 52 communities, from Altus to Miami and from Guymon to Talihina, were in line for benefits, the prospects for passage seemed quite good. As Representative Bill Willis put it, "We scattered that money out all over Oklahoma purely for the reason to get votes for it." Colleges and universities were slated for a third of the money and almost another third ($31 million) was earmarked for the Oklahoma Health Center. The remainder was divided among state hospitals, the Welfare Department, corrections, public safety, mental health, public health and other projects.[8]

The issue was billed as Oklahoma's "Pre-Paid" Improvements Campaign and voters were admonished to "Be a Hero. Vote Yes! on December 10." It did not require much courage to vote yes because, as the people were told, the "present cigarette tax will pay the bill." For non-smokers, the benefits were free; for smokers, the tax had already been levied and as long as they maintained their habit, they would pay that extra nickle tax on every pack regardless of the vote on December 10, regardless of their attitude toward health and education.

One of the keys to both fundraising and passage

The new University Hospital as designed by Frankfurt, Short, Emery and McKinley. (University of Oklahoma)

Construction of the first phase of the new University Hospital gets underway. (University of Oklahoma)

was the Alumni Association of the School of Medicine. Ed. L. Calhoon, M.D., of Beaver, Oklahoma, was president and the Association's executive secretary, Lawrence "Larry" Rember, J.D., did yeoman service coordinating a HERO Medical Task Force which or-

ganized these efforts among the doctors. As a result, the medical profession made its $15 thousand contribution quota and a number of county medical societies passed resolutions backing the bond issue. Of course, there was no way accurately to measure the influence of the physicians but their active support and their opinion molding position in every community in Oklahoma no doubt was a positive force. However, Dr. Dennis gave much of the credit to the alumni of the College of Medicine working through the county medical societies.[9] The public education program was scheduled to begin on November 18, 1968, so there would be more than three weeks to get the message to the voters. A week in advance, Bob Ruggles, education writer for the Oklahoma Publishing Company, began a series of articles in the *Daily Oklahoman* and the *Oklahoma City Times* which touted the advantages of passage. The final article pointed out that Oklahoma was short at least 1,500 physicians, perhaps as many as 4,886 nurses and at least 25,000 workers in health-related professions. These statis-

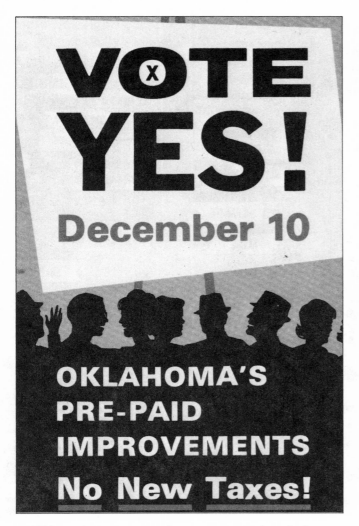

This succinct message to the voters appeared on the front of a brochure distributed by the campaign committee. (OHSF Collection)

tics, gathered by Dr. Tom Points' group, apparently convinced many people to vote for the HERO bond issue.[10]

Reasonable as the bond issue appeared, there was scattered opposition. A few people wrote letters to their legislators and to Robert Hardy, the bond campaign coordinator. Some unidentified opponents put up a billboard on Walker Avenue in Oklahoma City, south of the Canadian River bridge, encouraging people to vote against the issue.[11]   Bold, one-inch type across the top of the front page of the *Daily Oklahoman* on Wednesday, December 11, 1968, blazoned the results of the vote: "Bonds Carry By 3-1 Margin." Only three counties—Garfield, Grant and Major—failed to give the bond proposal approval and those rejections were by narrow margins. Ironically, Grant County voters did not support the HERO bonds despite the special

help Wakita was receiving from the Medical Center to establish community health service. Dr. Dennis said, "We have assured the future of Oklahoma in terms of health care. Our university medical center will indeed be second to none." Thus, the largest and most ambitious state bond issue in the history of Oklahoma was passed and, through mid-1985, there had not been another.[12] Reminiscing about the campaign, Gloria Bremkamp remarked:

> It was fun working on the HERO bond issue with E.T. Dunlap. What a power! What an organizer he was. I remember we had a meeting a night or two before the election. This dinner meeting was the final report and Governor Dewey Bartlett was there and, Lord o' Mercy, all of the heavyweight thinkers and the guys who were the movers and the shakers were there. Because of the coordinating job I had to publicize the HERO bond issue, I was there, too.
>
> Well, the next day or so came the bond election and of course it went over eight to one or some incredible vote. I got a call from Stanley Draper, Sr. Now, you must understand in my career over the years, I had been thrown out of several meetings by Stanley Draper, Sr., because I was a woman. That was typical of him. Came the vote and we were successful, I got a telephone call from him. He says, "Honey! I want to tell you, this is Stanley Senior talking. And I want to thank you for all your good work. Today, because of the election, you're the most beautiful *man* in Oklahoma!"

Gloria Bremkamp laughed heartily and continued, "To which I simply said, 'Thank you, Mr. Draper.' and he hung up and so did I. But that's the way he was and he'd changed, too, so this had a lot to do with women's lib, maybe. I never will forget that." She laughed again and shook her head.[13]

The passage of the HERO bond issue gave the OHC plan an aura of reality and success which may even have convinced Henry Bellmon. People at the Medical Center got the feeling it was all going to happen. Robert Hardy had the idea that a dramatic change in emphasis would set the OHC apart from all of the academic health care centers in America. As a planner, he was interested in the trends of the future, so he suggested to Dr. Dennis:

> Why don't we re-name this campus "The Oklahoma Wellness Center"? Health centers are everywhere—even Calico Rock, Arkansas has one! Besides, health can be good or bad. "Wellness" is unmistakable. What's more, we'd have the first wellness center in the entire country.

Dr. Dennis did not reject this idea out of hand. Ever the astute politician, he shook his head and replied,

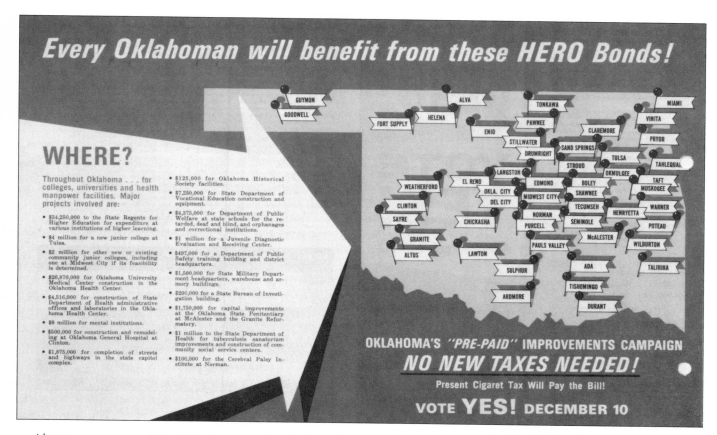

Almost every community in Oklahoma was slated to benefit from the HERO bond issue. (OHSF Collection)

"They're Real!!" (Sunday Oklahoman)

There was some opposition to the HERO bonds but it was not very strong. (OHSF Collection)

"I think that's a good idea, Bob, but I don't believe my colleagues could handle it."

1968 had been a very good year. The Oklahoma Health Center Development Plan-1968 had been printed and distributed, construction of the Basic Science Education Building was started and the Veterans Administration Hospital was well along on working drawings for a new research wing. An application for

103

E.T. Dunlap and Paul Strasbaugh tally the vote on the Hero bonds. (The Oklahoman)

Dr. A.B. Colyar, the new Commissioner of Health. (OHSF Collection)

federal funds to construct the university's health science library was approved and awaited funding, schematic plans for 300 student apartment units had been completed and the O.U. Regents had approved a specific plan for a School of Health Related Professions. Dr. William Schottstaedt was appointed acting director until a dean could be engaged.

Meanwhile, more federal money made its way to-

ward the Oklahoma Health Center. By this time, Howard Miles had taken over the Hill-Burton hospital construction program from Paul Snelson and A.B. Colyar, M.D., had succeeded Dr. Kirk Mosley as Commissioner of Health. The Oklahoma program had a state hospital planning advisory council which, in its February 9, 1969, meeting, recommended the City-County Health Department receive the first $150 thousand of an $800 thousand grant. The rest of the money would be allocated in subsequent years. In addition, $764,348 was approved to modernize the laboratory of the State Health Department, which was designed to be attached to the new 12-story office building to be built in the Oklahoma Health Center. The funding of the tower was expected to come from other sources, primarily HERO bonds.[14]

With passage of the HERO bond issue, the major hurdle of financing public health care facilities, including the university and the state health department, had been surmounted. As Dennis said, the federal government could not make this commitment legally, but informally said they would fund the Oklahoma Health Center plan as fast as local matching money became available. The Oklahoma State Department of Health, which administered Hill-Burton funds for hospitals and health centers, had already applied the expertise possessed by Paul Snelson and Howard Miles to garner federal money for construction of its 12-story headquarters and laboratory. Money for the Oklahoma City-County Health Department building was assured through the combination of federal Hill Burton and county millage funds.

Private hospitals, however, had no local tax support. Other than the meager $3.5 million, 1965 United Hospital Fund and possible Hill Burton money, there was no ready source of construction dollars with which to replace the superannuated, decaying facilities of Mercy, Presbyterian and St. Anthony Hospital. In addition, Baptist, South Community and Hillcrest Osteopathic Hospital had plans for additions totaling 170 beds, so the city's hospital system proposed to increase its complement of 1,507 acute, general hospital beds to 2,278, a net gain of 771 beds. Non-profit hospitals ordinarily had no capital funds because they almost never funded depreciation of their buildings and equipment from revenues so they could replace their capital investment when it became outmoded. Most private hospitals had difficulty just paying current costs from current income. Therefore, the hospitals in Oklahoma City looked outside their own

Three-term president Stanton L. Young in 1969. (Oklahoma City Chamber of Commerce)

Ray Anthony. (Oklahoma City Chamber of Commerce)

balance sheets for the money they needed for replacement and expansion beds.

In the spring of 1969, Stanton L. Young, vice chairman of the Presbyterian Hospital board of trustees, was in his third year of a three-term presidency of the Oklahoma City Chamber of Commerce. He and Paul Strasbaugh recognized as an area-wide problem the lack of any plan to assure capital funding for these private hospitals. Working with a group composed of Ray Anthony, chairman of the Health and Hospital Planning Committee of the Community Council, Dr. Dennis, Al Donnell, Don Ellison, the OHSF attorney, and Robert C. Hardy, they devised a financing plan which proposed to broaden the base of support for all of these institutions. Traditionally, private hospitals—institutions operated by churches or other non-profit organizations—had only two sources of money other than federal Hill-Burton funds for new construction. They could ask the public to contribute in a fundraising campaign, such as the United Hospital Fund drive, or they could borrow money and then assess their patients not only for the care they received but also for a portion of the cost of the building in which they received it. Both Stanton Young and Paul Strasbaugh believed the entire community should shoulder the burden of replacing worn-out hospitals. Otherwise, this obligation was dependent on the generosity of donors or placed an extra financial strain on hospital patients at a time they perhaps were least able to assume it.

The Chamber of Commerce cited a 1964 survey which had identified the need for 1,000 additional beds by 1970, but five years later, the city was still 412 beds short of this goal. In addition, about a third (578) of the beds in the system were "non-conforming," or did not meet state health department standards. All of these obsolete facilities were in three of the largest hospitals; Mercy, Presbyterian and St. Anthony. The first 352 such beds were in Mercy and Presbyterian which were planning totally new facilities in the Oklahoma Health Center.[15]

Simply stated, this critical situation could not be relieved without money—lots of it. The people not only had to be made aware of the problem but they had to understand the benefits an early solution would bring. This was a new concept in Oklahoma City—that good hospitals and health care are just as vital as good streets, dependable fire and police protection and other services which citizens routinely demand. Public support for health services had to be provided in the same manner that other services are demanded and supported. And that meant taxes!

The six institutions among which the 1,170 new beds were to be distributed were: Mercy Hospital, 400 beds; Presbyterian Hospital, 400 beds; Baptist Hospital, addition of a community mental health center and an extended care rehabilitation facility, 60 beds; South Community Hospital, extended care, 30 beds; St. Anthony Hospital, replacement of 226 nonconforming beds and addition of 200 beds; and Hillcrest Osteopathic Hospital, 80 beds.

Hospital construction costs in the late 1960s were averaging $50 thousand a bed and rising by the day. The total estimated cost to improve Oklahoma City's hospital system was $64.2 million. Interestingly, only Mercy Hospital had any capital money: $2.4 million in gifts and current assets. Hill-Burton and other funds were projected at $8.4 million and each institution was expected to borrow varying amounts through revenue bonds for a total of $20.5 million. This left $33 million of the tab to be raised through taxation.[16]

On June 19, 1969, when the first portion of this study was presented to the corporate board and executive committee of the Chamber, the only feasible financing method appeared to be municipal general obligation bonds. The city could call a bond election and there was no limit to the amount of bonds which could be approved by a majority of the qualified, taxpaying voters. The committee suggested that the city create a hospital authority for the purpose of building hospitals. They would be owned by the city, leased to the authority which would in turn use the leasehold as security for additional revenue bonds as necessary to construct the hospitals. The authority would lease the completed facilities to the respective hospital governing boards. The hospitals would have the right, when the bonds were retired, to purchase the facilities for their appraised value or the face value of the general obligation bonds committed to the facility, whichever was less. The bonds had to be retired in 25 years or less. With the problem well defined and an approved approach, the Oklahoma City Chamber of Commerce set about to convince the City Council the public had an obligation to improve the private hospital system in the area.[17]

While the chamber task force was at work promoting its financing plan, the problem continued to grow. Since 1966, the estimated cost of the new Presbyterian Hospital had risen 50 percent, from $16 million to $24 million and the Presbyterian Oklahoma-Arkansas Synod, meeting in Stillwater, Oklahoma, on October 7, 1969, could see no way to finance the project. Dr. G. Raymond Campbell, an Oklahoma City minister, said the Synod agreed to consider launching a fund raising campaign for the Presbyterian Hospital but thought it unlikely that enough money could be collected to get the hospital underway. To Dr. Campbell, who was one of the hospital's most enthusiastic boosters, the money problem seemed insurmountable.[18]

The Chamber leadership recognized the need to generate public support for private institutions in the metropolitan hospital system. (OHSF Collection)

By the fall of 1969, there had been no progress toward financing the expansion of the private hospitals in Oklahoma City with municipal general obligation bonds. Officially, "the unsettled financial climate, both nationally and locally, has prevented effective pursuit of this plan during the ensuing six months." As Paul Strasbaugh explained, "The city's attitude was the burden should fall on the people who used the hospitals, not the city taxpayer.[19]

However, the needs of the hospital system continued to grow and the hospitals continued to plan. With unabated optimism, the same Chamber of Commerce committee devised three alternative plans the members thought might be more acceptable to city and/or county officials. By December, 1969, construction had started on 200 replacement and 74 additional beds at St. Anthony, 78 beds at Midwest City, 61 beds at Deaconess, and, not to be outdone by other suburban, incorporated communities in the Oklahoma City metropolitan area, Bethany, despite recommendations to the contrary by the Health and Hospital Planning Committee, was building a brand new, 50-bed hospital. Also, a new projection of bed need indicated that over the next 13 years, 1,526 additional beds would be required in the area. By this time, the new University Hospital (Phase I) was under construction but was not included in the bed count because it served the entire state.

The original plan to finance hospitals with general obligation bonds was known as Alternative A. Alternative B proposed a one percent county sales tax. Enabling legislation would be required, passed by the state legislature, so the voters could decide by referendum whether or not to tax themselves. Half of the proceeds of this sales tax levy was proposed for hospital construction and modernization with the other half divided evenly between the county (25 percent) and the cities (25 percent), allocated on a population basis. The tax allocated to hospitals would have produced more than $6 million a year beginning in 1970, rising to $10.5 million by 1983, based on an annual growth rate of 5.7 percent. This revenue would have accommodated a $72 million general obligation bond issue, which was not sufficient to fund the entire system but adequate to handle 60 percent of the construction costs. Under this plan, the hospitals would have to sell $47 million in revenue bonds. At 6 percent, the county taxpayers would pay $50 million in interest over 20 years.[20]

The committee pointed out the disadvantages of this alternative. In 1969, the hospital system was operating at 81 percent occupancy, a comfortable level in view of the fact that 85 percent was considered full while still retaining the flexibility to accommodate the numerous classifications of patients such as male, female, adult, pediatric, obstetrical, surgical, medical, infectious, intensive care, extended care, etc. A single bond issue in 1970 would have permitted all of the 1,473 beds, planned or under construction, to be completed by 1974, creating a significant surplus of hospital capacity.

Because it was obvious both Mercy and Presbyterian would have difficulty filling twice as many beds as they were then operating when each had a new, 400-bed plant in the Oklahoma Health Center, Robert Hardy suggested a plan for sequential rather than simultaneous development of the two hospitals. He presented it to the trustees of Presbyterian Hospital. Hardy's plan called for a temporary merger of the two institutions, admittedly an ecumenical and perhaps impractical approach, but one which had great financial advantage for each of the hospitals. The idea entailed six steps to be carried out over a decade. It proposed to merge the two institutions and call the organization Mercy-Presbyterian Hospital. The next step was to build one 400-bed hospital in the OHC, open it by 1973 and operate it with the Presbyterian administration and personnel, expanded and supplemented as required by people from the Mercy or-

ganization. This would mean the new general hospital would be essentially full from the moment it opened its doors. Because the old Mercy physical plant was larger and in better condition than Presbyterian, convert it into an extended care facility. (At that time, under the theory of progressive patient care, those patients who did not require the full attention of a regular nursing unit could be transferred to a facility offering "extended care," which was a level of service between hospital and nursing home care. The cost of this care was reimbursed by the federal government under the Medicare program.) The availability of extended care would allow the new Mercy-Presbyterian acute general hospital to serve only the sickest patients while the mildly ill and convalescent patients were cared for in the old Mercy unit. This provided 200 additional beds as the demand for institutional care expanded. Mercy officials would continue to plan the second, 400 bed acute general hospital to be built in the OHC. With the combined Mercy-Presbyterian Hospital absorbing 27 percent of the total metropolitan demand for 102 new beds per year, its average daily census could be expected to grow at the rate of 28 patients per year. Thus in about seven years, or 1980, the merged Mercy-Presbyterian Hospital would be out of space. The fifth step was to begin building the second hospital in 1978 with completion scheduled for 1980. In the final step, the merged institutions would be separated and the second institution opened as the new Mercy Hospital. The first one would be renamed Presbyterian Hospital, the extended care facility closed and the two institutions would go their separate ways as though this temporary merger had never occurred.

This would have been a "marriage of convenience," so to speak, with no intention of establishing a permanent relationship. It would have made both units of the merged hospital economically feasible and permitted the second new hospital (Mercy) to be eight years newer in design and technological improvements. In addition, the slower expansion could have been staffed more easily with the ever-short nursing personnel absolutely essential to all hospital operation and expansion. The OHSF executive admitted his suggestion was "a bit foolHardy" but maintained it would have avoided much of the financial difficulty each hospital was destined to face. As Ted Clemens said, "The idea never got down to the staff level or I'm sure I would have remembered it. However, if it had gotten to the medical staff, I believe the Presbyterian doctors would have been against it. They felt themselves a cut above the Mercy staff."[21]

When the news got around, some people began referring to Jack Shrode, the administrator of Presbyterian, as "Sister Shrode." Sister Mary Coletta seemed to be concerned about the possible loss of Mercy's identity. She said to Hardy, "Suppose after seven years or so, it is determined there is no need for a new Mercy Hospital? What then?" All he could say was, "Well...." But Sister Coletta did not have to worry about the merger idea because it was never approved by the Presbyterian board of trustees.

The chamber committee's Alternative C also used the one cent sales tax as the source of money, applied it only to the city of Oklahoma City. It proposed that all of this revenue be used for hospital modernization and expansion. This would have produced $8.8 million in 1970, increasing to $14 million in 1981, sufficient to keep up with the annual rise in construction costs.

The unique feature of this alternative was the "pay-as-you-go" basis on which the money would be used. Also, it would pay the entire cost of construction except for Hill-Burton and institutional money, so no debt service would be involved. The two advantages of this proposal were that it would save taxpayers a lot of interest expense and it would rebuild the hospital system at a rate commensurate with the need for new beds, about 102 more beds each year. Furthermore, because the nurse staffing situation was critical, explosive expansion of the system merely meant many of the newly available beds could not be opened even if they were needed. This gradual growth idea, similar to Hardy's proposal for Mercy and Presbyterian, seemed to have all of the elements of reason and logic supporting it.

Alternative D, the final one, was a variation of the preceding pay-as-you-go idea, but assessed the entire county and dedicated 25 percent of the one cent sales tax revenues to the operating budget of the Oklahoma County government. Seventy-five percent allocation to hospital expansion would have permitted another 200 bed expansion of St. Anthony Hospital in 1982. Sequential hospital development was strongly recommended by Al Donnell and the areawide planners of the community council.[22]

Despite the logic of these alternatives, the chamber was unable to sell any of them. The city and county governments resisted all pressure to involve them in a problem they had not previously dealt with and were convinced was a responsibility which belonged elsewhere. Therefore, Report II met the same fate as Report I. These ideas for financing the construction of private hospitals were rejected.

CHAPTER 15
THE RISING CAMPUS: 1967-1970

During the week of July 31, 1967, construction began on the first new building in the Oklahoma Health Center, the Family Medicine Cinic at Northeast 15th and Phillips, two blocks north of the medical school. The O.U. Foundation financed the $144,000 building by selling bonds but the Department of Family Medicine was obligated to pay off those bonds with money it generated in patient fees. This was one more example of the variety of methods the Medical Center had to use to accomplish its goals.

The clinic building was modeled after private practitioners' offices so medical students and family practice residents could get realistic experience in a functioning general office practice. It contained examination and treatment rooms, x-ray facilities, laboratories, offices and a reception and waiting area. To get this building under way a scant 13 months after Dr. Roger Lienke arrived to organize a totally new department of family medicine was quite a remarkable accomplishment.[1]

Two and a half months later, ground-breaking ceremonies celebrating the start of the Basic Science Education Building were held on the Medical Center grounds just north of the old school of nursing. October 17 was warm and sunny, an ideal afternoon for "Operation Commencement," so called because it was said to launch the first building project in the greater Oklahoma Health Center development. Actually, this was the second building because it followed the beginning of the Family Medicine Clinic.

During the ceremony, Dr. Dennis pointed out that, "This great health education venture is no longer a dream. It is happening!" When he and President Cross unwrapped a plastic-covered model of the building carefully dug up from the site, they presented it to Stephen Campbell of Tulsa, president of the medical school's student council, "because the building belongs to the students," Dr. Dennis remarked.

The design, according to Dr. Robert Bird, represented a change in philosophy. Students would have their own "office" or study space in multi-disciplinary laboratories and the faculty would come to the students instead of vice-versa, as had been the tradition. The building was expected to have almost constant

Student Council president Stephen Campbell of Tulsa, George Cross and Jim Dennis admire the model of the Basic Science Education Building at the groundbreaking ceremony in the fall of 1967. (University of Oklahoma)

use because the students own space would be available to him 24 hours a day.

This new basic science education building, to be completed in 1969, would allow the entering class of the medical school to be increased from 105 to 125. The new University Hospital for which funding had recently been granted would provide the clinical experience for the expanded classes as they finished their first two years' study of the basic sciences. The construction bid of $3,007,200 had already been accepted by the O.U. Board of Regents and work on the basic science building was expected to begin as soon as the east end of the school of nursing building could be razed to make way for the new structure. By the time casework and other equipment was installed, the cost of the completed building would be about $4 million.[2]

Even though 1967 had not begun well because of the tragic death of freshman medical student Jeanette

The dean points the way to the future. (University of Oklahoma)

The University Family Medicine Clinic at 15th and Phillips. (OHSF Collection)

The waiting room in the new clinic. (OHSF Collection)

Morrone, the year ended with great promise. Since the mid-March meeting of the Oklahoma Health Sciences Foundation, the Operations Committee and their Gorsline Associates consultant, Lawrence Lackey, had been refining the Oklahoma Health Center plan. What had been ideas and inspirations, bits and pieces, had been dovetailed into a workable whole. It was complete with institutional roles better defined, relationships shaped and the master design perfected to achieve the central mission of increasing the supply of health manpower while simultaneously promoting the objectives of each individual institution.

The planning process seemed to generate a momentum of its own. Many people from all of the member institutions were involved, trying to make shared services practical, contributing their time and their talent and their experience. The level of communication and cooperation among the members of the Operations Committee and the subcommittees to it was exceeded only by the enthusiasm they brought to the project.

This rosy and perhaps idealistic view of the future reached its high point in The Oklahoma Health Center Development Plan—1968, which was completed by the end of 1967. As Robert Hardy recalled:

> Many of us did not appreciate that the OHC plan was only that—a plan. Lawrence Lackey once said to me, "You have to remember, Bob, planning is a process." He said a plan is only current the day it is published and even then it is probably out of date, depending on how long it took to print it. But I had the idea that once we

had agreed how the Oklahoma Health Center should be built and had completed a final plan, there would be no major changes. I quickly learned the loose consortium created to implement this plan was a lot looser than I had thought!

Forty-five months after Jim Dennis arrived in Oklahoma City to become director of the University of Oklahoma Medical Center, the first new building on the campus opened its doors. At an open house in the one-story clinic building on June 3, 1968, Dr. Dennis explained Oklahoma's serious deficit of physicians who practice primary health care—family doctors. He said this would be a model clinic for demonstration of comprehensive health care for the entire family. The *Daily Oklahoman* called it a step forward. "It may or may not halt the trend away from the small town general practice, a trend which is leaving more and more state towns and small cities with no traditional family doctor." "But," the editorial concluded, "it demonstrates again to the state Dr. Dennis' awareness of the problem and his interest in all components of family practice." At that time, 23 of Oklahoma's 77

The planned high rise housing for students. (University of Oklahoma)

Housing coordinator Bill Strickland and his assistant, Suzanne Marler, look over plans for the "community of scholars." (OHSF Collection)

counties had four or fewer doctors to serve an entire county and in five counties there was only one doctor.[3]

Two months later, in August, 1968, the O.U. Regents approved preliminary plans for two, 20-story apartment towers costing an estimated $4.4 million. This was the first step in the creation of the community of scholars which Dr. Bob Bird talked about. Intended to increase the security of students, the two towers were designed to contain 294 apartments and were scheduled for completion by the fall of 1969. The university opened an office to coordinate student housing and appointed William "Bill" Strickland as the manager.

While most of the people on the campus thought this represented great progress, Dr. C.G. Gunn was sure it did not:

> I was totally against that. That was supposed to be a compound, a community of scholars, fenced in to protect them from the community. I don't believe in compounds. I believe in coming out into this area [Lincoln Terrace] where the houses are already owned. I don't think we should *ever* teach people to live isolated from their community. The university should not be in the housing business—not for graduate students.[4]

About that same time, the innovators at the Medical Center found a way to provide temporary accommodations for new health sciences educational

programs that were expanding faster than buildings could be erected to house them. Dr. Dennis remarked that without this "surge space," the university programs would not have made the rapid progress they did toward meeting health manpower needs in Oklahoma. The first such space was a house on 15th Street, just behind the Faculty House, bought to meet one of the Kellog grant requirements for the Center for Continuing Education at Norman, which had to have an auxiliary station in the Medical Center. Early on, this house and the Faculty House were both used for continuing education.

The State Health Department was assigned the task of licensing nursing homes and extended care facilities which admitted Medicare and Medicaid patients. Dr. Kirk Mosley could not accommodate more staff in the building on Eastern Avenue, so he turned to W. David Steen, Ph.D., in the Division of Community Medicine to solve the problem. Steen recommended the formation of a private, non-profit trust which could purchase residences near the Medical Center. In October, 1968, this corporation, with Kirk Mosley, Raymond Crews, Joe Rogers, Bill Schottstaedt and Steen as incorporators, bought the first house at 627 N. E. 15th Street. The owners borrowed 100 percent of the value of the house and sold it to the corporation with that loan against it. The State Health Department then rented the space and the corporation, known as the

Old trees shaded 15th Street in Lincoln Terrace. The School of Health office was in the first house on the left. (University of Oklahoma)

Stewart Wolf's house at 14th and Lindsay, left, and its neighbor to the west provided "surge space" for new dental programs. (OHSF Collection)

Oklahoma Health Sciences Facility, used the rent money to make the mortgage payments. This system was used to purchase 28 houses on 14th, 15th and 16th streets for short-term use by the university.

Originally, the charter of the Oklahoma Health Sciences Facility, Inc., said that should there no longer be any need for the corporation, its properties would be given to a similar organization such as the University of Oklahoma. Essentially, the beneficial interest always rested with the university. When the School of (Public) Health was created, there was no space for it. When dentistry came along, it was in the formative years and needed space. The house which dentistry went into was first acquired at the request of Stewart Wolf because he had a $3 million heart research grant and he did not have a place to put that program. The Oklahoma Health Sciences Facility bought the house next door west of Dr. Wolf's home at 14th and Lindsay. Later, Wolf sold his home to the Dental Foundation for the dental hygiene program. This surge space was absolutely essential to the expeditious expansion

of the educational programs in the health sciences. Dr. Steen recalled: "We never put any money 'out front.' We got some criticism but [it was] never head on. It was implied on a number of occasions that I was making a pile of money, but these were mostly in-house [inferences] from the faculty of the school of medicine." Four years later, however, people outside the university began to view this corporation with more than a little suspicion.[5]

The section of a large, general hospital which contains the x-ray department, laboratories, surgery and delivery suites, kitchen and dining rooms, business office, medical records, housekeeping and other services is often called "the podium," not to be confused with the OHC parking podium. The new University Hospital was designed with a broad, multi-level podium above which rose three patient towers, one on the east for adult inpatients, a children's tower facing west, on Phillips, and an outpatient tower on 11th Street. Each tower would receive food, supplies and services from the centralized departments in the common podium. With this concept, both adults and children would be integrated into a single facility yet the age separation would be maintained by putting the kids in one tower and the grown-ups in another. This was expected to be less expensive and more efficient than operating two completely separate hospitals which the university was then doing.

Dennis was realistic enough to understand this new University Hospital, a complete, finished, 600-bed facility, could not be put in place all at once. To be sure, that would have been ideal but it did not appear to be politically feasible. Therefore, he chose to plan it in total, but build it in phases. The first unit, the Mark Everett Tower, was to be a 200-bed adult unit atop a portion of the podium. Located south of the clinic building, it was planned to connect with Old Main by way of the outpatient clinics. Of course, this was neither the most effective nor economic way to operate a hospital but it was the first step toward what was planned to be a highly efficient institution.

In June, 1969, the O.U. Regents accepted the Harmon Construction Company's low bid of $11,959,000 and by mid-July construction was underway. This initial unit, scheduled for completion in 1972, included surgery and gynecology/obstetrics services. The university obtained Hill-Burton and Health Professions Educational Assistance Program funds from the federal government to match HERO and other bond monies from the state to finance it.[6]

On January 27, 1970, five years and five months

Dean McGee turns to Governor Bartlett as he addresses the crowd at the dedication of the Basic Science Education Building. (OHSF Collection)

There was overflow attendance at the dedication ceremony. (University of Oklahoma)

after Dennis arrived at the Medical Center, the first major new structure in the Oklahoma Health Center was opened. Governor Bartlett, speaking at the dedication ceremony, challenged the Medical Center to increase enrollment. "As this center grows," he said, "the number of doctors who will serve the needs of the people of this state will grow." The Basic Science Education Building in which he was speaking made it possible to increase the size of the medical school entering class from 104 to 126 students.

The ceremony was held in one of twin, 175-seat lecture halls, the sharply-raked floor of which rose to the second level, permitting students an unobstructed view of the podium, the blackboard, the projection screen and six television receivers. Closed-circuit television connection to 16-student laboratory pods allowed close-up demonstrations to be seen by the student in his "office." Each medical student was assigned his own space where he kept his books, microscope and other tools, and did his experiments and his studying. Dr. Dennis emphasized that the study areas were open 24 hours a day which "is a surprise to those used to traditional buildings where labs lie fallow during portions of the year."[7]

This design was not a new idea. Charles Wagner, A.I.A., an architect in the Divison of Educational and Research Facilities who reviewed plans accompanying applications for funds under the Health Professions Educational Assistance [HPEA] program, explained the position of federal officials toward medical schools:

The theories of medical education change very fast.

When we first went in, in 1963, the 16-man, multidiscipline laboratory was in the ascendency. Dr. Leake had invented this in 1924 and everybody thought this was a great idea. We began to realize that maybe this wasn't going to work for everybody, but by that time, the "mill" was grinding out applications for funds and the easy thing to do, from the medical school's point of view, was to base it on the 16-student multidiscipline laboratory. We began to discourage them right away and they asked, "O.K. What's better?" Well, what was better hadn't been determined and a lot of medical schools, for instance the University of Southern California (USC), in the meantime had ripped out their 16 student lab.

Since 1924, very few medical teaching facilities had been built, so there was this lag. When the [HPEA] Act was passed in 1963, everybody wanted to get on the bandwagon right now. They didn't want to stall around, do a lot of studies of the efficacies of different kinds of teaching arrangements, so they took the 16-student thing, which was known, and just did it, all over the country. Very soon thereafter, we realized this was not going to work very well.

Different people handled it differently. George Harrell, at Hershey, came up with the idea of each student having a place in a laboratory but also a study space in the same building. Well, that meant a lot of extra space. George Harrell was an eminent guy so a lot of people thought if George does it, it must be good! In the meantime, George had discovered it wasn't such a hot idea after all.

It was ironic. We'd go to a medical school which was planning a basic science building and we'd say, "Look, this 16-student module is not working at USC for these reasons." But having already put in the application on the basis of the 16-student laboratory, they didn't have time to change so they just went ahead with it.

The east side of the Basic Science Education Building. University of Oklahoma)

A medical student inspects one of the controversial 16-man laboratories in the new Basic Science Education Building. (University of Oklahoma)

In the meantime, about 1970, the fashion in biochemistry began to dry up the laboratories. I think it was Jefferson [Medical College] in Philadelphia; the head of the biochemistry department gave up wet experiments altogether. But now, they're going back to them—it swings in cycles. It all depended on where you were in the 10 years of the (HPEA) program as to how you came out. We tried to encourage everybody to be more flexible.[8]

Did the design work at Oklahoma? A dozen years later, medical students seemed to be enthusiastic about it but, of course, unless they transferred from another medical school after the first year, they had no other system with which to compare it. One student said, "You get acquainted with the other students in your group, this is your home base, you have the television communication with the lecture halls and you can use video tapes on this equipment." He said the students liked it.

James W. Woods, Ph.D., professor of physiology, who was responsible for the operation of the Basic Science Education Building, thought "the arrangement for gross anatomy may have been the best I've ever seen." "The one thing that really worked," he added, "was the air flow. We kept cadavers in those inner labs, called the 'back labs,' and never had any problem. People were concerned that the cadavers would 'smell up' the building and they never did." Bodies for gross anatomy were treated with embalming fluid, a mixture of formaldehyde, glycerine and alcohol, which preserved them.[9]

L. Vernon Scott, Sc.D., who came to O.U. as an as-

sistant professor of bacteriology in the college of medicine in 1950, became head of the Department of Microbiology and Immunology, which bacteriology was later titled. He taught in the Basic Science Education Building from the time it opened in 1970 until he retired in 1983, over 13 years. When the Leake design was conceived, Scott explained, medical schools were almost monastic in regimen and spirit. Students were single, of single purpose and devoted most of their waking hours absorbing the facts and lore of medicine. They looked forward to the time, as interns and residents, they would be spending even more time in the hospital. But ideas changed in the 1960s and medical students adopted a different outlook. Dr. Scott agreed: "You're right. The life styles of medical students have changed. I think fewer of them are getting married now than during the sixties and seventies. Some students use the labs for study and some don't."[10] The Basic Science Education Building (BSEB) is a handsome structure with tall, square columns supporting the portico which shelters the main entrance at the north. The half-flight of stairs on the west leads to the entrance and gives the building an appearance of elevated position and importance befitting the scientific activities that go on inside. The exterior, in brown brick and beige, pre-cast concrete, set the earth-tone color palette intended for the entire campus.

The basic design is a "racetrack," with a landscaped courtyard that students can enjoy, well protected from the Oklahoma wind. At the front, the two-story lobby is flanked by the two large lecture halls previously mentioned. There are stairs ascending on either side of the lobby so students may enter at the upper level of these steeply-raked halls. Smaller lecture and seminar rooms are conveniently located close to the 16-

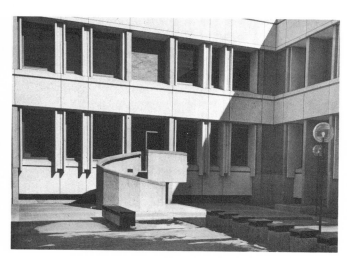

The courtyard. (University of Oklahoma)

Arthur N. Tuttle. (Courtesy Daily Oklahoman).

student laboratories, later revised to accommodate 20 students.

Because this building is the home base for the medical students during their first two years, it is also headquarters for the Medical Center registrar, a position held by Norman E. Goodwin until he retired at the end of 1983. This office handles admissions for graduate and undergraduate programs and academic records for all the schools. In the basement is a large storage area for the human bodies awaiting dissection in gross anatomy laboratories. It was on this level, the Centrex telephone system for the entire health campus originally was installed. After much negotiation, the university and the Oklahoma Health Sciences Foundation persuaded Southwestern Bell Telephone Company to install a system which would serve all of the organizations on the campus, regardless of their sponsorship. The university operates the system by maintaining a central switchboard and billing the other institutions. The system allows people to dial into the campus direct if they know the number of the station they want and permits people on campus to reach stations in other organizations by dialing only four digits. Only the V. A. Hospital retained an exclusive telephone system and even with a "178" tie-line, it takes seven digits to get from, say, Presbyterian Hospital to a specific station in the V.A. Hospital.

Although the flow of operating money for the university slowed after completion of the Basic Science Education building, the pace of planning and construction did not. The building of the new University Hospital went forward, a half-million dollar addition to radiology was under construction at the northeast corner of the University Clinics and a new dermatol-

ogy clinic, opposite the Presbyterian Hospital site, was expected to be ready for occupancy in June, 1970.

With these major projects under way, the university established an office of architectural and engineering services and, in early 1970, appointed Arthur N. Tuttle, Jr., A.I.A., to head it. He had been campus architect at the University of North Carolina, Chapel Hill, for 10 years. His job was to coordinate the plans for university construction with the long range plans for the OHC. Immediately, Tuttle began working on plans for the proposed School of Dentistry with Dean William Brown, the School of Health with Dr. Bill Schottstaedt and the Health Sciences Library with Dr. C.G. Gunn, chairman of the library planning committee, and Leonard Eddy, the medical librarian. He said, "The pace in the center at first was fantastic. We worked night and day and weekends. I met Bob Bird in his apartment and worked with him on grant applications on Saturdays, Sundays and lots of nights."[11]

During those early years of limited financial support, academicians in the medical school had to come up with innovative ways to get money if they wanted their department to move ahead. Dr. Mark Allen Everett, chairman of Dermatology, devised a method to build a headquarters for his department when all of the university's capital funds were earmarked for other projects. Ordinarily, deans of medical schools want the university to own and centralize patient treatment services in clinics and hospitals; it is a matter of control and efficiency. But when the medical school does not have sufficient money to expand those facilities, it may choose to permit departments to decentralize if and when private funding can be obtained. Dr. Everett described the situation in dermatology.

115

Mark Allen Everett, son of the former dean, was chairman of Dermatology. (University of Oklahoma)

The building did indeed resemble a castle. (OHSF Collection)

Jim Dennis at the dedication of the Dermatology Building. (OHSF Collection)

"The concept of a separate facility is such a worrisome concept to a dean. It suggests the removal of a department and its expertise out from under his control and indeed, from the "community" of the college. That is a threat, of course."

The impetus for dermatology's move was that the clinic operated in the hospital, but because dermatology, unlike other services such as orthopedics or medicine, did not contribute a large number of inpatients, it had little influence. Consequently, it was given very meager quarters in the hospital. However, the department was beginning to grow and needed space. Dr. Everett wanted to build a facility which had adequate outpatient teaching and faculty space which the hospital, for good reasons, could not and would not provide.

Out of his own pocket, he bought some land on the north side of 13th Street. Next, he had to convince the dean that developing a separate facility was a wise thing to do. Dr. Dennis was not enthusiastic about the idea and suggested Everett should get the approval of the hospital board. Everett spent about six weeks visiting every member of the hospital board, explaining the proposal in detail so when it came up in the hospital board meeting, it was voted unanimously, with no discussion.

Dr. Everett then got a letter from Ed Brandt, who was the associate dean, which said, "Now that you have received hospital board approval for this move, we

need to discuss it further." Immediately, Everett went down and arranged a bond issue with Charles A. "Chuck" Vose, Sr., chairman of the First National Bank and Trust Company of Oklahoma City, to finance the structure. He got the O.U. Foundation to issue the bonds and the bank to buy them at 7 percent interest. As Everett later commented:

Originally, I had not intended to give the land, so we would have some tax advantage during the period we were paying off the building, but it was clear we had to move quickly. I told Boyd [Gunning, director of the foundation] I would give the land as collateral for the bonds. We did all of that, the bonds were issued and bought, and *then* I replied to Ed Brandt's letter. Because the financing had been arranged and there were no problems about it, I never heard any more about it but I think it could have been stopped very easily.

The O.U. Foundation has the beneficial interest in the building. My partners and I have personally been paying off those bonds for the past 15 years, so it represents an enormous gift of our faculty, some $600 thousand.[12]

People are not ordinarily neutral about the architecture of the Dermatology Building. At first, people would ask, "When are they going to paint that castle?" Dr. Everett explained:

I instructed the architects, Seminoff and Bowman, to design a facility that could either be medical or an art museum. If, as originally planned, it had been owned by the faculty, we thought it might ultimately be given to the community as an art museum. During the process, I went to Ireland and Trinity University in Dublin had just opened a new museum. It was one of the very early poured-concrete buildings using cedar for the forms. I was so impressed we changed our ideas and used the same system.[13]

When he gave the keynote address at the Dermatology Building dedication on June 18, 1970, Dr. Dennis said the building was "symbolic of the total involvement of the Medical Center faculty with the long range program."[14]

CHAPTER 16

RISING COSTS: 1968

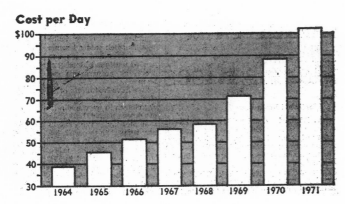

Cost per Day

The $100 per day hospital stay was expected to be a reality by the early 1970s. (Oklahoma City Times)

1975 $100 A DAY

$60 A DAY 1969

"Pocketbook Fever." (The Oklahoma City Times)

A corollary objective of the Oklahoma Health Center plan was to contain the cost of health care, which had been rising at an alarming rate. Hospital rates had more than tripled and doctors' fees had doubled since 1947, going up 50 percent faster than the general cost of living. As a result of advanced medical technology, more expensive equipment and specialization by doctors, health care had markedly improved and people did not hesitate to demand the best when they or a member of their family got sick. To meet this demand, hospitals expanded their facilities and their staffs, which pushed up costs. In 1950, it cost less than $16 a day to stay in the hospital; by 1967, that figure had shot up to a national average of $54 and, according to the American Medical Association, was expected to reach $100 a day by 1975. Some people predicted and many feared, if the trend continued, the average person would soon find it impossible to afford care in a private hospital.[1]

These conditions motivated hospitals to look for ways to contain costs. Five private hospitals in Denver, Colorado, formed a coalition called the Midtown Hospital Association to reduce competitive practices and increase cooperation. They were all clustered in the same vicinity in east Denver, not unlike the grouping proposed for Oklahoma's health campus. Their plans included utilizing a central laundry and a central heating power plant for all five hospitals. Other ideas were shutting down the maternity units in three of the five institutions, maintaining only one emergency center in one hospital and establishing a central computer for hospital records. They expected to continue group purchasing which had been saving them considerable money for some time.[2]

These notions of cooperation, central shared services and non duplication of expensive equipment were the same ones which impelled the planning by members of the OHSF Operations Committee. Both Mercy and Presbyterian planned to double their bed capacity but the new plants their architects were designing had to be four or five times the size of the buildings they then occupied. There was no questions their costs would go up rapidly when they moved onto the campus so Sr. Mary Coletta and Jack Shrode were looking for any operating efficiencies they could find.

The university and the administrations of other Oklahoma City hospitals were not the only groups concerned about the rapidly rising cost of health care. There was increased public awareness as the result of newspaper and magazine articles. The few patients who had to pay that cost themselves contracted "pocketbook fever" when they were handed their hospital bill.

Serious inflation was just getting a grip on the American economy. The process of health care cost inflation was being fueled by several factors. One of the most important was the third-party reimbursement system by which physicians and hospitals were paid, a system which gave patients little incentive to shop around for the best prices. With Blue Cross-Blue Shield or some other insuror picking up the bill, the patient had little reason to be concerned about what the service cost; he merely sent the charges on through for someone else to pay. In addition, many employees did not have to worry when the premiums for health care coverage increased, as they did regularly and significantly, because their employer paid them as a fringe benefit. Therefore, while the "public" was shocked by skyrocketing charges, only a small percentage of the people actually experienced the problem in their pocketbook. Care for the elderly and the poor was essentially free and almost everyone else had some kind of insurance coverage.

Moreover, because health care providers were reimbursed essentially whatever they charged, on a retrospective system, they had a built-in incentive to raise their prices, to pass on any increased costs they had, knowing full well there was no competition. Also, employees in hospitals, who were traditionally on the low end of the wage and salary scales when compared with similar jobs in industry, began to demand more money. Neither hospital administrators nor the public criticized this effort, because if hospitals did not keep up with wage and salary trends, they would soon find themselves unable to recruit scarce health professionals and they would also be threatened by union organizers. Additionally, this was an era of great advancement in the technology of medicine, requiring more sophisticated equipment and better trained people to operate it. Consequently, the average cost per patient day in the general hospital, which was less than $40 in 1964 and slightly more than $70 in 1969, was expected to exceed $100 a day by the mid-1970s.[3]

The improving scientific services coming on line in hospitals required more people. In 1968, general hospitals employed 2.5 people for every patient in the bed and the ratio continued to rise. The figures in the table below from the 1968 *Guide Issue of Hospitals*, published by the American Hospital Association, show the costs of Oklahoma City private institutions:[4]

Hospital	Beds	Expense	Payroll	Personnel
Baptist	364	$5,702,000	$2,920,000	871
Deaconess	111	1,952,000	1,131,000	302
Mercy	206	3,586,000	1,931,000	501
Presbyterian	193	3,432,000	1,928,000	431
St. Anthony	543	8,742,000	5,513,000	1,299
South Community	73	1,307,000	755,000	205
Midwest City	110	1,614,000	965,000	242

Hospital costs were climbing so fast that administrators were embarrassed by the shocking increases and tried repeatedly to explain and justify them to their public. Because hospitals were outside the free marketplace, there was no "invisible hand" to control prices. Administrators could do nothing about holding down general inflation and they had no reason to slow the advance of medical technology which always upped the cost of health care. Hospitals did not compete on the prices they charged but they were highly competitive in the scope and quality of their services. Each hospital wanted the latest equipment and the most comprehensive services. They were extremely sensitive about their image and reputation in the community.

Personal ambition also played a role in rising hospital costs as Al Donnell explained:

St. Anthony Hospital was going to be the biggest and best hospital west of the Mississippi River and it didn't make any difference if it killed all the cats in the county or not! And they had one Stu Cummings [an administrator] who really thought he was going to be able to do that.

All we had [in the areawide health and hospital planning agency] was the power of persuasion. It was like huntin' bears with a buggy whip! We started in developing a program and got attention from the State Health Department, Hospital Facilities Division. Paul Snelson cooperated in this effort of good planning and had us review every project in the Oklahoma City area that was submitted for Hill-Burton funds. But there was intense competition among the hospitals in Oklahoma City, even bad feeling of the voluntary hospitals outside the center toward the medical school and the hospitals in the Medical Center. It was hard to get the big hospitals to agree to do things together.[5]

In contrast, the hospitals in or coming into the Oklahoma Health Center were already planning together for central shared services on the campus in an effort to reduce costs. Mercy, Presbyterian, University and Children's and the V.A. Hospital eventually would total more than 1,800 beds, and their administrators could see the economy of scale this clustering could provide. By mid-1969, subcommittees of the Oklahoma Health Sciences Foundation's Operations Committee were well along in the planning of 21 such services.

Engineering studies of the central steam and chilled water plant had been completed and after two years of negotiation between private enterprise and the foundation, it was concluded the university should develop the heating and cooling service. In June, 1969, the University of Oklahoma Regents appointed Carnahan and Thompson of Oklahoma City as the design engineers. This system, which was expected ultimately to heat and cool all of the buildings on the campus, was scheduled for operation in 1971.

Arrangements had been made with the Central Oklahoma Transportation and Parking Authority (COTPA) to finance, construct and operate the parking blanket which would eventually accommodate 10,000 cars. Barton Aschman, traffic and parking experts from Chicago, had done an analysis of the need for streets and spaces and Bozalis, Dickinson and Roloff, local architects, did a schematic layout and design and figured out how much increments of the parking system would cost. They did this as a public service and turned their results in to Earl Sneed, president of COTPA. At that time, COTPA calculated it could build and amortize the parking blanket at an annual lease cost of $345 a space or $28.50 a month.

Plans for a central laundry and linen service for the entire campus moved ahead. Robert Hardy visited new cooperative laundries serving hospitals in Indianapolis and Pittsburgh to collect ideas. Proposals came in from private laundry companies in Phoenix, Arizona, Muskogee, Oklahoma and Oklahoma City. Laundry experts from St. Paul, Minnesota were brought in to conduct a feasibility study of alternatives. Early 1972 was the target time to get this central service in operation. The V.A. Hospital, however, chose to continue to operate its own laundry.

Policies of a proposed central emergency facility were established and physical planning was included in the second phase of University Hospital programming. To be located in the extended podium of the new hospital, the trauma center would be designed to serve all emergency patients brought to the Oklahoma Health Center. Staffing an emergency service around the clock is an expensive proposition, and the idea of centralization meant four of the hospitals on campus would not have to have this service. Patients were expected to be transferred by ambulance to the hospital of their choice after being treated and stabilized at the University Hospital Trauma Center.

Application for federal funds to construct a health sciences library and computer center had been submitted by the university in 1968. The design received highly favorable comment by the National Library of Medi-

"Life or Debt." (The Oklahoma City Times)

cine and was approved but not funded. Reapplication was scheduled for 1970. Other subcommittees were working on central laboratory services, high energy radiation therapy and radioisotopes, purchasing and stores, and extended care/rehabilitation which entailed the construction of a 100 bed institution on the campus. Central food service, a credit union, a cardiovascular diagnostic and treatment facility and mental health services were other central units in the planning stage. Another idea was to put all of the many private health and welfare organizations, such as the Cancer Society and the Heart Association, in a single building on the campus. Not only would this be convenient for OHC patients but it would allow the various agencies to communicate better and coordinate their planning and fundraising. They could use common meeting space, secretarial services and printing equipment. Still other committees worked on centralizing security services, grounds maintenance, a day nursery for employees' and students' children, a campus-wide telephone system and a waste collection and disposal service.[6]

Al Donnell said, "The OHC plan was very, very exciting. We had some awfully good people on that Operations Committee, Dean Chrislip, Don Ellison, the health science center people." He was right. Here was a great opportunity to build efficiency and economy into the operation of a group of hospitals and build it to a level which previously had not been achieved anywhere in the country.[7]

CHAPTER 17
TULSA ASPIRATIONS: 1968-1969

Senator and Doctor Richard Stansberry wanted to get ahead of the osteopaths. (The Oklahoman and Times)

The co-sponsor of the bill to construct a medical school in Tulsa was Senator Gene Stipe of McAlester. (Oklahoma Observer)

The "Oklahoma Plan," as the goals and design of the Oklahoma Health Center were known in Washington, D.C., had captured the imagination of almost everyone. However, in the midst of the enthusiastic support for the proposed health campus, a few small clouds were beginning to form on the horizon—some competitive, some critical. State Senator Richard D. Stansberry of Oklahoma City, also a physician, joined Senator Gene Stipe of McAlester, to announce, on December 15, 1967, they would introduce a bill in the next session of the legislature for construction of a medical school in Tulsa.[1]

Senator Bryce Baggett, a major supporter of the Oklahoma Health Center, reacted promptly and vigorously. "There is no way in the world, logically, that you can scatter and fragment medical training around the state without sacrificing quality. We have to really strain now to support one medical school—with help from federal funds and medical research funds,"

Baggett declared. He went on to describe Stipe's proposal as "disruptive of planning that has been done by the Medical Center, its consultants and the Health Sciences Foundation. It is not so much a recommendation as a dismantling job." He further opined that neither Stipe nor the co-sponsor of the proposal, Senator Stansberry, "has been noted for his constructive efforts."[2]

Naturally, Stansberry disagreed: " When I went into the legislature the first time in 1964," he explained, "I was real interested in getting the medical center funded. My ideas didn't necessarily agree with other physicians, and I got a lot of 'press' that I was trying to destroy the school." In 1963, about 120 out of 125 physicians contacted had signed a petition circulated at St. Anthony Hospital opposing the new University Hospital. Stansberry also had signed it and subsequently went into the legislature. He said this was the reason "they singled me out and said I was opposed to the medical center." Asked if he was in basic agreement with Dr. Dennis's effort to educate family doctors and get them to practice in small communities like Wakita, Dr. Stansberry replied that he had made many speeches on the Senate floor warning his colleagues that "if you don't take care of those problems, you're going to get an osteopathic physician in all those little towns because they realize that problem and have started addressing themselves to that problem."

Stansberry and Stipe tried to convince the physicians in Tulsa County that "if you don't do it, the osteopaths are going to put a school in Tulsa," but apparently the M.D.s were not particularly concerned. Things were quiet for a while and then the doctors decided maybe a new medical school could be established as a satellite of the one in Oklahoma City.[3]

This was not a new idea. As early as 1966, the Tulsa County Medical Society named Wendell L. Smith, M.D., chairman of a Medical School Survey Committee, the purpose of which was "to initiate a study of the need and possibility of a medical school in Tulsa." The committee thought about developing the school as a part of Tulsa University, but officials at that institution were not willing to raise the money to create and maintain it. The following year, 1967, the Metropolitan Tulsa Chamber of Commerce became interested, and both the society and the chamber agreed to contribute a maximum of $3,000 each for a feasibility study. By that time, Senators Stipe and Stansberry were interested in the idea. In January, 1968, a resolution was introduced in the legislature requesting the State Regents for Higher Education to conduct the study. Interestingly, the effort was rooted in two long-standing rivalries: Tulsa versus Oklahoma City and the M.D.s versus the D.O.s.[4]

Like heat lightning on the eastern horizon, other expressions of doubt about the proposed Oklahoma Health Center came from Talihina, which was concerned about the future of the tuberculosis sanitorium there, and from McAlester, where some people thought too much state money for health facilities was being concentrated in the Oklahoma City area. On December 27, 1967, the *Oklahoma Journal*, a Midwest City newspaper with a large metropolitan area circulation, ran an editorial in an attempt to correct some of the misconceptions about the OHC. It quoted one Oklahoma community newspaper as saying, "Our real battle is with the Oklahoma City proposal for a $189 million medical complex to house all state medical fa-

The Tulsa skyline in the mid-1980s. (Metropolitan Tulsa Chamber of Commerce)

cilities…. We believe that it is better to take medical facilities to the people instead of isolating medical facilities from people through centralization." The editorial went on to quote Dr. Dennis who explained the aim of the OHC was "to gird up the production of health manpower that is now in critical shortage in many areas of the state…and get the manpower we produce out into the state so people can get 90 percent of their health care in their home community."[5]

As promised, Senator Gene Stipe introduced a bill early in the 1968 legislative session to authorize a medical school in Tulsa. However, the Tulsa County Medical Society concluded in its February meeting that such legislation was "premature." While the society definitely favored a medical school there, it opposed all specific legislation introduced in advance of a feasibility study. As a native Oklahoman, Dennis understood the situation and realized the need to accommodate to it:

One of the first major talks I made was to the Tulsa County Medical Society. This was an obvious need because Tulsa always opposed anything Oklahoma City might benefit from. For a long time, some of the doctors up there had been discontented and were concerned about the possibility of a medical school in Tulsa. All I did was to go before the doctors and, with hat in hand, say, "Look, fellows, we have all of this pressure and you know the needs. I don't know whether there is enough funding available to support even one medical school. We certainly haven't supported the one we have."

They all agreed on that and I said, "We have a little over two million population in the state and it has been shown that two million people is the minimum base to support a medical school. As the state grows—and it usually takes 10 to 15 years to evolve a complete medical center—then Tulsa is the logical place for it. If you will help us get one adequately based and supported medical school, I will be the first to jump on the wagon and help you go after the second medical school."

I had the feeling that Stansberry and Stipe were strange bedfellows, in a way, but it was a good political ploy and when you get that kind of leadership coming to the doctors in Tulsa who had always wanted a medical school, you've almost got a major block of the legislature behind you before you go very far. The Tulsa group were hard-boiled negotiators and it wasn't easy to deal with them. They always operated from a position of power and they always bargained because they *had* that power. But things were premature in terms of the state's population and the needs.[6]

Premature as they may have appeared to Dr. Dennis, Tulsa continued to push ahead. The Tulsa County Medical Society saw the opportunity to get the State Regents involved in a project which could mean state money for a Tulsa medical school. The regents did get involved a scant six months after the legislative resolution requesting they conduct a feasibility study. They appointed an advisory committee made up of doctors, including Jim Dennis, educators, citizens and legislators and headed by Enid regent John J. Vater. At the same meeting on July 23, 1968, the State Regents authorized a contract with Booz, Allen and Hamilton, management consultants from Chicago, and the expenditure of up to $5,000 in federal funds, plus any other funds provided by Tulsans, for the study.[7]

The Oklahoma population in 1968 was approximately 2.5 million people. The U.S. Census Bureau population projection for Oklahoma in 1985 was 2,938,000. If indeed the minimum population base necessary to support the present medical school was two million people, it did not require any special talent to forecast the conclusion the consultants would reach.[8]

After three months study, Dr. Charles Edwards of Booz, Allen and Hamilton, the consultants, came to the conclusion that a Tulsa medical school would be a rather costly venture, requiring $21.5 million to build the medical school, $3 to $5 million a year to operate it and an additional $5 million to improve clinical facilities in Tulsa hospitals. He advised that the most economical way to increase the supply of physicians in Oklahoma was to enlarge the freshman class at the medical school in Oklahoma City from the current 125 to 200 by 1975. "In the final anaylsis," he said, "it boils down to economics." He told the Tulsa medical school advisory committee that a new state-supported medical school in Tulsa was not feasible at that time.[9]

Although the threat of a second medical school in Tulsa diminished, it did not disappear. The consultants suggested three actions Tulsans could take to prepare for the medical school they eventually expected to have: develop a joint residency training program in the Tulsa hospitals, establish graduate level basic science courses at Tulsa University, and correct the deficiencies at Hillcrest, St. John's and St. Francis Hospital so they met medical school teaching hospital requirements. It was also recommended that Tulsa expand working relationships with the O.U. College of Medicine in Oklahoma City.[10]

CHAPTER 18
PEOPLE: 1967-1969

In Norman, a committee of the faculty and the O.U. Board of Regents had been searching for a new president. George Cross planned to retire and in late May, 1967, the university announced its selection of J. Herbert Hollomon, Ph.D., to succeed him. Then 48 years old and the Undersecretary of Commerce of the United States, Dr. Hollomon previously had been the general manager of the Schenectady, N.Y., engineering laboratory of the General Electric Company. He was never quite sure how he became a candidate. However, he speculated that it was because he had gone to school at the Massachusetts Institute of Technology with the brother of James G. Davidson, a member of the board of regents.

There was some indication that Hollomon was chosen because he had contacts in Washington and possibly could get federal support for university programs. As regent Nancy Davies commented:

> I think that was a concern. We did want someone who knew his way around the federal bureaucracy and certainly he did. He had those credentials.
>
> You see, Cross had been there for 25 years and had done an excellent job. But throughout the state and the university, everyone kept saying it was time for some new ideas, time for a change. Certainly, you expect anyone coming in to have a chance to present a plan.[1]

The scheme for succession was somewhat unique, possibly because Dr. Hollomon's administrative experience had not been in academia. Dr. Cross was not to retire until mid-1968; during the interim, Dr. Hollomon would spend his time at the campus becoming acquainted with the people and the programs, learning about the challenges facing O.U. and working on a plan for the future of the university. An editorial in the *Oklahoma City Times* opined that "...Hollomon is a first-class choice, a man any university would be proud to have. The outlook for O.U. now is brighter than ever."[2]

During this period at the Medical Center, there also were changes in top-level leadership positions. Dr. Joseph M. "Joe" White, associate dean of the medical school, resigned in September, 1968, to become dean and vice president of the University of Texas Medical Branch in Galveston. "I left," White recalled, "not be-

Forty-eight year old J. Herbert Hollomon was selected to succeed Dr. George Cross. (University of Oklahoma)

cause I didn't like Oklahoma, but because there wasn't any place for me to go." He continued:

> I'd been associate dean for seven years. Dennis was both vice president and dean and it didn't look as though he was going to give up either one of those jobs. He made me Dean of the Medical Faculty, which was kind of a "nothing" job. So if I was going to be a dean, I had to move out.[3]

As Joe White was leaving, Dale Groom, M.D., a cardiologist from the University of South Carolina, arrived to take over the Oklahoma Regional Medical Program. Born in Bristow, Oklahoma, Dr. Groom had been recruited by his friend Jim Dennis. In South Carolina, Groom had taught cardiology and was associate dean for continuing education which was just coming to the fore. While medical centers previously had not paid much attention to continuing education, it was a primary objective of the Regional Medical Program [RMP]. Basically, the idea was: the federal

Dr. Dale Groom, head of the Regional Medical Program, talks with a student. (University of Oklahoma)

Registered nurses Vicki Camp and Sharon Denton on duty at Presbyterian's Central Monitoring Unit. (Presbyterian Hospital)

government would give grants to the states for continuing education and other projects having to do with improving medical care, and those grants would be administered locally. A local board was set up to decide how to appropriate funds for the best interest of the state.

The Regional Medical Program was geared to heart disease, cancer and stroke, which were the leading causes of death, then described as the "killer diseases." Dr. Michael DeBakey, a cardiac surgeon at the Texas Medical Center in Houston had the initial concept and sold it to the federal government. Actually, the idea of fighting heart disease, cancer and stroke sold itself because everyone in Congress had some relative who had died of one of the three and even if they did not, they regarded them as major threats. Every medical school in America got behind the Regional Medical Program, partly because it was another avenue of support for new programs which medical schools wanted.

There was a catch phrase which described RMP: "from the bench to the bedside." This had to do with hastening the day from the consummation of research resulting in new medical knowledge to the application of that research to the care of the patient at the bedside. That, of course, could best be done by the continuing education of the physician looking after the patient.

One of the projects initiated under RMP was the teleconferencing network, connecting the medical staffs in hospitals around the state, and sponsoring continuing education conferences emanating from the Medical Center and from different hospitals. This form of professional communication caught on; the physicians would meet at lunch in their own hospital and participate in case presentations with physicians

of other hospitals. Dr. Groom also believed the remote coronary care monitoring was a signal success. Using telephone lines, certain large hospitals in Oklahoma City and Tulsa monitored on oscilloscopes the electrocardiograms of patients in rural hospitals. The local physicians could talk with the cardiologist in the large hospital night or day. This was a solid achievement which advanced the treatment of coronary artery disease.[4]

With coronary monitoring, the heart attack victim could have the benefit of specialist care without having to be transported to an urban hospital. This was often a life-saving advantage. The Presbyterian Hospital's remote coronary monitoring system later became the largest in the United States, serving 22 outlying hospitals.

Meanwhile, at the Oklahoma Medical Research Foundation, another change in top-level leadership occurred. Leonard Eliel had been director of research since 1954, following two other directors who had only short tenure. In addition, there was a lay administrator, first Hugh Payne and then Reece McGee. As Dr. Eliel put it, "We had sort of a two-headed organization with nobody the supreme boss. This did create problems at times." He laughed and added, "Sometimes I characterized it as a 'two-headed monster'." He recalled:

I think I was there too long in the top position. You get stale, you run out of impetus and energy, there are factional problems which [at OMRF] became overwhelming. It was a very interesting development in terms of philosophy of research in an academic setting, in re-

125

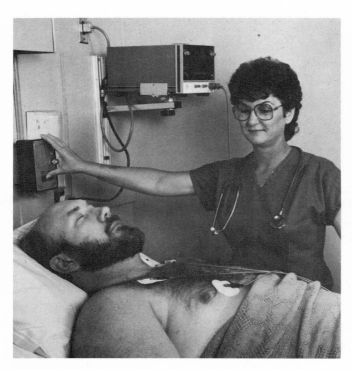

Patient, hooked up to a coronary monitor, is attended by a nurse. (Presbyterian Hospital)

gard to the relationship of OMRF to the Medical Center. We were engaged in a tug-of-war, almost from the outset, from the time the foundation was created until I left.

It should have been a symbiotic relationship. The Research Foundation was brought into existence in an effort to upgrade the academic status of the O.U. School of Medicine when the school had no full time faculty. The foundation made recruiting a full time faculty possible because it was a key factor in recruiting Stewart Wolf, Jolly West and others.

Dr. Eliel's inclination was to develop closer rapport with the medical school faculty. He believed that only with vigorous interactions between the two institutions could either of them really thrive. The foundation could not exist isolated from what was going on in the rest of the Medical Center. Others at OMRF, because they had very specifically focused and directed research interests, felt it was a threat to their territory and their access to the resources of the foundation to bring in new people. Hence, the tug-of-war. Dr. Eliel said, "I wanted Dr. Stewart Wolf to have a greater role in the research programs. He already had a section there but was not personally very active in the research program, which was basic science-oriented and Dr. Wolf was more of a clinical investigator. This ultimately resulted in an insurrection within the institution."[5]

Harvey Everest, center, chats with Mayor Patience Latting and John Rogers, Tulsa attorney.

As an apparent result of this unrest, some of the Foundation's directors were persuaded Dr. Eliel should be replaced. Medical administrators are often quite vulnerable to such pressures, as indicated by Dr. Dennis's description:

Len was the image of the research investigator for the OMRF in the state. I thought he had done a good job and gotten along very well with the faculty. But one morning about 11 o'clock, Lora said Harvey Everest and [B.D.] "Babe" Eddie [OMRF directors] had called and insisted on seeing me as soon as I could. Neither had been in my office before and I found that very strange. They came in, sat down and said, "We've decided we have to have new leadership over at the Medical Research Foundation and Len Eliel's got to go." That was the first hint I'd had from anyone that Len was anything but the fair-haired boy over there. That shocked me because I knew it would have reverberations among the faculty.

They wanted to get rid of him right now. My first reaction was, "You know, you can't do this to him because your institution will suffer. You've spent many years building up his image and you're going to throw that away in one fell swoop? Let's look at this as an academic problem. If I had Len over here and felt he could no longer function, I'd try to protect him. If you're going to dump him, let's see if we can't give him a sabbatical. The man deserves to go with honors. He hasn't done anything, as far as I know, to be kicked out." They hemmed and hawed, said they'd think about it and come back.[6]

The Faculty House, replica of Mount Vernon. (University of Oklahoma.)

Members and their families enjoy the Faculty House pool, courtesy Dr. Jolly West. (University of Oklahoma)

Professor Oz Parsons, psychologist. (University of Oklahoma)

"I guess one of the most traumatic things that ever happened to me," Eliel recalled, "was that I was called down to see Harvey Everest in his office; he was then president of Liberty National Bank. He told me— after 15 years he said, "I think it's time for you to go.""[7]

In the spring of 1968, the medical school began to lose some of its top faculty. Jolly West decided it was time to move on and resigned to become chairman of the department of psychiatry and biobehavioral sciences at the University of California, Los Angeles (UCLA), School of Medicine. Rainey Williams laughed as he related a story about Jolly. Apparently, Dr. West had always been more interested in the ends than in the means. The Faculty House was one of the few amenities at the Medical Center and had always been important. Stewart Wolf bought the house at 14th Street and Lincoln Boulevard and gave it to the faculty association. When Jolly was president of the association in the mid 1960s, he decided the house ought to have a swimming pool. As Williams recalled, "He went to the directors of the association and said, 'I want you to sign something.' He had it covered up so you really didn't know what you were signing but we ultimately found out we were each signing a note to the Liberty Bank for, I think, $10 thousand! Then he borrowed the money and built the pool." West was a nationally-recognized leader who went from Oklahoma to a very prestigious position at one of the best centers of psychiatry in the United States. According to Oscar "Oz" Parsons, Ph.D., professor in Jolly's department in Oklahoma, West was extraordinarily successful at UCLA.[8]

In the fall of 1969, the Medical Center lost two more of its important leaders: Ed Brandt, associate dean of the School of Medicine and Stewart Wolf. Dr. Joe White, then the vice-president and dean of the Med-

ical Branch of the University of Texas at Galveston, told how he recruited them:

> The first person was Ed Brandt who had replaced me as associate dean at Oklahoma. He had gotten into this squabble that Dennis was in with Hollomon and was not happy with that. Ed and I had worked very closely together so his recruitment was a natural one for me when I was looking for an associate dean.[9]

In fact, White had offered Brandt the position of associate dean at Galveston in July of the previous year. As Brandt recalled:

> At that time, Jim talked to me pretty hard and I decided not to go. Then, I became somewhat more disillusioned. I thought Governor Bartlett's attitude about higher education in general and the Medical Center in particular was going to kill any hope of everything com-

Dean Dennis shakes his hand as Associate Dean Ed Brandt says farewell to the Medical Center. (University of Oklahoma)

ing to pass. The general attitude of the Oklahoma people and Bartlett was that higher education was utilitarian. The purpose of sending someone to college was to make it possible for them to get a better job, and the purpose of the faculty was to teach and make sure these people got jobs. There was a failure to recognize the other aspects of higher education as it relates to society in terms of research and creative abilities. That's one big difference I found in Texas. One of the first things that amazed me was, when that state had a problem, it turned to the university to solve it.

I thought we had gone so far down the road in Oklahoma that we couldn't shift. We had no alternates available to us. Beside that, Galveston was starting to build and had a lot of money. It was the opposite extreme; it had all kinds of money and not much plan. So it seemed time for me to get onto something that looked a little safer.

And I might say the whole issue of Hollomon—it wasn't boiling up, but it was there. I worked with Hollomon a lot and I got to know him pretty well. It was very clear to me that the Medical Center was not high on his priority list and he was not going to allow the Medical Center in any way to escape from the general policies of the University which were adapted to the main campus. Furthermore, you could see the increasing conflict between Hollomon and Dennis. I would hear about it from both of them. Also, Hollomon's relationship with the State Regents at that time was deteriorating as was his relationship, as far as I could interpret, with the state legislature.[10]

Joe White continued:

Stewart had resigned as chairman of medicine and was over at the Oklahoma Medical Research Foundation.

Auld House at Totts Gap research farm in eastern Pennsylvania. (Stewart Wolf)

And he was in an unhappy situation. Bob Bird called and asked me if there was anything I could possibly do for Stewart. We happened to be developing this marine biomedical institute, so we got Stewart down [to head it], not that he knew anything about marine biomedicine. But he was such a helluva recruiter and promoter, such a dynamic leader, that he was a natural for it. Within a week, he had the damnedest speech about marine biomedicine you ever heard in your life! It was primarily a research institute and he recruited researchers to do the work. So that's why Stewart came.[11]

Stewart Wolf's unhappy situation was a bit more involved than Joe's brief explanation indicated. Dr. Dennis said when he arrived in Oklahoma City, Stewart Wolf had been running the Medical Center as a surrogate for Mark Everett. He was a creative thinker and understood what Dennis was trying to do although he may not have been too sympathetic with the concept of needs out in the rural areas. In recounting the events, Dennis pointed out that:

Stewart became a problem in an obtuse way. He had this big farm in Pennsylvania which he had acquired with funds left to him by a grateful patient while he was at Cornell. He wanted to establish a "research farm," which again is creative. He was redoing some of the 100-year old buildings and building housing for staff. In the summer months, he'd take his family and some of his staff up there. They could spend the summer refreshing and recreating their energies and at the same time be continuing their research which, I think, was a good thing. They called it the "Oklahoma Research Farm."

But Stewart was a lot like Jolly West—he had no sense of budgets or living within budgets, which caused me great difficulty without his meaning to. His department was always in the red. If they needed to do something, Stewart and Jolly both just did it! And I think that's great; I think that's why the place was moving.

But a lot of Oklahoma money was going up to people who were staying in Pennsylvania. The main problem was the legislators were jumping on me about all the telephone bills—long distance calls from Pennsylvania to Oklahoma. People were talking back and forth all the time and these calls were coming in on the university telephone system.

I always thought the farm was a most unique and creative thing and had great potential for attracting federal funding, but the resistance to it and the pressures to do something about it became very, very great. Finally, I talked to Len Eliel and Harvey Everest, as I recall, about Stewart transferring to the Medical Research Foundation. Stewart had been chairman of medicine for 10 years or so and some of the old time, conservative, Oklahoma physicians resented "these guys from the East who are not our kind of people." I was not at all sympathetic [with that attitude] but I thought if we could get him to the OMRF, pay his basic salary there and the telephone calls could come through the Foundation, it could be a good thing because they were both private and they were both in research. The OMRF response was positive and I talked with Stewart. I think he understood, although he had a paternalistic feeling about the department and the institution. He gave up the chair [of medicine] but not his professorship. He was never too happy after that.[11]

Of course, Stewart Wolf viewed the situation differently. "I really didn't think," he countered, "that was much of a problem. I understood why Jim was concerned about it because they had all sorts of brainless inspectors that came around who didn't understand what *enormous* benefit these young people from Oklahoma were getting by being here in the East with the opportunity to meet all of the big wheels in the [medical] schools around here. Both Jim and I understood what the objectives were, but he needed some protection with respect to the accounting and budget process. Jim and I never had any difficulty working together." Wolf said he was not reluctant to give up the chair of medicine. "Quite the opposite! Jim had no interest in my giving up the chair of med-

Medical student Paul Ruoff studying cardiac arrhythmias with Dr. Wolf at Totts Gap. (Stewart Wolf)

icine." Dr. Wolf had an offer to be vice chancellor and dean of the medical school at San Diego, California. This brought up all the old conflicts about whether he was happiest running things or when "closer to the production line." He said, "The answer is both! So you've got to have a situation where you can do both, which we had at Oklahoma for quite a while. I had become much more of an administrator than a doer and a father-figure which I had been before. This was not Jim's fault or anybody else's fault. It was just part of this phenomenon of growth, where you've got to have layers of administration."[12]

When Leonard Eliel was deposed, Robert H. "Bob" Furman, M.D., and Dr. Wolf were the leading candidates for the presidency of the Oklahoma Medical Research Foundation. Stewart Wolf reviewed the circumstances:

Bob Furman had very obviously been responsible for unseating Len Eliel, with a lot of help from Condit [Paul T. Condit, M.D.], who had been recruited by Len to take charge of the cancer section. Fairly early in the game, Paul started undermining Len and so was Bob. They *were* the insurrection; there was nobody else involved. Condit became very influential because he had managed to take full control of the inpatient unit. But he did not have any power with the Board.

Bob Furman, on the other hand, was the doctor for "Babe" Eddie and Ben Wileman. At this time, OMRF had a very distinguished national advisory committee, about as good as you can get. The Board of Directors

129

Dr. Robert H. Furman visits one of his tiny research patients. He was associate director of research and head of the cardiovascular section at OMRF. (University of Oklahoma)

thought these people were great, in a social sort of way, and gave them wonderful big dinners with the best kind of champagne. Then, when we had the meetings where we got the advice from them, the board paid no attention whatsoever to it. The prime advice was that they should develop a unified relationship with the medical school. The board was against it completely.

Bob Furman told the board members I was weak, passé, and had no support from Washington—all sorts of stuff like that. I am sure about this because I had enough close friends who were party to those conversations. Harvey Everest, I think, had a lot of confidence in me, without knowing me too well. George Cross did not exert his influence at all but he was fully in my corner. So was Rainey Williams, who is also a powerful person who doesn't use his power, a very dangerous situation to be in.

Very shortly after Len was fired, Harvey Everest called me at the farm and said he wanted to meet with me but we'd have to meet in a neutral place. He said, "This'll sound funny to you but I don't want you to come to Oklahoma City and I can't come to Totts Gap. We'll meet in the Chicago airport." I figured there was some real diplomatic problem.

Harvey said, "We'd like to have you be director of OMRF. Would you be willing to do this and let Bob Furman run the place on a day-to-day basis?" I said, "No, I wouldn't, Harvey." and he remonstrated a little bit. I told him I couldn't operate that way. If they were going to make me director of the Foundation, I was going to run it, with the permission of the board. I would not select Bob to assist me because his relationship with me was such that I couldn't possibly trust him. So, like the rich young ruler, Harvey went away sorrowing.

Harvey didn't have the strength to make this happen. He and Ben Wileman and "Babe" Eddie were running the place and Ben and "Babe" were patients of Bob Furman. But they didn't appoint Bob Furman because

Harvey wouldn't let them. Harvey always played his cards close to his chest but I understood that Harvey recognized what I was saying. So very shortly after that, Furman left. Then they were without a director and I had already accepted the post in Texas.[13]

Shortly thereafter, the O.U. Board of Regents learned that four more medical school faculty members were resigning. Loyal Lee Conrad, M.D., professor of medicine, took a position in Albuquerque at the University of New Mexico medical school; Marion de-Veaux Cotten, Ph.D., professor and chairman of pharmacology, went to the University of Nebraska; Harry J. Parker, professor of preventive medicine, became associate dean for allied health professions at the Texas Southwestern Medical School in Dallas; Eugene Pumpian-Mindlin, M.D., professor of psychiatry, joined Jolly West at the University of California at Los Angeles (UCLA). In explaining why O.U. was losing top faculty people to other medical schools, Dennis pointed out that:

People are just jumping all over the institutions which have the money. With a retraction of federal support and limited state support, we simply cannot compete. O.U. has supplied deans to three out-of-state medical schools in the past four years. For these men, it is the opportunity of a lifetime. We can't sit around and cry about it. We give them our blessings. After all, most of the senior people here were developed by other institutions.

Once the medical school loses a faculty member, you can't replace him at today's prices. We simply have to get bright students and develop our own. If I'd had 15 associate deans last year, they all would have received top offers from other places. Both Dr. Brandt and Dr. Wolf have turned down jobs repeatedly. But sometimes the dream opportunity comes along.[14]

The resignations were partially offset by the success with which the Medical Center had recruited new people. Of course, the experience of the departing faculty would take time to replace. Dennis said, "We got lots of new people this year."

In the meantime, additional clouds formed along the horizon, forecasting some turbulence in the otherwise bright future of the Oklahoma Health Center. Dr. Maurice L. Peter, Sr., who had been director of the Oklahoma City-County Health Department for 15 years, died of a heart ailment on September 29, 1969. The continuity of long term leadership was thus broken and John Gales, M.D., Dr. Peter's assistant, took over. Claribel Peter, the doctor's widow, talked about her husband's successor, who had come in a year

Dr. Maurice L. Peter, Sr., Director. (Mrs. M.L. Peter)

or so before. "Maurice was not too pleased with Dr. Gales, to put it nicely. Dr. Gales was real good handling money, making the finances work toward the new building and all, but he was a very apprehensive gentleman...." How the City-County Health Department relationship with the health campus would unfold was unknown.[15]

CHAPTER 19
TROUBLE: 1969-1970

The HERO bond issue solved the problem of state matching money for university and State Health Department construction and the Oklahoma City Chamber of Commerce was moving ahead with the municipal bond concept to finance the private hospitals. Nonetheless, the rapidly growing University Medical Center began to run short of essential operating funds. The state legislature appropriated money for the Medical Center as it did for the rest of the higher education system in Oklahoma, based on the assumption each institution would grow at about the same rate and that a five to six percent increase in the budget would cover inflation. The Medical Center, however, was experiencing 20 percent cost increases per year in many areas of its operation. Much of this extraordinary increase involved hospital costs. For example: a box of x-ray film that cost $64.41 in 1968 cost $80.63 in 1969. In addition, the state legislature had just set the minimum wage at $1.50 per hour, an action that cost the University Hospitals $90 thousand a year, or 11 percent of the total increase in state appropriations which the Medical Center had received in FY 1969-1970. As a result, the center needed another $400 thousand in operating funds just to stay even.[1]

To complicate the funding problem, the expansion of existing schools and the emergence of new programs such as dentistry and health related professions were calculated to require another $400 thousand that year just to make minimal progress toward solving the health manpower supply problems of the state. Likewise, the continuing uncertainty of federal medical programs which paid faculty salaries, funded research and helped pay the costs of treating indigent patients, added to the problem.

Inadequate operating funds would mean cutbacks, Dr. Dennis warned— laying off some employees and curtailing services to the sick. He also cited figures from the Association of American Medical Colleges (AAMC) which showed that state appropriations for medical schools nationally had risen 167.2 percent in 10 years but in Oklahoma, the increase had been only 53.3 percent, less than a third of the average. During that period, the cost per patient day in the University Hospitals had gone up from $28 to $63, a 125 percent

(The Oklahoma City Times)

increase. Enrollment in the entering class of the medical school had been increased to 126 students in 1969.[2]

These statistics reemphasized the precarious financial situation in which the Medical Center found itself. The dean updated the dimensions of the problem. One and a half million dollars would be necessary in 1969 "to continue last year's level of operations," and an estimated $2 million more would be needed to make minimal progress.[3]

According to President Herbert Hollomon, the O.U. Medical Center's financial status was indeed precarious. Governor Bartlett, however, did not believe the situation was that bad and released a letter he had sent to John Houchin, president of the O.U. Regents, which described Hollomon's statements as "misleading" and said no financial crisis existed at the university. This controversy was an expression of a growing feud between the governor and Hollomon, one into which Dennis said he did not want to be dragged.[4]

Another problem destined to affect the financial plight of Oklahoma City's hospital system was the care of indigent patients. On February 1, 1969, St. Anthony Hospital had announced it would no longer accept county welfare patients because the county paid only $5 for a clinic visit and $35 a day when the patient was admitted. Oklahoma County retaliated by refusing to accept any more bills from St. Anthony Hospital, the commissioners figuring they were being billed for people who were not bona fide county patients.

As a consequence, Presbyterian, University and Mercy hospitals were hit with an overload of indigent patients. The Sisters at Mercy Hospital had a policy they would not refuse service to anyone because they could not pay so that hospital was particularly vulnerable to charity overload. Patients, and especially ambulance drivers, were aware they would not be turned away.

By October 1, the County Commissioners approved $26 thousand in back payments to St. Anthony and the hospital agreed to accept county patients at the old rate. Although this was about half the hospital's cost, the institutions decided they were going to get the patients anyway and 50 percent collection was better than nothing.[5]

In the spring of 1970, federal funds allocated to the Medical Center for research were slashed; 15 percent cut by Presidential decree and another 15 percent held up by the Bureau of the Budget. The general research support grants, which are used for paying the difference between a grant and the actual cost of research, were being cut by 20 percent across the board. Dennis pointed to federal emphasis on research while there was virtually none on education of health manpower. These cuts, the government said, were to bring the two into balance, but then nothing was added for education. This meant doing more for less, which was not realistic, because the government was simultaneously exerting tremendous pressure to raise the output of health manpower.[6]

These cuts set the Medical Center back to the 1968-1969 budget level. Also, federal officials said they would allocate funds for "education" but not for "teaching hospitals," despite the reality that medical students spent much of their last two years of training in the University Hospital. This downward trend in federal funding, coupled with rising construction costs, placed the university portion of the Oklahoma Health Center plan in jeopardy. Dr. Dennis predicted drastic reductions in research, services and construction at the Medical Center. Because the university was the nucleus of this massive project, this anticipated slowdown did not bode well for the overall progress of the Oklahoma Health Center.

CHAPTER 20
THE MOVERS: 1970

This is the way the architects visualized the new Mercy Hospital. (Sunday Oklahoman)

In late November, 1969, it was reported that Mercy Hospital was having second thoughts about moving to the Oklahoma Health Center! The rumor was that sometime earlier Sister Mary Coletta, just returned from a five-week summer retreat at the Motherhouse in St. Louis, Missouri, was talking with the chief of the medical staff about all of the great things they would accomplish when Mercy became a teaching hospital affiliated with the university on the campus. The chief of staff listened for a while, so the story went, and then said, "Well, Sister, you can go out there if you want to but we're not going with you!" It seems the doctors had discussed the matter and a majority had voted against the plan to move next to the university. Boyd Shook, M.D., director of medical education at Mercy, recalled the vote:

> We did, in fact, conduct a poll of the staff members. We took a vote and allowed commentary in addition to the numerical vote. It was almost a 50-50 proposition. The 50 percent who did not want to move to the university were split quite a bit on where they did want to move. So the poll was inconclusive. If you weighted the poll for the doctors who were heavy contributors to Mercy Hospital [those who admitted the most patients], there

was a very strong vote for going to the university. If you weighted it in the direction of the people who had more clout in the community, it was strong for going to the northwest area. I think it was the community clout that really counted.[1]

Gary Theilen, who succeeded Al Donnell as director of the Health and Hospital Planning Committee of the Community Council ("B"Agency), outlined the four major problems Mercy cited as reasons for having second thoughts about moving to the Oklahoma Health Center. They had to do with capital financing, access to the OHC, the charity patient load and the relationship of the Mercy Hospital medical staff with the doctors at the other institutions in the health center. Four task forces were formed by the B Agency to look into these potential difficulties and report their findings to Mercy by the first of January, 1970. Theilen declared, "We want Mercy to stay in the Health Center if it is desirable and feasible. If it isn't, it is a whole new ball game." With Baptist and Deaconess planning to expand and a new hospital slated for Bethany, the movement of Mercy in that direction would add to the anticipated glut of hospital beds in the northwest quadrant of the city. The Oklahoma City Chamber of Commerce was already studying the problem of capital financing and the Oklahoma Health Sciences Foundation researched the problem of improving streets, boulevards and expressways. The community council took on the study of distributing the charity patient load among the city hospitals and Dennis appointed a group to look into medical staff relationships.[2]

What a difference a year made! After sailing smoothly through an outstanding 1968 which terminated with successful passage of the HERO bond issue, the Oklahoma Health Center was now running into heavy weather. To be sure, the momentum had continued, with University Hospital starting under construction, planning on all fronts moving forward and the Basic Science Education Building nearing completion. Also, there was ample state money for further expansion of the university and building the Health Department. But the winds of resistance and the tides of change were getting stiffer and higher. There was financial trouble at Wakita, a hefty short-

In February, 1968, John Kirkpatrick, Sr. Mary Coletta, Wayne Parker and Architect David Benham looked to the Oklahoma Health Center as the future home of Mercy Hospital. (Oklahoma Journal)

Joyce Swingle was friend and confidante of Sr. Coletta. (Mercy Health Center)

fall of operating funds at the university Medical Center, health care costs were exploding, the relationship between Dennis and Hollomon was deteriorating, the availability of construction money for the private hospitals was a major question, leadership at the Oklahoma City-County Health Department was untried and now Mercy Hospital was having second thoughts. Despite its great plans and rapid progress, the Oklahoma Health Center seemed awash with problems and some of the most experienced faculty were leaving the ship. Batten the hatches! Or to use a metaphor more appropriate to land-locked Oklahoma—circle the wagons!

While it is difficult to reconstruct the exact timing, apparently Sister Mary Coletta had already made up her mind to move shortly after the news was released on November 27, 1969.[3] She said the chamber's effort only strengthened her resolve:

> The thing that *really* made us change our minds was the fact that when the Chamber of Commerce was notified we were planning to move somewhere else…we didn't know then where, whether northwest or southwest or where…they set up all kinds of task forces. Mr. [Wayne] Parker was not only a vice president of the Oklahoma City Chamber of Commerce, he was also the chairman of our board. After one of those meetings, he came into my office and said, "Sister, as a vice president of the Chamber, I really want the University Health Center to

be built and become a progressive University, but as far as being on your board of directors, I have to tell you, if you go out there, you'll be broke in a year!"

In the book *Coletta, A Sister of Mercy*, Wayne Parker was quoted as saying to her, "Even if the city gave us the hospital, already built free of cost and with the sheets turned down on the beds, we still would be bankrupt within a year if we located in the center, because we will be expected to care for more than our share of the charity patients."[4] Joyce Swingle remembered the situation:

> Sister was disappointed that Mercy could not go to the Health Center [but] she had no choice. When she talked with me confidentially, she blamed certain individuals…. I'm not going to say "blamed" because she wasn't vindictive. She understood their side of it and she understood their reasons but still she was disappointed. In many respects, she was bullheaded and in other respects she was very flexible. She was the most adaptable person I ever knew in my life. She could take a situation, no matter how bleak it was, and make the best of it…make it bloom and blossom.[5]

Sister Coletta reported that some Mercy doctors said they had been told by the university staff that if they came out there, they'd have to be on the bottom of the totem pole. When it came to getting residents and interns, university would be first, Presbyterian would be second and Mercy would always be last. Because the physicians felt they would be dominated by O.U. and Presbyterian, a task force was organized to look into medical staff relationships. On Monday, January

Charlie Bennett was particularly interested in improving hospital care for the people of central Oklahoma. (Oklahoma Publishing Company)

Sister Coletta, Beverly Marko and Dr. Boyd Shook, medical education director, look on as Dr. Michael Marko, one of 12 new interns, signs on at Mercy Hospital in mid-1969. (Mercy Health Center)

5, 1970, the group reported it was optimistic about the progress which was being made.

Meanwhile, the four task forces continued to work to remove the major stumbling blocks which seemed to be impeding Mercy's move to the Oklahoma Health Center. Ray T. Anthony, of the C.R. Anthony stores, was chairman of the Health and Hospital Planning Committee. He asked the task forces to summarize their conclusions by the second week in January. Mercy administrators were fearful "an increasingly inequitable share of the cost of caring for the medically indigent" would be aggravated by a move to the Health Center inasmuch as the hospital "would be even more centrally located." Actually, the move was from 700 Northwest 12th Street to 600 Northeast 10th Street, not important in relation to the geographic center of the city but highly significant in their minds because the new site was "on the other side of the tracks."

Charles L. "Charlie" Bennett, managing editor of the *Daily Oklahoman* and *Oklahoma City Times*, was very active in the Health and Hospital Planning Committee's effort to reach solutions which were, in the view of the committee, best for the community. As he recalled:

My role in those discussions had aroused the ire of a

number of doctors associated with a couple of the hospitals. One of those physicians was attending me in the hospital after I had surgery for an acute appendicitis attack. He came in one morning and said, "Charlie, I want you to know there was a meeting of the county medical society last night and they voted to wish you a speedy recovery—by a very narrow margin![6]

On January 12, the Health and Hospital Planning Committee endorsed a report of the four fact-finding task forces which recommended that Mercy Hospital continue plans for relocation in the Oklahoma Health Center. The report called for the Chamber of Commerce, the foundation, the Medical Center and the State Highway Commission to assist in the planning and completion of the Health Center and the move of Mercy Hospital thereto. Four days later, it was reported that two Mercy Hospital lay boards urged Wayne Parker and Sister Mary Coletta to delay until July 1 any decision on whether or not the hospital would move to the OHC. They wanted to see the final reports of the task forces.[7]

The director of medical education at Mercy, Dr. Boyd Shook, did not like what was happening. He said Sister Coletta was dealing openly with Ralph Neely of the Health and Hospital Planning Committee, Jim Dennis and Bob Bird in numerous committee meetings after she had signed a contract to go out northwest. When he found out about this, he called her up and said, "I cannot work under these circumstances." and she said, "That's all right. You don't have a job, anyway." That day, he moved out of Mercy Hospital and has not practiced there since. He commented, "I felt the concept of the Oklahoma Health Center that we envisioned absolutely mandated Mercy's presence, Mercy's participation."[8]

The Mercy Hospital location decision, pending for two and a half months, was clarified on February 11, 1970, when the special committee headed by Dean McGee received a letter from Sister Mary Coletta laying out the conditions necessary for the hospital to move to the Oklahoma Health Center. The administrator said Mercy Hospital must have the community's guarantee of a new hospital built by 1974 plus funds to operate it. Ironically, the letter admitted that "Mercy is aware there is no way community leaders can guarantee certain points the hospital directors consider essential since these are practically impossible demands." "But," Sister Coletta asked, "if they [community leaders] cannot assure the hospital that they can and will assume these [specified] risks, then does it not follow that neither should they ask the hospital to assume them since the administration is aware that operating expenses would greatly exceed the operating revenue under present circumstances?"

The Mercy conditions were tough. In addition to adequate financing, the hospital wanted the cost of the OHC site brought in line with the cost of land elsewhere; assurance the charity load would be distributed equally among all private hospitals in the Oklahoma City Area Hospital Council; a budgetary subsidy from the university to help defray the cost of additional teaching programs; and efforts to obtain loyal and concrete support of private physicians and private patients in the OHC.

Sister Mary concluded, "If this cannot be done immediately, so that Mercy can survive, then Mercy is willing to relinquish the place assigned to it in the center." Moreover, Mercy wanted "the community and its agencies" to approve and support construction of a hospital at a site selected by Mercy's board and consultants. Sister Coletta pointed out that if there were more delay, other hospitals would build northwest and Mercy would eventually be told there were already too many beds in that area. This was a legitimate fear because a building permit had been issued to Drs. Charles L. Reynolds and J. Hartwell Dunn to construct a $7.8 million, 216-bed hospital on North Portland at the Northwest Highway. In addition, completion of the first 50-bed phase of a city hospital for Bethany was scheduled for mid-July, 1970, Baptist Memorial Hospital had completed a long range plan to double its bed capacity and Four Seasons Nursing Homes, an Oklahoma City based national

Quail Creek Country Club. (OHSF Collection)

firm, was planning to expand into the hospital business by building a new hospital in the vicinity of the Baptist Hospital. With these conditions and comments on the table, it was not difficult to see that Sister Mary Coletta had made up her mind.[9]

Less than a week after Sister Mary Coletta's letter was received by the Chamber of Commerce-sponsored special committee, the chamber got a second letter announcing the Mercy Hospital board of trustees' decision "to continue as a good community hospital at a location in the northwest sector of Oklahoma City." "Their decision doesn't change anything," Dr. Dennis maintained. "When the Oklahoma Health Center plan was first developed, there were provisions for two private hospitals and any hospital was eligible provided its management was willing to make the commitment to education by operating as a teaching hospital. Apparently, Mercy Hospital has decided to go another direction, feeling they couldn't afford the change." He pointed out that altering a private hospital to an affiliate teaching hospital would add perhaps 20 to 25 percent to the total construction cost by the time classrooms, extra labs and the like were added. Jack Shrode, administrator of Presbyterian Hospital, said, "There has been no change in our plans since our decision was announced three years ago. We feel this hospital is very much oriented toward the health center. We believe in it and have faith it will be accomplished."[10]

The following week Sister Coletta said the new Mercy would be built on a 40-acre site on the west side of Portland between 122nd and Memorial Road. This location, across the street from Quail Creek residential areas and the golf course, quickly drew opposition from the people who lived there. Residents organized to fight rezoning of the site for the hospital and for commercial development west and south of

Mercy. Sister tried to calm her new neighbors in a meeting at the Quail Creek Country Club. She described how nice the new institution would be and extolled the advantages of having a hospital close at hand, but the residents were not convinced. As one man put it, "My kid has to cross 122nd twice a day going to school and back. It will be little comfort to have the emergency room five minutes away if he gets run down by a speeding employee who is late to work at the hospital." An editorial in the *Oklahoma City Times* observed, "There is something ironic in the fact that Mercy Hospital decided to move out where the affluent live; and now finds the neighborhood in which it wants to locate doesn't want it."[11]

Mercy withdrew its application for rezoning of the controversial site on North Portland on March 25, 1970. As Sister Coletta said, "We've been offered 40 sites and we want to study the best of them before making a final decision. The Oklahoma City planning department had opposed the rezoning because it would cause access problems when north-south and east-west expressways programmed in the area were constructed. The Areawide Health Planning Organization [the new name for the Health and Hospital Planning Committee] opposed the location because it projected a surplus of 831 beds in the northwest sector in 1975 while hospitals in the southeast and northeast areas were expected to be crowded beyond capacity.

One of the members of the medical staff told how the new site for Mercy Hospital was selected. Turner Bynum, M.D., had held practically every job on the Mercy staff. He had been secretary, chief of medicine for ten years and on the hospital board since 1955:

Mr. E.K. Gaylord talked to Sister Coletta several times and one day actually took her out and showed her a site for the hospital. He was very important in convincing Sister she ought to go out there. I was with Sister one day at noon when Mr. Gaylord came to pick her up and take her out and show her that acreage. I don't think he put any pressure on her. He just said he thought that would be the ideal spot for her to build her hospital. I talked with her when she came back that afternoon. She was just all buoyed up. It seemed to be pretty well settled if Mr. Gaylord said that was the thing to do. She wanted me and some of the others to look at it. I've never seen any girl be more ebullient over her relationship...like a debutante after her first date. From that day on she was convinced that was the right thing to do and Mr. Gaylord was on her side.

I was very disappointed at the time. I own this little

Dr. Turner Bynam's office was across the street from Mercy Hospital. (Mercy Health Center)

Ebullient....(OHSF Collection)

138

The Oklahoma City-County Health Department building at 23rd and Kelley. (OHSF Collection)

building [on 12th Street across from the old Mercy Hospital]. It was 15 miles out there.[12]

Charles Bennett said that, "Mr. Gaylord was quite fond of Mercy Hospital and its people because of the way he had been treated there. Whether this led him to believe Mercy would be better off on a stand-alone basis or not, I do not know."[13]

C. Harold Brand, an Oklahoma City realtor, said it was he who took Sister Mary Coletta, two priests and Bert Loy to visit the site at Meridian and Memorial Road on Christmas morning, 1969. He persuaded the developers of The Greens to sell 40 acres at their cost of $3 thousand an acre to Mercy Hospital. The book, *Coletta, A Sister of Mercy*, does not indicate when this transfer occurred, so it is hard to say precisely when Sister Coletta made the final decision about this site. In 1984, a 92-acre parcel within half a block of the hospital sold for $5.7 million or about $62 thousand an acre.

Finally, on May 14, 1970, the present 40-acre site of Mercy Hospital at Meridian and Memorial Road was recommended for rezoning by the city planning commission. Mercy's change of course was complete.[14]

During the period Mercy Hospital was trying to decide whether or not to remain a part of the Oklahoma Health Center plan, Frank Lynch, chairman of the Oklahoma County Commission, announced the purchase of a 10-acre tract for the City-County Health Department. It was *not* in the Oklahoma Health Center. The Commissioners' March 4, 1970, purchase involved a site at 23rd Street and Kelley Avenue, a mile north of the campus. They also planned another building on this tract to house both the state and county welfare departments.[15]

There had been rumblings of discontent before. At a meeting of the Oklahoma Health Sciences Foun-

Dr. Gales and his assistant examine schematic plans for the new health department building. (OHSF Collection)

dation on June 24, 1969, Dr. Peter had voiced two problems. The health department building was to be constructed above the two-level parking blanket, a design which brought up the legal question of erecting a building using the "air rights" above a structure owned by some other agency of government. Dr. Peter had asked for an opinion from the district attorney. Also, he objected to clients and staff being required to pay for parking inasmuch as that was not the current policy.[16]

Another major question which made Dr. Peter dubious about moving to the Oklahoma Health Center was whether the central heating and air conditioning service would be available by the time the City-County Health Department's new building was ready for occupancy. Given these two problems and Dr. Gales' apparent feeling of independence, the County Commissioners decided to build elsewhere. Dr. Gales said the Board of Health decided against the site in the Oklahoma Health Center because the proposed "underground" parking would have been too costly.[17]

Thus, another major health facility was forever lost as a part of the campus. It was the only county health department in Oklahoma which, by geographic circumstance, could have taken advantage of the synergism close relations with the State Health

Department would have afforded. Quite probably, the self-chosen isolation of the City-County Health Department was more disadvantageous to it than to the other institutions in the Oklahoma Health Center.

Despite Dr. Dennis's assertion that Mercy's decision "doesn't change anything," it and the City-County Health Department's decision to withdraw from the OHC plan had their effect. It could be said you cannot lose something you have never had, but both institutions were part of the plan and would have made the health campus a more comprehensive center. These events had a substantial psychological effect on the planners of the Oklahoma Health Center. Dennis said:

> I was disappointed, particularly in the Mercy move. Sr. Mary Coletta had come into the original conceptual phase starry-eyed and idealistic. She could see the vision. Although Mercy had been kind of the G.P. hospital and was looked down on a little bit by the university and the St. Anthony and the Presbyterian crowd, they were doing an awful lot of emergency care and taking care of the poor. I felt this was an element of care the university needed to have some relationship and interface with. I envisioned Mercy as a place the family medicine group could get going. We had one of the first university family medicine clinics in the country but we had to go to Mercy to deliver babies because the chairman of the department of obstetrics would not let anybody deliver babies in University Hospital unless they were going to be certified residents. We were running into this kind of unionism and Mercy appeared to be a good clinical experience for producing family practitioners. So their move northwest disappointed me and the fact the City-County didn't move out there [to the OHC] was discouraging, but I never felt it wasn't going to happen. It just wasn't going to be as big as we thought.[18]

HOLLOMON VS. DENNIS: 1970

Dr. Hollomon and Dr. Cross enjoy a happy moment to-gether. (University of Oklahoma)

After about a year working with Dr. Cross, J. Herbert Hollomon, Ph.D., became acting president of the University of Oklahoma on June 13, 1968, and president on July 1. He was formally installed as president in elaborate outdoor ceremonies on the Van Vleet (South) Oval of the main campus in Norman on October 18, 1968. When asked how working with President George Cross had been, he replied:

> Difficult. He was always cooperative but it was difficult. The institution reflected his ideas and his plans and therefore, anything different from that was difficult to formulate. But George was always cooperative. We sat down together; we discussed things with no difficulty whatsoever. He gave me his views and I gave him my views.[1]

During the year both the president and the president-designate were on the campus, Dr. Hollomon organized the development of a plan for the future of the University of Oklahoma. In this massive study, he involved nearly 600 persons on 24 committees and panels:

> What I was primarily trying to accomplish was to get an interplay between the people who were there so they

felt the plan for the university was their's. I'd had some success at such things in the past—to get the people involved to develop their own future. My major thought was to say, "All right, fellows, let's us decide what we want to do." I tried very hard simply to be a stimulant, a motivator, an integrator of what they said. I felt that, particularly with the old president leaving, if we could establish a climate in which the people of the university felt it was their university and they participated in the planning for its future, that would be a great accomplishment. That's what I was trying to do.

> I had very little concern for the substance of the plan; that was not something I had thought through. I did not come there with an idea of what a university should look like. I came there with an idea, which I have had all of my management life, that the way to manage a group is to get people to work with you and trust you. That was my purpose in trying to establish a plan.[2]

Dr. Hollomon had come to the University of Oklahoma in the middle of the late 1960s, a period of unrest among the younger generation which was upset with the authority and decisions of an unpopular establishment. Protests against the war in Vietnam, the massacre of students at Kent State University and the civil rights movement, the opposition to which precipitated the assassination of its leader, Martin Luther King, punctuated the period. As the first chapter of *The Future of the University* observed, "There are mighty forces at work in the world which we do not understand....There is rebellion and resistance. It seems directed against those in established positions of authority throughout our institutions and against abstract organized authority itself."Because young people are learning to think about and prepare for the world in which they will live as adults, they tend to be the group most interested and active in bringing about change.[3]

Many students did not like what they saw in the 1960s—the military draft, a protracted, brutal and seemingly unwinnable war in the Far East, racial bias, sex discrimination and mores and folkways which held them down, restricted their freedom and inhibited their lifestyle. They reacted to this situation with drug experimentation, sexual liberation, rock music, the peace movement, draft evasion, violence, protest marches, sit-ins, informality in dress and behavior and

A time of protest. (The Oklahoman)

High noon. (OHSF Collection)

constant questioning of all authority...in the home, the school, the workplace, everywhere. Two slogans floating through the college-age community reflected the spirit of the times: "If it feels good, do it!" and "Don't trust anybody over 30." The sheer number of students in their late teens and early twenties added impact to the ferment. These were the students Chancellor Dunlap and the State Regents were preparing for in the early 1960s. These were the babies of the post-World War II population explosion, grown up. And the single institution outside the home which was most affected by and involved with these young adults of the late 1960s was higher education, the colleges and universities of America.

As the O.U. planning group examined the university in the world, it concluded: "Universities thus find themselves in a role which, in serving their ancient tradition, must seek to preserve what is, while lending protection and courage to face the new, to understand the nature of change and to cope with it." But "the new" was threatening to the faculty. In Dr. Hollomon's observation:

> The culture of Oklahoma was less open, there was less acceptance of new ideas, less trusting of individuals, more dependence on bureaucracy, more dependence on power. And there was more willingness to have what I

consider an unfair fight, that is, to have a fight and keep a dagger behind their back!

On the other hand, it is not a great distinction. There's a kind of "cowboy culture" residue in Oklahoma and Texas, a "High Noon" kind of characteristic where someone has to win and someone has to lose. This is less so in Boston or Washington. I do not believe one gets along with major substantive questions by "facing them down"—I think that's a term cowboys use.[1]

But change was happening at an increasing pace and in recognition of this fact, the plan recommended that "every major position taken in this report should be reviewed at least every five years."

Dr. Hollomon continued his thoughts about the process of developing the plan for the future of the university:

> I had very little suspicion as to how it might come out. Therefore, the only thing that surprised me—it doesn't surprise me today but it surprised me then—was the great resistance of the faculty to think about activities that cut across departments and laboratories. I'll give you an example: At that time, and it continues to be one of the major issues in the country, was the environment. It was very clear that the people who could engage in research on that issue, and teach it, are multi-disciplinary. They have to be. I was surprised at the resistance to that. It doesn't surprise me one whit today because I've lived longer; I've seen more universities. You see,

142

the power in a university lies traditionally in the disciplinary departments and anything that threatens that power is resisted. Departments in universities *are* independent fiefdoms, generally. I remember quite well the day someone—I even know who did it—got up in one of the meetings and said, "I wish to propose a program of education and research on environmental matters that cuts across all the departments and centers of the University." He proposed a graduate degree in environmental sciences. You could have heard a pin drop. There was so much antipathy toward what he said![5]

"Many people don't understand Herb Hollomon because they think he was a product of Ivy League liberalism. He wasn't." Mark Johnson said, "He was a street fighter from Atlanta, Georgia, and when I say 'street fighter,' I mean literally. He roamed Atlanta streets with a group which in Brooklyn would have been a gang." Dr. Johnson continued:

His father was a small-town minister and Herb was the "ornery preacher's son." He was a vagrant juvenile who slept in ambulances that were owned by the funeral home where he worked as a janitor and assistant embalmer. He had an absolutely fantastic history. He educated himself, won scholarships, entered the intellectually elite as a parvenu. He had one of the most agile, one of the most fertile minds in one of the most impulsive and imprudent personalities I think I have ever encountered.[6]

Dr. Hollomon's management style did not please Governor Bartlett. On May 12, 1970, O.U. students opposed to the war in Vietnam staged a demonstration as the R.O.T.C. students were conducting a ceremony on Owen Field, the football stadium. The governor wanted President Hollomon to call out the national guard to assure order and avert violence but Dr. Hollomon, trusting the students, refused. He talked about the incident:

We had a group of people who had agreed to keep the peace. These were students, employees, faculty. On the day of the "demonstration," they were out there, keeping the peace. I took the uniforms off the policemen, had them wear just what I've got on today, slacks and a red jacket. I told them no force would be used.

The "rebellious" students asked me if they could meet with the chief of [campus] police and find out how far they could go without being in trouble. The chief met with them, told them they could go to the end of the football field; as long as they stayed behind that—no trouble. Then we had the damn R.O.T.C. ceremony in front of them. They began to yell and scream, to run up a Vietnam flag, but at no time did they come into physical contact with the R.O.T.C. students.

I sat there and watched the committee, with their red

Vice President David Burr, Security Chief Bill Jones and O.U. Attorney David Swank assemble student marshalls (with arm bands) to help control the demonstration. (Oklahoma Publishing Co.)

Students display their sentiments as R.O.T.C. troops pass by. (The Oklahoman)

arm bands on, pick people up who were getting boisterous and carefully take them off the field. Nobody hurt anybody. We were keeping the peace.[7]

At their May, 1970, meeting, the O.U. Regents approved the appointment of Dr. Bob Bird as dean of the school of medicine and Dr. Len Eliel to the new position of director of medical center research and graduate affairs, effective July 1. As early as the previous October, Dr. Dennis had said he wanted to be relieved as dean of the medical school to devote full time to the vice presidency. He pointed out that in the previous three years the number of students in the Medical Center had doubled, and the academic units had increased from two to five. He recommended re-structuring the Medical Center administration to include a full-time dean of medicine, a full-time registrar, a research director and a fiscal affairs officer. Perhaps if Dr. Joe White had remained at Oklahoma, he would have been promoted to the deanship. Dr. Dennis talked about his problems:

> I was the one who put the heat on Len Eliel. I wanted him back because at the time we were going like mad, moving new programs into the houses [on 14th and 15th Streets] and we needed someone to coordinate research and graduate programs. We had a "second class cousin" relationship with the Norman campus. A person on that campus was actually serving as our vice president for graduate affairs but that didn't work very well.
>
> And I thought this would be a way for Len to come back with honor. He was a very sound academic administrator and research leader and could interface with the community in that regard. I think it was a logical move.[8]

Later that month, on May 26, the *Oklahoma Journal* carried a story which said Dr. Dennis had been offered three major positions elsewhere and was trying to decide whether to accept one. These administrative jobs were at the University of Arkansas Medical Center in Little Rock, the University of Tennessee Medical Units in Memphis and the University of Texas at Austin. He would not publicly discuss his relationship with President Hollomon but said, "It isn't any secret I haven't been very happy." It was known, however, that Dr. Dennis had resisted attempts to move the Medical Center administrative functions to the Norman campus and take over the Medical Center budget, then about $20 million, including the University Hospitals. The vice president was quoted as saying, "I really think the time is coming when this institution must report directly to the [O.U.] regents."[9]

The suggested changes in the organizational relationship between the Medical Center and the parent University were outlined in Dr. Hollomon's *The Future of the University* which proposed a vice president for the University of Oklahoma at Oklahoma City. This expanded urban campus was expected to accommodate other educational programs, such as the practicum aspects of urban development and public health. The vice president of the Oklahoma City campus would report to the president of the university for all non-academic functions and to the provost on the Norman campus "as regards academic programs and

J. Herbert Hollomon in the early days of his presidency. (University of Oklahoma)

academic budgets." Dr. Dennis harked back to the early days of his relationship with Dr. Hollomon:

> When Herb first arrived, he came to the Medical Center, had a visit, looked around. He was a jovial, extroverted, "hyper" guy. He liked what we were doing, felt it was the best thing that was going on in the University. At least, he said he did and I think that was true.
>
> I found that whereas I was able to converse and communicate very easily with George Cross, I never got a response from Herb. Once a week, I used to summarize things and send to George by mail. Often it would be a legal question; I'd ask his opinion and ask if he wanted to discuss it further. Then I'd go visit him.
>
> I would send things with very important considerations on which I really needed Herb's feedback, things I needed to have in writing, and they were never acknowledged. I'm not sure he got them; I don't know what happened. I wrote letters to his office and went to see him now and then. He put Gordon Christenson in as manager; perhaps he ignored them.
>
> Then Herb organized what he called his cabinet. I had the title of vice president and he viewed me the same as the vice presidents on the Norman campus. There was no way I could function that way. He would have meetings down there once or twice a week and I couldn't talk with him about Medical Center things. He always had an agenda which did not relate to the Medical Center and it took up so much of my time, I was unable to get my work done in Oklahoma City. I couldn't get answers on policy and things we were doing about which I needed answers. I became very disillusioned

with this and I was literally in a position of being insubordinate because I began to miss those meetings. It was a total waste of my time.

Before Hollomon had come, we organized a branch of the University Foundation at the Medical Center. Lee Teague ran it. We had the idea we could handle research monies [through the foundation] and develop a fundraising operation, get a program going that would bring in some money you could spend. There were many days I would have given a thousand dollars to have been able to spend 50 under the circumstances. This was very successful because by the end of the first year, we had several million dollars.

Herb had spent an awful lot of money—his investiture was, as someone said, "like the annointing of the king"—and all of a sudden they were in difficulty down there in finances. Gene Nordby was made vice president for finances. Nordby was very aggressive and bright and apparently sold Herb on the idea of getting control of the O.U. Foundation money in the Medical Center branch. I dug my feet in on that! I just was *not* going to do that because the next step was [for Herb] to take over your budget. I had already found it prohibitive to spend the time I had being what amounted to a staff man. I did not come there as a staff man; I came there as a responsible executive and head for a [separately] budgeted agency.

As the pressure built up on the Norman campus, another thing that happened really did disturb me. I found out that a group of the liberal activists on our campus had been meeting with Hollomon, including Ben Heller and Jolly West. I could see the loyalty of the faculty being split. This was where Herb was a master, taking a small group of people, getting behind them and then splitting the whole thing wide open. That's exactly what he did down in Norman.[10]

But Hollomon appeared totally different to Ben Heller, M.D., the internist who ran the clinical laboratories at the hospital:

At that time, I was on the University Senate as a medical school representative and I was on President Hollomon's advisory committee. In addition, I was very close to Jim Dennis and it was my feeling that this [struggle between them] could do nothing but bring harm to the university and the Medical Center. I felt that Jim was wrong in this struggle. The surprise was that, on one occasion, Jim promised me he would meet with President Hollomon and he never made the effort to do so. It was obvious he thought the rift was irreparable and I was very disappointed in his action. I think Hollomon was willing to give to a considerable extent and I don't think the health center should be totally independent of the university.

I was impressed by the fact that Hollomon was a good

Internist Ben Heller headed laboratory medicine and was also chief of staff of University Hospital. (University of Oklahoma)

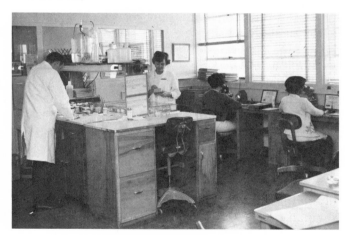

The clinical laboratory in the 1960s. (University of Oklahoma)

administrator, that he was very knowledgeable and that he was a very considerate person. I thought he was a good president and I don't think one can judge Hollomon's performance by Dewey Bartlett's response to him.[11]

Others on the faculty had a high opinion of the president. Bill Campbell, the campus architect at Norman, declared:

He was a neat guy! I loved him, absolutely loved him. I think he did some of the greatest things and made some of the worst mistakes of anybody I've ever known. It was either one extreme or the other.

I think Herb was the right man at the wrong time. Had he come at a time when we were not involved with all of the student unrest of the late 1960s and early 1970s, Vietnam and all of that business, I think he would have been much more successful than he was. But he had an awful lot of support on the Norman campus.

He'd get me on such an emotional elevator sometimes when I was around him, I'd almost break out in tears. I remember a recruitment day for high school seniors who had come to the campus from all over the state. After some presentations, he opened the floor for questions. There was a black girl sitting up in the back who asked him why, after three or four efforts to get in touch with the student aid office, she had not been able to get a response. She had a 3.95 or some such grade point average and wanted to come to O.U. but her parents couldn't afford to sent her and she needed some financial help. Hollomon said, "Is that 3.95 supportable?" and she said, "Oh, yes." She was very nice, a clever young lady; I was impressed by her. He said, "Can you meet me in my office in 45 minutes?" and she said, "Yes, sir." Then he said, "Fine. You now have a four-year scholarship to the University of Oklahoma." Just like that! I practically broke down when he did that. He was that kind of guy.[12]

Dr. Hollomon's rapport with the students at O.U. became legendary. Asked about his philosophy and the approach he used to achieve such a warm relationship with the students, he replied, "There's no trick, no secret about how to get students to have faith in you. Simply love 'em! If you love people, they love you back. That's all there is to it; I just loved the students at Oklahoma." But there was another part to his approach as this story indicates:

Furthermore, I trusted them. Oklahoma and that campus had a heritage of mistrust of students. The parents did not trust the students when I was there. Let me give you a story: a very well-to-do gentleman said to me, "My daughter's coming down there next September and I want to tell you something, Mr. Hollomon; she is *not* going to live in a coed dormitory! If she does, I want you to have someone following her all the time to find out what she does." I said, "She's going to be treated like the rest of the students on this campus. Furthermore, Mr. So-and-So,— I'd looked him up—you have another daughter who is a stewardess on American Airlines. Do you treat her that way, too? Do you go running around telling American Airlines where she can sleep and that they have to follow her?" He got very angry with me. People don't trust their children so all I did was very simple; I trusted their children.[13]

To understand the antipathy toward President Hollomon on the part of the governor and many others, an explanation of the general Oklahoma attitude concerning the "Eastern liberal establishment" may be useful. At least, this is how the Okie mindset appeared to Dr. Hollomon:

I think there is a deep, justified mistrust of Easterners in Oklahoma which comes about from the fact the state was once controlled by Eastern money. It has not been long since the state was controlled by the banking industry of New York and Boston. Texas and Oklahoma developed their own banking system fairly recently; [before that] they had to depend on huge amounts of borrowed money from the East for development of their state and the development of industry. Then you are a second class citizen. That's an idea of my own; I never read it anywhere.[14]

The mistrust of J. Herbert Hollomon appeared to be widespread in Oklahoma. From Governor Bartlett on down, influential Oklahomans were disenchanted with his presidency. State Senators Ed Berrong of Weatherford and John W. Young of Sapulpa said they now believed the employment of Dr. Hollomon was a mistake. The head of the O.U. alumni group in Oklahoma City called for his replacement on the basis that Hollomon "does not have the team pulling together."[15]

Former O.U. Regent John Houchin, president of Phillips Petroleum Company of Bartlesville, Oklahoma, predicted Hollomon would resign or get fired. He said:

Unfortunately, Hollomon has a faculty for generating controversy. Much criticism has come to the regents concerning Dr. Hollomon, much of it unjustified. While I have been critical of Dr. Hollomon on occasion, I was constructively so. But the regents now have a terrible responsibility. They must determine in their own minds the question: Is Hollomon an asset or a liability to the future of the University of Oklahoma? That's the way I would look at it.

If they act as I predict, it will not be because of political pressures.... The caliber of the board is such that political pressure would be resented and reacted against.[16]

There was strong political pressure from Governor Bartlett who wanted the regents to get rid of Hollomon. This influence was an element in the discussion scheduled for the regents meeting on Thursday, June 24, 1970. On June 10, Governor Bartlett had appointed a Bartlesville physician, V.M. Lockard, M.D., to replace John Houchin whose term had expired in April. It was rumored Lockard held the deciding vote

The O. U. Board of Regents in 1969. (Clockwise from the left) Quintin Little, Barbara James, John M. Houchin, Reuben Sparks, Jack Santee, President Hollomon, Nancy Davies, Huston Huffman, Horace "Tony" Calvert and Emil Kraettli. (University of Oklahoma)

Jim Dennis and newly-appointed regent V.M. Lockard. (The Oklahoma City Times)

on whether or not Dr. Hollomon's contract would be renewed.[17]

The issue between Dr. Dennis and President Hollomon came down to who was going to control the Medical Center. As a separately budgeted unit of the University, the Medical Center enjoyed a degree of independence from the main campus which Dr. Hollomon, feeling responsibility for the entire institution, believed was too great. He put it this way:

The arrangements were such it was extraordinarily difficult to integrate the Medical Center with anything else in the University because they had wiggled themselves into a power relationship with the statewide Board of

Regents and the legislature. Therefore, the power of the central administration or the faculty or anybody else on the other campus...any cooperative arrangements were extraordinarily difficult.

My basic issue with Dr. Dennis was relatively simple; that is, I didn't think the money was being handled properly. I suspected deep down in my gut there was something funny going on and I wanted an accountant up there...someone I trusted to discharge what I thought was my responsibility to keep people honest. Second, I felt this being an academic part of the University, it should be under the general control of the provost of the University and I charged him to do some integrating. Those were the two issues; they are quite different.

You see, I thought there were some shenanigans going on up there. Private fee money was one of them and the other was money used by Dennis for his private purposes. I'm not being slanderous; I can't prove it. I wanted a bookkeeper to go up there and find out. I found out that my suspicions were probably, *probably* well-grounded. I never could trace in detail how his house was built...how it was bought or how it was built. I will bet you almost any amount of money you want to bet that the lumber and the equipment for that house was paid for by the Medical Center.[18]

When questioned about whether the house was purchased or built, Dr. Hollomon said, "I think it was built. I'm not sure about this." Dr. Dennis talked about how he came to move into the existing house provided for him in Nichols Hills:

This house came about when Ralph Stumpp [Director of the Research and Development Office] and Reece

147

Jim Dennis's new home in Nichols Hills. (The Oklahoman)

McGee [Vice President and Director of Administration of the Oklahoma Medical Research Foundation] came to me and said, "Jim, you need to have a larger house." We had that nice little Cape Cod house on Avondale but it was very small and when we had receptions, it was very crowded. I was probably the lowest-paid medical center administrator in the country and most of them had parsonages for their director. They said, "You and Virginia find a house and the Foundation will purchase it." I really don't know about the financing of it. I was until this day [July 10, 1983] under the assumption there were no university funds at all in that house. I did have some concern about some of the furnishings Reece McGee's interior decorator put in there. Of course, we had our own furniture which we moved into the house. When we left, we went over every bit of the furnishings that belonged to whomever had the title to that house.... Again, I thought it was OMRF. We itemized everything that was left in the house.

That house was a mistake, I'll grant you, [because it] became an issue for those looking for issues. I would never do that again but it was a customary thing to do. Every state college had a house [for its president or director]. To my knowledge, there was no misuse of funds. I never had any [University] funds, personally. They asked me to turn over the utility bills to Ralph and Reece.[19]

McGee corroborated Dennis's assumption there were no university funds involved. He said the money for the house came from the Physicians' Trust Fund which was then administered by OMRF. This fund consisted of private patient fees earned by the faculty of the medical school. The departments kept 75 percent of the money, 15 percent went to the Dean's enrichment fund which allowed him to supplement the basic science department budgets because they had little or no opportunity to earn extra money, and 10 percent was used to pay billing and recordkeeping expenses. The house in Nichols Hills was purchased as an investment and when it was sold after Dr. Dennis moved, the proceeds went back to the Trust Fund.[20]

Previously, the Norman home of Earl Sneed, former O.U. law school dean, was purchased for Dr. J. Herbert Hollomon. At the University of Oklahoma, it was customary to provide a house for the president but not for university vice presidents. The house provided for Vice President Dennis was a perquisite which the O.U. Regents had not authorized. This apparently irritated Dr. Hollomon and made him suspicious.

The headlines across the first page of the *Oklahoma City Times* on June 25, 1970, shouted the news: "Regents Retain Hollomon." On a four-to one vote, the regents renewed the president's contract for another year. H.K. "Tony" Calvert, who presided in the absence of Chairman Reuben Sparks, a Woodward attorney, cast the single dissenting vote. He said he felt the president had lost the support of large numbers of O.U. faculty members, students and alumni and charged that Hollomon had "credibility problems." Dr. Lockard, the Governor's newest appointee who was thought to hold the balance of power, abstained from voting. Nancy Davies talked about why the vote went the way it did:

> Everyone who voted for Herb was a Bartlett appointee. That day at the meeting, the question came down to whether the University was going to be governed by the regents or the governor. I agreed at that time that Hollomon could not last long. He had made enough enemies and caused enough trouble, although I think he did a lot of good things. But at that point, to fire him because of the governor's request was wrong.
>
> I think the problem was mostly Hollomon's own personality. When he found out he was irritating somebody, he would just dig in. He had a lot of good ideas; I think he did not have the tact and the patience and the personality to work it around. He would sometimes go behind people when he should have gone through them. I think he was perceived as an Eastern liberal and he didn't deny that. I believe Oklahomans just have their own ideas and I don't think they were always exactly right, either. It was really a clash of personalities. He didn't fit here.[21]

The president's office, where this crucial meeting was held, was jammed with about 100 newsmen and other spectators. A burst of applause followed the action of the board. Hollomon pledged to try to bring together "the divergent, differing attitudes and forces." After the vote, there was a 15-minute recess when most of the jubilant gallery left the meeting. Smiling broadly, Dr. Hollomon emerged to thank his friends and supporters. "As many of my friends know, I love this university and this state and if there are things I have done that have hurt people, I hope they can be used in such a way as to bring the university and the people together."[22]

Previously, in the same meeting, agreement had been reached in the controversy about administrative control of the Medical Center. James L. Dennis was granted the title of Executive Vice President of the University for Medical Center Affairs. The regents specified that under this title, Dennis had full authority and responsibility for everything, including financial matters, at the Center. This change gave him the access to the board of regents he wanted. In his comments at the meeting, Dr. Dennis said, "To insure the plans and future of the Medical Center, I have informed the regents that it is essential that whoever heads the Medical Center be provided the opportunity for open communication with its governing board—a privilege I have been denied for the past two years."[23]

Thus, the tension and suspense were broken. President Hollomon had won a vote of confidence, Dr. Dennis had his status redefined and opportunity for a new relationship between the campuses of the University was created. Everybody won—at least something—except Governor Bartlett.

That same evening, there was a two-hour meeting of six of the O.U. Regents with the governor at his mansion in Oklahoma City. Ironically, three of the four regents who had voted for Hollomon had been appointed to the Board of Regents by Dewey Bartlett. It was apparent that Bartlett was not happy with the regents' decision and accused them of not considering enough issues in reaching their conclusion to retain Hollomon for the coming year. Reuben Sparks, a known critic of the president's administration, said he did not show up for the Thursday morning regents' meeting "in the interests of harmony." Bartlett suspected the regents took the action they did because they feared student reprisals, which he believed was akin to blackmail, but Jack Santee of Tulsa and Walter Neustadt, Jr., of Ardmore denied that.[24]

Nancy Davies described the climate of the meeting with Governor Bartlett as:

Very cool! He wanted us each to say why we had voted as we did. Certainly, the idea that the regents did not want the governor telling them how to run the university came across. It was pretty stiff and formal. I think he found out what he wanted to know.

Governor Bartlett sincerely believed Hollomon was so bad for the state he had to get rid of him and he went about it just as hard as he could. I think Hollomon saying there was a crisis at the Medical Center seemed to cause as much ill feeling between the governor and the

Nancy Davies knew a real financial crisis was on the horizon. (University of Oklahoma)

regents and Hollomon as anything. That upset Bartlett because he had worked for education and he thought education was fairly funded. He didn't think it was fair for Hollomon to come out and say there was a crisis in funding education.

But I think we had a real crunch, yes. New buildings were being built and coming on line and there were no support funds. That was the general attitude of the regents.[25]

In a statement the next morning, Governor Bartlett made his displeasure clear:

I disagree with the action of the board voting to retain Dr. Hollomon as President of the University of Oklahoma. It takes strong, statewide support to build a strong state university. It is obvious that the present Oklahoma University administration does not have such support. The citizens of Oklahoma have lost patience with a divisive and less than professional performance by the university administration.[26]

The next headlines came swiftly. On July 7, 1970, the front page of the *Oklahoma Journal* carried the message in two lines of heavy type: "Dr. Dennis Quits For Arkansas Job." When he announced his resignation to become vice president for health sciences at the University of Arkansas Medical Center in Little Rock, Dr. Dennis told the newspaper, "It is my considered opinion and deep conviction that the future of the University of Oklahoma Medical Center will best be served by new leadership." He described in more intimate detail his personal view of the situation in which he found himself:

By that time, the whole Board [of Regents] had changed so much. Walter Neustadt was solidly behind Hollomon and it was obvious there was a group of so-called intellectual liberals pushing hard. I really felt I was going to get pushed over the cliff and very, very rapidly. I was being put in an untenable position.

I was shocked when the Regents gave Herb a vote of confidence at a time when Governor Bartlett was demanding his resignation. I felt this was a vote of confidence for Herb Hollomon and a vote of less confidence in Jim Dennis, although it wasn't stated in that way. At the same time, I was getting calls from Dewey Bartlett, who was encouraging me. "Stick in there, boy! We'll stay with you."[27]

Meanwhile, E.T. Dunlap was doing the same thing:

Jim Dennis left at a critical time. I had talked to him and said, "Don't leave. That guy won't last down there long. Dad gum it, just stay put! That [situation]'s going to take care of itself. Be patient." Of course, Hurricane Herbie wanted to take over the Medical Center and run *it*, too.

The Board upheld Dennis's hand and then this guy kept on pushing. So Jim got enough of it and took off. [I think] Jim acted a little bit impetuously.[28]

Dennis continued:

But then I found Hollomon was going to be there. Their plan was to keep him on another year, why, I don't know. Another year, the way it was going, I could not have survived. At that time, I had three offers in my pocket, from Texas, Arkansas and Tennessee. I was knocking on the door of 60 years of age and I knew I had one more move. When I sat down and thought about it, I knew Arkansas had the same challenges as here and I thought I could do something about them. I went to Texas and I ran from that one in a hurry. Then I went to U.T. in Memphis and I didn't care much about what I was finding over there, either. Actually, they never did make me an offer but I did have one from Texas.

What I saw was that the Board of Regents had swung around strongly in support of Hollomon and that in the next go-round, the people who controlled it and had the same philosophy as Herb would move in.[29]

But Nancy Davies was surprised when Dr. Dennis resigned. "I was very sorry because we had worked for weeks and felt we had worked out a compromise that both Dennis and Hollomon could live with. In talking with Dennis, we thought he had agreed to stay

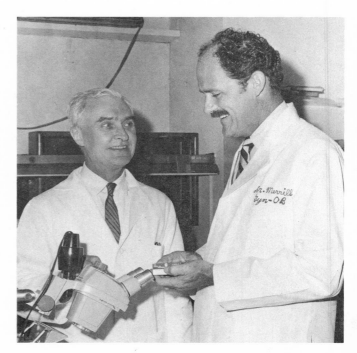

Gyn-OB Chief Jim Merrill with Dean Bob Bird. (University of Oklahoma)

but, on the other hand, he got a good offer and—who knows?"[30]

Dr. Dennis went on:

I think, looking back, for any academician to take on the job of chief administrator of a modern medical center is almost a death wish! Your vanity leads you to do it because you think you can accomplish some things you couldn't get done otherwise. But there's no way you can win. You can just count on five years, maybe only three years.

Of course, the Oklahoma Health Center is one of those things that can happen only once in anybody's lifetime. Here I was, a guy coming home after 25 years, going into the right circumstances with the right people. Everything came together! It was a marvelous, marvelous experience. But we moved so fast and upset so many deeply rooted territories, it was a wonder an explosion didn't blow me out of the water a long time before. One of the reasons it didn't was because guys like Dean McGee and Governor Bellmon and other hard workers went along with it. They saw it was a great advancement for the state.

It was a great privilege. Virginia (Mrs. Dennis) often observed that I did more work and had more challenges and responsibilities in those six years than I had in any 20-year period in the rest of my life. The Oklahoma Health Center was a concept whose time had come and that did it, not I. I would never have survived if the "power structure" had not emerged. They came along at a time I was beginning to feel I couldn't pull this off.[31]

150

There were different opinions about Dennis's actions in his controversy with the president. Dr. Mark Johnson said: "I viewed this as a great misfortune because Jim Dennis had lost sight of the fact that he *was* a part of the University of Oklahoma and he had a responsibility to support the chief executive of the university or resign. And he did neither. I viewed it as disasterous for Dr. Hollomon [although] I realized that Dr. Hollomon was one of the most imprudent individuals I had ever known." Dr. Stewart Wolf took the opposite stance. "I think Jim was very wary of Herb Hollomon. I sided with Jim, of course, because Hollomon was in no position to run the Medical Center; Jim was. Hollomon lacked the perspective to run the Medical Center so I strongly supported Jim."[32]

Interestingly, James A. Merrill, M.D., Chairman of the Department of Gynecology and Obstetrics of the School of Medicine, subscribed to the same principle but sat on the other side of the controversy. "I thought President Hollomon was a breath of fresh air and I supported Hollomon fully in his difficulties and conflict with Dennis. Hollomon wanted to have more university responsibility and authority over the medical school and I thought, and still do, that's a good thing. If you are going to have interest and responsibility you must simultaneously have authority; you can't have one without the other.[33]

Gordon Deckert, M.D., head of Psychiatry and Behavioral Sciences, looked at the personalities of Dennis and Hollomon this way:

> Those who looked at that conflict in depth saw it as a power struggle between two individuals who had very different personalities. Jim Dennis, in order to accomplish what he needed to, by-passed the usual university regential process and he involved himself with key figures of business leadership in downtown Oklahoma City and key figures in the political scene. Jim Dennis's vision, which started this process and for which he deserves much credit, left a legacy that we're still dealing with. That legacy was a certain suspicion of the medical center, its leadership and its autonomy at the level of the O.U. Board of Regents. The faculty did not view Hollomon as someone who became knowledgeable about or who was terribly interested in the medical center. Many viewed Hollomon as a kind of a "shear bolt" in a way; many predicted he would be a transitional president, an easy prediction for one who knows anything about systems.[34]

Less than three weeks later, in a hastily-called executive session on July 23, 1970, the O.U. Board of Regents accepted Dr. J. Herbert Hollomon's resig-

The strain shows in Dr. Hollomon's face at the time he resigned the presidency of the university. (Oklahoma Observer)

nation, effective September 1, and appointed Dr. Pete Kyle McCarter, university provost, as acting president. Earlier that day, at the regular monthly meeting of the board, Dr. Hollomon had surprised the regents by announcing his decision to resign. In his statement to the board, he said in part:

> In voting to continue me as President in June, this Board acted for the best interests of the University after I had refused to resign under pressure. Had I resigned in those circumstances, the University's independence and academic freedom would have been jeopardized. If you had dismissed me, your own constitutional independence would have been undermined.

> Shortly following the meeting, comments by the Governor, and his appointment of a member of his former staff as a regent, made it clear to me that the assaults on the University and on me personally were to continue. The issue of my continuing as President as raised publicly in these statements raise a deeper question concerning the fundamental values of our country's institutions of higher learning. The survival of these institutions depends on the projection of values which, when threatened, pose the possibility of the demise of our society's deepest tradition of liberty and free institutions. Among these values are freedom of the university from outside political or ideological interference, the freedom of expression and dissent, the freedom to teach, to learn and

to inquire without coercion, and the freedom of the academic community to govern itself justly under law.

These freedoms which lie at the heart of the university are being threatened in Oklahoma.

When my continued presence becomes the excuse for denying citizens and members of this community those fundamental values on which our way of life depends, then I can no longer stand in silence. I cannot and will not be so used. To allow this would violate the confidence and support of all those people who have worked so hard for this institution and its potential for excellence.

So I give you my resignation, though with hesitation and anguish. It is to be effective September 1st of this year. I have implicit faith and trust that you and the University community will oppose the very real threat of tyranny we now face. I know you will reaffirm the greatness and spirit of this place and of what you called on us and the hundreds of members of our planning venture to begin nearly three years ago in a time of hope and creativity. *The Future of the University* must not be shelved.[35]

Bill Campbell told this story about the support for Dr. Hollomon:

When Hollomon had resigned and was leaving, Gordon Christenson and his wife had a party for Herb over at their house and invited quite a few people. As far as I knew, everybody who was invited came. George Henderson [professor of sociology and the first black man on the faculty at Norman] and his wife Barbara were late getting there. When they came in the door, George said, "Who are all these people?" Someone standing there said, "They're all Hollomon's friends." and George's response was, "Where the hell were they when he needed them?" The point of that story is: he had an awful lot of friends but they weren't in a position to help him. Nobody mounted an effort to keep Hollomon here at all costs.[36]

Jim Dennis also had many friends who were distressed by his resignation. Governor Bartlett praised Dennis's leadership by saying, "He has done a wonderful job. Dean Dennis is a most capable administrator and he will be missed. Under his leadership, the $170 million medical center complex was designed and is now under construction. When completed, it will be one of the finest health centers in the nation." Editorials in all three Oklahoma City papers conveyed the same sentiment.[37]

Bob Hardy, who had worked closely with Dr. Dennis in Arkansas and Oklahoma, lamented his impending departure in conversation with Bob Bird:

Dr. Bird's reaction was a surprise to me. He said that perhaps now was the appropriate time for Jim to move on. "Jim's talent is in conceptualization and planning,

not in day-to-day administration. He lives 10 years out in the future. His development of the Oklahoma Health Center idea will be a lasting contribution to medicine in Oklahoma. Now that it is underway, maybe his job here is finished."

Later, Dennis expressed the idea that he wished he had held on as he had been advised to do, but, on the other hand, he did not feel he was abandoning the project. Characteristically, he put it in pediatric terms:

I felt I had left a thriving baby which, though in the diapering phase, would continue to grow if given tender, loving care. I felt confident I was leaving a situation that was basically pretty good. A concept had been delivered.[38]

Hardy continued:

Then I suggested to Dr. Bird that he was the logical successor as vice president for medical center affairs and again I got an answer I wasn't expecting. First, he reminded me that he had a heart condition, something I guess I had known but had forgotten. Bob's genial, outgoing personality never called attention to his personal problems. The main reason he wouldn't be a candidate for the job was this: "I guess I'm a snob, but the vice president has to spend an awful lot of time with people I would not care to be with. Life's too short to spend your time with people you don't enjoy."

Many people were affected personally by these two resignations which had happened in such quick succession. Arthur Tuttle was one:

One of the biggest shocks of my life was to pick up the paper one morning and read Jim Dennis's comment about Herb Hollomon along the lines…the only trouble with the guy is you can't trust him. I was unaccustomed in North Carolina having a provost of a health sciences center and the president of the university get quoted so directly on the front page of the local tabloid. I really wondered whether I'd made a good decision when Jim Dennis was pulling up stakes and Hollomon was resigning. The stability I had looked for seemed to be dissolving before my eyes.[39]

Another was Leonard Eliel who had just returned from Seattle and reported to his new position as director of medical center research and graduate affairs on July 1, so he was not aware of the political situation in the University:

I guess the most devastating thing that happened at that junction in my history was that within a few days of my return, Jim Dennis resigned. That was a blow because I had no inkling this was going to happen. Then John Colmore took over as acting vice president for medical center affairs and Pete McCarter was acting president.[40]

PART THREE

CRISIS:
1970-1975

CHAPTER 22

THE NEW PLAYERS: 1970-1972

Dr. John Colmore took over as acting director of the Medical Center. (University of Oklahoma)

Pete Kyle McCarter was acting president of the university at Norman. (University of Oklahoma)

On September 18, 1970, when Dennis left for Arkansas, John P. Colmore, M.D., a 49-year-old internist, took over the post of acting vice president. A search committee was formed to find a permanent vice president. Unfortunately, Dr. Colmore was able to hold office only a few short weeks because he became gravely ill with hepatitis and died in University Hospital on November 26, 1970. For the second time in three months, the top Medical Center position changed hands as 56-year-old Leonard Eliel assumed the post of interim executive vice president following his appointment by the O.U. Board of Regents on December 3, 1970.[1]

Bob Terrill's forecast of trouble 18 months earlier was accurate,[2] a fact of academic administrative life Len Eliel learned quite promptly:

We ran into problems almost immediately; one of them was at Wakita. It turned out the program there had been illegally funded with University Hospital funds, according to the State Regents for Higher Education. The Medical Center was then obliged to refund the money, so to speak, to the State Regents. It was very complicated. My memory is a little vague on this issue but it

was inappropriate for the Medical Center to use University Hospital funds to finance this construction at Wakita even though it was a teaching facility. I'm not even sure that the medical school could have done this without approval of the State Regents for Higher Education.

I had to break this news to [acting president] Pete McCarter. We were at a meeting somewhere around the state with the University of Oklahoma Regents. I remember sitting in Pete McCarter's room in a motel one night and breaking this news to him which was sort of devastating to him as well as it had been to me. I think the State Regents dug this up, found out how we financed it. I don't know who rang the gong on us. At any rate, the issue was raised to me by E.T. Dunlap and his staff and we had to answer to it.[3]

Chancellor Dunlap commented:

I think the university may have made a payment on the building up there when it had no authority to use current expense money for capital purposes. Also, the University Hospital was expected to use its operating money for the purposes for which it was originally appropriated. I don't recall the precise situation but I know

The new president, Paul Sharp. (University of Oklahoma)

there was no money refunded to the regents. We probably told them they could no longer spend hospital money that way up at Wakita.[4]

Wakita was just one problem. Faced with a rapidly expanding educational program which would need a lot of new tax money for operations, Dr. Eliel promptly ran up the warning flag in an interview with Ervin Watson, medical writer for the Oklahoma Publishing Company. He described in specific terms the ambitious Oklahoma Health Center plan and the University of Oklahoma Medical Center's part in it:

> We now see a number of things happening toward this end [assuring a healthy future for the people of Oklahoma] such as a sharply increased enrollment of medical students. We have seen the enrollment rise from 104 to 136 this year and expect it to rise to 150 in the next few years. As our state's population grows, we will begin to think in terms of a second medical school in Tulsa. This requirement probably will be reached by 1980.
>
> We are optimistic at the moment although we are subject to the problems of funding like most medical schools across the nation.[5]

After listening to the plans for rapid expansion of O.U.'s health sciences educational offerings, the reporter accurately diagnosed the problem in this headline which appeared in the *Sunday Oklahoman* on January 24, 1971: "State Health Cure: Big Dose Of Money."[6]

In early June, 1971, during the interview process, Paul Sharp, Ph.D., candidate for the presidency of

the University of Oklahoma, was taken to the top floor of the new Rogers Building to visit with Dr. Eliel in what Dr. Sharp called "his rather impressively furnished office":

> I liked Len Eliel immediately. I think he is one of the finest gentlemen I ever worked with and I enjoyed working with him through the years we were together. We talked about the future of the University of Oklahoma in the health sciences and Dr. Eliel referred to the long-range plan which had been completed in 1968.
>
> In a modest way, I felt like our Lord who had been taken to the mountaintop, shown all the riches of the world and told they were within his grasp. But I was too weak to resist temptation. It seemed to me the planning was *very* exciting. I had, of course, had experience as chancellor at Chapel Hill [the University of North Carolina] with medical schools, dental schools, the professional schools in the health sciences and with teaching hospitals. It struck me as I listened to the plan that here was an integration, a development which was far beyond anything we had thought of at Chapel Hill, consisting of public and private agencies, with statewide constituency and public and private support. The development of schools which at that time did not exist or were only in embryonic form entailed, for the university, the very exciting task of not only building buildings but bringing in the quality people to do the teaching and research which are suggested by a major health sciences center.
>
> Dr. Eliel was very persuasive. He had captured the dream from Dr. Dennis and I must admit, it caught me up, too! Here was an opportunity if the state had the resources. When I asked that question, Dr. Eliel suggested that, well, there were some problems but at that moment, the federal government was so committed to the support of the health sciences, it appeared we would find subsidies to build the buildings and underwrite a good bit of the research the university wished to undertake. It was somewhat later I learned the University of Oklahoma did not have to do the extensive research in the health sciences that a university such as North Carolina had to undertake because of the separate and privately funded Oklahoma Medical Research Foundation, a very strong ally in the research component of the Medical Center. I was given the impression that the state had made the commitment to underwrite the expansion of the Medical Center.[7]

The new president of the University of Oklahoma, Paul Sharp, promptly named Dr. Leonard Eliel executive vice president of the university for Medical Center affairs. This happened on August 20, 1971. It is not unusual in academia for the acting or interim leader to be chosen for the position he is filling after

Number Two, Number Three and Number One in Oklahoma: 1971. (Department of Human Services)

a search committee has failed to find a better candidate. Commenting on the appointment of Dr. Eliel, a 1940 graduate of Harvard Medical School, President Sharp said, "In his 20 years at the O.U. Medical Center, Dr. Eliel has proven his ability as an educator-scientist and an administrator. The Medical Center is now in the midst of a multi-million dollar expansion and Dr. Eliel's leadership during this period of rapid growth has been exceptional."[8]

Dr. Sharp had not been ensconced in the president's chair many weeks when he received a call from Senator Bryce Baggett who said he would like to have lunch with the new chief executive of the university. The president recalled their meeting at the Faculty House in Oklahoma City:

> In the course of our conversation, Bryce made this suggestion, "Now, the way to get along with E.T. [Dunlap] is to treat him like "The Godfather." I thought that was a bit strange and said, "What if we don't agree?" The Senator replied with an observation, "Well, you know what happens to people who don't agree with The Godfather!"[9]

When David Hall was elected Governor of Oklahoma, like most politicians, he was pleased with his newly acquired power. Larry Brawner, the Governor's assistant, recalled the afternoon following the inauguration in January, 1971:

> One of the first times I saw David Hall very angry he was in his office, people were coming and going, shaking his hand, congratulating him. I don't remember who it was, but someone, trying to be funny, told David Hall that, as governor, he probably presumed he was the most powerful man in the state but he was actually third; the first was Lloyd Rader [director of the state welfare department] and the second was Gene Stipe [state senator

from McAlester]. He did not appreciate that but that was the perception and [it was] probably not totally inaccurate.[10]

The big dose of money the Medical Center needed was just not available, according to Representative Bill Willis:

> It was a critical time for Oklahoma. [Governor] Hall called me during the recount [November, 1970]; you recall the race between Hall and Dewey Bartlett was that close. Well, Hall was so confident that the recount would come out in his favor, he called me in Tahlequah and asked me if I'd come over and brief him on the state's financial condition. It was terrible! We got money during the sixties through such things as the 1968 [HERO] bond issue. We borrowed money instead of pay-as-you-go, as we have been doing [since].
>
> He asked me how much money he had for new programs or to enrich programs that were ongoing. I said, "Right there's what you've got!" [Willis held up his hand, making a cipher with his thumb and forefinger.] Our growth was so tiny and college enrollment at that time was still going up—as I recall, 12.5 percent that year. We didn't have much inflation, maybe three or three and a half percent.
>
> I said, "By the time you pay for the new college enrollment and take into account the inflationary impact on other functions, you're going to slide back a little bit, just as we have been doing." He said, "What do you do about it?" and I said, "Well, you have to get more money." He said, "Where do you get it?" and I said, "From the people…where it all comes from." He said, "You mean a tax increase?" and I said, "That's what I mean!"
>
> The upshot of the meeting was he wanted to know how much money we'd need so I said, "Give me two weeks and I'll tell you. In the meantime, you go to the Tax Commission and talk to them about our whole tax structure. Pick something out we're undertaxed on." I came up with a modest figure of $45 million, but, of course, that was a lot of money in those days. The Tax Commission told Hall that the income tax and the gross production tax [the wellhead tax on gas and oil, also known as severance tax] would be the best areas to go into.
>
> We came with those two bills, raising the gross production tax two percent—it was five percent; we raised it to seven—and the income tax revision. The Tax Commission misfigured the income tax increase so we got more than the $45 million we were searching for. We bled ourselves bloody out there on the floor [of the House], passing those bills.
>
> J.O. Spiller worked almost exclusively for me in appropriations. Hall said, "I've got a favor to ask of you. Can I have J.O. Spiller as my budget director?" and I told him yes. J.O. balked like everything but I said it

The new governor depended heavily on Representative Bill Willis of Tahlequah. (The Oklahoman)

was more important for the state that he become budget director. Then Hall said, "One more favor....Could I have your secretary?" I told him, "Well,...yes." and that *was* a sacrifice because she'd worked with me on appropriations for a long time. Then to cap it all off, he said, "Would you make my first budget?" And I wrote his first budget—J.O. Spiller and I.

The legislature passed Hall's tax increases in the first legislative session of the new governor's administration. Willis recalled that historic struggle:

We passed the severance tax and the income tax bills and, boy, we bled like hogs over them. I kinda realized we were making history then because I'd been through the decade of the sixties and saw us just creeping along, not keeping up with other states...borrowing money. Well, we cured that with the 1971 tax bill.[11]

Pressured by the need for additional funding, Dr. Eliel reasoned that federal money might be somewhat easier to get if the name "Medical Center" were updated better to reflect the broad scope of its educational programs. He recommended it be changed to the "O.U. Health Sciences Center" (OUHSC) and on Veterans Day, 1971, the O.U. Regents concurred.[12] This effectively met the requirements of the university but left the public forever confused about the difference between the entire multi-institutional health campus and its academic nucleus. As Bob Hardy said:

If the newspaper reporters can't get it right, you can't expect the public to understand the difference. It is very

confusing to have the O.U. Health Sciences Center within the Oklahoma Health Center. Sometimes, I describe the OUHSC as the jelly in a jelly doughnut but rarely do people remember, so I've given up trying to explain it or expecting people to get it right. What's more, I get at least three wrong numbers a day, people telephoning the Oklahoma Health Sciences Foundation when they are trying to call the O.U. Health Sciences Center. Oh, well....

By the last month of 1971, it looked as though some of the Health Science Center's capital and operating costs were easing, at least through federal resources. The bill providing "capitation grants" to the schools for medical and dental students had been enacted and on December 6, U.S. Senator Henry Bellmon announced that HEW had approved a grant of $1,192,993 for construction of the third-floor, dental addition to the Basic Science Education Building. This enabled the dental school to plan on accepting its first class of 24 students the following fall. The whole project was expected to cost $1.8 million with the balance of the funds coming from HERO bonds.[12]

One of the shocks of university health sciences administration came to Dr. Eliel as he became acquainted with the financing of teaching hospitals:

I learned of the financing problems of University Hospital which related largely to uncollected bills amounting to several million dollars. Bob Terrill was in charge. Although I had not uncovered it personally, I had some vague idea of the magnitude of the deficit the hospital was facing. It subsequently turned out that all kinds of records, paperwork and billings had been piling up, like Fibber McGee's closet, and simply were not being handled. The billings had not been done properly and they had not been systematically "writing off" the older ones. So the "write-offs," [those bills deemed uncollectible] were not being reflected in the financial statements. I think it had accumulated to the point where the management of the hospital was incapable of taking care of it.

To Bob Terrill's credit, he said he hadn't been able to get from the administration of the health sciences center the managerial support that he needed. It was partly that he couldn't get enough people in the business office to do the job and partly that the staff he had just didn't have the capability of handling the problem.[13]

Dr. Sharp commented on the hospital's financial problems from a different perspective:

The legislature did not appreciate the magnitude of cost involved. First, the teaching hospitals had been operated at very low cost and, as a result, had rather low standards. The budget for the two hospitals that we got from the State Regents was $2.75 million. The legislators misunderstood the high cost of health care and of course, it was developing, too. Teaching hospitals are probably as expensive a venture as universities can get into. The second thing was, I don't think the university had anything resembling an accurate appraisal of what it cost to operate a teaching hospital. That was accompanied by slipshod accounting procedures; we just simply were not running it as a hospital ought to be run and had to be run to survive.

In addition, there were several senators in the leadership, Senators Hamilton, Berrong, men of that kind, who genuinely believed that if they just eliminated the waste and duplication and reformed the accounting procedures and developed other agencies, such as the [medical] practice plan, the teaching hospitals could be relatively self-sustaining and would not have to be heavily subsidized by the state. I think that was something of a self-deception.

The third thing—and this gradually burdened me more and more—was in the 1970s Oklahoma as a state did not have the wealth to underwrite all the things it was trying to undertake, including the health sciences center and the dream to build the other colleges, even though the federal government contributed heavily to the capitalization and the HERO bond funds were available and earmarked. That's only a small part of this kind of expansion. As I projected the *operational* costs, it was almost horrifying![14]

To add to Dr. Eliel's mounting problems, the resentment of the black community toward the Medical Center and urban renewal continued to smoulder and flared again in the spring of 1972. On March 5, at a panel discussion held at the Center, three black activists charged that the Medical Center had been unresponsive to the needs of residents in the area and warned of future racial conflict. In contrast, Dr. Frank Cox, the dentist, was a local leader who, despite the expression of his intense personal feelings, was a calming influence on some of the more radical people in the black community. He recalled the period:

I made a speech before a group of people in the Health Sciences Center and threatened to burn it down! I was very angry. I always felt guilty in that I was in a position of leadership at that time and could not supply my mother's needs. I was an only child, very close to my mother, and I always kind of blamed that additional tension [of her home being taken by Urban Renewal] which she was under for what I felt was her early demise; Mama was 60. I became much more angry after she died than I was before. It would have been impossible to do anything about the acquisition of her prop-

erty but I guess when your emotions get involved…. I was president of the Urban League at the time and was invited to speak. Marshall Schecter, Gordon Deckert, a lot of people were there and I really unloaded on them.

There were some really radical people around [in the neighborhood]. We had this guy they called "Cheetah" who invaded the swimming pool at the Faculty House once. Cheetah was just itchin' to do something dramatic, and I was in direct contact with him. This was during a period everybody was demonstrating about something and didn't mind burning something down to make a point. Then I knew the Black Muslims were going to get started here. I'm sure I had within my power at that time to turn some of those people loose on this campus. But that wasn't my goal. Our unspoken goal was to demonstrate that you couldn't mistreat a section of the black community and not involve the entire black community.[15]

At the panel discussion, Minister Theodore G X, head of the Oklahoma City Black Muslim temple, told the Medical Center people, "You're building a Frankenstein monster here," and warned, "You're not going to sit here and be safe. You're going to deal with us." He complained about the lack of medical resources for blacks and poor hiring practices in the Center.

Donald "Cheetah" Gates said, "If you're white and living in this area that's 95 percent black and not doing anything, then that's the problem. There are people in this neighborhood without a job watching some of you go to work. That man's a threat. He's got no security; he's the one that will burn your Medical Center down." Gates went on to urge support of job training programs to secure equal employment for blacks. But Gates' "in the system" approach was castigated by Minister X, who urged separation of the races, the standard Muslim approach, as "the only solution."[16]

Along with these threats from the black community, Leonard Eliel faced a new budget inadequate to support the steady growth of the educational programs in the Health Sciences Center. The proposed 1972-73 appropriation, at $10.2 million, was $2 million less than the need and the outlook for more money was dismal. Senator James Hamilton of Poteau, president pro tempore, related the problems of the legislators as they appropriated funds for state projects and services:

People in the bureaucracy sometimes don't realize the position the members of the legislature are in when they're not able to fully fund a project [or agency]. They say, "Well, you're not for us." Maybe you are for them

159

but you just don't have the money to reach everything they'd like you to do because you've got 10 other people who also have projects [that are] just as vital.

Also, you've got the budget-balancing amendment that says you can't spend more than you take in. It's a lot tougher serving in the Oklahoma legislature than it is in the congress. [Up there] you just appropriate a little more money and, whether you have a deficit or not, you just keep going. [But in the legislature] it's a tough job. We should get that [budget-balancing] requirement up in Washington. If we don't, I think something catastrophic is going to happen to our national economy.[17]

It was apparent that something had to give. It appeared to Bob Terrill that:

Leonard had the best in mind for the Center. He was devoted to the cause and he believed he was going to bring order out of what he saw as chaos. He had difficulty arriving at decisions, particularly regarding financial matters. It appeared he would listen to first one and then the other and play them off against each other. For example, he might listen to Ralph Stumpp for a time and then call me over and present the same questions or issues to me and find out if I said something different. He seemingly wanted to verify that what each person said was accurate.

It was obvious that educational activities were increasing, buildings were coming on line, the school of nursing was growing. It was obvious we needed money and we were not receiving enough to cover all the new programs and to continue the programs that were there. About this time, costs had begun to escalate so tremendously in the hospital world, starting in 1968 and 1969. Although our percentage of reimbursement was continuing to go up, we were still requiring so much more. I went there in 1965 and our budget was $7 million; by the time I left it was $16 or $17 million. This was seen as causing problems with the State Regents for Higher Education.

Eliel was trying to cut down the amount of money the hospital would have. He told me I would have to take a $2 million cut and demanded I come up with various possibilities. I told him I could not take a $2 million cut and keep the hospitals operating the way they were. He said, "Fine. Go across the street and come up with alternatives." I simply went back and gave him alternatives. [I said,] "Here is what we can do with $2 million less."

My various alternatives for dealing with the $2 million cut were presented to President Sharp and then to the board of regents, which voted to accept the recommendation that the hospitals' budget be cut by reducing services. Eliel called a special session of the chiefs of the hospitals' medical services to explain the action. He announced that one of my recommendations was to

Cardiovascular surgeon G. Rainey Williams was Dr. Schilling's right hand man. (University of Oklahoma)

close Children's Hospital. The idea was if we had to cut down we could put both children and adults in Old Main and operate more efficiently, reducing the number of beds on all services. We could be a smaller hospital, consolidated into one building. We had 350 to 380 beds in University Hospital and 125 in Children's.

Rader sent word to me via one of his people that he was greatly disappointed and that if I had intended to close Children's, I should have, as I had always done in the past, gone out and talked with him. But I never dreamed Children's would be closed. I simply suggested to Dr. Eliel that, if you are going to take $2 million away from us, we obviously have to do something to live more economically and here are things that we can do. These [alternatives] are open for discussion and review.

Another alternative was to close the emergency room, [a suggestion] which brought the TV reporters out and caused great problems. These alternatives became the basis for so much unpleasantness over the next few months that Len called me to his office and told me that because I had become seen as the problem in the hospitals, I should begin looking around [for another job]. I told him I did not want to prevent a solution from being found so I would leave.[18]

From the viewpoint of many others on the faculty, Terrill's suggestion the two University Hospitals be consolidated was not all that drastic. As G. Rainey Williams, M.D., Professor of Surgery, remembered:

The faculty, in a sense, was shell-shocked. One crisis

after another had occurred or was about to occur. The people I talked with, I thought, felt some things had to be done and were willing to try to do them. Children's had gotten much the tail end of everything and was even worse than the adult hospital in terms of shabbiness and the inadequacy of its physical facilities. I remember thinking that closing Children's was a viable alternative in the sense that we envisioned adding wings to the new Everett Hospital; that we would add a children's wing and get away from the two hospitals, which I thought was a good idea.

It meant reduction of surgical beds and amalgamating operating rooms, a major issue. In retrospect, I'm not sure much money could have been saved because more capital would have had to be spent in order to accommodate the children. But at the time, I did not think it was a shocking idea.[19]

But Senator Hamilton was appalled by the suggestion of closing Children's Hospital. He was quoted in the *Oklahoma Journal* on April 19, 1972, referring to the medical school appropriation which had increased from $6.3 million in 1969 to $10.7 million in 1972:

It would be completely demoralizing to the general public to know that a facility that has received a 70 percent increase in funding during the past three years would purport to close these needed facilities because of a so-called financial plight. The crisis simply would not exist if the administration would take steps to properly administer the funds that are on hand. The records reveal that the *total* expenditures of the medical school increased 50 percent, from $18 million to $27 million, which includes revenue from various sources. I don't know of any other state agency that has had such a large percentage of increase. I am hopeful that the administration will reevaluate its position and take a closer look into the complete operation of the medical school before taking such drastic steps as have been proposed.[20]

By quoting total Health Sciences Center budget figures, the president of the Senate neatly obscured the fact that between fiscal years 1964-1965 and 1970-1971, the *state* appropriation to the hospital had risen only $199,168, which meant that state support as a percentage of the total hospital expense had *dropped* from 55 percent to 27 percent.[21]

Jeptha Dalston, Ph.D., who succeeded Terrill as administrator of the University Hospitals and who had worked as an assistant to him, commented on the alternatives Terrill suggested: "He may have had a strategy by suggesting such a thing, feeling it was impractical but trying to show that $2 million just couldn't be cut out of his budget. Or he may have just been carrying out a management assignment. I did not talk with him at the time. But he sure did get cut down by it!"[22]

Bob Terrill had turned down an offer to become administrator of the teaching hospitals at the Indiana University Medical Center in Indianapolis but promptly renewed his connections there, received the appointment and departed a few months later. In looking back at the situation, Terrill said:

The buildings were there, about to be opened; the area which had been just short of devastation was taking form as a center. We were at the point of bringing in the people who would give life to the new programs, such as in nursing and dentistry. And simply, at that moment, there wasn't money to do it all or we were *told* there wasn't money to do it.

Our response was to begin looking for other ways to do the job. I believe now that was a mistake, that we should have said we have done what we had been asked to do. Instead, we tried to come up with the money for new programs by taking from programs that were already underfunded.

The hospitals were simply not able to shoulder the entire burden. We were already operating well below the average cost for teaching hospitals. The task of providing added educational programs…[was the responsibility of] the people of the state, not the indigent who went to the hospitals for service. Unfortunately, we looked inward for a solution to our problems and were caught up in the business of collecting money. In so doing, we lost the opportunity to finish the job that was so well begun.[23]

When asked about Dr. Eliel's reaction to the uproar Bob Terrill's alternatives created, Dalston said, "I don't know that I was well enough informed to have a reaction to that. My general reaction to Len is that he was a very well-meaning, honorable, earnest person who was way, way over his head in what he was dealing with."[24]

Gordon Deckert was the hospital chief of staff in November, 1972, when the next traumatic event occurred:

The visible crisis was precipitated, literally, when Bob Bird walked into my office, ashen, saying, "Gordon, my God, what are we going to do? I've just learned we can't meet the payroll in the hospital in one or two weeks!" He was surprised; I'm not sure exactly where that knowledge came from. It certainly was a surprise to me. There wasn't exactly that much budgetary information presented; Terrill presented all kinds of things in a way that was viewed then by the chiefs of the various services [as] in a competent fashion.

As chief of staff, Gordon Deckert was in the middle of the hospital crisis. (University of Oklahoma)

The incident, frankly, was that a large check, due University Hospital for services rendered to patients, was ordered locked up by the president pro tem of the Senate. At least, that's what the story was, even though the leader of the department of human services [Lloyd Rader] was reluctant to do it. That precipitated a major cash-flow problem.

Len Eliel was equally disturbed. I suggested what we were going to have to have was essentially a crisis management operation. In the space of two days, there was then created what was called "Big Mac," the management advisory committee. It was made up of key deans, Len Eliel, the fiscal officer, Bob Terrill. We knew we needed a very competent staff person and Jeptha Dalston got picked. That committee literally met every morning at eight o'clock from November 1972 to March, 1973.

The view then was: the damn university has not effectively managed the hospital—in essence, the dollars earned by the hospital have been siphoned off to support educational enterprise and on top of that, there was the suspicion the doctors were earning all kinds of dollars. It was really a paranoid time. That was a ring-tailed doozy of a crisis! There was a maneuver that I was involved in—which frankly I'm not willing to share—that rather quickly effected the release of that check which made it possible for the payroll to be met. It never was clear what the president pro tem was trying to prove.[25]

CHAPTER 23

GOVERNOR HALL: 1972

Larry Brawner (right), former assistant to Governor Hall, eyeballs a later Oklahoma governor, George Nigh. (University of Oklahoma)

In September, 1972, a few weeks before the University engaged Herman Smith Associates to examine and analyze the fiscal problems of the O.U. Health Sciences Center, Governor David Hall commissioned Robert E. Lee Richardson, LL.D., an attorney on the faculty of the University of Oklahoma Law School, to conduct an independent investigation. Larry Brawner, the governor's assistant who later became associate provost of the O.U. Health Sciences Center under Dr. Clayton Rich, explained why the governor was worried:

Probably the impetus for Governor Hall's investigation was [that] there never seemed to be a coherent policy toward the Center. It was more a "crisis management" situation between the state government and the Health Sciences Center. There was always the threat that one of the entities down here was going to close its doors. To a politician, it would be very important if *any* hospital were closed, much less Children's Hospital.

The crisis—I don't know whether it was manufactured or not; I suspect it was—the crisis [was that] we were literally within days of closing Children's Hospital. The issue presented to the legislature was, "Do you want to go home and justify to your constituents that you closed a hospital [and] that killed babies?" Kids and medicine are buzz words in politics. It didn't have anything to do with the university—it was babies, *sick babies!*

In trying to deal with it, to get a handle on it, Governor Hall, although he is extremely bright, did not have the background to deal with it from a government administrative level. So, in his dealings with individuals at the Center, he was probably offensive to them [but] not in a knowing way. In some of the things he did and suggested, he did not recognize the academic part of the institution. Their [the faculty's] responses to him were equally hostile and these hostilities built up to a point that he began to believe a lot of the things outsiders say about doctors making too much money, and this and that. The hostility that was constantly escalating was probably the reason for the investigations. I would say the trust [between the governor and the Medical Center] was next to non-existent…flowing both ways. I don't think any governor before or since has regarded the physicians down here as anything other than state employees—hired hands. And that's true of all state government's attitude.[1]

Dr. Sharp related his reaction to this review of the Health Sciences Center crisis:

As I contemplate what may have been the reasons that Governor Hall acted as he did…when one searches for motivation, of course, it's problematic. My staff and I saw three or four things in Governor Hall's actions. It seemed quite clear he was representing a point of view from Tulsa and eastern Oklahoma that was consistent with his supporters' interests. This, of course, disturbed the balance of power substantially in many issues involving the university but much of it came to focus at the Health Sciences Center. Second, he had a genuine interest in improving health care and health professional education in the state. I think he had the politician's concern that here was a crisis that might engulf him, he had the responsibility of doing something about it and hence, the studies he authorized.

One of our lawyers down here did a study of the Center for Governor Hall—Bob Richardson. We were hoping it would be helpful, pointing major ways in which we could resolve some of these problems. My staff and I were looking forward to it. We thought, "Here's going to be a blueprint to help us out of this…"[2]

But Dr. Eliel looked at it differently:

I felt Governor Hall was trying to make political capital out of the Medical Center and use his investigation of it as a feather in his political cap. Richardson was purely an investigator of the prosecutorial type who

Governor Hall's investigator, Robert E. Lee Richardson, was on the faculty of the O.U. Law School. (The Oklahoman)

pursued thing relentlessly. It was a very uncomfortable situation.[3]

In comments prefacing his Study Report dated February, 1973, Dr. Richardson said people employed at the OUHSC had been misled about the future growth of the Center and were now disillusioned because of its financial condition. He also observed that many faculty members did not consider the Center a state institution because most of the support money came from federal and other "non-state sources." Thomas E. "Tom" Acers, M.D., chairman of the Department of Ophthalmology, recalled a fascinating incident which reflected this attitude and how it rankled state officials. Dr. Acers and David Hall had gone to school together and their families were life-long friends:

> I presented the problem to David. I said, "You use that term in the newspapers—that physicians on the faculty should be considered state employees—and they resent it! His comment was, "I don't care whether they resent it or not, it's a fact. They have to follow all the rules and all the regulations and as far as I'm concerned, they deserve to be treated like any other state employee."
>
> So we set up a breakfast meeting to talk about it and fairly early in the breakfast, he made that same statement. Well, Rainey Williams and Ted Clemens and Walt Whitcomb—the people I had assembled as even tempered, well-thought-of people in the field—it just re-offended them!
>
> It started off so nice; it was really a fun meeting and David was in a real good mood. He'd lost about 40 pounds and he told some jokes.... It started as a very pleasant breakfast in the sunroom of the governor's mansion. It abruptly turned about!
>
> I had obviously overestimated my influence as a me-

Dr. Tom Acers, long-time friend of David Hall. (University of Oklahoma)

diator. I thought I could go to him and say, "Now, David, just lay off and tell the guys when you have breakfast with 'em you just meant they had to follow state rules.... All of us do that. But don't talk to them like they're street cleaners." I thought he'd take my advice.[4]

Dr. Richardson's primary concern was whether or not Oklahoma could afford the planned expansion of the O.U. Health Sciences Center. He predicted, "The problems faced by the Center during this fiscal year are minimal in relation to the problems which will occur in future years." He pointed out that while university officials stated the major money problem was the hospitals, the state appropriation for them was $3.1 million in fiscal year (FY) 1964-1965 and had risen only nominally [to $3.3 million] by 1970-1971. The proportion of hospital costs had dropped from 55 to 27 percent during that period. This reflected the advent of Medicare and Medicaid reimbursement as well as the hospital administrator's effort to convert the state charity hospital to a system of charging patients according to their ability to pay. Bob Terrill commented on collections:

> When I went to the University [in 1965], about 10 or 15 percent of the monies [$7 million] on which the hospitals operated came from patient care. That was, of course, prior to Titles 18 and 19 [Medicare and Medicaid]. I'm not trying to suggest that anything I did was

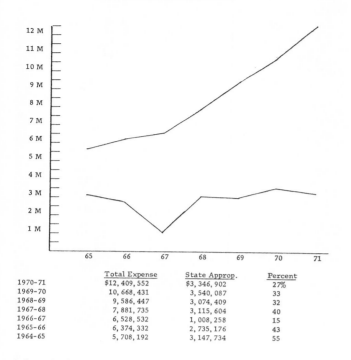

COMPARISON OF STATE APPROPRIATION
TO TOTAL OPERATING EXPENSE

	Total Expense	State Approp.	Percent
1970-71	$12,409,552	$3,346,902	27%
1969-70	10,668,431	3,540,087	33
1968-69	9,586,447	3,074,409	32
1967-68	7,881,735	3,115,604	40
1966-67	6,528,532	1,008,258	15
1965-66	6,374,332	2,735,176	43
1964-65	5,708,192	3,147,734	55

Information obtained from Wolf & Co. audits for the Fiscal Years 1965 through 1971.

The cost of the Medical Center was rising rapidly but the State of Oklahoma's share was almost level. (Study of the University of Oklahoma Health Sciences Center by the Governor's Oklahoma Health Sciences Task Force: 1973)

Senator John McCune, a veteran Republican from District 47. (Senator McCune)

magical to raise that to a 70 percent level [which was achieved] within about two years [mid-1968]. I was never able to push it much above the 70 percent level; I could get it to 72, 73 percent and then it would pull back. I found by looking at other teaching hospitals across the country that were constituted much like ours and had about the same type of patient population, we were running fairly consistently with them. So when you talk about a shortfall, I have to turn around and say the problem was that the larger the total operating cost became, the larger became the sum which had to come from the state.

All monies were appropriated by the State Regents to the Center, not directly to the hospitals. Then the appropriation was divided by a planning committee working within the Center. We prepared our budget requests and submitted them to this Center committee but, of course, the State Regents would confirm the allocation between teaching and patient care.[5]

The 1972-1973 state appropriation for the Health Sciences Center was $10.5 million, about $2 million less than needed, according to Dr. Eliel. For the next year, he had submitted a budget requesting an $8.2

million increase. But the State Regents for Higher Education divided the money it received from the Legislature for all institutions of higher learning according to a set formula, and it appeared the Center would receive only $15.8 million, about $3 million less than Dr. Eliel thought was required.

One of the factors which made the Center's request appear out of proportion was that educational programs in other Oklahoma colleges and universities were leveling off as the post-World War II baby boom essentially had been accommodated. But growth of the health sciences programs, stimulated by federal incentives, was just beginning to hit its stride, a fact the legislators probably did not fully comprehend. Dr. Richardson said that by FY 1975-1976, the Center would need $28.4 million in state appropriations, up almost three times. He was not convinced this magnitude of growth was either needed or affordable. Senator John McCune, Republican from District 47 in Oklahoma City and Logan County, had a different attitude. "We all realized it was going to be costly but, on the other side of it, some of those things were necessary. It seemed to me ridiculous in a state of almost three million people we didn't [yet] have a school of dentistry. We were having to subsidize our students going to Washington University in St. Louis and other places."[6]

Because the Richardson and Herman Smith reviews of OUHSC operations were conducted simultaneously, Governor Hall's investigator quoted findings and attitudes of the Smith consultants. He noted there was a marked difference of opinion between Dr. Eliel and Bob Terrill on one side, who thought the Health Sciences Center's accounting and billing system was being reorganized properly and, on the opposite side, the Herman Smith consultants and Associate Vice President Gerald Gillman, who stated flatly, "There is no system!" In fact, Herman Smith Associates decided it had to pull out or go into a management contract [as opposed to a consultant contract] for 90 days and saturate the place with temporary business office workers in order to restructure the financial operations at the Center. William Nix, another Herman Smith consultant, said at best the billing system was deplorable. At times, bills simply disappeared and "You cannot track an account through the system." But Jeptha Dalston, Ph.D., who became administrator of the University Hospitals in January, 1973, viewed both parties as "right" although they looked at the same conditions from different perspectives:

New University Hospital administrator Jeptha Dalston took an objective but realistic view of the institution's problems. (Oklahoma Journal)

> There was consultant "hype" in Jack Dumas' [Herman Smith Associates] report but, by and large, I felt things were pretty bad. I had respect for Jack and the firm; I had known him before and so I had my own bias. I was impressionable; these high-flying people came in, with national credibility, made these assertions and I believed them.
>
> Bob Terrill's perspective was one of having lived there and worked with that monster for years and years. He recognized all of the [accounts receivable and accounting] problems. The consultants came in, applying standards of the field as a whole and, by comparison, it was a deplorable situation. I'm talking about the efficacy of the [accounting, billing and collection] system. If you compared that operation with this one [the University of Michigan Hospital at Ann Arbor] or most teaching hospitals across the country then, it was substandard. Bob knew that, I knew that, we all knew it. So the consulting firm was right.
>
> Bob was the classic scapegoat! He was absolutely scapegoated and it happens regularly in that situation. You've got to kill somebody so the first person to go is the weakest figure on the scene—that's the hospital administrator. Of course, it ricocheted up. I worked with six people my first six months at the hospital. First Bob went, then Len's financial officer, then Len himself. It was just a series. I felt Len was scapegoated for the same reason.[7]

Richardson quoted Jack Dumas' highly critical statements about the capital planning process. The Herman Smith people implied "that no actual plan-

David Steen teaching a group of students in the Basic Science Education Building. (University of Oklahoma)

ning had been followed but that applications for facilities had determined the planning." Here Mr. Dumas was quoted as saying, "If the hospitals are to survive, there must be a change in image away from charity hospitals.... A danger exists in putting them under a state agency because such would tend to make them appear even more to be indigent hospitals." Inexplicably, he then turned around and recommended that Children's Hospital be transferred to the Welfare Department, the very name of which connotes indigency.

Robert E. Lee Richardson criticized the way the university used trusts for accomplishing its purposes. He was particularly suspicious of the Oklahoma Health Sciences Facility, Incorporated, which by then had purchased 20 houses on 14th and 15th Streets to provide temporary "surge" space for the new and growing academic programs in the health sciences until permanent quarters could be planned and built on the Oklahoma Health Center campus. The original Articles of Incorporation "did not list any entity which was to receive its benefits," so on November 10, 1972, this corporation stipulated that "all real property…is held in trust for the Board of Regents of the University of Oklahoma." This, according to Dr. David Steen, had been the intent of the Board of Directors all along. With an attorney's penchant for detail, Richardson wanted everything written down, with all the t's crossed and the i's dotted.

Both the Bureau of Public Health Research and the Research and Development Office of the O.U. Foundation were created to facilitate the management of grants. Ralph Stumpp, Director of the Research and Development Office, said a separate corporation was needed because, once funds were deposited in a state account, all state laws applied and under grant management principles, it was impossible to run the office effectively and comply with state laws.

Richardson also discussed the relationship of the Oklahoma Health Sciences Foundation with the University and the actions proposed in this planning organization which had not been approved by the Regents of the University. He noted that Robert Hardy, the executive officer of the OHSF was paid entirely from state funds even though he worked full-time for this independent, non-profit corporation. The report did not explain this was the way Dr. Dennis had been able to contribute to the funding of the Foundation whose primary purpose was to further the plans and programs of the university. In addition to major support by business and industry in central Oklahoma, Presbyterian Hospital and the Oklahoma Medical Research Foundation also made annual contributions to the Foundation budget. Dr. Paul Sharp talked with Hardy about his prompt removal from the O.U. payroll when the Richardson report was released:

> You were one of the casualties and that wasn't a very happy thing to do. You see, my conviction was, and still is, we have a good many faculty members who play key roles that are not involved in teaching. But the legislature at the time saw the function of the university only in its teaching role…that research was secondary, public service was somewhere down the line. I recall so well one of the legislators saying to me one day, "Paul, I walked through the English building down on the campus and I didn't see anybody teaching." And I said, "What time was it when you were down there?" He said, "Oh, it was

about four in the afternoon. All of the faculty members were in their offices reading!"[8]

There were also college and department "trusts," separate accounts used by the College of Dentistry, two departments in the College of Health and, of course, the oft-discussed accounts of the clinical departments in the College of Medicine. Richardson said there were at least 28 separate accounts in the department of surgery which were not included in the state budget. The dean's philosophy of fiscal control was quite foreign to the legally rigid, bureaucratic mindset of state officials. Dr. Robert Bird recognized that "the work gets done at the department level" and told his chairmen in the College of Medicine to channel the money to get the job done. He deliberately did not hold a tight rein but said, "I think I know what is going on." He admitted, however, that in the future, funds would have to be made visible "because the Health Sciences Center is a public institution."

Some of the clinical departments used the "Physicians' Trust" or University of Oklahoma Medical Center Trust Fund, as it was officially titled, which was managed by the Oklahoma Medical Research Foundation. But there was little consistency in the way the clinical department heads deposited and managed the money in their numerous separate accounts. These non-state funds were used to supplement faculty and staff salaries, pay intern and resident stipends, refurbish faculty offices, subscribe to professional journals, purchase and maintain office equipment and furniture, buy books, pay travel expenses, renovate and alter departmental space and hire additional personnel. For example, Radiology spent half a million dollars to expand the outpatient clinic building in June, 1970, so it could have more space for diagnosis and treatment.

These money-handling procedures and the criticism leveled at them stimulated the O.U. Board of Regents to establish principles for a new private practice plan at the Center. In addition, three of the four people who, Richardson noted, were being paid by the State but did not work full-time for the State were removed from the state payroll. Although Dr. David Steen spent considerable time managing the Oklahoma Health Sciences Facility real estate, he was also Associate Dean of the College of Health and remained on the university payroll.

Dr. Richardson questioned the expenditure of

$340,000 a year to rent space outside the Center. The O.U. School of Nursing building was demolished to make way for the new Basic Science Education Building, so the school leased seven residences on 13th and 14th Streets just west of Lincoln Boulevard. Because the owner, Winston Howard, also worked for the State as budget director, there was suspicion he had an "inside deal" because of his political position. This idea was not expressed in the Richardson report but the implication was there. According to Winston Howard, officials of the School of Nursing approached *him* because they were desperate to find quarters for their program and he was the only owner who had several contiguous houses close to the Medical Center. Before entering into the lease agreement, he checked with the state attorney general's office which said there was no conflict of interest because the O.U. Board of Regents was a constitutional board separate from state government. Despite this, which Raymond Crews agreed was the precise situation, the university felt pressure to terminate the arrangement with Mr. Howard as soon as possible after the release of the Richardson study. Fortunately, nursing was soon able to share with dentistry the new Interim Building at 12th and Stonewall until its permanent facilities were available.

The report went on to list the 20 houses on 14th and 15th Streets east of Lincoln Boulevard owned by the Oklahoma Health Sciences Facility and used by the College of Dentistry, the College of Health, the Physicians Associate Program and other university departments and services. In addition, O.U. rented space from OMRF, Christ United Methodist Church, the Oklahoma Dental Foundation and Mistletoe Express Company. But as Dennis had said, without the off-campus surge space, the steady growth of the academic programs designed to relieve the acute shortage of health manpower would have been impossible.

Unlike the Herman Smith consultants who advised major, sweeping changes in organization, finance and control, Dr. Richardson went on to discuss detailed procedures which did not conform to Center-wide standards if, indeed, such existed. The people at the Center by necessity had devised ingenious ways to accomplish the job at hand, whether that was getting enough money to survive, recruiting the right people, finding space in which to work, or executing the principal tasks of teaching, medical investigation and taking care of sick people. They were quite casual about *how* it was done and did not keep elaborate records of the process. Thus, Dr. Richardson had ample reason to question the method if not the motive. When President Paul Sharp read the report, he reacted this way:

> It turned out to be a real disappointment to us. Instead of analyzing on a major scale, it was a micro-study—a nit-picking type of study. Not that it wasn't correct in terms of these small items and correcting them should have been done and we did. We tried to move as quickly as we could. But that report did not address the overarching problems that we faced, particularly in finance. To save $1,000 here or $1,200 over here or $800 here really wasn't the kind of approach we needed. We needed the "megabucks" approach and we were disappointed.[9]

The last half of the Richardson report dealt with conditions intolerable to well-organized and documented bureaucratic operation. These included suspected nepotism, high personnel turnover and the lack of a job classification and salary plan. Richardson noted that the salaries paid administrative assistants varied from $560 to $1,015 a month. Because the money to pay salaries came from so many different sources—grants and contracts as well as the state—there was no Center-wide policy which specified how much jobs ought to pay.

Even though the Central Oklahoma Transportation and Parking Authority's plan to develop the OHC parking system already had been scuttled, Richardson criticized the operation of the university's parking lots and and the fact that employees were required to pay $10 a month. This change followed a long tradition of free parking for employees, so there were numerous complaints, not only because they now had to pay but also because parking for some university employees behind the houses on 14th and 15th Streets was still free. Richardson said, "It is possible to have a parking program at the Center which will allow personnel to pay a *yearly* rate of $15—a rate comparable to that paid by personnel on the Norman campus...." However, he did not say how this could be done and also develop the planned multi-level parking system. Richardson's map merely located various lots for surface parking and did nothing to prevent the campus from becoming an enormous sea of automobiles.

The study report went over much of the same ground covered by Herman Smith Associates concerning hospital accounts receivable exceeding $6.5 million of which $2 million were over six months old. In one year, the hospitals "wrote off" over $3 million in accounts for "charity patients" and teaching patients as well as discounts for physicians, students and

The block south of the Mark Everett Tower was a vast sea of automobiles. (OHSF Collection)

employees. The report also said that the Wolf and Company audit report did not include funds from non-state sources, the university did not allocate costs to the units which incurred those costs and it ignored the auditor's recommendations about billings and collections. Equipment procurement for the new Everett Tower had been delayed because money was "borrowed" from this fund to complete equipping the Basic Science Education Building and the necessary funds had not been transferred back to the Everett Tower equipment account.

The governor's investigator raised other questions about purchasing procedures, how much teaching the geographical full time doctors accomplished and the failure of the administration to answer questions he had presented the previous September.[10] Dr. Eliel commented:

> At any rate, the Richardson affair was sort of a sordid one. Paul Sharp's vice president for public relations gave me a scrap of paper one day with some scrawlings on it. He said, "This investigator, Richardson, wants a lot of information about your faculty's productivity, utilization of time, hours spent in teaching, research and patient care." I didn't take it seriously because it wasn't a formal request from the president of the university or anybody else. They began pressing me for it later on and by the time the deadline for submitting it to Richardson arrived, it wasn't ready. I never heard the end of that! The legislature just pounced on that. We gave them a lot of data he requested but not a detailed analysis of [the faculty's] time and effort. That was really what he wanted.[11]

Richardson raised the basic question of the future role of the University Hospitals by asking, "Should these hospitals have as one their principal purposes the health care of indigent citizens or should their role be limited to laboratory facilities for Center students?" This was the same question posed eight years earlier by the State Regents in their Self-Study of Medical Education in Oklahoma and by the Herman Smith consultants. Jeptha Dalston had these observations:

> It is pretty clear in my mind the University Hospital was an inner-city teaching hospital with a "county hospital" role added. It was never valued sufficiently over time to make it "solid," to make it right. The poor people it served, the other patients and the university were not valued and that troubled me greatly.
>
> I think Jack [Dumas] was incorrect in the first instance. You cannot change the image away from a charity or welfare hospital. You cannot do that. I remember standing on the portico of the Everett Building with our board members and all of us wringing our hands saying, "If this building were located out where Sister Mary Coletta's hospital is, we could do that, but because it's here, we can't, at least not in our lifetime."[12]

While the Richardson report implied that everything was wrong at the Health Sciences Center, it included no specific recommendations which Governor Hall should require the University to follow. However, this was the public report; in a separate and voluminous report to the chief executive, Dr. Richardson suggested numerous policies and procedures he thought the administration should initiate. He talked about his public report and the confidential second section of his study:

> I got a varied reception at the Center. By some, I was well received. Probably to a great extent, the medical staff didn't want anybody looking at the place. They paid little attention to regulations, sometimes to state law. For example, Eliel had his daughter on the payroll down there, clearly a violation of state law. There was little attention to fiscal management according to state policy in the way the houses on 14th and 15th were procured

and then rented back to the state. Money was funneled into private bank accounts; all kinds of things that were contrary to state law. And they didn't want anybody to mess with any of those. It was a morass, an unbelievable thing as far as I was concerned, fiscally speaking. That's the reason I recommended some type of fiscal integrity.

What I found was that the hospital wasn't in bad shape; it was the fact it was being bled by the various educational departments that gave it such difficulties. All kinds of things that should have been under the educational budget were coming under the hospital budget.

I don't think anybody particularly looked at what Oklahoma could afford in a health sciences center. You had a group of leading citizens in Oklahoma City that wanted this beautiful, impressive, excellent Health Sciences Center. I don't think the legislature was aware and I recommended it have an on-going study as to the projected cost of the Center. If you went down to the Health Sciences Center and checked on projected cost, it wasn't the same information you got at the State Regents office. The Center was projecting tremendous cost; the State Regents *weren't* projecting tremendous cost. So the end result was, the legislature was unaware of what was coming.

I think the attitude was: the federal government is going to pay for most of this and it's really not going to cost the state much. The actual cost of the educational units was increasing tremendously but it didn't show up in the Regents budget as to educational costs.

The thing I think the Health Sciences Center projected to the legislature was that the big problem was the hospitals. To me, that was incorrect. The big problem was *not* the hospitals. There seemed to be the feeling, "If we can just get rid of these hospitals, things will be solved.[13]

Larry Brawner's reaction to Dr. Richardson's work was not enthusiastic:

It was really a compendium of bitches and complaints that you hear out of any major organization. You could have set up an interview booth downtown and asked anybody who had a complaint about the way the Health Sciences Center was run to come in and tell you about it and you could have written that report. I wasn't too impressed with Bob's work, even though I didn't have anything against Bob—still don't—but I didn't think he was very realistic in his approach to a lot of things. I can remember some of the impressions I had. He could have written it without ever talking to anybody on the campus. I don't think that happened because I believe he has more integrity than that.[14]

CHAPTER 24
THE CRISIS: 1973

Leonard Eliel and President Paul Sharp were convinced the University Hospitals *were* the major cause of growing fiscal problems at the O.U. Health Sciences Center. At least they were the immediate problem, but there were other difficulties, as Dr. Sharp described:

> It was quite clear there were two or three different levels of problems. One was the teaching hospitals; another was within the Health Sciences Center itself with respect to the management of departments, organization and the teaching and research functions. The third, of course, was the political umbrella under which all this operated. That led to legislative investigations which, in turn, led us to bring in Herman Smith Associates.[1]

In early autumn of 1972, Dr. Sharp and Dr. Eliel were not aware that the study of the Center then being conducted by Dr. Richardson would emphasize that the request for increased support for the hospitals represented less than 15 percent of the total need for more money to run the center. Of the $8.2 million increase in state funds requested for FY 1973-1974, the estimated increase of hospital expense over income was only $1.2 million.

Be that as it may, on October 18, 1972, the O.U. Board of Regents authorized Herman Smith Associates, hospital consultants based in California and Illinois, to assist the university with a reorganization of the governance and fiscal support of the University of Oklahoma Hospitals and the "design and installation of a fiscal management system for the O.U. Health Sciences Center." Moreover, the regents thought it would be helpful to get the consultants' observations regarding the total governance of the center.[2]

Although the approved organization of the OUHSC as it related to the administration at Norman gave Dr. Eliel great operational latitude, the pressure on President Sharp to do something about the threatening money problems at the Oklahoma City campus was intensifying. Getting advice from "an expert from out of town" seemed to be the first step, as Leonard Eliel recalled: "The first thing I did was take the hospital problems up with Paul Sharp. I recommended this hospital management consulting firm from California be employed to come and take a look at the situation. That was one of the smartest things I did while

I was there, one of my major contributions amongst the few I made."[3] Dr. Sharp related what happened then: "They sent Jack Dumas who quickly appraised the situation and, almost from the beginning, became an advisor to Mr. Rader rather than to the university. We were paying him but he was providing a great deal of data and information to Mr. Rader."[4]

Consultants, by the nature of their profession, tend to exaggerate. They need to express alarm at the seriousness of the situation they find so they may then point with confidence to the also exaggerated results the changes they suggest will achieve. Of course, consultants come in, stay a short while, gather opinions, analyze data, make up a report which neatly recommends effective solutions to existing problems, collect their fee and depart. They rarely stay around to bask in the glory of successful solutions; neither are they present if the action they advise results in disaster.

As excoriating as their language often is, they invariably give credit to the people who cried for help. In this case, Herman Smith Associates said, "In many ways, the Health Sciences Center, and in particular the Medical School, has operated very successfully in spite of 'the system'." In a final paragraph of Section One, "An Overview of the Problems," in their March 9, 1973, Interim Report, they also wrote, "We would like to remind everyone that the School of Medicine has assumed one of the greater teaching commitments of any medical school in the country, and yet ranks in the *lowest quartile of costs* for training medical students. The quality of these students and their training certainly ranks above the lowest quartile, leaving many wondering why the problems which are surfacing now did not arise earlier." This is somewhat like the pathologist's observation about a deceased patient, "The wonder is not what the patient died of but what he lived with!"

Another characteristic of consultant reports is they tend to recommend what their client wants to hear. To illustrate: the governor's office "took over" John C. "Jack" Dumas and his helpers from Herman Smith Associates or perhaps, as Dr. Sharp opined, the consultants found out where the power was and gravitated thereto:

> I did not talk with Dumas about this but several of my

associates did. He quickly concluded the university would never have enough money to make these hospitals effective institutions. We gradually concluded that was true. The State Regents were not going to ask for the millions of dollars it would take as an appropriation to higher education for teaching hospitals.

I think the general reputation in the legislature of the management of the hospitals was so low that *they* were not prepared to appropriate monies, either. Dumas quickly and clearly understood Mr. Rader was, in fact, the center of power, perhaps in the state, but certainly in these situations. He had wealth, a dedicated tax, federal funds, he had patronage—all the things the university did not have—that made him very attractive to Dumas. I was quite surprised to be told by my colleagues he was working with Mr. Rader. He ultimately went into Mr. Rader's employ. Despite this, we did not particularly suspect that Mr. Rader wanted to take over the hospitals.[5]

This shift of allegiance was probably the reason the consultants advised that "the present University Regents Task Force on the Health Sciences Center should be reconstituted to include representation from the governor's office, the Senate, the House, the State Regents and the Department of Institutions, Social and Rehabilitative Services (DISRS)." The latter was the department which Mr. Rader headed, previously known as the Welfare Department and later called the Department of Human Services.

Between mid-October, 1972, and March 9, 1973, the date a Senate Committee for Investigation and Study of Health Care Facilities in Oklahoma, created by Senate Resolution 9, required the consultants to submit proposed solutions, Jack Dumas and his colleagues found many conditions about which they were critical. The larger problem, they said, began with the total governance of the university. "The Oklahoma State Legislature, the State Regents for Higher Education, the O.U. Board of Regents and the OUHSC as a constituent agency in the state system *predictably* all lead to conflicts and competitiveness. This led the citizens to be confused and dismayed about 'education' due to overlapping roles of governing bodies." Said another way, there were too many cooks in the kitchen! The consultants thought the legislature and the O.U. Regents should re-examine the authority and responsibility of each group, think how they should communicate and decide which group should make what decisions.

Jack Dumas went on to identify the major problems of the Center, claiming: the role of the O.U. Regents in operating and managing the University was

Members of the O.U. Board of Regents in 1972 were (from top left clockwise) Thomas R. Brett, Mack M. Braly, Huston Huffman, Walter Neustadt, Jr., Horace K. "Tony" Calvert, and Jack H. Santee. Mrs. Nancy Davies of Enid was the first woman chairperson in the history of the board.

ineffective and perfunctory, and there was serious controversy nationally over the quality and quantity of health manpower needed. Previous data were no longer adequate and health sciences centers, such as OUHSC, had to decide if they were going to train health professionals for local needs only or try to meet regional and national requirements as well.

The consultants also contended the isolation of the Health Sciences Center as a constituent agency of the state system instead of a fully integrated part of the university was "inexplicable and unfortunate." Of course, this separation had been further emphasized by the power struggle between Dr. Dennis and President Hollomon and the executive powers granted the OUHSC director by the O.U. Board of Regents on June 25, 1970. Dumas thought this action made the president of the university merely a ceremonial head of the Medical Center and the regents had abdicated their responsibility, an action for which, he said, they were now paying a severe price. Furthermore, the dependence on federal funding and other soft money, which had promoted a laissez faire atmosphere for the past decade, helped to create the financial crisis as these sources of funding declined. There was no back-up plan to provide alternative funds nor did the governing or legislative bodies express much sympathy or compassion when the Center got into financial difficulty. Concern often had been expressed about the percentage of soft money but little had been done to provide state money when the situation changed.

The consultants decried the delegation of master planning responsibility to "an umbrella agency," the Oklahoma Health Sciences Foundation. They said, "It is apparent the Foundation's planning concepts, process and efforts do not have a sufficient understanding by the O.U. Regents, university-wide administration, State Regents or the legislature to gain their full support. Unfortunately, this has complicated the planning and decision-making process at the Health Sciences Center to a substantial degree." Dumas probably would not have written this had he taken the time to learn the history of the Foundation and how it operated. Apparently he was not aware that the president of the O.U. Regents and the chancellor of the State Regents for Higher Education were trustees of the Oklahoma Health Sciences Foundation, that Dr. George Cross was president of the Foundation, and that the current president of the university, Paul Sharp, was also a trustee. Of course, the OUHSC directors—first Dennis, then Colmore and later Eliel—were leaders in the work of the Foundation's Operations Committee. The governor of Oklahoma was also a member of the board of trustees of the Foundation. Henry Bellmon and Dewey Bartlett were heavily involved with the Foundation, but Governor David Hall never answered communications or invitations to meetings sent to him by OHSF. Sometime later, he resigned from his position as *ex-officio* trustee of the Foundation, citing "conflict of interest." It was apparent consultants do not always have "sufficient understanding" of the situation they are purporting to analyze. After all, the Oklahoma Health Center plan had been generated within the University with full knowledge and concurrence by the O.U. Regents, the State Regents for Higher Education and the previous governors.

The OUHSC administration was "crisis oriented, on the defensive and had lost a degree of credibility," according to the consultants. It also ignored the parent university until it was in trouble, according to some, while others the consultants talked with thought the university was overly permissive. The consultants said "the [Health Sciences Center] leadership came, used up the environment—or was used up *by* the environment—and left (three vice presidents in four years)." This was an accurate statement based on the arbitrary date the consultants used to begin counting. Apparently, Dumas counted back four years from March, 1973, to March, 1969. Dr. Dennis was at O.U. about six years but given credit for only 15 months. Dr. John Colmore was vice president less than three months

and died in November, 1970, while in office, so he hardly had the choice implied by the consultants' statement. Dr. Eliel had served two and a half years by March, 1973. To be sure, the average tenure of OUHSC directors since 1964 was not long, only 2.8 years, but consultants have interesting ways to impress their clients. Had Herman Smith Associates wanted to make the opposite point, they could have included Dr. Mark R. Everett and the count would have been four vice presidents in 24 years.

They went on to talk about the lack of communication, lack of confidence, management by committee to avoid risk, and an attitude of defeat. Above all, they said there were too many solutions, plans and planners, which they classified as "the most serious, disquieting and potentially destructive problem affecting the entire University of Oklahoma at this moment." Too many cooks! Jack Dumas then listed the many ways in which these problems at the Center were specifically manifested.

Money to operate the University at Oklahoma came from 10 sources: state appropriations; student fees; overhead or indirect cost payment from grants and contracts; the sale of departmental services to outside organizations; hospital patient services; food service operations; gifts, grants and contracts; professional fees (primarily charged by College of Medicine faculty but also by the Colleges of Dentistry and Health); support from affiliated hospitals (for example: the V. A. Hospital provided $1.5 million a year in faculty and other staff salaries); and auxiliary services (computer center, plant operations and others). Despite these many funding sources, the result was fiscal insolvency. The hospitals were required to take care of the medically indigent and thus could not control the outflow of money for this purpose. There was no way to predict how much support would come from professional fees, grants, contracts and gifts so fiscal planning was ineffective. The absence of a well-designed accounting and control system resulted in unmanageable accounts receivable, a critical reduction of cash flow, freezes on salaries and travel expenses, restrictions on capital funds and general deterioration of personnel effectiveness, physical plant and other resources.

Inevitably, the consultants concluded, there was a lack of confidence in management. Also, because of the "structure of governance," financing solutions and overall planning of patient care facilities "have been less than desirable or have failed." Oddly, after all of this criticism, the consultants said, "Some feel that if

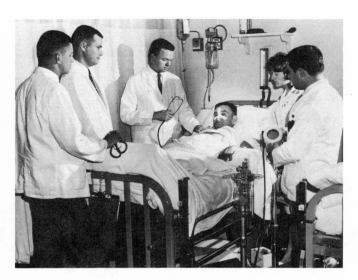

Many of the patients in University Hospital were slow in paying for their care and Bob Terrill could not get sufficient budget and personnel to collect delinquent accounts. (University of Oklahoma)

'prudent' management had been exercised, none of the above would have occurred. This charge can neither be supported nor refuted except subjectively. Unfortunately, there has been enough evidence of mismanagement that the latter is generally accepted and blown out of proportion." It was hard to tell precisely what the consultants were saying. How much mismanagement had actually occurred? How was it measured?

To correct this myriad of problems, Herman Smith Associates had solutions—immediate solutions and long range solutions. The immediate steps Jack Dumas recommended concerned the financial and organizational stability of the hospitals and the center. In their effort to "design and install a fiscal management system," the consultants brought in a team of eight full-time and eight part-time people to get bills out to former patients and their insurers who owed money to the hospitals.[6]

Bob Terrill believed he could have accomplished the same goal if he had been authorized to spend the money to bill and collect the delinquent accounts. Terrill had been in a kind of "Catch 22," knowing the bills had to be collected but unable to get authorization to pay sufficient business office manpower to get the job done. It often happens that consultants can recommend and achieve action which managers on the scene are unable to get through, even though both advise the identical solution to the problem. Terrill looked back on those days with these comments:

In part, we had problems getting enough people but we also had problems getting enough space. We built an accounting office in the basement of the hospital which was the first time we had any place at all; before that we were in various houses around the place. We were able to pull them [the accounting and billing personnel] together and begin working. We needed more people and we needed more space.

I understand in talking with Jim Rice [former University Hospital assistant administrator] and others who were there while this was going on, they [the consultants] simply pulled accounts and got them to pay which would have paid eventually anyway. You can step up the whole process and get your money in quicker and I'm not saying you shouldn't do that. But I don't think they captured money which was lost.[7]

The consultants took major credit for reducing an estimated $3 million shortfall to $1.7 million by collecting hospital accounts and installing "a wide range of fiscal and administrative reforms." But the latter included a freeze on salaries and travel and because the wages of lower-paid employees had been frozen for more than a year, the consultants warned of future labor problems. Jack Dumas also claimed, through their effort, "fiscal and administrative responsibility had been achieved and they would soon be able to assure 'the greatest of doubters' that fundamental and lasting changes had been made." Therefore, they recommended the legislature provide a supplemental appropriation of $1.7 million to cover the expense of the current year; $777 thousand for operations and $955 thousand to open the new University Hospital building. They warned the supplemental appropriation was only a stop-gap to keep the center from being closed at the end of June, 1973, and the amount of money needed for the next fiscal year (1973-1974) would be substantially higher. Herman Smith Associates recommended a minimal supplemental appropriation sufficient to keep the OUHSC standing in place until a long range plan could be worked out and presented to the legislature. They warned that relations with faculty and personnel were critical, particularly concerning their futures, and the situation at the Center was "extremely brittle if not volatile" at that time.

The consultants admitted they had insufficient knowledge or insight to recommend appropriate governance for the entire University as it related to the State Regents for Higher Education and the legislature but said the University Hospitals needed to relate immediately to a university organization which was "strong, supporting and understandable."[8]

Jeptha Dalston, the newly appointed hospital administrator, and a number of the clinical chiefs thought the hospital needed a board of trustees which would define the role of the hospitals, articulate policy, relate the institutions to the community and state and provide talent and judgment of business leaders to the decision-making process. The consultants concurred. They also agreed the hospitals needed independence in order to respond to the demands placed on a teaching hospital and should not be "buried in the organizational morass of an academic, health sciences center and treated as a laboratory for students." If the situation were left as it was, the consultants were convinced the hospitals were "programmed for disaster."

Jack Dumas then recommended the hospitals become a "separate entity" within the University, fully accountable to the O.U. Regents through the president. To appreciate this recommendation, the attitude then current should be noted. Historically, most universities which did not control their teaching hospital facilities were anxious to gain either ownership or at least full operating control. The consultants were aware of this, but their recommendation that the administration of the hospitals report direct to the president of the university implied that the medical faculty and the vice president at the Medical Center would have no direct authority over hospital operations.[9] Dr. Sharp explained his position:

> We made a survey of what universities around the country were doing with teaching hospitals—Chapel Hill, Temple, Pennsylvania, Texas—and found we all had exactly the same problems. It seemed to us, basically, as desirable as it was for the university to control the teaching hospitals, and that meant the professional staff—the doctors—to insure the right environment for instruction and research under the conditions that existed at that time, there was simply not enough money for us to do that.[10]

Herman Smith Associates also recommended the Health Sciences Center be governed along the functional lines of other colleges. This meant removing the "Executive" and "Director" words in Dr. Eliel's title so he would become Vice President for Health Sciences, reporting to Dr. Sharp for academic programs only. "Other functional vice presidents and administrative officers [at Norman] would have authority for non academic matters." The consultants also recommended centralizing support services on the Norman campus insofar as possible. This would help "break

New buildings were beginning to rise in the Oklahoma Health Center in 1972 as the old residential neighborhood disappeared. (OHSF Collection)

down the artificial barriers" between the Norman and Oklahoma City units and the image of two distinct campuses. These recommendations were reminiscent of Dr. Hollomon's organizational approach in *The Future of the University.*

A proforma budget for the hospitals was prepared by the consultants, covering full activation of the new Everett Tower, for a total of 478 beds. They listed three alternatives which might be followed if operating funds were *not* significantly increased: relieve the hospitals of the obligation to admit charity patients; operate only the 214 beds in Everett Tower and scale down supporting services accordingly [an alternative very similar to the one which got Bob Terrill fired]; or shut down the hospitals completely which would effectively close the medical school.

Jack Dumas was quite aware of the way out of this money crunch. Just who originated the idea may never be known, but the Herman Smith Associates recommended the transfer of ownership and control of Children's Hospital to the State Welfare Commission, effective July 1, 1973.[11] Jeptha Dalston said:

> Intuitively, it occurred to me then, as well as in retrospect, it was quite apparent Lloyd Rader was not going to bring the full force of power, money and influence to the benefit of the Health Sciences Center unless he owned it. Jack Dumas was influenced by Lloyd; he deferred to him. When it appeared Lloyd wanted Children's Hospital, Jack changed his logic.
>
> There was a lot of speculation at the time but I really

don't think Rader wanted both of the hospitals. As I talked with him and understood him—and I've wondered about it a lot—but sensing the man, [it appeared that] he could achieve what he wanted to do *without* that adult hospital. He just didn't need that one, too. It got him too close to the university. And the one thing that Lloyd feared was the university. I rarely saw him anxious, but I did see him anxious in meetings a couple of times; he was really intimidated by the university.[12]

From his vantage point in Governor Hall's office, Larry Brawner recalled: "At the time, we thought it was *our* idea, which goes to show you the genius of Lloyd Rader, if in fact he put it together. The university had no choice but to give up those hospitals [because of] the funding mechanisms of the Constitution."[13]

This proposed transfer had the advantage of taking the charity patients to the source of charity money, the Department of Institutions, Social and Rehabilitative Services (DISRS). The Department had two cents of the four cent state sales tax earmarked for its use and the booming Oklahoma economy in the early 1970s made more money available each year for these services. The legislature conveniently could thrust additional social service-related responsibilities on Lloyd Rader, DISRS's astute and dedicated director. This was not a new practice, by any means, and the Department had become a garguantuan operation. In 1973, it administered about $325 million in state and federal funds providing welfare and health services for the poor and the sick. So it was natural for the legislature to take the problem of the University Children's Hospital to the source of the money rather than appropriate money from general state funds to solve the problem. However, not all state legislators agreed with this practice. Senator John McCune was one:

> I've always been opposed to earmarking sales tax to the Welfare Department. They end up spending more money than we [legislators] appropriate and we are responsible to the people; they are not. I think we should have the responsibility of making the decisions of what money goes where.
>
> But that's what they've continued to do over the years. Anytime they [the legislators] come up a little short, they transfer that particular agency to the Welfare Department and can stop worrying about its funding.

Asked about the tendency of legislators to be more interested in roads and education than in social services, McCune, who had been in the Senate since 1968, said, "I've never been in the situation where I've had

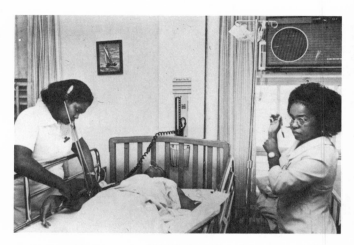

Nurse aide Lacey and LPN Caroline Curry care for a patient in Children's Hospital. (Caroline Curry)

to make those decisions but I would hope we were responsible enough we would not let down anybody dependent on that department, either needy or ill."[14]

Fundamental to this recommendation, according to the consultants, were these conditions: that the legislature generate capital funds to replace the Children's Hospital; that diagnostic, treatment and support service be shared where possible to reduce operating costs; that a board of directors be created by the legislature consisting of state officials, O.U. Regents and university deans and administrators to formulate policy for Children's Hospital operations; that management be coordinated between University and Children's Hospital; and that conflict over treatment of adolescents and young adults be reduced so patients may be admitted to the hospital best equipped to care for the patient. Also, if patients were admitted specifically and exclusively for teaching purposes, it was proposed the university would be responsible and pay for this care from their educational funds.[15]

Physicians reacted differently to this idea of turning Children's Hospital over to the Welfare Department. Jolly West, while no longer personally involved at Oklahoma, thought it was fine:

> I look at results. Jim Dennis's grand design was going no place for lack of resources until that transfer came. As far as I'm concerned, whatever works is right!
>
> If you were to ask me to name three men, outside the faculty, who exerted an influence that shaped what was to become a great center, I would name Mark Everett, George Cross and Lloyd Rader. For many years, Rader was seen as somebody whose responsibilities were almost on the other side of the fence. Welfare was competing for taxpayers' dollars with health and education. But Rader was not a narrow man and he always saw

Lloyd Rader, Director of the Oklahoma's Deaprtment of Institutions, Social and Rehabilitative Services. (Department of Human Services)

how health, education and welfare related to each other. He pitched in when he could, he understood, he was a smart man and not a selfish man. He understood the uses of power and played on the political system like an expert on a harmonica. Particularly with regard to children, he was determined to see that good things happened there and in the long run, I think to a considerable degree on his account, they happened.[16]

Dr. John Schilling did not agree:

Academically, it was the ultimate of disasters when the university lost their hospitals. By the same token, I was very close to Lloyd Rader over the years in a variety of ways because he helped us with patient referrals, the medically indigent, when we needed patients and I sat on his advisory committee. I always thought that Lloyd Rader was sort of the "Herbert Hoover of Oklahoma." He was the champion of the poor and it really didn't make much difference how he did it! But he did do it and he was honest. I can see in a power structure how this would happen.

But we lost the University Hospitals because we couldn't fill them clinically. I just think that's a disaster and the university ought to have back the control of the University Hospitals.[17]

From the viewpoint of the president of the university, the situation looked this way:

We concluded the university would not resist this move to separately finance the hospitals with state funds. We felt the primary obligation we had was to assure quality patient care and a proper environment [in which] to educate doctors and other health care professionals. We were not able to provide that money.

Many of the legislators felt they were taking the hospitals away from the University. I kept seeing newspaper references to that, so our strategy was quite successful. I had a number of legislators come to me later and say, "You know, we didn't take those hospitals away from the university. You *gave* them to us, didn't you!"[18]

The Herman Smith organization also had long range solutions for the ills of the University of Oklahoma Health Sciences Center. Governance seemed to the consultants the greatest barrier to effective operation. While they had no suggestions as to what changes were appropriate, they strongly recommended the O.U. Regents determine how better to communicate with and relate to state agencies and the legislature. They again predicted "with near certainty" if the sensitive and complex issues of hospital governance were not resolved, the problems discussed in their report would recur with increasing intensity.[19]

Jack Dumas said serious underfunding compounded by major cutbacks in federal funds required a close look at the university's educational programs with possible merger, reduction or elimination of programs and possibly colleges. Dr. Sharp commented:

There was a very high public concern for health care in Oklahoma. Somehow, people felt we had fallen behind in that and we really deserved not only a better center but all the benefits that flowed from it so people would not have to go to Houston or Mayo's in order to get the first class medical treatment that Oklahomans ought to have. At the level of leadership in the private sector in Oklahoma, I think there was a great deal of that feeling; that public and private resources ought to be devoted to developing major and acceptable higher education facilities surrounded by and mixed with private facilities in terms of clinics and hospitals and research, the fusion of which, working together very closely, would provide unusual strength.

That's part of the excitement I sensed when I came. After I'd been here a little while, I discovered that, in the public sector at least, we didn't have all that kind of money. So we kind of fought a guerrilla war for about four years (1971-1975).... That's not really quite the right term to use.... We were engaged in fighting brush fires, trying to work out ways in which we could reach those ultimate goals without too many compromises.

But during those four years, when it was so formative and tentative, I had people all over the state asking me, "Well, is the medical school really going to be open next year?" Those were the strenuous years and the word "crisis" was often used but there were aspects which took on a temporary crisis nature. For example: the federal government precipitously withdrew funds at various levels, for research, capitation grants, etc. Each one of those hit us particularly hard because we were operating the whole thing marginally anyway and to accommodate to those losses created very difficult situations.[20]

The consultants advocated reorganization of the Medical Center on a functional basis with much of the decision-making power moving to Norman. The Medical Center faced federal funding cutbacks of $2 million and possibly another $300,000 reduction in state support. They said that any money previously available from the State Regents for Higher Education for the care of indigent patients had to be redirected toward teaching or there would not be any health professionals to care for the sick poor regardless of who underwrote the cost.

Long term funding for adult patient care was possible, they said, if these *alternatives* were selectively followed: DISRS reimbursed University Hospital for the full cost of the medically indigent; [or] the adult hospital were converted to a non-profit community organization or a *separate* state agency with its own board. If successful, Children's Hospital could then be placed under this board [ironically, this control was destined to shift in the opposite direction]; [or] the responsibility for indigent care were placed directly on the counties of Oklahoma or the law were changed to place total responsibility for this care on DISRS; [or, finally] the clinical (junior and senior) years of the College of Medicine were transferred to Tulsa. Of course, this latter alternative would have eliminated the need to operate any university teaching hospitals in Oklahoma City but would have seriously complicated the indigent care problem.

The consultants also strongly recommended permanent separation of "educational costs from uncompensated medical care, installation of a financial management system capable of setting rates and rendering bills for identifiable costs of patient care, and a full scale feasibility study to see if reprogrammed academic and service programs could be supported."

A moratorium was recommended on further construction except those projects underway or funded.

Norman Bagwell. (Oklahoma City Chamber of Commerce)

The consultants said a campus-based university teaching hospital was essential and the V.A. Hospital affiliation was critical to the academic program of the University of Oklahoma. After a superficial review, they concluded the new Presbyterian Hospital site was too far away to provide "efficient physical interrelationships" which might help the University Hospitals.

Herman Smith Associates deplored the "welfare-indigent hospital model," pointing out that this concept had been eroding for 25 years through Social Security and other health care legislation. They went on to predict that national health insurance was inevitable and would replace the current myriad of medical care assistance programs. In addition, they forecast the return of the federal funds then being cut off from the University of Oklahoma Health Sciences Center. Twelve years later, neither of these events had come to pass so it would appear that the experts often cannot predict the future any better than their clients![21]

The Oklahoma City Chamber of Commerce responded quickly to the Herman Smith interim report by producing a position paper the very next month, April, 1973. A medical education task force, headed by Stanton Young, also represented the areawide health planning effort of the Community Council with Ray Anthony and Norman P. Bagwell, who were successive chairmen of the planning committee, and Charles L. Bennett, managing editor of the *Oklahoman* and *Times*. Donald S. Kennedy, Dean A. McGee and Charles Vose, Sr., trustees of the Oklahoma Health Sciences Foundation, were on the committee.

This group recognized the Medical Center's financial crunch as a serious crisis which could place "the entire future of health care in Oklahoma…in danger of progressive deterioration." These leading citizens pointed out that to reconstruct the medical education system would cost far more tax dollars than to shore it up then. Additionally, future generations in Oklahoma would not have high quality medical care if the health sciences education system were allowed to founder.

In describing the problem, the task force said there were not enough health professionals to go around and made these comparisons of manpower to population:

Professionals per 100,000

	Oklahoma	U.S.
Physicians (M.D.'s and D.O.'s)	117	171
Dentists	35	47
Nurses	234	353

The central mission of the Oklahoma Health Center was to produce more health manpower for the state and this mission was in jeopardy. Since 1966, the student enrollment at the OUHSC had almost doubled, from 920 to 1,750, and the construction program was well along so there had been substantial progress. The task force said, "It is absolutely vital to the future of Oklahoma that the Center continue to train health manpower in growing numbers." They urged the legislature to act promptly and decisively to solve this financial crisis.

With hospital billings and collections improved and a better cost control and management system in place, the Chamber of Commerce made its recommendations for future action, either agreeing or differing with the consultants.

The task force supported the idea of a $777 thousand supplemental appropriation for the current (1972-1973) fiscal year's operation and $955 thousand to open the new $12 million, 214-bed Mark Everett Tower. They warned that the federal government could demand its grant money back if the university did not move into the new facilities in a reasonable period of time. An increase of $3.7 million for the teaching budget was also recommended for 1973-1974 in view of the cutback of federal support as well as the growth of academic programs. The legislature was urged to commit the "revenue-sharing" funds which were just beginning to flow to the states under new

policy of the Nixon administration. The task force supported the O.U. Regents request for a $4.4 million increase to operate the University Hospitals. The chamber apparently saw the value of the hospitals' dual purpose of teaching and indigent care and was not offended by the "indigent care model" of the teaching hospital.

The idea of separating the hospitals from the university was summarily rejected by the chamber. While it recognized the desirability of separating the hospital budget from the teaching budget, the task force said if a new hospital board *were* created, it should be *directly responsible to the O.U. Regents.*

The chamber, consistent in its philosophy, also opposed the idea of turning over Children's Memorial Hospital to the Welfare Department. The task force saw this transfer as a desperation move by the university, not a solution in the long range interests of the Oklahoma people. "Separate funding to finance the operating budget of Children's Hospital, either directly through the legislature or from welfare department sources, appears to the task force to be the only viable answer."

The members said private patient fees of faculty doctors should continue to be used as enrichment funds to pay resident salaries, buy equipment, books and other essentials. Furthermore, these funds should *not* be placed in central accounts run by the State and their use thus be subject to approval outside the Medical Center.

The chamber thought the legislature did not understand the purposes and advantages of the "health campus" idea and pointed out how the Oklahoma Health Center enhanced the teaching effort of the university and contributed to the production of health manpower. The task force said that adequate funding by the legislature would stimulate further private funding of affiliated health organizations on the OHC campus. They agreed with the consultants that the remaining $8.5 million in HERO bond funds should be spent promptly for the university building program, despite the decline of federal matching money, and further recommended the university submit a total long range plan to the 1974 legislative session.

The Chamber, in a carefully worded statement designed to avoid offending legislators, agreed there were too many cooks in the kitchen and recommended that "the legislature should delegate to the educators and the health professionals the development of plans and administrative decisions by which these broad goals can be met and the policies of the

"*Grand Finale.*" (*The Oklahoman*)

legislature carried out. The O.U. Regents' responsibility for the operation of the Medical Center should be reaffirmed by the legislature and the regents should be held strictly accountable for efficient and effective management."

A year earlier, the legislature had passed a resolution authorizing the creation of a College of Osteopathy and a branch of the O.U. College of Medicine in Tulsa. It was obvious to the Oklahoma City Chamber of Commerce that promoting new medical edu-cation programs in Tulsa at the same time the health sciences programs in Oklahoma City were critically underfunded did not make a lot of sense, particularly at a time Oklahoma ranked *last* among the 50 states in its per pupil expenditures of state money. For this reason, the task force emphasized that "estimates of the need for people with special skills must be kept up to date and look ahead to how many doctors, dentists, nurses and other health experts Oklahoma would need in the future." Then available resources should be allocated on a priority basis on "appropriate evidence for new and expanded training programs as the gap between the demand for and the supply of health manpower in Oklahoma closes." The chamber insisted the survival and improvement of existing programs in the O.U. Medical Center ranked at or near the top of the priority list.

They also observed that merely graduating more doctors who went elsewhere for residency training and stayed where they went would not solve the problem of getting more doctors to practice in Oklahoma. In 1971, 40 doctors out of the 111 medical school graduates went to out-of-state internships and residencies. It was patently obvious the state needed additional post-doctoral training opportunities before additional undergraduate medical education programs were created or the entering class of the O.U. College of Medicine was expanded.[22]

CHAPTER 25
THE PERILS OF PAUL: 1973

Jim Killackey, medical writer for the Oklahoma Publishing Company, came to Oklahoma City in the spring of 1973. As a former reporter for the *Tulsa Tribune*, he had these first impressions of the O.U. Health Sciences Center:

It seemed like there was very little understanding in the legislature how a medical school and health sciences center are run. That seemed to me the basic problem; a legislature which was relatively naive as to how they're operated. The medical center was run primarily from the Norman campus at that time. It didn't seem there was enough leadership or defined role at the health sciences center which could articulate their needs, explain how they were operating. It was some kind of transition period. I can remember Paul Sharp jokingly saying his tenure would last longer if he didn't have a medical school; that was an administrative burden on a university.

It seemed there was a mandate for Oklahoma City to become a tertiary center for the whole state. Jim Monroe [who became a member of the board of University Hospital] talked about the impact of University Hospital on Idabel [Oklahoma, his home town] and I thought, "Gee, that's a long way away."

My wife was going to nursing school at O.U. and everything seemed to be so spread out and disorganized. Of course, they were in those houses. It seemed as though the health sciences center succeeded in spite of itself. Certainly, if you went over to Children's or University or V.A. or the medical school, it seemed like a chaotic situation, both from an administrative and facilities standpoint. Everything was helter skelter and it was going to take both facilities growth and administrative expertise to kind of put it all together.[1]

Paul Sharp was particularly aware of the latter. Tom Tucker, then a university attorney, assessed the situation:

Prior to this time, the [state] government had not supported the health sciences center in any substantive way. It authorized a college of medicine and a college of nursing, gave it a pittance and said, "Good luck!" The people who built it—the physicians who came out here and did that—were frontier types. They were wheeling-dealing—and I don't mean that adversely—entrepreneurial types, admirable frontiersmen. What they built strongly reflected their personalities and mannerisms. When this health center got big enough, it was, in a bureaucratic way, like civilization coming to the fron-

Medical writer Jim Killackey, recently of the Tulsa Tribune. (Oklahoma Publishing Company)

tier. We had to hang up the guns and put a little law and order into this environment.

Early in that period, near the end of Dr. Eliel's term, we suffered what seemed to me basically an organizational collapse. I've never seen anything quite like it. People had paper on their desk and they didn't know where it went next. They didn't know what to do. The bureaucracy, in its inspired but patchwork, hip-pocket design, no longer meshed well. It was simply essential for someone in Dr. Eliel's position, if he was going to manage the center, to impose some kind of system.

Among all the individuals, as there would be in a frontier town, there were those who said, "This is progress and I'm going to participate in this new growth." There were others who said, "I'm going to move on someplace where I can [still] be an individual, where we don't have these terrible bureaucratic constrictions." Some moved "further West," as it were, and some stayed to participate as councilmen, law officers, mayors and all the positions a town develops as it goes on from being a frontier community.

The center had outgrown its bureaucracy, which broke down because it could not cope. We had a young, vig-

The North Oval of the Norman campus. (University of Oklahoma)

orous environment without any depth of administration. An improved bureaucracy, while largely and roundly damned at the time, was needed.

In Norman, the university had a very old, sort of stale environment that had more bureaucrats than they knew what to do with. So it seemed very reasonable to take some of the well-seasoned bureaucrats who knew how to manage all the systems and bring them to the health sciences center. In essence, the center would simply import an already-made bureaucracy to get the place on its feet. And we did!

But it had some very interesting and unexpected results. Those people on the Norman campus who were anxious to control the health sciences center picked their most loyal and dedicated subordinates to come up and manage those areas which would be subordinate to them. [This followed Jack Dumas' recommendation for a functional organization based in Norman.] But what happened within a very short period of time: the trusted and loyal subordinates advised their superiors in Norman, almost invariably, "If you want to make the damn decisions, you get up here and make 'em!" Essentially, they seceded from the union.

I have a theory on this. Let me put it in an anecdotal framework. As counsel for the university in Norman, if a librarian had a legal problem, he would write me a memo and send it across the sidewalk from the library to the administration building. If he had a written response in two weeks, he was thrilled with the service. In the health sciences center, if Sid Traub [chairman of radiology] had a legal question, he didn't write a memo. He picked up the phone and called and if I couldn't tell him the answer on the phone right then, he would assume I'd call him before the day was over. The time frame is so much shorter.

That time frame is largely set by the urgency of dealing with life and death crises and it affects everyone. If you have an electronic problem in Norman, maintenance will get around to it when they can. At the health sciences center, maintenance men take [radio] alarms home in their truck so if something goes wrong with [equipment such as cardiac] monitors, they can come back in the middle of the night and fix it. The expec-

tation of immediate action on the part of health professionals, who must act immediately themselves, affects the administration. If you need something done or you need some information, you need it *now*. The pace is entirely different.

Tucker laughed lustily as he recalled that:

I drew the diagrams for Jack [Dumas' proposal for a functional organization based in Norman] in the very first instance and thus, myself, shared monumental blame for that disaster. Though, in hindsight, I don't know what else we could have done to have dealt with this emergency. To train a bureaucracy takes a good period of time, they *do* get things done, and the center needed one. We did solve that problem but the organizational design clearly was not functional for the long term.

The Norman campus is egalitarian and this quality extends to all members of the academic community except students. The president and the deans are basically faculty members and they engage in discussion about the course of events. The Health Sciences Center is basically hierarchical. The intern can be disciplined by the resident, the resident by the attending physician; the attending physician can be called on the carpet by the chief of the service who, in turn, can be dressed down by the chief of staff. This is very much a matter of rank which so permeates the place and is so completely understood, it is not even a topic of discussion. When the president came up here for his first discussion with the medical faculty, which was in a state of turmoil and distress as a result of what was referred to as "the Norman invasion," I talked with him about this distinction and suggested that if he were to be successful in addressing the faculty he would have to *understand*, and *believe*, and *feel* he was the commander-in chief.[2]

It was apparent to President Sharp that cutbacks were necessary in order to keep the Health Sciences Center in operation. Services like media information and the alumni office were eliminated. Dr. Eliel and the president had little choice but to withdraw all support for the Wakita project. Nancy Davies remembered the February 8, 1973, regents meeting clearly:

It was in the meeting held in Enid, when I was president, that we finally dropped Wakita. It was embarrassing and painful to me because a lot of my friends from the area were at the meeting, including John Day Williams. It was a good idea but unfortunately, we wouldn't keep it. It was never meant to be permanent; it was always billed as a demonstration project but we felt like we'd cut it off a little soon and just left it hanging.[3]

The Wakita banker understood the university's

The steam and chilled water plant. The front of the build-ing (right) is on a rise above N.E. 8th Street. (University of Oklahoma)

The OHC campus is laced with tunnels carrying huge utility lines. (University of Oklahoma)

plight but he, too, believed the project was deserted prematurely:

> The med center got into trouble and the State Regents jumped on them. The way I understood what happened; the State Regents told the University Regents they had no authority to get into this kind of venture without the State Regents approval. Of course, the health center was having other problems at the time. So they gave us two weeks' notice that they were going to cease to be the operator and we had to take it back over. Our little operating company, at that point, had $700![1]

Because Dr. Graves was there when the university withdrew its support, Wakita still had medical service, but Tom Points said, "Knowing what I do today about Wakita, I probably wouldn't have done it…without backup financing which we were promised from the university. They were going to subsidize the physicians until the project took off."[5]

Paul Sharp was having his problems at the State Capitol as well. With the Herman Smith and Richardson reports filed, legislators were looking askance at any and all activities in the Health Sciences Center. The university proposed to expand the steam and chilled water plant, taking it over from the O.U. Development Authority and legislative hearings were held on this and other subjects:

> The steam plant was way out there…looked like it was in the "southwest 40" and everybody was really quite critical. "What are you putting it way out there for? The health science center will never reach that. That's just stupid!" I can remember any number of critical comments. In fact, we had so many arguments and the legislators were always dragging us over the coals about that and the various bond issues, I used to say to my colleagues, "Every time the legislators start talking about it, I both heat and chill!"

There were two or three things in the hearings the

Senator Ed Berrong of Weatherford…"around the barn." (Oklahoma Observer)

legislators were concerned about. One was whether the regents were familiar with the problems in the health science center. It quickly transpired that Huston Huffman and Nancy Davies were well informed which was, I think, a surprise to many legislators. Second, we tried to make it quite clear the University of Oklahoma didn't have the money in higher education [to make the University Hospitals first class institutions.] I remember

Senator Berrong was always talking about the indirect way in which we managed the hospitals. There was a phrase that became a standard recollection of those hearings…"Berrong's Barn." He was always talking about the way we were always going around the barn rather than doing things directly. I suspect he was quite right because in the nature of things, we could not afford the direct approach. We had to get money from many sources. At that time, the Feds were cutting back on grants to health care professionals and as a result we were experiencing withdrawal of federal money which aggravated our problems considerably. Inflation was another factor that was terribly important. We just couldn't ride that inflation.

There was a lot of concern in the legislature about what appeared to them the affluence of the health-related professions as symbolized by the Oklahoma Health Center. I've often speculated about this. I have a very deep feeling that much of it was a personal resentment against doctors, their monetary success, their prestige and their social status.

And to Paul Sharp, it did not appear the doctors were about to put any of these on the line in behalf of medical education:

How wonderful it would have been, as we went through those legislative hearings, if the (state) medical association had spoken up. They were always there but they never said anything. It was as if they were disinterested observers who were watching the Titanic go down! I often wondered, "What *was* their real interest and role in seeing that medical education was kept at a high level?" I remember having a sense of both frustration and awe that they could stand there silently, watching the ship go down.[6]

CHAPTER 26
ENTER LLOYD RADER: 1973

It did not take the legislature much time to respond to the recommendations Jack Dumas had included in Herman Smith Associates Interim Report on the University of Oklahoma Hospitals, submitted March 9, 1973. As E.T. Dunlap recalled:

Hamilton couldn't get out of the university people the kind of information he wanted so the legislature didn't have confidence in the hospital management. The reason was, one, they wouldn't collect the bills; two, they came to the legislature with bad information and they couldn't bring proper information; and three, there was no leadership over there. Everything was in an acting capacity. So [Senator] Hamilton said, "By gosh, we'll take those two hospitals away." Well, I went to see Jim because I was opposed to that notion. He wanted to give them both to Lloyd Rader who could take sales tax money and fix them both up.

I told him these were teaching laboratories for the education and training of physicians and of course, to some extent, of dentists and nurses. I said these hospitals ought to be a part of the University Health Sciences Center. He said, "We can't support them. Lloyd's got some extra sales tax money and he can fix 'em up and manage them. He'll do a better job of managing them." I never did agree it was good policy to do this. Rader said he didn't have the money to fix both of them. He finally agreed to take the Children's Hospital.[1]

Lloyd Rader remembered discussions about the proposed transfer:

So far as this grandiose transfer Dumas outlined, I never heard of it until Jack unveiled it. I had never seen him before. Well, as I sat there, the wheels began to turn and I decided that taking over Children's would be all right. I could see that I could finance it without any problem. So I began to dream about where I could pick up federal money. I never said a word.[2]

But when Senator Hamilton suggested to Mr. Rader that he take over *both* hospitals, he turned white as a sheet and said, "Hell, no, Jim! We'll all be broke together because I can't finance it." The senator insisted, but Rader was just as insistent:

Like hell! I didn't ask for this job. I came over here to be welfare director, not funeral director. Sonovabitch's not going to fold up around *my* ears. Get you another boy![3]

Children's Hospital as it appeared when Lloyd Rader took it over. The Basic Science Education Building is at the top right. (University of Oklahoma)

On April 25, 1973, the Senate passed and sent to the governor the bill transferring operation of University Hospital from the O.U. Board of Regents to a new board of trustees. It appropriated $5,494,771 to operate and maintain the hospital, a boost of $2.2 million over the allocation in Governor Hall's original budget. This was made possible through use of federal revenue-sharing funds which President Nixon had initiated. The bill also provided for the transfer of $1,635,000 in bond funds to equip and activate the new Everett Tower and a half million dollars to renovate "Old Main".[4]

The Children's Hospital had already been transferred to the public welfare department by a previous bill but another half million dollars in bond funds was made available for renovating Children's. Both transfers were scheduled to take place on July 1, 1973. The new board of the University Hospital was to be composed of six members appointed by the governor and confirmed by the Senate and three members selected by the O.U. Regents. Chancellor Dunlap said, "I caused Jim Hamilton to write into the law a special committee of educators to advise the board of trustees that was going to run the University Hospital."[5] Dr. Eliel talked about the transfer of the hospitals:

It was strange for the university to give away its hospitals and I think it was rather without precedent. Other university hospitals reviewed at the time, such as the one at Duke [University], demonstrated that the relationship with the university is probably the best way to go. Nevertheless, the regents were sufficiently disenchanted with the magnitude of the problem, they wanted to get it out of their hair.

The investigation by Robert E.L. Richardson was my nemesis, if anything ever was. I think it was largely a political move by Governor Hall. The investigator was undoubtedly appointed because of the problems we'd had with Wakita and University Hospital and all kinds of collateral problems which arose because of suspicions the faculty was not utilizing its time properly and was not generating enough income. The question was whether or not the state was getting a proper return for its investment in the faculty for teaching and patient care—whether the guys were spending too much time in research—issues of this kind. The investigation broadened, partly for political reasons, because academic institutions are often the butt of legislative scrutiny and inquiry. The matter of persuading legislators and politicians to adequately support higher education is always a thorny one. If they can pin something on the institution that would justify some kind of punitive action in terms of appropriations, they like to grab it—it makes good publicity.

The fact we didn't give Richardson all he wanted came out again in legislative hearings, so finally, I just went to Paul Sharp one day and sat down with him in Norman. The relationship between Paul Sharp and me was always very cordial; he played it quite straight with me. I said to him, "I want you to let me know if you think I am a political liability to the presidency of the university." He said, "Well, you've asked me an honest question and I'll give you an honest answer. Yes." So I said, "I'll resign anytime you think it is appropriate." Not long after that I submitted my resignation. That's the way *that* came about.

I like Paul Sharp very much and he appreciated my candor in dealing with him. Basically, I think he was a very good university president but, being an historian, he had no concept nor did his staff of what a medical center was all about. I think that was the main fallacy in trying to assume more responsibility for managing the Medical Center from Norman. But, on the other hand, I think the magnitude of the problems almost dictated…in fact, he was virtually directed by the legislature to "take charge and get rid of this mess!"[6]

On June 1, 1973, William E. Brown, D.D.S., dean of the College of Dentistry, donned the additional hat of Acting Provost of the O.U. Health Sciences Center, a chapeau he was destined to wear for the next 22 months.

Jeptha Dalston had been appointed administrator of the University Hospitals on January 12, 1973, two months after Bob Terrill left. Asked how he got this opportunity, he said:

Orthopedist and sports medicine expert Don H. O'Donoghue chaired the new board of trustees of University Hospital. (University of Oklahoma)

I was just there. I had disconnected myself from the hospital for reasons unrelated to all this crisis. I was asked by Len or Gordon Deckert, who was chief of staff at the time, to lend a hand with their management committee. So I went to help and got acquainted with Jack Dumas and those people.

I was interested [in becoming administrator] and the consultants said, "You seem to have the credentials and you speak the language. You are acceptable here." They recommended me and Eliel offered me the interim job but I told him I'd take it only as a permanent job. I was excited about the whole scene—not about what happened to Bob or the general condition, which I thought was very bad—but I was excited about the opportunity to make a contribution to something I liked very much. I felt those hospitals were important and I wanted to do something positive.

In commenting on his new board, which was headed by Don H. O'Donoghue, chief of orthopedics, and which took over on July 1, 1973, Dalston laughed as he recalled his earlier experience:

When I was at Children's Hospital, Don had an orthopedic unit over there. We had some tough times; I think I was a thorn in his side. I wanted to do things administrators do and that interfered with what he wanted to do. I thought he was cantankerous, obstreperous and narrow minded. That was *his* hospital and

186

he didn't want anybody messing around in it and I was trying to do what I thought I was supposed to do. I grew to love Don O'Donoghue, absolutely love that man! My personal relationship with him was very warm and very close.

The board came as a result of legislation. The first meeting was up in Lloyd Rader's conference room, which I resented deeply. There was the issue of who would be secretary to the board. Lloyd or somebody wanted a legislator to do that but I felt, if it's my board, *I'm* going to do it. I didn't want the person who filled this role to be a spy for somebody else.

In that first meeting, Bryan Arnn got up to leave and Lloyd said, "Where are you going?" Bryan said, "I've got an appointment. I did not think the meeting was going to last this long." Lloyd said, "Well, you can't leave. Sit back down!" Bryan said, "I'm sorry, but I've got an appointment," and he left. Lloyd held court up there in his conference room and [almost] all the subjects did his bidding.

That board met every week for three months in order to know enough to get into it and fulfill their trusteeship role. My relationship with them was productive, positive, businesslike and very rewarding. I think the board had credibility with the legislature.

Lloyd Rader certainly was "the man to see" on the larger issues. He never expressed himself on our internal operations but I spent an awful lot of time in Lloyd's court because our hospital was financed by him. The relationship between Children's Hospital, which he operated, and our hospital was integral. I think he was a tyrant, a benevolent dictator for areas of his interest, but he could be ruthless. I think he was ruthless with Pete Riley [Harris D. Riley, M.D., chairman of pediatrics]. Pete sold his soul to Lloyd and Lloyd did him in. But I think Lloyd was a political figure who just operated that way; I'm not making value judgments, just observations. That's the way the political world works. If somebody gets in the way, you get rid of them. He did that with Bob Terrill.[7]

Lloyd Rader agreed with Dalston's observation of his modus operandi. He said:

I never meddled in *anybody* else's business. I've been guilty of a lot of things but not meddling in other department's business. I learned that lesson many years ago. I ran my own shop. Anybody got in my way, I knocked hell out of 'em, politically—not personally, but when they got in the way of my department and my programs.[8]

Jenell Hubbard talked about life at University Hospital with Dr. Dalston as administrator:

I'll have to say it was a lot more exciting working for Jep simply because of the way he operated. He was so in-

Lloyd Rader had his own administrative style. Here he confers with Senator Miller. (Department of Human Services)

tense in everything that he did. Everything had to move so fast, you'd think at times you'd pushed yourself to the absolute limit and he'd demand more. I worked 16 hour days for months getting the Everett Tower ready to open. And the resources available weren't sufficient to carry out some of the things he wanted.

But things were beginning to improve. He was the most knowledgeable person I had worked with about the inner workings of the legislature. We would spend hours and hours providing the kinds of information the legislature needed. We were always preparing for what were known behind the scenes as "dog and pony shows," presentations for the new board and the legislature…charts, graphs, statistics, that sort of thing.[9]

In April, 1973, when the legislature approved the transfer of Children's Hospital to the welfare department effective July the first, Lloyd Rader hit the ground running. Less than a month later, on May 23, 1973, the public welfare commission approved $1.3 million to remodel and expand the 1928 vintage hospital. Plans were under way and were expected to be put out for bids on July 1. The idea was to make the hospital functional for acute care until a new 150-bed facility could be built to the east, a matter of three to five years. Then the old children's hospital, planned to be connected to the new hospital, would be used as a long-term care hospital. Plans included expansion of pediatric clinics and the emergency room, which would be open 24 hours a day beginning in July.[10]

Of course, this approach did not follow the original Oklahoma Health Center plan at all. Bill Campbell commented on long-range planning as a process:

Too many times we give lip-service to the idea and we crank out a few typewritten pages and put it together with some photographs, send it to the printers and have

187

a thousand copies cranked out, distribute it to all the proper people who look at it and say, "How nice!" and throw it on the shelf and that's the last of it. But if we have a plan and head in the general direction—we may detour slightly, left or right—but as long as we keep our eye on the goal and keep trying to achieve that which was conceived 'way back, something good will come of it.

But too many times, it's merely words on paper and a few graphic presentations and nothing ever comes of it. We just keep right on doing the same *expedient* things. We put this building here because this man has a loud voice in the legislature and this is what he wants so if we can get "X" million dollars through his efforts, by all means put it there. Even though it's not the best place for it, we'll live with it— make do. I'm not suggesting we do that constantly but we do it enough it disrupts things rather severely.[11]

Arthur Tuttle expressed his opinion. "The decisions made by DISRS [the welfare department] to completely rebuild an obsolete, outmoded children's hospital and spend huge amounts of money...personally, I don't believe that money was spent wisely. I did not believe it at the time it was occurring and the end result is not a contemporary hospital."[12]

Bids for remodeling and expanding Children's Hospital were not opened until November 6, 1973, and, at $1,790,000, came in 40 percent higher than estimated. Meanwhile, welfare department work crews had begun improvements, so by that time the original hospital was being expanded to the north and to the south. Frosty Troy did not like the way Mr. Rader went about it:

We had a lot of duplication, a lot of waste, a lot of overlap....No one'll ever know. The first year he took that thing over, the figure hangs in my mind, he had a surplus of somewhere around $50 million, just give or take. Then he decided he'd start the reconstruction over there and he'd pay cash. Well, we had a lot of facilities problems in a lot of the eleemosynary institutions in Oklahoma at the time. Contrary to all of the little annual reports you saw, with all their beautiful facades, we had yet to do it *right* in the programs for which those sales tax dollars were earmarked. They [the other institutions under DISRS] just went by the boards while he paid cash [at Children's Hospital]. That was the dumbest thing the state ever did. That was really, really spectacularly ignorant to do it that way.[13]

According to Donald B. "Don" Halverstadt, M.D., the pace and amount of activity in renovation, expansion and preparation for separate accreditation of Children's Hospital by the Joint Commission on

Frosty Troy, editor of the Oklahoma Observer, did not agree with Rader's priorities. (Oklahoma Observer)

Accreditation of Hospitals was such that it became apparent it was more than one man could be expected to handle. Pete Riley had been chief of staff and medical director of the hospital since July 1, 1973. Halverstadt told how he started to work for Lloyd Rader:

On Christmas eve [1973], a representative of Herman Smith consultants was sent to talk to me. I never knew exactly why they picked my name out of the hat, but the story goes that Jack Dumas raised my name to the commission and the director and suggested the duties in Children's Hospital be split up and a chief of staff be appointed separate from the medical director position. They suggested my name for reasons I have never been aware of. Up to that time, I had never done anything administratively.

I was sitting in my little office over in Children's Hospital; I was running the pediatric urology service at that time. He simply asked me if I'd like to be chief of staff. I said, "Well, don't know. Be happy to talk about it." He walked off.

A week later, I had a meeting in Lloyd Rader's office on Saturday morning [New Year's eve]. We spent four hours, with Mr. Rader recounting the history of the agency and the importance which he felt resided in the development of the Children's Hospital. Then he asked me if I'd be willing to help him.

At that point, I think he felt the session was over, but I said, "Well, there are a few things you need to know about me before you take me on." We spent four more hours, with me doing most of the talking. At that point in time, I was going through the evolution of some dis-

Pediatric urologist Donald B. Halverstadt became chief of staff at Children's Hospital on January 1, 1974. (Presbyterian Hospital)

agreements with policy in regard to the full-time faculty in the university [over a newly established site-of-practice regulation ordered by Governor Hall]. I told Lloyd Rader my disagreement with the philosophical posture of the university was such that I either would have to resign or be fired in the not-too-distant future and he might be taking on more of a liability than an asset. I think that intrigued him; he had spent his life championing the underdog. The upshot was he said more than ever he wanted me to be chief of staff. So on January 1, 1974, I started.[14]

On February 1, 1974, the welfare commission said it would present to the legislature a plan for a new, 150-bed children's hospital to be built to the east and connected to the old building. It announced a 39 member, state-wide planning committee for the building, named Dan Macer to head it, retained Hudgens, Thompson, Ball and Associates (HTB) as architects and hired the Herman Smith consultants to assist.[15]

It appeared that Oklahoma was fated to have an academic, tertiary health care center whether or not state leaders countenanced the idea or felt Oklahoma could afford to operate it. Certainly, when it transferred the University Hospitals to the Welfare Department and to a board which had funding separate from the State Regents for Higher Education, the legislature took a giant step toward the level of support the Medical Center had always needed and never got. As Dean McGee said, "I feel the Welfare Department's involvement was all to the good."[16]

The Oklahoma Health Center juggernaut moved ahead, despite legislative consternation, impoundment of federal construction funds, changes in university administration and other transitory impediments.

CHAPTER 27
THE COST BATTLE: 1970-1975

In the early 1970s, with both the demand for and the cost of health care rising, the idea of federal payment for health care was becoming politically more acceptable. Efforts in this direction had been made even before the Truman administration in the late 1940s when the Murray-Wagner-Dingell bill was beaten down with the cry of "socialized medicine." A generation later, federal health care again became a political issue in the 1964 elections. Congressional candidates discovered vast, grass roots support for medical help for the aged. Although organized medicine lobbied vigorously against it, Medicare became effective in July, 1966. Opposition to the principle of federal health care, i.e., payment by the federal government for the cost of health services, evaporated.

Five years later, in early 1971, rising costs motivated President Richard Nixon to call attention to the "crisis in the national health care system." Public opinion had so changed that it appeared certain some form of general health plan would soon arrive, with the federal government playing a key role. The argument was not over *whether* but *how*. Many ideas were set forth. President Nixon proposed "Family Health Insurance" for the poor and near-poor, replacing Medicaid and providing preventive, hospital and surgical care. The tab was estimated at $2 to $3 billion a year and the money was expected to come from general federal revenues. Catastrophic insurance, covering all persons, would pay hospital bills after 30 to 60 days of care and 80 percent of medical bills over $2 thousand. This cost was estimated at $2.3 billion a year from Social Security funds. Both would use the private insurance system. And there were many other schemes:

"Ameriplan," proposed by the American Hospital Association, would create 400 Health Maintenance Organization (HMO)-like health care corporations nationally. This would eliminate Medicare and Medicaid, with the federal government paying the premiums for the poor and the aged. The hospital group did not estimate Ameriplan's annual cost.

"Healthcare" was a plan drawn up by the Health Insurance Association of America. It proposed to extend private health insurance coverage to all Americans, with the states and the federal government

"Get Away From Me With That Filthy Stuff—You... Socialist!!" (Washington Post)

paying the premiums for the poor and the near-poor. Federal standards would assure uniformity of benefits. Employers with substandard plans would lose half their tax deductions for premiums until they upgraded their plan. Cost: $3.2 billion the first year.

"Human Security." The most sweeping plan of all, this national health insurance scheme was written by Senator Edward "Ted" Kennedy and Representative Martha Griffiths, both Democrats. It would be totally federal, eliminating Medicare, Medicaid *and* private coverage. It would emphasize group practice and comprehensive care. The authors estimated it would cost $53 billion a year but HEW judged the tab would run closer to $77 billion.

"Catastrophic Illness," reintroduced by Senator Russell Long of Louisiana, would protect 95 percent of all Americans, paying hospital bills after the first 60 days of care and 80 percent of an individual's medical bills exceeding $2 thousand. Cost: $2.2 billion, financed by extra Social Security taxes.

"Medicredit." This was the American Medical Association's entry, allowing people to choose their own health coverage by giving them income tax credits to buy insurance from private companies. Credits would be scaled to income, with the federal government buying coverage for families paying less than $300 federal income tax a year. The main feature of this plan was that it did not change the system of delivering care, a principle highly important to the private enterprise-oriented medical profession, and it provided maximum freedom of choice within the private insurance system. It was expected to cost the government $16 billion annually.

"Minimum Health Benefits" was a blend of HMO, Ameriplan and area health-education centers (AHECs) recommended by the Carnegie Commission on Medical Education. It would create federally-chartered regional health corporations financed by individual, federal and employer group insurance payments. Fee-for-service charges would be eliminated; doctors would be salaried employees of the corporation. They had not yet calculated how much this arrangement would cost.

"Optional Extended Medicare" was put up by Senator Jacob Javits, a New York Republican. The idea was to extend Medicare benefits to all Americans under 65 who chose it. People could buy private insurance if they wished. It emphasized comprehensive care through prepaid groups, HMO's and private insurance plans. Again, the government would pay the premiums for the poor. All others would pay through payroll taxes on individuals and employers. Proposed to be implemented gradually, this plan was expected to cost $66.4 billion a year when fully operative.[1]

Inevitably, there were heated clashes between the proponents of the various plans. Organized labor and Senator Kennedy predictably and vociferously opposed the administration's plan. The Senator charged it would give Americans too little medical care for their money. Leonard Woodcock, head of the United Auto Workers union, called the Nixon plan "a cruel hoax" and contended it was "developed to accommodate special interests rather than the general public interest."

Defending the Nixon ideas, HEW Secretary Elliot L. Richardson said it would use the best of the present health system and improve it, rather than starting all over again with "a single, post-office-like nationalized system." At a Senate health subcommittee hearing, chaired by Senator Kennedy, Secretary Richardson also made a wistful health wish. Reporting that Americans' health was improving despite many problems, he said, "I do wish medical scientists would discover how to enable us to be as obese as Winston Churchill, smoke as much as he did, drink as much as he did and live as long as he did—and, oh yes, be as smart as he was—instead of discovering that we shall survive longer if we give up tobacco, alcohol and fine foods."[2]

The arguments about national health insurance were destined to continue for many more years than it then appeared would be required to arrive at a way

Edward M. Kennedy and Elliot L. Richardson clashed on ways to improve health care. (Washington Post)

to assure protection for all Americans against the high cost of health care. Thirteen years later, while the effort to enact national health insurance stalled out, the problem which gave impetus to this effort had become greater than ever.

For seven years, the Oklahoma Health Sciences Foundation had assisted the institutions planning for shared services in order to hold down the rising cost of health care at the Oklahoma Health Center. While subcommittees of the Operations Committee had labored hard and long, it became obvious that sharing central facilities was strikingly unsuccessful and conditions for further promotion of this idea were not favorable. After 81 meetings, the Operations Committee was officially discontinued; the last one was held on June 6, 1973. Of the 21 proposed sharing projects, ranging from parking to emergency treatment facilities to a computer center, only the steam and chilled water plant had been implemented, a completion rate of 4.76 percent. As Al Donnell had commented earlier, "It was a noble thought, much easier said than done."[3]

Perhaps it was naive to believe that even closely related organizations on the same campus would cooperate to the extent of sharing central facilities and services and thereby avoid duplication and save money. Stewart Wolf was right. Twenty years later, it is less difficult to understand why this process of sharing, so hopefully and enthusiastically begun and pursued, did not work. The answer is territory and pride! Health professionals and health institutions want to *control* the services which are essential to their operations and

The new director of the Oklahoma City Veterans Administration Hospital was Dan Macer. (Dan Macer)

Governor Hall and Speaker Carl Albert. (The Oklahoman)

their success. They also want to believe that because they have the latest and best of everything, they *are* the best. They love to point with pride to their institution. Why, then, was the steam and chilled water plant an exception to the twin motivations of ownership and ego? It was not. Who cares where the heat and the cool air come from?

The tenure of V.A. hospital directors is about as short as that of academic health care center provosts and medical school deans. During the 20 years this history covers, eight directors served the Oklahoma City Veterans Administration Hospital for an average length of stay of 2.5 years. Dan J. Macer, a fellow in the American College of Hospital Administrators, became director on May 18, 1971, the fourth one since 1964. He had served with the V.A. for 27 years but came to Oklahoma City from the University of Pittsburgh where he was assistant vice chancellor and professor of medical and hospital administration in its graduate school of public health. Perhaps it was this latter experience which stimulated his interest in comprehensive health planning and cost containment.

Macer had headed the planning committee for the new 150-bed Children's Hospital about a month when, in early 1974, he presented an innovative scheme to bring the V.A., the university medical school and the state hospitals closer together. He thought the Oklahoma Health Center plan was inadequate because:

It left the V.A. Hospital isolated geographically and did

not recognize the tremendous role the Veterans Administration was playing. The V.A. had the majority of residents, the majority of the interns and the majority of the teaching persons from the college of medicine who were on duty in the Veterans Administration Hospital. I felt the plan was moving toward separation and a lack of recognition of this important role. I want to hastily add that I thought the plan was an excellent beginning of a total integration of programming.

There should be one point of entry [for patients] into the Health Sciences Center. This point of entry should then be focused on child and maternal care, the various specialties and adult care, with a closer integration of programming. There seemed to be no reason for the V.A., Presbyterian, University and Children's each having a separate emergency service. I thought the OHC plan needed considerable modification if we were going to have an integration of programming that would best meet community and educational needs.[1]

To pursue this idea, Macer asked Governor Hall's Health Sciences Center Planning and Advisory Committee on March 12, 1974, to approve a $100 thousand feasibility study of expanded resource sharing between the V.A., Children's and University Hospital. This idea had been endorsed by the Oklahoma congressional delegation the previous week, as Lloyd Rader recalled:

We had a hearing up there in Speaker Albert's office—Governor Hall and all the Oklahoma delegation. David had made this affiliation agreement and they were going to get a lot of federal money. Well, you never got anything out of the Veterans Administration in your life you didn't pay for it 10 times. That's my experience down through government. So I walked into Carl Albert's office and all bets were off! I was going to build a little, new, modern children's hospital [on the east] where Nicholson [Tower] stands, which was a parking lot then.[5]

Mr. Rader had been planning to abandon the old children's hospital when the new one was built. "I was going to tear the old one down, just like I tore the old University Hospital down." He continued:

> I was told in Carl Albert's office, "We're going to tie onto the V.A. Hospital." They had this grandiose idea, you know, with these wide walks across there, two levels, possibly three, all the lab work and all that stuff was going to be in that...[double-loaded corridor, bridge building spanning 13th Street]. But, hey, I knew they weren't going to get any federal sharing. Bullshit! I was the only administrator in the bunch that had experience. Not that I wasn't for it, but my judgment was, you wouldn't get anything but promises. You have to be realistic when you are an administrator. You can't just buy dreams, boy. You have to be a cold-blooded, businessman type.
>
> I called up Ed Hudgens and said, "Ed, you gotta build her on the west side." He said it was impractical and I said, "I *know* it's impractical but we agreed in the speaker's office. We had Johnson, the V.A. man, in and we're committed. It has to be. You've got to turn the damn plan over!"[6]

Governor Hall appointed a "Federal-State Sharing Subcommittee" consisting of Dr. Robert "Bob" Mitchell, chairman of the O.U. Regents Health Sciences Center Committee, James Monroe, chairman of the University Hospital Board of Trustees, Stanton L. Young, chairman of the Presbyterian Hospital Board of Trustees and Lloyd Rader, with Dan Macer as chairman. The subcommittee appointed Robert "Bob" Douglass, an architect-planner previously with Herman Smith consultants, to begin the feasibility study. As Douglass recalled, "The objective was to bring the total resources represented...in the Health Sciences Center into a more rational and economical application...." When asked if he actually believed two levels of government could cooperate and share when the institutions on the campus had been trying unsuccessfully for seven years to get together, Douglass replied, "We had the benefit of naivete' and just the kind of impertinance that goes with being a young planner. We didn't know all that history. We listened to Mr.

Macer and Mr. Rader and Governor Hall and interviewed people on campus and came to the conclusion that, yes, it *was* possible."[7]

As Dan Macer pointed out, "There were many things being shared then. For example, many of the procedures being done by Children's Hospital were being done in the V.A. Hospital."[8] Bob Douglass continued: "I didn't know what Mr. Rader's plans were for the old building, but in our evaluation of Children's Hospital, it wasn't *that* old a building, and there was nothing about the services in there that made sense to walk away from. We recommended building a new bed tower on the west and allowing horizontal expansion of existing services and probably saved several million dollars."[9]

Ironically, several years previously, Mr. Rader had advocated abandoning the entire health center and building out north:

> [There was] a section of land due north of here, just this side of Edmond, almost on a line with Mercy Hospital. I was on a deal to buy that [with some others], put a little ranch in. I thought we'd be getting a little thin and didn't buy it. So I went to Henry [Bellmon] and I said, "Now, Henry, just abandon all that crap down there." You had Everett Hospital stickin' up there, too. It was about the time Mr. Loy [Bert Loy, business manager of Mercy Hospital] made the decision to not come down here. I said, "Bert, you proved to be the only smart one in the whole damn bunch!" I propositioned the governor to move the entire center north where you'd have expansion. The whole damn thing."[10]

As planning began on this altered track for maximum sharing, Dan Macer proposed to assemble the people involved, such as the acting provost of the university, the dean and department heads of the college of medicine, the administrator of University Hospital and others who would be affected. But that was not the way Mr. Rader operated. He told Macer, "Forget it. We're not going to deal with the hired hands. You and our committee'll make the decisions."[11]

Asked if Mr. Rader displayed his skepticism about this project openly, indirectly, covertly or in any other way, Bob Douglass answered:

> Mr. Rader never failed to convey his skepticism in all those ways! My impression was he felt very incovenienced by the "do-goody" flavor of this attempt to seek cooperative arrangements. I think he felt he could run his show better and more effectively without the inconvenience of having to cooperate with others.
>
> But despite his skepticism, he eventually accepted the concept and then supported it effectively through some

Architect Bob Douglass and Dan Macer discuss the model of the Federal-State Sharing project. (Dan Macer)

pitals had to buy—food, drugs, medical supplies and the like. Inflation, then running 11.1 percent a year, was pushing the cost of operation up while the federal government was trying to keep the lid on with price controls. Jeptha Dalston was caught in this squeeze.[13]

The Federal-State sharing idea gathered momentum. At mid-year 1974, Dan Macer unveiled plans prepared by architect-consultant Bob Douglass for the concourse-bridge building between the V.A. Hospital and Everett Tower. Lloyd Rader had no choice but to follow the Congressional mandate to build on the west side of Children's Hospital so it could be linked with the concourse building. He apparently had agreed with Douglass that the original, 1928 building "wasn't *that* old" for he had embarked on $20 million of construction on all sides of it. A $1.8 million addition on the front and a $989,000 expansion to the rear were under way. The construction of a $10.6 million, seven-story addition on the west for acute care inpatients began in October. Bids were received on November 7, 1974, to add a three-story, 100-bed unit to the east for convalescent patients. These expansions were designed to raise the bed complement from 106 to 348. The money was budgeted from "growth revenues and other sources" rather than through the issuance of revenue bonds.[14]

Lloyd Rader was not the only one displeased by the order to reconfigure the plan for Children's Hospital. Dr. Vernon Scott was upset. "The addition to the Children's Hospital ruined the front of the Basic Science building. It really irks me. We [the university] lost control when Rader took over." And Arthur Tuttle had much the same opinion: "I have the feeling that the Department of Human Services, largely under the direction of L.E. Rader, did the greatest damage to the overall concept of the health center. I think the concept that was developed by Gorsline, Lackey and Frankfurt, Short, Emery and McKinley— a major hospital center [consisting of] a series of bed towers interrelated to a podium—is a much superior concept."[15]

Called the "main street" of the health center, the two or three story concourse building proposed by Macer was designed to connect the west side of the V.A. Hospital, bridge over 13th Street and continue southward to 11th Street, with easy access to Children's and University Hospital as well as the Basic Science Education Building. Bob Douglass explained the goals:

> We were trying to get an arrangement whereby critical

stages of its development. I have never worked with quite as colorful a person. My naive beginnings in this project were really those of an architect. I wanted to get things in functional relationship—connections—proximities. He was a lot more attuned to the political and financial strength of the respective entities. Every time I'd want to get Children's Hospital connected to or integrated with the University Hospital, Mr. Rader would bang on the table and say, "Mr. Tucker...." For some reason, he was convinced through most of the project I was Mr. Tucker [perhaps Tom Tucker, the university attorney]. "Mr. Tucker, don't you try to brother-in-law me again!" Somewhere there must be a story about getting tied up with your brother-in-law who doesn't have any money.[12]

Lloyd Rader had every reason not to get tied too closely with that improvident "brother-in-law," University Hospital. The bare bones supplemental appropriation from the legislature for FY 1974, coupled with pressure from the governor's office to hold down expenditures, as well as control by the Cost of Living Council so charges remained well below the cost of providing hospital care, made management of University Hospital a hand-to-mouth nightmare. During the Nixon price control period governing hospital rates, controls did not apply to the commodities hos-

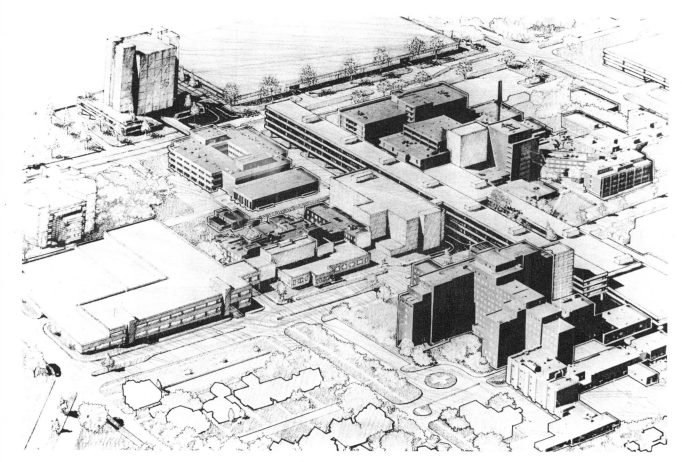

Artist's conception of the Oklahoma Health Center with the proposed Concourse Building connecting the VA Hospital, University Hospital and Children's Memorial Hospital. (Robert Douglass Associates)

and expensive resources of this place could be used most effectively in a cooperative way. The most critical and most expensive resource then, and probably now, was the time of the professional staff, so proximity and a convenient, weather-protected physical connection, especially connecting the "right things" with the "right other things", was the dominant single concept.

We also tried, through trading and relocation of responsibilites, to achieve a certain amount of centralization. When we started, there were 140 sharing arrangements in place between V.A. and the other entities in the center. So sharing wasn't a new idea.

The V.A. at that time had extended benefits to the dependents of veterans [for specialty care not available elsewhere in the community] so we had a man's hospital with responsibility to provide specialty care for wives and kids in some fashion. Across the street, we had a kid's hospital and across the street the other way, we had a good general hospital so we thought the common ground that would allow the rational homogenizing of these [services] was ambulatory care. We were going to

fill the void between the three hospitals with an ambulatory care zone that could be used every sort of way. After all, it was all one medical staff. Even though the political and administrative levels felt they needed above all to protect their turf and identity, at the level where the care was delivered, they were already unified.[16]

Dan Macer said the V.A. Hospital needed 176,353 net square feet of additional space or a total of 446,560 net square feet. By relocating clinics, laboratories and administrative offices in the new building, space could then be freed in the hospital to reinstate 105 beds previously closed. The V.A. director proposed "renting" six unused operating rooms in Everett Tower, thus saving the $1 million it would cost to duplicate them across 13th Street. Also, 81,795 net square feet of space would be released in University Hospital for use by the colleges and hospitals in the sharing program. In summary, the concourse building was planned to house clinical laboratories, specialty labs, rehabilitation medicine, ambulatory care, radiology and pharmacy.

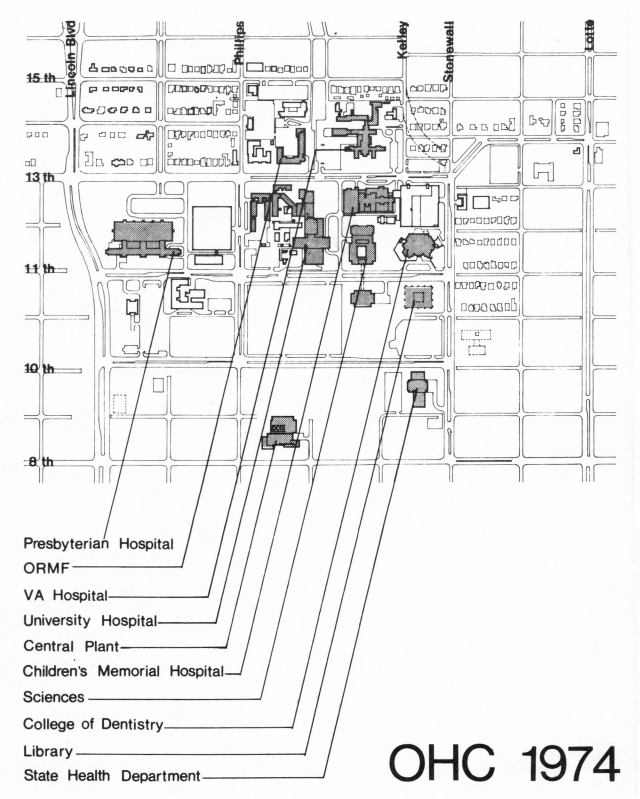

Presbyterian Hospital

ORMF

VA Hospital

University Hospital

Central Plant

Children's Memorial Hospital

Sciences

College of Dentistry

Library

State Health Department

OHC 1974

(Robert Douglass Associates)

196

The specialty labs included respirology, electrocardiology, hematology, gastroenterology, neuromuscular procedures and the blood and blood products laboratory. The plan also extended westward to include Presbyterian Hospital. An east-west pedestrian bridge over Phillips was proposed to link Presbyterian with the University Hospital so patients and staff could circulate freely among the four hospitals. A great idea.[17]

In 1974, Douglass estimated the project would cost $60 a square foot or about $15 million. A year later, detailed design had reduced the square footage to 240,000 and inflation had upped the estimated cost to $20 million. Senator Henry Bellmon, who was very supportive of the sharing concept, introduced this request into the V.A. appropriation bill and construction was expected to begin in late 1976.[18]

A year and a half after schematic plans were unveiled for the Concourse/Bridge building which would become the heart of the Federal-State Sharing program, Dan Macer, his committee and their consultant, Bob Douglass, published the development plan dated February, 1975. By achieving connection and centralization, the plan expected to accomplish these aims: 1. Create a new Ambulatory Care Center which would meet the projected needs of the V.A. Hospital, Children's Hospital and the University Hospital. 2. Satisfy all requirements of the proposed V.A. Hospital 5-year expansion program. 3. Establish centralized radiology, clinical laboratory and food preparation services with ready access to the V.A., University and Children's Hospital. 4. Integrate the internal circulation of the three core OHC hospitals so they could operate as a single functional unit. 5. Make centrally located space available for teaching, research and public service functions. 6. Reclaim space for 105 beds in the V.A. Hospital previously closed by Mr. Macer to accommodate critical ambulatory care needs. This was to be accomplished for the cost of remodeling instead of the cost of new construction. 7. Achieve

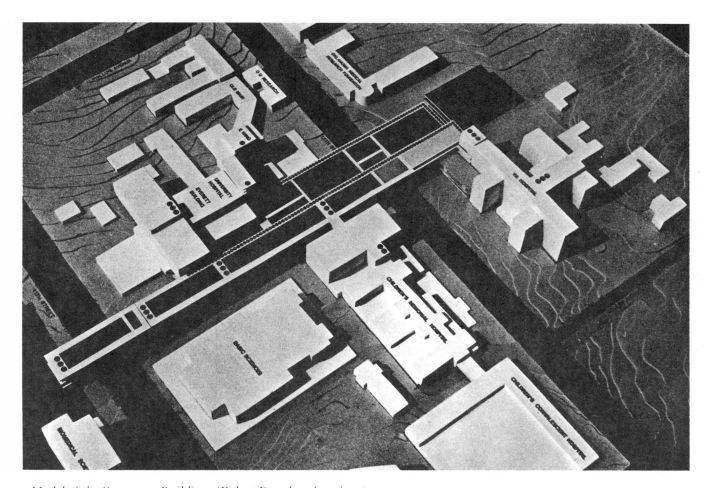

Model of the Concourse Building. (Robert Douglass Associates)

197

effective utilization of space and facilities in University Hospital and the colleges of the University of Oklahoma, while satisfying a significant amount of the V.A. Hospital expansion requirement. 8. Effect. savings of several millions of dollars in capital expenditures and operating costs. 9. Establish a functional framework for growth of new programs and services. 10. Accomplish all of the above with less than the total amount of new construction projected in the V.A. Hospital expansion program.[19]

It was not difficult to see why this idea was attractive to Senator Bellmon and the Central Office of the Veterans Administration. Potential savings to three of the four involved institutions were estimated in the range of $10 million, with a half million savings in operating costs each year. A survey the following year indicated that another $345 thousand in travel time would be saved by having the connection between the University and the V.A. Hospital across the street.

Curiously, the summary mentioned only *access* to the Children's Hospital. Services to be shared by or with the DISRS-managed institution were conspicuously absent. Under the heading Laboratories in the development plan, the assumption was that Children's would have selective participation initially in the single clinical lab that would centralize all V.A. and university lab work. It looked as though Mr. Rader was not about to be "brother-in-lawed" by either institution.

The relationship between the V.A., University Hospital and the medical school, the major participants in the sharing program, was carefully thought out from concept to organization and the concourse building was tailored to fit these relationships as well as the physical space between 13th Street and Stanton L. Young Boulevard. Access, circulation, connection, orientation, functional integration, parking, the character and design of the structures, phasing and growth and cost implications were all examined. The steps required to implement the plan were programmed.

All that remained was to line up local legislative support for the idea and get commitment for the money to match V.A. funds to continue planning and ultimately to finance this $35.5 million project. With the Federal-State Sharing Program Development Plan under his arm, Dan Macer set about to get the backing of the new governor, David Boren, and the Oklahoma Legislature.[20]

On the national scene, although Herman Smith Associates had predicted in 1973 that national health insurance was inevitable, a proclamation that had been made by Representative Wilbur Mills (a Democrat from Arkansas who was chairman of the House Ways and Means Committee) and others as early as 1971, half of the decade had gone by without the passage of such a program. By 1975, for a number of reasons, the concept was in trouble. The burgeoning cost of Medicare for the aged and Medicaid for the medically indigent flashed a yellow caution light to the members of Congress. Moreover, inflation was accelerating and the benefits of these two federal programs were specified as health services rather than denominated in dollars. As hospital costs climbed 15 to 17 percent a year, the expense of these entitlement programs exploded.

In addition, there had been a major split as to the best approach for providing national health insurance. Senator Edward "Ted" Kennedy (D-Massachusetts), the leading proponent, wanted the federal government to handle costs and administration but President Nixon favored a major role for the private health insurance industry. By the time Kennedy and Mills had moved toward a compromise with the Nixon position in 1974, the President was mired in the Watergate scandal. Succeeding Nixon, Gerald Ford had other things to think about, including double-digit inflation during an economic recession, growing deficits, rising unemployment and the collapse of the American military effort in Vietnam.

Moreover, the Social Security program was going broke, an eventuality predicted for 1980 or 1981 if drastic changes were not made. Medicare was a responsibility of the Social Security Administration and, while the retirement and disability benefits were paid from funds separate from Medicare, the revenue source and the responsibility were the same. A *Sunday Oklahoman* editorial on May 25, 1975 observed, "It isn't clear how the already troubled Social Security System could support the incalculable additional burden of womb-to-tomb national health care."

Although the previous January, Oklahoma's Carl Albert, Speaker of the United States House of Representatives, had assured the chairmen of the appropriate committees that "national health insurance would be one of the first bills—if not the first"to come before the House in the 94th Congress, it was still in limbo at the end of 1975. President Ford threatened to veto any new spending legislation because the federal government had experienced a $43 billion deficit for fiscal year 1975 and anticipated a $90 billion shortfall the following year. National health insur-

Note the striking similarity of Mercy Hospital to the proposed 1963 University Hospital shown in Chapter 4. (OHSF Coll.)

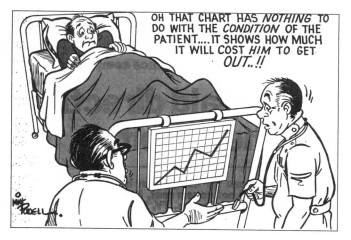

"The High Cost of Being Sick." (The Oklahoman)

ance, visualized since the Truman administration as an easy solution to the problem of making health care accessible to everyone, had disappeared like an attractive but ethereal mirage.[21]

In central Oklahoma, the rapid expansion of hospitals in the four county [Oklahoma, Cleveland, Canadian and Logan] area had resulted in a surplus of beds, an easily predictable result of construction activity during the early 1970s. The 1969 Oklahoma City Chamber of Commerce Report II on financing new hospital construction had forecast a glut of 763 extra beds in 1974, a surplus they said probably could not be fully utilized for seven more years. The Areawide Health Planning Agency (AHPO) expected the oversupply to grow to 1,000 beds.[22]

In October, 1974, a few months after Mercy Hospital had moved into its new facilities on the northwest edge of the city, it was 50 patients short of the 150 average daily census Sr. Mary Coletta said it needed to break even. It was losing $100,000 a month. The room and board rate for the all-private room hospital was $65 a day.[23]

AHPO estimated it cost a general hospital $18,250 a year to maintain each unoccupied bed. At this rate, the surplus beds in central Oklahoma were costing the community about $14 million a year. As Presbyterian and Mercy were opened, occupany rates in the hospitals at Edmond and Guthrie declined, prompting an AHPO task force to recommend "the planned closing of hospitals experiencing less than 50 percent inpatient occupancy—based on licensed capacity—for two consecutive years." This idea caused so much concern among the doctors on the staffs of these hospitals that AHPO ruled it out the next day, February 14, 1975. An influenza epidemic that winter had temporarily filled the available beds and the hospitals could not open more beds immediately because of the nurse shortage.[24]

To add to the confusion about the need for beds, the federal government, under new legislation called the Health Planning and Development Resources Act, decided to set up a new system. This did away with the state "A" agency and seven areawide "B" agencies in Oklahoma and instead proposed "health service areas" for which planning would be carried out by "health systems agencies (HSA's)."[25]

Thus, the struggle to hold down rising health care costs went on. By the end of 1975, there was the promise that federal-state sharing on the OHC campus would result in significant savings. Elsewhere, there appeared to be no relief in sight.

CHAPTER 28
THE COLLEGES: 1970-1974

In addition to building accommodations for existing institutions and planning more new buildings, brand new educational programs were emerging, health professions not previously taught in Oklahoma. William D. "Bill" Stanhope was brought in to organize an educational program for physicians associates:

It began because there were two separate needs that came together in 1969 and 1970. First, there was the obvious problem of rural health manpower. Secondly, there was a significant problem with the non-dean's committee V.A. hospitals, such as the one in Muskogee, Oklahoma. Dr. Schottstaedt, Dr. Steen and Dr. Lynn were concerned with the whole question of rural health manpower and primary care. At the same time, there were some people in the department of medicine, namely, Jim Hammarsten and Bill Horsely, who were concerned about the quality of services in the V.A. Hospital at Muskogee. These parties got together and thought the introduction of the P.A. [physicians associate] might be an answer to some of the rural health manpower problems. The V.A. people felt that if you could find somebody to do a lot of the day-to-day ward activities of patient care, you could make the place attractive for young, academically oriented physicians. Without that kind of person to do much of the "scut-work," the V.A. would never be a fun place for young physicians to practice.

So in 1969, the [O.U.] regents were approached and in 1970, the leadership at the center made the decision to start a P.A. program. In July, 1970, the request was put before the State Regents. Not only did they approve the program but they mandated that it be started immediately! We were told we had to have the curriculum developed, students identified and recruited, selected and in class by the 4th of October, 1970.

One of the first things I did when I got here in August was make a protocol visit to the State Board of Medical Examiners and found the secretary to be a fellow named Dr. Edgar Young, who was then in private practice in El Reno [Oklahoma]. It turned out that Ed had known Gene Stead, who started the whole P.A. business at Duke [University] and had in fact been to Duke and some of the conferences. So Dr. Young was a very active proponent of the P.A. program. It was just a serendipitous blessing so that when we really got down to the business of developing the law, in September, we had the support of the State Board of Medical Examiners.

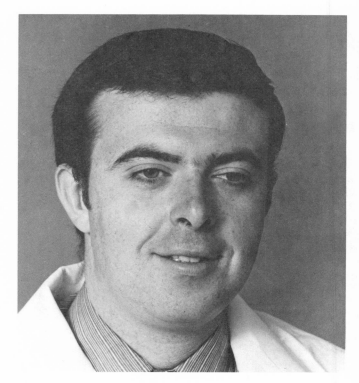

Bill Stanhope headed the new Physicians Associate program. (University of Oklahoma)

There were never any serious problems that I was aware of. When we got ready to negotiate for teaching time and curriculum, Bob Bird sent out a one-line memo to the faculty of the college of medicine, "We are starting a P.A. program and your cooperation is expected." Period! Now there were a lot of skeptics. A lot of people said, "Gee, I don't think this is going to work." But there were never any active opponents that I knew of. We started with nine students, one never showed up for class, one dropped out and we graduated seven two years later, in October of 1972.[1]

"Talkback Television" made its debut on the Medical Center campus on February 1, 1971. The State Regents for Higher Education established a closed-circuit, microwave television network connecting the Medical Center, the O.U. campus at Norman, Oklahoma State University at Stillwater and the University of Tulsa. This televised instruction system was designed to take the college classroom to industry and business in Oklahoma City, Tulsa, Bartlesville, Muskogee, Ponca City, Enid, Duncan and Ardmore. The

200

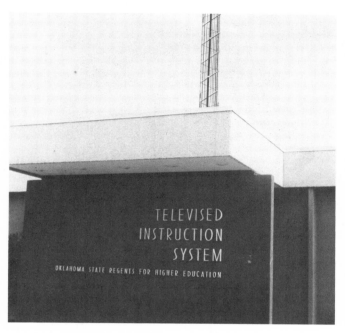

Talkback TV headquarters. (OHSF Collection)

Mark Johnson was Chancellor Dunlap's physician. (University of Oklahoma)

system not only allowed the employee/student to see and hear the professor but to talk back to him as well during class and counseling sessions.

The universities offered seminars and short courses in addition to regular course work. Halliburton Services, Continental Oil Company, Phillips Petroleum Company, Kerr-McGee and Oklahoma City's Fidelity Bank were some of the organizations in which receiving stations were set up throughout the state. Also, students on one campus could take courses offered on another campus without having to commute. By the fall semester that year, the system was in full-scale operation. The sending station at the Medical Center was in a low, flat-roofed, windowless building of rose-hued precast concrete located on Phillips where 14th Street tee's in. It had a 300-foot tower behind it with four microwave dishes on the top and three others at lower levels.[2]

Dr. Mark Johnson, who by this time had gone off the O.U. Board of Regents and rejoined the volunteer faculty of the medical school, did not like the way the State Regents had commandeered the site for this transmitting studio/classroom:

One day when I drove into the lot behind the medical school to park, I noticed many of the parking areas had been blocked off. When I learned what was happening, I became curious about how the State Regents acquired that land. First of all, the State Regents are prohibited by law from owning land. I realized, though, the television authority legislation empowered them to do this.

The president of the O.U. Board of Regents was a friend of mine and I said to him, "Hey, I'd like to see the motion the University Regents made granting this land to the State Regents. Did you sell it to them?" He said, "No, they just told us they wanted it." Then I asked Len Eliel and Bob Bird about it and they said, "We didn't give that land to the State Regents."

So I went back and reviewed all the minutes and there was not *ever* one resolution to dedicate, lease, sell or give that land away. There wasn't even an acknowledgement that the State Regents had moved in and taken over that land, which is, in effect, what they did. It is illegal today!

E.T. Dunlap is a patient of mine so I asked him, "How come you stole that land?" And he said, "Now, Mark, there you go...." But I said, "You stole it and I may decide to sue you all and the regents of the university," and he said, "Now, what would you sue us for?"

"First, for taking my parking place and second, for stealing land from the University of Oklahoma and not paying 'em for it!" Of course, E.T. just kinda laughed.[3]

The dean of the School of Health was quite optimistic. On February 4, 1971, Dr. William W. Schottstaedt announced that Murray-Jones-Murray, Tulsa architects, would start on working drawings that week for a new $10 million building to house the school. The U.S. Department of Health, Education and Welfare (HEW) had approved the Medical Center's application for a $7 million federal construction grant the previous July "subject to the availability of funds."

Tulsa architects Murray-Jones-Murray built this model of the proposed School of Health. (Oklahoma Journal)

Dr. LeRoy Carpenter, new Commissioner of Health for Oklahoma. (University of Oklahoma)

While the dean had not yet received notification that funds had been awarded, he was confident they would be forthcoming within the year. The federal money would be matched with $3 million in HERO bond funds.[4]

At that time, the three-year-old school was jammed into several residences along 15th Street. The 101,000 square feet of space in the proposed new building would permit the 1971 enrollment of 146 graduate students to triple. It was to be located on 10th Street, across from the new State Department of Public Health building then under construction. The school structure was designed as two interconnected, five and six story towers.

Dr. Schottstaedt's program offered degrees in biostatistics and epidemiology, parasitology and laboratory practice, community health and environmental health, the traditional public health disciplines. In addition, it had developed education in human ecology and health administration. The school awarded four degrees: master of science, master of public health, doctor of philosophy and doctor of public health. Eighteen residents were in postdoctoral training doing advanced work in general preventive medicine, occupational medicine, aerospace medicine and family medicine. The physicians associate program was also based in the School of Health.

These plans were highly exciting and encouraging to the faculty. As Dr. David Steen recalled, they had great expectations:

> I would say that traditionally in the United States, schools of public health have been "second class citizens" as part of the academic community. They are not, in reality, second class people but because of the flow of cash.... Now during the 1940s, post-World War II, with the ad-

vent of preventive medicine programs in the National Institutes of Health (NIH), money flowed into preventive medicine and public health like it had never flowed before. It became very popular on campuses. The head of preventive medicine and public health was invited into many situations because it was through the school of public health access to NIH funds for other research was available.[5]

So with an approved $7 million grant in his pocket and the state matching money assured, Dr. Schottstaedt had only to wait until Washington released the money and public health at the University of Oklahoma would have a new home.

That same month, Dr. LeRoy Carpenter was elevated to state commissioner of health, so the continued symbiosis between the educational programs and the practice of public health was assured. Dr. Carpenter immediately outlined an ambitious program of environmental quality control, family planning and genetic counseling, consumer protection and improved medical services for rural communities.[6]

Another new paramedical program got under way on August 30, 1971. Sixteen young women began a four-year curriculum in dental hygiene, a program initiated by the School of Health Related Professions [now Allied Health] in cooperation with the School of Dentistry. Temporary clinical facilities were set up in the house once owned by Stewart Wolf at 14th and Lindsay, anticipating space in the new School of Dentistry building. Dean William Brown had made application for a $7.8 million construction grant in mid-February but federal money was beginning to get tight. Nancy Davies, who was chairman of the Regents' Medical Center committee, said it was uncertain whether the dental school could open in the fall of 1972. "The dental school needs a $1.2 million addition to the Basic Science Education Building and an $11 million clinical facility. Requests totaling $300 million have been made by health schools throughout the country and only $99 million is expected to be available this year. We have contacted our congressional delegation on this matter and they are working very hard to do something about it."[7]

It was in 1972 that the university's budget problems grew to crisis proportions. Jack Santee of Tulsa, chairman of the university regents OUHSC committee, broached a money-saving idea which Philip "Phil" Smith, Sc.D., who had become the dean of the College of Allied Health, recalled:

> Out of the blue, he announced there was so little money that the University had the option of having five mediocre colleges or putting their money on three good colleges and the regents had agreed that medicine, dentistry and nursing were worth keeping. They proposed to discontinue public health and allied health. Fortunately for us, the State Regents for Higher Education gave O.U. the word that they had created a health sciences center, they had recommended there be a school of public health and a school of health related professions and *only they* could discontinue these schools. Even though they did not discontinue these colleges, appropriations were not increased, so Paul Sharp was faced with the responsibility of doing something to cut down expenses.[8]

Also, according to Dr. David Steen, John Dean, Dr. Sharp's vice president for public relations, made the statement in a legislative hearing that if the legislature did not fund the budget, the university would cancel the school of health. A faculty member went to the press and told the story. Steen said:

> The public reaction to threatened closing of the school of health was about the same as if you were to throw a rock in a gravel pile. Nobody noticed. The public didn't know we existed. Most of public health activity which gets noted is punishing people for selling rotten milk or contaminated food, so it is punitive to the people who really know about it.
>
> Our faculty had the same kind of feeling that anyone has who has committed a lifetime to their work only to have the rug pulled out from under them without any

The University's Vice President for Public Relations John Dean. (University of Oklahoma)

participation in the decision. It was as though someone had said, "By the way, you don't exist any longer!" Ironically, we'd had site visits from outstanding people in the field of public health who had said, "This is *the* school of public health in the United States. This is the school which has the opportunity to bridge the gap between medicine and public health because of the concepts of the people working here."[9]

Dean William Schottstaedt commented:

> What was going on at that time put the Medical Center in a very awkward position because the University felt the same way. President Sharp and the regents of the University were complaining that the Medical Center was the tail that was wagging the dog...that we were taking money away from the Norman campus. There was [just] so much money to go to education and if we got more, that meant they got less. As I looked at it, we did not have any real support from our own [main campus] administration. There was a lot of feeling on the Norman campus that the Medical Center was too big and out of keeping with what the state could afford. Obviously, Dr. Sharp agreed with that even though he was president of both campuses.[10]

Dr. Sharp explained the attitude on the main campus:

> The problems on the two campuses are quite different—costs are quite different, just the whole role of clinical costs, for example. The people at Norman never really understood that. They were always complaining

203

about the health science center budget. Actually it was consistently my judgment that the health science center was more seriously underfunded than the Norman campus ever was. The attitude [of the Norman campus people] was always very critical of the health science center and I think this was partly [a consequence] of envy but it was also partly because they never really understood the difference in functions at all levels in health professional education. We tried to create the sense of one university and worked very hard at it but there were three or four things that work against you. At Chapel Hill, the non-health professional faculties always looked with a combination of contempt and envy at "pill hill." That shocked me and I never did get used to it. When I came to Norman, I discovered that feeling, which is apparently endemic in faculties, was exacerbated by the 25 miles that separated the two campuses. There were occasions in which the two seemed to be hundreds of miles apart. Yet, it would be my observation there were a great many faculty members who did want to work together and saw the urgency of interdisciplinary effort.[11]

Dr. Schottstaedt continued:

On top of that, there were a number of new people in the legislature hostile to developments there [in the OUHSC]. The school of health was investigated by at least three different groups during that last two-year period. They thought there must be something illegal going on because we were able to acquire all those houses without having a special appropriation for doing it. The legislature felt it didn't have control over the School of Health because they hadn't had control over the buying of the houses [on 14th and 15th Streets]. Those buildings were painful because they were the focal point for all of the investigations of the school of health.[12]

On April 27, 1973, it happened. Phil Smith recounted the climax:

It was the biggest shock of my life! We were called down to the Norman campus…all the deans from the OUHSC. We had been meeting regularly with the president and his staff. After finding out from Schottstaedt and me which programs in the two schools could be eliminated, Dr. Sharp announced, "At this stage, we are going to combine public health and allied health and we'll pool the resources of the two colleges."

Eliel may have had some inkling this was going to happen but the rest of us didn't. As we were going out, dumbfounded by what had transpired, Dr. Sharp's secretary signaled me. When everybody was out, Dr. Sharp asked me if I would be willing to serve as the dean of the combined colleges. I was in a state of shock.

The next day, I agreed to be acting dean until a formal search could be made. Then, I told him, if I'm se-

lected, I wouldn't mind that, but I won't accept a direct appointment as dean.[13]

Dr. Eliel had not known what the president was going to do:

As a result of the financial strictures we were being subjected to, the fact we were faced with inadequate appropriations generated a lot of unofficial political activity on the part of some of the graduate students, particularly in the School of Health. They went up and lobbied on their own initiative in the legislature for a better appropriation for the Health Sciences Center. This got back to the president and his vice president for public relations, John Dean, and they were furious. It was not very long after that, at a meeting of the president's council of vice presidents, Sharp announced, completely to my surprise and everybody else's, that Phil Smith would prepare the budget for both the College of Allied Health and the College of Health. [He did this] without consulting me. What this amounted to was a proposal that we consolidate the two schools as a cost-saving measure. I think it was very dubious whether it would have saved us any money but as far as the president was concerned, it represented a gesture to economize in the operations. It also got rid of Bill Schottstaedt.

I had to present this to the legislature in a hearing and unfortunately Paul Sharp wasn't there to explain the problem. So I was left there, holding the bag, trying to explain the president's decision. I didn't do it very well. I remember both Bob Bird and Bill Brown were absolutely furious about the whole situation. That led to a temporary administrative committee of deans who were in an advisory capacity to me, so we could get over the rough humps.

I think if I had been astute enough, I would have raised questions the moment he requested Phil Smith to develop a joint budget. In retrospect, I think I should have resigned at that point because he hadn't consulted me nor given me a chance to consult with our deans. This was just another of the events that contributed ultimately to my resignation. I tend to think that whoever had taken the position at that time, because of the terrible problems anybody would have had to face, would have fallen by the wayside. To be perfectly honest, I really wasn't cut out for that kind of job.[14]

Bill Schottstaedt reflected on that now famous meeting:

The crux of the matter was, Dr. Sharp didn't think I was loyal to him. Initially, the students were very upset when it was announced the school had to be discontinued for financial reasons. The students went to the legislature and there was a great deal of "to-do." He saw

The deans of dentistry and health, Bill Brown and Bill Schottstaedt, in 1969. (OHSF Collection)

The acting dean of medicine, Dr. Tom Lynn. (University of Oklahoma)

me orchestrating all of that. I didn't orchestrate it but I was not inclined to stop it.

The specific instance which resulted in my being fired right on the spot was one in which he *thought* I was trying to get the faculty of the school transferred to another university. One of the faculty members had talked to someone at the University of Texas at San Antonio who had suggested it would be awfully nice if they could have a school of public health down there. Neither of them who had that conversation had any responsibility or the authority to do that. Dr. Sharp indicated to me he'd heard there was such a thing afoot and I said, "Yes, I'd heard that, too." In almost the next sentence he told me I was fired and Phil Smith would take over. It was unexpected, to say the least, and final. Absolutely, that was the end of it.[15]

President Sharp saw this change as highly appropriate under the circumstances:

We put together the two colleges for reduction of administrative and instructional costs, not because it was particularly educationally wise. But when you're faced with problems of that sort…and where I'm sitting now, if this [1983] financial crisis goes on through the years, they'll be put together again under the importunities of financial stress.

When asked why he fired Bill Schottstaedt, Dr. Sharp replied:

Redundancy. We didn't need two deans for one role. Schottstaedt displayed a good deal of public disloyalty

to the whole planning process, insisting on his own interpretation. In other words, he went public with a matter that was an in-house…. He wasn't a team member, at all. But it was deeper than that. He simply refused philosophically to accept the point of view they could be put together whereas Phil Smith believed they could and it could work. It wasn't the best of all solutions but we lived in an imperfect world. Whatever it is now, it was then an imperfect world!

When you go through those crises—and for a period of seven years on the Norman campus, we never had enough money—your strategy is to maintain the vitality and strength of your core programs, looking for that better day when you can add to them. And that's exactly what we went through those four years (at the OUHSC), looking forward to a better day.[16]

While things looked just a shade better for University Hospital, they were looking several shades darker for the O.U. College of Medicine. Dr. Tom Lynn, head of community medicine, was made acting dean of the college of medicine when Dr. Bird departed. In June, 1974, a "pre-accreditation team" from the Liaison Committee on Medical Education, composed of representatives of the American Medical Association and the Association of American Medical Colleges, had visited O.U. and was so negatively impressed it recommended moving the full review up by two years. Accreditation inspections were ordinarily done on a six-year cycle.

The events and conditions which upset the visitors

were: the fact that there were only three full-time faculty members left in surgery. According to Dr. Glen Leymaster, an AMA representative, "no medical school can retain accreditation for long with a surgery faculty of only three"; the separation of the hospitals from the College of Medicine, which caused the team great concern; and the plan to operate the Tulsa branch as a virtually independent, two-year school. "We do not and never have accredited two-year medical schools," Leymaster said. The Tulsa branch had a dean and an assistant dean but no faculty. It needed at least one full-time teacher in each of six major departments.

Dr. Lynn also cited the low budget. "We are below the national mean in dollar expenditure per student, no matter how you calculate it. The average outlay per student is $17,000 per year while at O.U. it is between $12,000 and $13,000." Leymaster described the College of Medicine's difficulties as "major operational problems" of a "fairly critical" nature.[17]

By the time the medical school accreditation team returned, Dr. Rainey Williams had begun recruiting new surgery faculty and prospects for that department were much brighter. In addition, the medical school had received substantially more money in the fiscal year beginning July 1, 1974. According to Dean Lynn:

> The biggest problem was the "Tulsa flap." It was the fact that the Tulsa branch was independent which bothered the accreditation team. Had it been set up so that the dean at Tulsa was an associate dean reporting to the dean here, the problem never would have come up. It was solved by making the provost of the OUHSC the "executive dean of the College of Medicine" so the dean of the Tulsa branch reported to him. We received full accreditation but not for six years—it was two years as I recall. We were not put on probation.[18]

Meanwhile, on November 14, 1974, the O.U. Regents appointed William G. "Bill" Thurman, a pediatrician and dean of the Tulane University School of Medicine, as the new provost for the O.U. Health Sciences Center. He was slated to assume the $70,000 a year job on April 1, 1975. Thurman said the financial problems at Oklahoma were being experienced by health care institutions across the nation and cited the unstable program at Harvard as an example. "It is not unique to Oklahoma. Costs are going up. You have to expect it."[19]

Costs were indeed going up. In a little over a decade, the job of director of the Medical Center no longer carried the active responsibilities of dean of medicine

Dr. Eleanor Knudsen came from California. (University of Oklahoma)

and the pay had gone up 180 percent. When legislators complained about the salary which would be paid Dr. Thurman, President Sharp defended it. "It looks large to everybody but it is consistent with salaries of leaders in medical schools across the country. It is necessary to attract and retain a highly specialized professional."[20]

The College of Nursing had lived from pillar to post for 10 years after its building on campus had been demolished to make room for construction of the Basic Science Education Building. Gloria R. Smith, Ph.D., had joined the faculty in 1971 and had become interim dean in 1973. After the search committee had scoured the country for 32 months to find a leader for the school, the members discovered they had one who was already in the job and performing well. This is not an unusual result of search committee efforts. The "interim" was stricken from Gloria Smith's title in September, 1975, and she continued as dean for the next eight and a half years. She remembered the early years:

> When Eleanor Knudsen came here in 1970 [as dean of the college of nursing], the idea was that O.U. would prepare faculty for the various nursing schools in Oklahoma. In order to do so, there had to be a master's program. That was the main *new* thrust for the school—to get graduate education going. Eleanor was the first dean prepared at the doctorate level.
>
> What she found was a small school with a small, dedicated faculty who had been kind of churning out undergraduate nurses and doing a fairly good job. They'd

Two of the houses on 14th Street which served as offices for the College of Nursing. (Oklahoma City Chamber of Commerce)

Christ United Methodist Church on Kelley Avenue. (OHSF Collection)

The University's Interim Building served both Nursing and Dentistry. (University of Oklahoma)

been planning a new curriculum for years but hadn't done much about it. [According to the current O.U. president, Dr. William S. Banowsky, "Universities are very conservative. The faculty is liberal about everybody else's business but it's very conservative about its own. Changing a curriculum and moving a cemetery are tasks of equal magnitude!"[21]]

Some of the faculty were not even master's-prepared and Eleanor was expected to begin graduate education. She decided she needed more time, which she didn't get. The graduate program began in 1973, ready or not! The State Regents and the legislature couldn't afford to give her more time because there were new nursing programs opening up in the community colleges around the state which required qualified faculty which meant people with master's degrees in nursing. We weren't getting enough prepared people migrating into the state so we had to produce our own.

I took over in 1973 with three new graduate faculty, a new graduate program that had not been fully implemented and a faculty bewildered by the sudden departure of a dean they had spent two years recruiting. Eleanor said she left because she could not adapt to Oklahoma. [She had come from California and departed to Reno, Nevada.] I think if she had delayed her decision about six more weeks, she'd still be here.

Things were moving so rapidly, it's kind of hard to remember when we were not in these wonderful, luxurious surroundings we are now in. We started outgrowing the classrooms; that was the first thing. You see, during the short time Eleanor was here, the student body doubled, then it tripled! The faculty doubled and tripled. In 1972, we graduated the largest class we'd ever had—88. The usual size class was 60 some. Within two or three years, we were up to 100, 120 and were beginning to look at the possibility of 150 in the entering class. But by the time we got to 120, it became apparent we were not going to have resources fast enough to keep up with that kind of growth so we limited enrollment for a while.

At the same time, we had an application in to the fed-

eral government for matching money to construct a new building. We had offices on 14th Street and classrooms in a church up on Kelley, Christ [United] Methodist [at 17th Street]. We were lucky because the church permitted us to have classroom space we didn't have to clear out at the end of every day or on the weekend. They gave us space we could set up as a [nursing] practice lab. This was pretty satisfactory but we outgrew it almost before we were in it. We had moved from a situation in which we were trying to hold classes in the living rooms of those houses on 14th Street, so the church was just like paradise by comparison.

Then we got into the Interim Building [in 1974].… That was wonderful! We used the Annex for offices [a two-level motel on Stonewall and 12th Street, around the corner from the Interim Building]. What helped that move to come about so rapidly was the Richardson Report. The houses we were in were owned by Winston Howard and apparently there was some kind of rift between Winston and David Hall. The report covered two

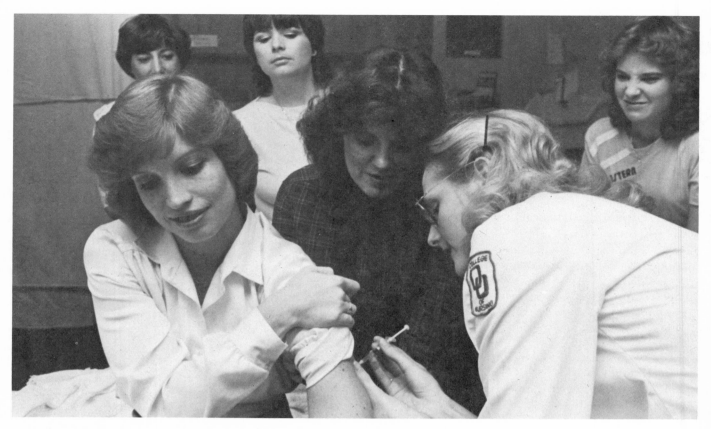

Student nurses practice "giving shots" by "sticking" each other. (University of Oklahoma)

Gloria Smith, Ph.D., Dean of Nursing. (University of Oklahoma)

areas of concern about the school of nursing. One was that we were not in state-owned facilities, which I think was aimed at Winston and we were told to get out [of the houses he owned] almost immediately. That was when we moved our offices into the Annex, before we got into the Interim Building. We were still teaching at the church. It was a very rapid move but it worked to our advantage.

The other thing was: we had moved into a new curriculum and we were using a concept of structure nobody understood. Richardson thought we had too many administrators. We had moved from departmental chairmen to the concept of "lead teachers," as we called them, and of course, coordinators and level coordinators. All of these people had full-time teaching responsibilities but the Richardson report thought we had layers of managers and that created some confusion.[22]

There was indeed turbulence among the programs in health sciences education as a result of the financial crisis during this period, but the university was responding to the need for health manpower. It was determined to meet that need despite budgetary strictures, inadequate facilities, faculty turnover and the legislature's lack of confidence in university leadership.

208

CHAPTER 29

STAYING AFLOAT: 1973-1975

President Richard M. Nixon, in a nationwide address on January 28, 1973, declared "it is time to get big government off your back and out of your pocket." He proposed holding the line on taxes and slashing several popular programs which had been "regarded as sacred cows in the past." Among them were the Hill-Burton hospital construction program and urban renewal. He proposed a new (1973-1974) federal budget of $269 billion and vowed to keep the current year's spending to $250 billion by withholding congressionally-approved funds. "Impoundment" was about to begin. The president was emphatic. "What is at stake is not just a big, impersonal federal budget," he said. "What is at stake is your job, your taxes, the prices you pay...."[1]

What was at stake for the O.U. Health Sciences Center was the new, federal capitation grant program which paid schools of medicine and dentistry several thousand dollars for each enrolled student. Impoundment of Hill-Burton funds was not particularly serious because this was not a highly significant source of funding for construction of OHC hospitals. The overbuilding of hospitals in the Oklahoma City area, forecast by the Chamber of Commerce in 1969, had begun. Bob Nichols, state director of the Medical Committee on Human Rights, pointed out that the Areawide Health Planning Organization in Oklahoma City had recommended against construction of additional beds but the facilities division of the State Department of Health, which administered the Hill Burton program, was providing funds anyway. New hospital construction, especially by Baptist, Mercy and Presbyterian, was expected to produce about 1,000 too many beds. Kent Corey, head of Oklahoma Consumer Protection, Inc, a non-profit, volunteer organization, said this needless expansion would cost citizens some $200 million over the next 10 years.[2]

The Oklahoma Health Center seemed to acquire a momentum of its own, despite the alarm of the legislature about the cost of operating the OUHSC. Senator James E. Hamilton explained the thought process at the Capitol and out in the state:

> A lot of people in the legislature and the general public are deceived by the ongoing costs that are going to be initiated by the building of a new structure. People have the idea, well, that's not a recurring expense. [They think] the capital outlay of so many millions of dollars to build a building is better than expending it on other things because it's just a one-time expense. Speaker Bill Willis and I had several discussions about how much additional operating expense we'd have for personnel, equipment and keeping these new buildings up.
>
> I think when they planned that capital outlay [for the Oklahoma Health Center] they just sort of glossed over the amount of expense that was going to be involved in developing central steam and a lot of things that weren't anticipated. It's just like everything else. We just don't face up to the issue until the crunch is on. That's the way we are up there [at the legislature] right now [February, 1984]. We've got our backs to the wall.[3]

In March, 1974, the idea of turning the University Hospital over to the Welfare Department surfaced once more but was squelched after a meeting of Governor Hall, Speaker Bill Willis, President Jim Hamilton and Senate leaders. Undoubtedly, Mr. Rader again expressed himself on the subject. On April 1, looking at the record of the legislature, the *Daily Oklahoman* was anything but complimentary:

> The legislature has fumbled the ball in all directions on the Oklahoma Health Sciences Center, destroying much of the prestige it once held as a medical school and turning much of the operation over to the welfare department as a way of dodging its responsibility. Money is being spent in floundering efforts to establish a second medical school in Tulsa while the existing one at Oklahoma City is grossly underfinanced.[4]

A month later, there were rumors the University Hospital might close, a possibility Senator E. Melvin Porter of Oklahoma City attributed to a conspiracy. Many of his black constituents depended on the hospital and clinics for their medical care and its threatened closing made the senator nervous. Finally, on May 6, 1974, the Senate passed a $6.68 million appropriation bill to support University Hospital during the next fiscal year. Despite the fact this was $1.2 million more than the current appropriation, Jeptha Dalston said he would have to cut expenses $160 thousand a *month* beginning July 1 to break even. He said he needed $1.9 million more. Otherwise, educational programs, which the hospital supported to

Senator E. Melvin Porter was fearful University Hospital might close. (The Oklahoman)

the extent of $4.7 million a year, would be adversely affected. Accreditation and licensure of the hospital would also be in jeopardy. Dean Robert Bird said inadequate support of the hospital could force a cutback in residencies and internships which would reduce the number of doctors available to practice in the state. Apparently, the legislature was not impressed because it did not increase the hospital's appropriation.[5]

In the waning days of the 1974 session, the Senate passed a resolution requiring an interim study of a possible merger between the V.A. Hospital and the Mark Everett Tower. The seven key senate leaders who authored this resolution, including the president pro tempore-elect, Gene Howard of Tulsa, George Miller of Ada and Dr. Richard Stansberry of Oklahoma City, said the legislature would weigh this merger "before any consideration would be given to supplemental appropriations for operation of University Hospital in FY 1974-1975."[6]

Dan Macer originated this merger idea as an upshot of the Federal-State Sharing concept. He hoped to add 144 beds to the V.A. Hospital and because Everett Tower was expansible to 800 beds, he thought it could accommodate both University and V.A. requirements quite handily. The proposed bridge building would provide expanded outpatient clinic space at the single point of entry to the Oklahoma

Health Center which Macer advocated. This arrangement would result in savings and efficiencies for both the state and federal governments, he said. "We would never consider taking over University Hospital because it is failing financially," Macer added. "We would only take it over because we must expand." But neither Governor Hall nor O.U. President Paul Sharp thought this was a good plan. The governor said he would call a special legislative session in December (1974) if it were necessary to supplement financing of University Hospital.[7]

The contrast between the financial fortunes of Children's and University Hospital was not lost on the newspapers. On June 6, 1974, the *Daily Oklahoman*, under a headline, "The Poor Relative," editorialized:

> The $17 million expansion of Children's Memorial Hospital authorized this week by the Oklahoma Welfare Commission emphasizes the striking contrast between that fortunate institution and its desperately poor relative, University Hospital.
>
> The public interest and general welfare demand the health services provided by both institutions. Yet Children's is embarking on a major program of capital improvement and service expansion at a time when University is tottering on the brink of financial collapse.
>
> This paradox of poverty versus plenty in the comparative status of the two hospitals is probably not understood by the average citizen but it is easily explained. Although both are state-connected, University must depend on the annual largesse of the Oklahoma Legislature while Children's has no such problem....
>
> Meanwhile, poor cousin University was able to get only $6.68 million of the $10 million it requested.... This compounds an already strained financial picture at University, forcing it to reconsider reductions in patient services as well as teaching services rendered to the O.U. medical school....
>
> But it's a strange system that enables the one to forge ahead with a $17 million building program by simple administrative action while the other fights for survival because of legislative neglect.[8]

Whether cousin or brother-in-law, the University Hospital was a poor relative Lloyd Rader was inclined to shun as much as possible.

By this time, Acting Provost Bill Brown was well immersed in the dual task of keeping the University of Oklahoma Health Sciences Center afloat and operating a fledgling college of dentistry:

> David Hall, with whom I played tennis, was a delightful, very pleasant person, yet in terms of professional dealings at the State Capitol, it was quite a different

The model of the Dental Clinical Sciences Building planned for the corner of 11th and Stonewall. (Oklahoma City Chamber of Commerce)

feeling. It is extremely difficult to educate people [about the complicated field of health professional education] who don't have time to listen. My feeling is that David Hall probably wanted to help but I don't think he really understood that much about what we were trying to do. There was a great deal of suspicion about this place then and, in some ways, [it was] justifiable. One of the things I had to do during my tour of duty was try to reestablish credibility with the legislature. Bit by bit we got more and more support.

None of the vice-presidents had worked closely with Lloyd Rader prior to my coming on. Len Eliel had one occasion during his tour—one occasion! When the hospitals were transferred, whether he or I liked it, we were going to be working together a lot. There were few days that went by that we were not talking. My days were pretty long; I'd usually hit the house about 6:30 at night. I rarely got inside the door before the phone was ringing; there was Mr. Rader, wanting to talk to me. I was very fond of the man; he was very straightforward, easy to deal with.

On one occasion, he caught me after a meeting and said, "Sure would like that property where you're going to build your dental building for a parking lot for Children's Hospital." I'd heard rumors he'd wanted it for a long time. This [conversation] took about two minutes. I said, "We've got an $11 million grant [application] in. It's for this site and it requires site plans and architectural drawings. If we try to move it at the eleventh hour, forget it! We'll be dead! We might as well fold our tents and go home." He said, "That's fine. You can't do anything else. I won't ask you about it again." And he never did.[9]

Meanwhile, the financial and political tension was having its effect on the medical school faculty. Dr. Eliel, who had become head of the endocrinology section

of the department of medicine said in March he would leave his current position at the end of May, 1974. Dr. John Schilling, the head of surgery, also announced he would be leaving at mid-year. As Dr. Rainey Williams said:

> He told me at the time he simply thought the problems at Oklahoma were sufficiently great that the institution would be crippled for several years and whoever dealt with that ought to be somebody younger. At the same time, Jim Hartsuck left, Lazar Greenfield was appointed head of the department of surgery at the Medical College of Virginia and Ide Smith [pediatric surgeon] had left several months earlier to go into private practice because of the [physicians practice] plan and what he saw happening at Children's. At the beginning of the July, 1974 academic year, there were three full time people in the entire department of surgery, including all its divisions and all three hospitals. The complement was ordinarily ten to twelve.[10]

Some of the unrest certainly was due to suspicion that a few of the medical college faculty were not adhering to the rules of the physicians practice plan. The plan had been adopted by the O.U. Regents in April, 1973, to comply with a law which directed that "all funds which are generated by the doctors as part of their duties as faculty members shall be considered as state money and handled accordingly." On June 11, 1974, Jack Cochran, director of public relations at O.U., confirmed that an investigation was being conducted to determine if physicians at the College of Medicine were withholding professional income from the university. He said, "It appears that some of the physicians are not depositing money according to the plan." However, during the first 12 months of its operation, more than 250 faculty doctors had contributed nearly $4 million.[11]

In addition, some physicians were suspected of violating the "site of-practice" directive which required faculty members to put their private patients in University or Children's hospital beds if any were available in order to increase hospital income. Dr. Williams continued:

> The practice plan was punitive and was intended to be punitive because of questions about the physicians' trust fund which nobody ever understood. It was really a very altruistic thing rather than a questionable thing. Fortunately, John Schilling and Roy Lytle [an Oklahoma City attorney] were able to negotiate out most of the really repressive parts of the practice plan. As I see it, the legislature was punishing the faculty for alleged misuse of professional earnings, which was never proven.

I can remember when there were five legislative investigations of the Center going on at one time! To my knowledge, nobody *ever* had any evidence there was any actual wrongdoing. The faculty bitterly resented it because what they were doing was supporting the school with their [private] practice earnings.[12]

Tom Lynn chaired committees which put the private practice plan together:

The O.U. practice plan is a good one from the standpoint of the faculty and has allowed the university to be competitive nationally for clinical faculty. Geographic full-time faculty of a medical school are employed with the understanding the university will pay them a set figure per year for their teaching function and they will be allowed to practice medicine and generate income from that practice. The practice plan which is now in place in almost all medical schools in the country sets out the way the income is to be used. At the University of Oklahoma, the money is pooled by department. Then, based on the amount generated and the individual's academic rank, the doctor can retain a portion of the income he has generated. If you don't generate any money, you don't get any more money. On the other hand, if you are an assistant professor and generate a *lot* of money, you don't get to keep all of that, as much, say, as a full professor would get to keep. The percentage is based on your rank.

Of the money which is left over, the dean's office gets 10 percent and the remainder goes to the department for expenditures such as residents' salaries, secretarial salaries, supplies and equipment. The only part that is centralized is that which goes to the dean and that which is used to pay the expense of billing, collection and accounting…administrative overhead.[13]

Apparently Don Halverstadt did not wish to be restricted by the practice plan. He said:

The problem was the regents' site-of-practice policy which they put in effect to help keep the beds full in the teaching hospitals. I said, for better or worse, I'd put my patients in the hospital where I thought they'd get the best care. [I felt this] was a medical decision, not an administrative decision. At that point in time, unfortunately, [the best care] was not in the regents' hospital. It was over that single item I ultimately elected to resign from the full-time faculty.

He requested to go from full-time to voluntary faculty but was turned down by the O.U. Board of Regents. Instead, the regents accepted his resignation and took him off the list of 10 to 15 physicians who were being investigated to see if they had withheld professional income from the University. Thus Dr.

Halverstadt relinquished his $27,000 faculty salary but he was receiving $23,985 a year from the welfare department as chief of staff. L.E. Rader said that because Halverstadt had a faculty appointment when he joined Children's his status there should not be questioned.[14]

Dr. Jim Merrill was not at all pleased with the regents' investigation. He said the probe by "a vindictive O.U. Board of Regents" could signal a rash of faculty resignations. "If the regents do not stop their harassment, they may find themselves with no college of medicine at all." The physicians felt that income generated before July 1, 1973, should not be considered part of the practice plan but the regents said the plan covered all money received regardless of when it was earned. Dr. Merrill talked about the situation immediately before the physicians practice plan became effective:

The money that was supposed to go into that was money collected for service rendered to non-private patients or things that were done on contracts and what have you. Just before the physicians practice plan was started, a three-man committee consisting of myself and John Schilling and one other was appointed by Bob Bird to look into compliance. We actually made a report to the faculty in which we described instances of non-compliance. The most flagrant non-complier was Donald Halverstadt. It was because of that he went off the faculty and then came back on the faculty as a volunteer, not a full-time. He was not complying and would not comply.

Most people handled their private patient income themselves and some made more than the permitted 50 percent [of their base, faculty salary].[15]

Halverstadt disagreed vehemently:

I would say that is an uninformed statement which is incorrect. I played by the rules. As a matter of fact, for a while I was one of three trustees of the [old physicians trust] fund. Eventually, I was the only trustee left when there was a $270 thousand tax lein put on it by the Internal Revenue Service.[16]

Dean Bird said the O.U. audit of physicians income had caused a great deal of resentment and anxiety in the medical school. "Before the practice plan, individual doctors did their own billing and had departmental trust funds. The misunderstandings are a reflection of doing things the old way and being ignorant of the new way." Dr. Harris D. "Pete" Riley observed, "The problem is that we have contributed voluntarily in the past and don't want to be told what to do." On the other hand, Jack Santee, the president

Dean Bird resigned as a result of the physicians practice plan controversy. (Oklahoma Journal)

of the O.U. Board of Regents, said the audit was necessary because the board had "been too lenient" in enforcement of the physicians practice plan and the site of practice directive. He said the board, "could not back off from the execution of the law."

The controversy wore on for weeks, with efforts at reconciliation coming from both the faculty and the regents. James F. "Jim" Hammarsten, head of the department of medicine, said the major point of contention was "simply a difference of interpretation of the law." He referred to the date the practice plan was effective, the physicians claiming the law should not be retroactive and that income for services performed before July 1, 1973, should not come under the practice plan.[17]

Jim Killackey commented about the origin of the practice plan legislation:

> There had always been this undercurrent of the legislature being suspicious of what doctors in administrative positions were doing in the health sciences center. Heck, that's true even now (1983). The legislature always thinks the doctors in the health sciences center are making too much money, they're doing too much. There is a basic distrust between the lawmakers of Oklahoma and the medical administrators.
>
> In fact, my major introduction into the health sciences center was during the physicians practice crisis, the summer of 1974. That's when I met Schilling, Halverstadt, Merrill...all the leaders. The animosity between that group and the O.U. Regents had reached its peak. It was a very confusing time. I did a week of page-one stories on that crisis. It was a real gut-level issue; how much power the regents should have over the doctors.[18]

Dr. Robert M. Bird became a casualty of the con-

tinuing crisis in the O.U. Health Sciences Center. On July 12, 1974, he announced his resignation as dean of the College of Medicine. He refused to make any remarks that might be critical of the O.U. Regents' probe into the medical faculty compliance with income visibility and limits policy but he said his unexpected decision was "obviously influenced" by the recent financial and personnel problems besetting the school. He left on September 1, 1974, to become director of the Lister Hill Institute for Bio-Medical Communications, a division of the National Library of Medicine in Bethesda, Maryland.

Audrey Clonce, who had been his secretary since the mid-1960s and during the four years Dr. Bird had been dean, said that a year earlier he had attended a meeting of the regents and when he came back:

> We typed up a copy of his resignation. He told them that he would not turn his professional faculty into state-paid employees, which is what he felt they were trying to do. Of course, a year later, he did resign. He knew it was coming all that year. Once you tangle with the regents of the university, you're on your way out. I'm sure Dr. Hollomon found that out!
>
> What the state wanted to do was have all the [private fee] money go into the pot and then be "salaried out" and Dr. Bird wouldn't have that. That's what it all started over and it just sort of mushroomed. Dr. Bird could see a split developing and he couldn't have that happen to his beloved medical school. He felt the risk would go away if he went away. He was a very selfless man.
>
> He'd been asked several times during that year to go to the Library of Medicine and he'd turned it down every time. He'd had offers to become dean of other medical schools but he turned them down. He felt he had to finish what he had started and he was going to leave when he was ready to leave.[19]

Money troubles at the University Hospital continued. At mid-year, 1974, it was "still in a fix" and "more than $1 million short of a balanced budget." Dr. Dalston recalled the struggle. "I felt as though I was trying to row a boat in a raging storm at sea, being tossed about by the cross-currents of interests, personalities, conflicts and dynamics of that political scene. It was power politics at its best...and worst. The interests of the patients and the poor people were like a pawn moved around a board."[20]

With the legislature now heavily involved in the debate over the funding and the future of University Hospital, political cross-currents affected the relationship between the Presbyterian and University Hospitals. Originally, the medical school faculty was expected to teach and care for some of their patients in Presbyterian Hospital as a way to broaden and enrich the clinical experience of the medical students and house staff. But the financial crisis and the site-of-practice directive imposed on the faculty changed the rules of the game. The university directed all clinical faculty to admit all of their private patients to University Hospital assuming facilities and services needed for their care were available.

Senator E. Melvin Porter, again suspecting a conspiracy, said on July 23, 1974, that Presbyterian "has planned for years to raid University Hospital for income-producing patients." He said the wording of the Presbyterian's 1972 bond prospectus "clearly indicates that all money-making patients at University Hospital would go to Presbyterian. That would mean the end of University Hospital." Then Senator Porter added, "I'm going to make sure University Hospital is not gutted for the benefit of Presbyterian."

But Senator Richard Stansberry took the opposite view, saying the affiliation agreement between O.U. and the hospital "severely hurts the chances of survival of the new Presbyterian." However, the chairman of the hospital board, Stanton Young, said Presbyterian "should be able to generate an adequate number of patient days from its own staff." The affiliation agreement stipulated that faculty would be free to admit patients to Presbyterian Hospital "only when beds are not available at University or Children's Memorial Hospital."

Former state senator George Miller, who had joined the welfare department, said, "It will be difficult for the University and Presbyterian to 'co-exist'," and added, "I'm beginning to wonder why Presbyterian located here in the first place. Problems have become very serious because of its location." Representative Hannah Atkins said, "Key legislators and the people must realize that a private institution is going to drain [paying patients] from a public institution." Representative A. Visanio Johnson echoed these ideas: "Someone in the private enterprise section is pulling against everything we're striving for at the health sciences center." Of course, Porter, Atkins and Johnson, all local legislators, were worried about the future of University Hospital because it represented the only source of medical care for many of their constituents, the blacks in the Oklahoma City area. The politicization of the Oklahoma Health Center program had distorted its original intent and suddenly Presbyterian Hospital was the bad guy.[21] Hospital president Harry Neer was not perturbed, though:

I did not like to see the plight the university and the University Hospital were in, but it probably helped us with the private practitioner. Some people were quite opposed to the site-of-practice [directive], thinking it would do Presbyterian in. I was silent because I thought site-of-practice was the best thing that could have happened. There was a whole lot of "town and gown" [feeling] among the physicians in the community. One of the things they were worried about was the university taking over Presbyterian Hospital. This made it easier for us because I could say to the physicians I was trying to encourage to practice at Pres., "They're weak. Don't worry about them taking over Presbyterian, and running the departments." That was probably the single thing they hit me with [most often].... There was a real fear of the university taking over. Of course, the doctors who had been active at Pres. were not worried; they had been working with the university all this time. It was the new guys.[22]

In the interim, Skipper Dalston was steering the University Hospital toward calmer seas. By careful financial control, program costs were pared and revenues increased, generating $450 thousand toward reduction of the budget shortfall. In August, 1974, Dr. Dalston said the hospital deficit was still running about $90 thousand a month, $1.08 million a year. Billings were speeded up and uncompensated charity care was reduced from $5.7 to $4.5 million in the course of a year.[23]

By mid-December, 1974, the trustees of the University Hospital had decided not to ask for a $1.7 million supplemental appropriation when the legislature convened the next month. Seven months previously, it looked as though the hospital would amass a huge deficit during the fiscal year but a number of developments wiped out that threat. Remodeling of Old Main, which would permit activation of 70 beds there, was delayed along with 17 other new programs that were to have been established. Fundamentally more important, the hospital was getting many more patients than it anticipated and was garnering substantial income from them. Occupancy was 14 percent higher than the previous year. In fact, by the following month, the University Hospital had topped 90 percent occupancy and had established emergency procedures to transfer patients to other hospitals in the city as required. Jeptha Dalston attributed the improved census to more physician referrals from around the state and recognition of "the high capability of our physicians in treating acutely ill patients requiring tertiary care."[24]

Despite its still precarious though improving finan-

The 40 million electron volt linear accelerator at University Hospital. (University of Oklahoma)

cial situation, University Hospital was striving to expand its patient services. At the start of 1975, it was vying with Baptist Medical Center to win approval of the Areawide Health Planning Organization (AHPO) to establish a 10 or 12 bed burn center for which it needed a million dollar legislative appropriation. On January 9, voting six to one to counter a staff recommendation, AHPO favored Baptist because it could get the burn center in operation by mid-year at one-fifth the projected cost of the one proposed by University Hospital. Greg Harmon and the AHPO staff had given first priority to the University Hospital location because of "its capability to provide a comprehensive teaching and research program over the long term." Although burn care is monstrously expensive, Dr. Dalston said a unit at the University Hospital, with a high percentage of third-party reimbursement, could be self-supporting in a year. Harmon surmised Baptist wanted the unit more for its public relations value than its income potential.[25]

The Oklahoma Health Planning Commission had committees, too, and Al Donnell headed the Blue Streak Committee which evaluated these applications:

> We met in the medical school to hear University [Hospital] and Baptist present their cases for a burn center. Of course, Brother Lloyd [Rader] was going to get his burn center in Children's Hospital no matter what. I'll never forget how intense that was and how they fought for it. The committee recommended Baptist and the Commission—Mr. Rader—went along with that.[26]

On February 21, after months of study, debate and discussion, the authority to develop a burn center was given to Baptist Medical Center.

Undaunted, University Hospital officials planned expansion of medical services in a different direction. On March 21, 1975, the *Daily Oklahoman* reported the hospital was studying the feasibility of acquiring a 40 million electron volt linear accelerator, a unique radiation machine for the treatment of cancer. The advantage of this machine was that it could be focused accurately to kill deep-seated tumors without damaging the surrounding healthy tissue. The project was expected to cost $1.5, $1.2 million for the machine and $300,000 for the building to put it in. There were only 14 such machines in the country at the time, the closest located in Houston, Texas, and St. Louis, Missouri.

The legislative committee, headed by Al Terrill of Lawton, seemed favorably inclined toward this new machine but it was primarily concerned with the need for the hospital to create a sound financial base. The committee recommended that county ad valorem tax collections be used to reimburse University Hospital for indigent care. Other alternatives being considered were: development of the hospital as a public trust operation; sharing of services in the health center; emphasis on major health provision grants; and development of the hospital as a health maintenance organization.[27]

In contrast to all of the legislative concern about how the University Hospital could create a sound financial base, there seemed to be no reluctance to fund one-time capital improvements. On June 5, 1975, Governor Boren cut through the ubiquitous bureaucratic red tape to get the proposed linear accelerator approved by the Health Sciences Center Planning and Advisory Committee, which he chaired, and the State Health Planning Commission. By this time, the estimated cost of the building needed to house this cancer treatment machine had escalated so the entire project was edging toward $2 million. The necessary money was then included in the appropriation bill for University Hospital. Governor Boren said the machine could attract patients from six states.[28]

On April 1, 1975, the new provost, Dr. William Thurman, arrived on schedule. Asked why he took on the challenge of the OUHSC when it was still very definitely in crisis, he replied:

> That's been my history. I've always taken on challenges that needed both administrative skill and some rebuilding. I came on April first and on April second, I was in front of the House Appropriations Committee about why we had a $4 million deficit. It was still in crisis and needed some more reorganization and administrative

tightening, things like that, plus [here was] a major building program to be accomplished.[29]

Gordon Deckert, M.D., the chairman of psychiatry and behavioral sciences, said that Thurman was brought in as a "hatchet man" to get rid of some of the deadwood in the organization.[30] The provost agreed:

No question! That is a very correct statement. I had that history in Virginia; I had that history in New Orleans. I think the University of Oklahoma became interested in me because I was willing to take on the challenge of…"How do you nicely get rid of deadwood, avoid the tenure problems and try to get people back on the main track of education as a priority related to the money available?" The charge was very clear from the O.U. Regents and Paul Sharp. There *had* to be significant change on this campus and I was brought in to do it.

President Sharp remarked:

I had a great deal of regard for Bill Thurman as an administrator. He was not very popular with the faculty, partly because it is extremely difficult to move through a crisis like that without taking [controversial] actions and partly because of his style. Crisis management requires a different style and we were moving through a genuine crisis.[31]

Shortly thereafter, Jeptha Dalston told the board of the University Hospital he was resigning, effective September 1, 1975, to become administrator of the 1,100-bed University of Michigan Hospital at Ann Arbor:

It was time for me to leave Oklahoma. I had the bruises and scars of 30 months of very intensive effort and I could not effectively carry it to the next stage. I felt it was a war, an absolute war, and I'd had to align myself in ways to advance the interests of my organization and give that organization strength. That meant incurring enemies. I had to be single-minded to do what I could for that adult, general hospital. I believe we achieved that at a considerable price.

I felt those prices would be a burden moving to the next era which was integrating with the university. Clearly, I had made enemies of the university, its administration, Paul Sharp. The way for me to gain strength for the hospital at that time was through the legislature and Lloyd [Rader]. They were the key to achieving stability and strength. There was the power! When we became stabilized, I felt the situation was ripe for moving toward reintegrating with the university. I was tired, too. I was worn out!

Two weeks before, Dr. Dalston's 14-year-old son

Christopher had died of injuries received in an automobile accident, a tragedy which added to the administrator's exhaustion and undoubtedly increased his desire for a change of scene.[32]

Paul Sharp also must have been worn out for he breathed a sigh of relief as he reflected on the years since he became president. On May 13, 1975, commenting on the events of the last academic year, he said the single most important event was the turnaround at the Health Sciences Center. In a way, the transfer of the hospitals in 1973 marked the beginning of that turnaround:

Yes, there was a certain reality and a certain symbolic aspect to it. To have that burden off our shoulders freed us, administratively and financially, to move on to the internal problems which the health sciences center had.

Following that, our budgets showed an improvement and there were several things we did, such as put together the schools of health and allied health. I certainly recall there was a very real feeling throughout the university and particularly the Health Sciences Center there was an easing of our financial crunch.

Dr. Sharp went on to say the turnaround had been accomplished in Oklahoma in spite of the fact that medical centers around the country were still in deep trouble. While the university and the University Hospital were not yet entirely comfortable, the fear of being swept away by political and financial storms had subsided and clearing weather was definitely on the horizon.[33]

Some of the unrest among the medical school faculty over the physicians practice plan and the transfer of Children's Hospital to the welfare department had eased, as well. About the latter, Frosty Troy told this story:

What's really funny about that was these doctors who were howling and yelling, violently opposed to it. One of the senior faculty over there said he'd just pack up and leave. It wasn't a year later I saw him at a party one night and I said, "You still here? I thought you were going to leave." And he said to me, "Let me tell you. That Lloyd Rader's a much misunderstood man!"

Frosty laughed uproariously.[34]

Bruce Perry was 32 years old when he took over from Jep Dalston as administrator of University Hospital on September 1, 1975:

I hadn't been on the job a week when I received a visit from the president of the university. I guess that was an unusual happening for Paul Sharp to journey all the way from Norman to see the young kid who was the

Bruce Perry…"the new kid on the block." (Presbyterian Hospital)

new administrator of University Hospital. He wanted to let me know he thought the university and the hospital needed to work more closely and he'd do anything he could to help. However, in my judgment, he didn't take any more personal interest in developing those relationships; he pretty much left that to Bill Thurman.

Perhaps Dr. Sharp was convinced of the efficacy of a "strong provost" form of Health Sciences Center administration and felt it now appropriate to back off from day-to-day involvement at the Oklahoma City campus. Perry continued:

> One of the things most exciting and most challenging about the hospital was the trauma it had come through. Jep had really worked very hard developing relationships with the legislature and Mr. Rader. He did not have time to develop the systems in the hospital and to get hospital operations in "sync"[hronization]. And he had not developed relationships with the university because he'd had to make some very unpopular decisions

to befriend the political side…moving the neonatal unit from University Hospital to Children's was one. It was a political necessity rather than something he really wanted to do but it alienated him from the department of gynecology and obstetrics. Jep thought getting the linear accelerator would create a good image for the Center but that alienated a lot of people. He really had to court the legislature.

> Then there was a new governor [David Boren], another young kid with new brooms to sweep the street clean. He had no real sense of the history of the separation [of the hospital from the university] and no real interest in it. The governor's office was a major problem in terms of developing programs because there was very little understanding of the issues and the governor had a very thin staff in terms of health care issues. Relationships had already been established with the power brokers in Oklahoma, specifically Lloyd Rader.

> In retrospect, I probably should have checked with him on policy decisions, day-to-day changes and financial problems but I did none of those things. My approach was to get the hospital on a sound operating basis and through this accomplishment [we could] develop the credibility to begin moving in different directions…a very naive view of Oklahoma politics, if I might say in retrospect!

> I did visit with Mr. Rader. He was one of the first persons I met when I got here. He took four or five hours telling me stories, expecting I would get the point of all those stories as the new kid on the block. I probably did not get the point. He was trying to let me know how the state worked and that my job was to take care of the folks and pretty much do what I was told. One thing he was saying was that a new kid on the block had *no* credibility so don't try to do anything new. I didn't pay much attention to that because I naively believed that working within those relationships, you could make happen the things which the university faculty and the [hospital] board wanted to happen.

> I would characterize my relationship with Mr. Rader during the four years I was chief executive of University Hospital from non-existent at one end of the continuum, to "strained"![35]

CHAPTER 30

THE DOCTOR SUPPLY: 1971-1975

Tulsan Finis Smith confers with Senator Jim Taliaferro. (Oklahoma Observer)

Meanwhile in Tulsa, two years after it appeared the Booz, Allen and Hamilton study had postponed plans for a new medical school there for a long time, the idea surfaced once again. This time, the "second medical school" flag was hoisted by none other than Senate President Pro Tempore Finis Smith, himself a Tulsa Democrat. "We can't afford to wait. Oklahoma is fast approaching a crisis and positive steps must be taken. We must accelerate the time schedule to produce health manpower which includes not only doctors but dentists, nurses and skilled technicians in the allied health fields."[1]

Senator Richard Stansberry suggested the proposed Tulsa School of Medicine could be a branch of the University of Oklahoma Medical School. He sponsored a resolution asking for a second study of the feasibility of establishing a medical school in Tulsa. It was introduced on April 21, 1971, by Senator James Hamilton, appropriating $12,500 for this study plus another $12,500 to determine if establishing a college

of osteopathic medicine and surgery, also in Tulsa, could be accomplished successfully.[2]

In 1971, there were no standards to indicate just how many health professionals of what kind were actually needed to care for all the sick people in a given population. All that could be done was compare the health manpower in one state with the ratio of doctors or nurses or technicians to population in the nation. Oklahoma, according to figures released by Dr. E. T. Dunlap, required an additional 870 physicians, 267 dentists and 1,889 registered nurses to bring its complement of health care professionals to a level equal to the national average. He again quoted the estimate the Department of Health, Education and Welfare had made about 10 years previously—the United States had a shortage of 50,000 physicians. "In the event that an additional 50,000 physicians were added to the national total, Oklahoma would require an additional 1,500 physicians over current levels to measure up to the national average," he said. That year, Oklahoma had 2,988 physicians, 874 dentists and 5,611 registered nurses.[3]

The Tulsa effort, promoted by the Chamber of Commerce there, put Dr. Eliel in a difficult position. He did not want to oppose the idea of another medical school but he recognized the enormous need for money to support the burgeoning Medical Center:

During a hearing at the legislature, Senator [Ed] Berrong [of Weatherford] asked me what my opinion was of establishing a medical school and a school of osteopathy in Tulsa, whether I was for or against it. I guess I gave an answer which wasn't politic. I said we were concerned about being able to fund this many schools in Oklahoma and I thought our approval would be contingent on assurance there would be adequate funds. I was told afterward that was the wrong thing to say.

This job takes someone who is an instinctive politician. I always counted Bryce Baggett as a good friend because he was a very intelligent man. He knew about the problems we were having; he was nobody's fool. He gave me a lot of good advice. At a luncheon one day at the Faculty House he said, "You know, the trouble with you is that you project the picture of a Harvard don. What you've gotta do is learn to crawl in bed with these guys. If you want to get along with the state legislature,

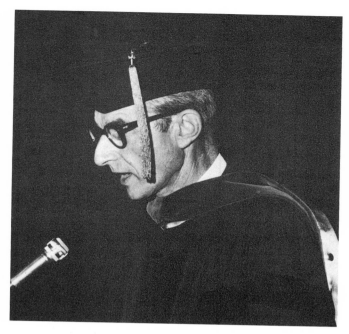

"The Harvard don." (University of Oklahoma)

you've gotta be a "good ole boy!" That was something I could never do. I'm just not that kind of person.[1]

Despite the increasing money drought on the federal level and the rapidly expanding funding requirements of the Medical Center, the push to develop a new medical school—perhaps two—in Tulsa continued. On September 8, 1971, Governor David Hall named five Tulsa physicians to serve on a special committee to study the feasibility of establishing a medical and dental school in Tulsa. It was not difficult to predict that committee's conclusion given the attitude of many Tulsa doctors.[5]

Dr. Eliel tried to get more information about the legislative attitude toward the creation of a medical school and a school of osteopathy in Tulsa so he asked Larry Rember to find out what he could. Larry promptly reported that the consensus was just the way House Speaker Bill Willis of Tahlequah phrased it, "Those schools are going to fly together or they'll die together!"[6] Furthermore, Dr. Eliel said:

> In one of the nice clubs over there, a senator who represented Tulsa told Bob Bird and me, right to our faces, "I don't care whether you want a medical school over here or not, there's going to be one!" We knew the handwriting was on the wall then and there was nothing we could do about it even though all the data would suggest another medical school was unnecessary in a state with our population. It is amazing the way the political pendulum swings from one side to the other.[7]

The second medical school in Tulsa. (OHSF Collection)

President Paul Sharp's opinion was:

> I think the necessity for trained personnel in some cases was tied too much to political estimates rather than professional estimates. We were led into the Tulsa Medical College for political reasons rather than health care reasons. We did not feel at the time we had enough resources to develop a first-rate medical school in Oklahoma City, let alone try to finance one in Tulsa. But I always have to remind myself that whatever you're doing is never enough to a professional. However good you are, you're never quite good enough to a real professional so they can alway demand more resources. As a lay person, one never knows where that line is. You rely on professional judgments but there is always a certain amount of self interest.
>
> I think on the whole, the Tulsa Medical School experiment was not an unreasonable educational experiment but it certainly split our resources and left us without the kind of resources we felt we needed in Oklahoma City. None of the politicians ever believed us when we told them what it would actually cost to mount the programs there. We estimated to get the college on firm ground would take $8 million a year. I think we got a million and a half.[8]

A dozen years later, in fiscal year 1982-1983, the budget of the Tulsa Medical College was $13.5 million. As far as the school of osteopathy was concerned, Tom Lynn reported that:

> The people around the medical school, Bob Bird included, thought the introduction of a bill to establish a school of osteopathic medicine was a joke. They thought it was a threat by the legislature: "If you don't do what we want you to, we're going to pass this bill!" They didn't take it seriously because at that time, only Michigan had a state school of osteopathy.[9]

219

(OHSF Collection)

John Voorhees, D.O., practices in Oklahoma City. (Oklahoma Osteopathic Association)

But of course, the osteopathic physicians in Oklahoma took it seriously, as John Voorhees, D.O., of Oklahoma City recalled:

There was a serious need for primary care physicians which was not being satisfied by the O.U. med school. About 80 percent of the graduates were going into specialty training, if not more, and about 80 percent of the M.D.s trained in primary care in Oklahoma were leaving the state for other locations.

The reason to put the school in Tulsa was the proximity to a large osteopathic hospital with an excellent clinical teaching potential. The group of doctors in Tulsa who were the prime movers was headed by Dr. Ed Felmlee. A feasibility study was made by the American Osteopathic Association for the legislature. We [in Oklahoma City] were supportive of the concept but I was not confident that the bill to establish a college of osteopathy in Tulsa would get through the legislature. I figured the allopathic [M.D.] profession in the state would pull out their big guns, call in their markers and start things rolling. I really thought it would be shot down.

The leaders in Tulsa believed the D.O.s could relieve the severe need for primary care physicians in the rural areas which were underserved. Eighty percent of the D.O.s in practice today are primary physicians and 58 percent of the ones in Oklahoma practice in towns of less than 50,000 population. I attribute at least part of this to the clinical training years because we have maintained the concept of the rotating internship for the first postgraduate year. Also, we require senior students to spend a month in a general practitioner's office. They

may select the location and many get exposed to the smaller hospital and they realize you can practice good medicine without being neck-deep in subspecialty men. This is where I feel the fault lies with allopathic training, as in the Health Sciences Center, where [students] are taught by specialists who [for example] are convinced in their own mind no one but an otorhinolaryngologist should treat tonsillitis.[10]

Dr. Bird and Dr. Eliel had got the message, so they decided not to fight any longer. Speaking at an open meeting of the Board of Directors of the Tulsa Medical Education Foundation on October 16, 1971, they said a two-year branch of the University of Oklahoma School of Medicine at Tulsa could be a reality by the fall of 1972 if funded by the legislature. They made this statement even before the Booz, Allen and Hamilton consultants began to update their study which resulted in their second report, submitted to the State Legislative Council on January 14, 1972.[11]

While the Tulsa doctors and the Chamber of Commerce renewed their effort to create medical schools in northeast Oklahoma, the "Millis Report", a new study supported them by calling for drastic changes in medical education to produce "an army of physicians," with emphasis on "healer-teacher" doctors helping people stay well. The idea that people had more long-term influence over their health than their doctors was just beginning to penetrate the public awareness. Dr. John Millis said, "A crisis in medical education must be overcome because the American people have determined that health care is a right, not a privilege." The author, president of the National Fund for Medical Education, also cited the need for at least 50,000 more doctors and urged training of more black, Indian and Spanish-speaking physicians, a reduction in the years required to educate a physician, and establishment of a non-governmental Commission on Medical Education.[12]

The Congress was also thinking in the same direction. Senator Edward Kennedy of Massachusetts and Representative Paul Rogers of Florida, both Democrats, drafted and, in November, 1971, pushed through a $3.8 billion, three-year plan to boost enrollments in the nation's 106 medical schools, shorten training by a year and develop new kinds of health workers such as physicians assistants (known as physicians associates at O.U.). This was the beginning of the famous "capitation grants" which would provide $2,500 to the school for each student of medicine, dentistry and osteopathy during his first, second and third years, $4,000 for each one in his fourth year if he is graduating and $6,000 for each one who graduates in the third year as a result of a speeded-up course. The legislation also liberalized current loan and scholarship programs and provided money to build classrooms, laboratories and libraries. Geared to end the doctor shortage by 1978 or 1979, the bill was great news for the financially-strapped O.U. Medical Center.[13]

But there were some different, even contrary ideas beginning to be expressed at that time. James E. Hague, associate director of the American Hospital Association, agreed there was a need for more doctors across the country but pointed out that the shortage "is confined mainly to rural areas and ghettos." To him, the main problem was the uneven distribution of physicians.

Within weeks, the National Health Service Corps was created. It was described as a pioneer effort to cure lack of medical treatment in high crime and low income regions where private doctors hesitate to practice. On December 16, 1971, government-paid physicians, dentists and nurses got their marching orders to begin providing health care in doctor-poor city slums and rural areas, implementing the 1970 Emergency Health Personnel Act. The Corps provided free care for poor people and sliding scale fees for others unable to pay the full cost of medical treatment. This $13 million program "is not socialized medicine," interim director Dr. H. McDonald Rimple

was quick to point out. "It is designed to alleviate the critical manpower shortage in these doctor-starved areas."[14]

Jude Wanniski, writing in the December 11, 1971 *National Observer*, a weekly newspaper based in Washington, D.C., said it was reasonable to assume the nation could rest easy about the doctor shortage because President Nixon had signed the $3.8 billion Kennedy-Rogers bill. With this support, there was plenty of incentive for medical schools to "crank out more and more graduates, perhaps as many as 14,000 a year by 1974, up from 9,000-plus in 1970. The well-advertised shortage of 50,000 physicians would be ended by 1978 when there would be 436,000 practicing physicians compared with 332,000 now." But a few people in Washington were worried. As the architect for the Health Professions Educational Assistance Program, Charles Wagner, expressed it, "The trouble with the federal government is that it responds too late...with too much!" Those few were concerned that government was doing so much tinkering with the doctor-producing machine that "it will not only end the shortage but run amok and produce a surplus."[15]

When the second Booz, Allen and Hamilton report was turned in to the legislature on January 14, 1972, it said a four-year medical school in Tulsa was still not feasible but a clinical medical school, affiliated with O.U. and offering the last two years of medical education, would work. The consultants went on to say such a school could take 50 students a year and eventually expand into a free standing, four-year school of medicine. The two-year clinical program could be accomplished at moderate cost [$1 million a year], and would support expanded residency programs in Tulsa and serve to retain doctors in Oklahoma.

Expanding the entering class of the medical school in the O.U. Health Sciences Center seemed to Booz, Allen and Hamilton to be the least expensive way of adding to the physician supply in the state. But they emphasized that the increased medical school enrollment should be coupled with expanded intern and residency training. The study made it clear the paramount objective of a new medical school in Tulsa was to alleviate the physician shortage on a *state-wide* basis. However, it then went on to illustrate, not the doctor *supply* problem but the doctor *distribution* problem by noting that two-thirds of the physicians in Oklahoma were located in seven counties of the state. Approximately 56 percent of the M.D.s and 51 percent of the D.O.s were located in Tulsa and Oklahoma Counties. Why the consultants implied that the newly gradu-

Medical students at work in 1966. (University of Oklahoma)

ated M.D.s from the Tulsa program would be more inclined to practice in small towns and rural areas than earlier graduates was not explained.[16]

Some of the legislators were convinced this would happen. At least, they had been convinced by the osteopaths that *they* would solve the problem of providing medical service for rural areas. As Dr. E.T. Dunlap recalled:

> Jim Hamilton was in the president's office [president pro tempore of the State Senate] and he was irritated at the whole educational community because we didn't put any family practice physicians out in the country. So he was the one responsible for the Oklahoma College of Osteopathic Medicine in Tulsa…he and Bill Willis, country boys from over in the mountains. Osteopaths had a history of rural community service. He authored the bill but Finis Smith from Tulsa handled it for him. In the same session, on the same day, March 10, 1972, the two bills went through and were signed by Governor Hall establishing the two—the Tulsa Branch of the O.U. College of Medicine also. Finis Smith ushered both of them through.[17]

Bill Willis explained his point of view:

> A good long while ago—and this may sound like a campaign speech—I became more interested in the State of Oklahoma as a whole than I did just my single district. Back in those early years, there was a shortage of doctors. Jim and I both felt the school of medicine down here could accommodate more enrollees; in other words,

we could have a greater output than we were producing. We were unsuccessful getting that accomplished, that is, enlarged enrollment. So we came up with the osteopathic medicine school; we provided for the creation of it. Of course, we authored the bill but we didn't push for another M.D. school. We thought we had already provided for [more] practicing physicians in Oklahoma. I personally took the attitude, "Well, if that will give us still more to have the [M.D.] branch over there and enroll more here, fine and dandy!"

We discussed extensively [the tendency of osteopaths to serve rural communities] before we considered the final plans for putting the school over there. It was our intention to get D.O.s or M.D.s, whatever branch of medicine they followed, out into the rural areas. Many, many of the smaller towns in Oklahoma flat didn't have the services and we wanted to get the services out there. I think Tahlequah is well served now and that's a far cry from those earlier days.[18]

Not every Tulsa doctor went along with the idea of a new medical school in Tulsa. A group of 51 members of the Tulsa County Medical Society criticized the then current residencies in Tulsa and the Tulsa Medical Education Foundation. They recognized a strong need for a family medicine residency program but thought a new trust should be formed to sponsor it. The 51 signatories of an open letter declared, "We stand opposed to the current proposal to establish a branch medical school here in Tulsa." The primary reason given was the failure of the Oklahoma legislature to fund adequately the existing O.U. College of Medicine and the Health Sciences Center in Oklahoma City. They thought it would be more feasible to expand the teaching program there before moving to Tulsa.[19]

Senator Baggett opposed the Tulsa medical schools, but as Senator Hamilton said:

> We were legislative antagonists! He represented the liberal viewpoint and I represented the conservative viewpoint on a lot of issues. He sat right in front of me and we were personally good friends and I had a lot of admiration for him. But we debated a lot of bills, practically every one that came along. He had a lot of talent.…[20]

The way physicians organized themselves to deliver health care influenced the number of doctors required. On October 20, 1972, the Oklahoma Health Sciences Foundation had completed an eight-month study which explored the attitude of doctors and hospitals toward the health maintenance organization (HMO) concept for Dr. Dale Groom and the Oklahoma Regional Medical Program. The first HMO in the entire country had been started at Elk City, Oklahoma, by Dr. Michael A. Shadid in 1930, years before Kaiser-Permanente had the idea to develop an HMO in California. The Oklahoma plan was based at the 30-bed Farmers Union Cooperative Hospital. It cost $18 a *year* for a family of four to receive all of its medical and hospital care, but of course, this was in the depth of the Great Depression. Members of all health maintenance organizations pay a flat fee for complete medical and hospital care in contrast to paying a fee for each service they receive. As a result, the physicians who care for them are motivated to keep the members healthy and out of expensive hospitals; hence the term "health maintenance."

With the advent of Medicare in 1966, the Elk City plan was abandoned after 36 years of service. Oklahoma doctors were not much in favor starting any new ones. Hillcrest Hospital in Tulsa attempted to organize an HMO but met resistance. As Bob Hardy, who did the survey, reported:

> I could find very few physicians who were in favor of HMOs. A doctor I interviewed in Miami, Oklahoma, told me, "If the other members of the (hospital) staff knew I was talking with you about HMOs, I'd be in real trouble. You've got to remember, the doctors up here are about two steps to the right of the John Birch Society!"

The time for the second HMO in Oklahoma had not yet arrived.[21]

Dr. Leonard Eliel shared the concern of the Oklahoma City Chamber of Commerce about the true need for physicians in the state. The legislature had authorized two new, state-supported schools of medicine in Tulsa without knowing if they were really needed. True, Oklahoma had only 117 doctors per 100,000 population compared with the national average of 171. Dr. Rainey Williams said, "The original report in 1958 which led us to believe there was a shortage of doctors and started the whole thing felt that 140 physicians per 100,000 population would be approximately a fair number."[22]

Looking only at the raw ratio of doctors to people was misleading. There had been no scientific determination of the need, i.e., how many doctors was enough to take care of sick people. The distributive range was very wide—from 69 physicians per 100,000 people in Alaska to 199 per 100,000 in New York. Dr. Dennis had previously estimated the need for physician service in Oklahoma. By 1973, the entering class was up to 148, a 41 percent increase since 1966. Dennis recalled:

Jim Dennis foresaw a practical limit to the production of physicians in Oklahoma. (Oklahoma City Chamber of Commerce)

> We talked realistically about getting 165 or 175 students in a class. At that time, the largest medical school in the country was Michigan with approximately 200 students per class. We did not foresee any need for that. We felt that if we could establish a family medicine program and find a way to keep the trainees in the state, we would be producing more than enough physicians to meet our needs, realizing it would take a decade to do it.[23]

Dr. Eliel wanted to know if 175 in a class was still an appropriate target. Where should the medical school enrollment plateau? He asked the Oklahoma Health Sciences Foundation to find the answer to the question, "How many physicians does Oklahoma need?"

This question was not simple because it generated other questions, such as: how many doctors do we need to do what?—take care of sick people, conduct medical research, teach medical students, administer medical institutions such as health departments, hospitals, medical schools and other health science schools? How many of what kind of doctors do we need?—doctors of medicine, doctors of osteopathy, generalists, specialists? What kind of specialists do we need?

Even if an ideal ratio of physicians to population were established, it would not speak to the important considerations of: where the doctors are—how they distribute themselves in cities, towns and rural areas; what they do—whether they take care of sick people or do something else, like research, or teaching or administration; whom they care for—whether they serve rich and poor, black and white, Indians and other minorities, veterans and non-veterans, welfare and Medicare patients; what they specialize in—whether they take care of families for their total health needs or treat referred patients for special problems— whether they have a general specialty, such as pediatrics, or a satellite specialty, such as pediatric urology.

Another extremely important consideration was the kind of health care delivery system they work in. Are they in: private, solo practice; partnership with one or two other doctors; group practice; institutional medicine, such as V.A. hospitals or state mental health centers; health maintenance organizations; or hospital outpatient clinics and emergency rooms? Complicating these questions was the *certainty* that the health care delivery system would change over time and the *uncertainties* of how, how much and how fast.

It appeared, then, that merely striving to achieve a doctor population ratio in Oklahoma as high as the average ratio in the United States was not an appropriate goal. The average might be completely inadequate to provide needed and expected health services in Oklahoma or, on the other hand, it could provide a surplus of physicians. And it was entirely conceivable that it could do both simultaneously, i.e., furnish more than enough doctors in some places in the state and less than enough in other places.[24] Dr. Sharp pointed up:

> One very basic question: when we talk about highly specialized and trained personnel in health care, we are talking also about societal needs and we are trying to match the two. What may appear to be a professional surplus to one group is still a shortage to another, depending on where one sits. There are elements of qualitative and subjective judgment here, politically and socially.[25]

The Foundation study had two purposes: to find out how many physicians Oklahoma needed and to suggest ways by which the state could improve its health care delivery system. The title of the study which Robert Hardy completed in June, 1973 was a bit misleading. It repeated Dr. Eliel's question, *How Many Physicians Does Oklahoma Need?* but it answered the question, how much medical service do the people of Oklahoma *demand* and how much can the physicians in the state provide? In addition, it figured out what the supply and demand situation would be a dozen years later, in 1985. A simple market study.

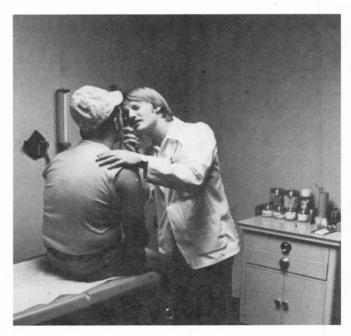

The OHSF market study compared patient demand for care with the capacity of Oklahoma doctors to meet that demand. (University of Oklahoma)

In fact, it was so deceptively simple, it was incredible that the method previously had not been used to measure the health care market. To be sure, it did *not* measure the unmet need for physician care of people who, because of insufficient education, financial resources or motivation, did not seek or were deprived of health services. But it measured how much service people wanted and were able to pay for, a quantity heretofore unmeasured. The title might better have been, How Many Physicians Does Oklahoma Require to Meet the Demand for Health Care?

The study made two basic assumptions which seemed entirely reasonable: people in Oklahoma were as healthy as people elsewhere in the United States and visited their doctor about the same number of times each year as the average person; and doctors in Oklahoma were as educated, qualified and hardworking as the average physician in the United States. Each Oklahoma doctor provided quality health care to a number of patients equal to the average number seen each year by physicians throughout the United States.

The average number of visits which Oklahomans made to their doctor each year was compared to the number of patient visits the doctors in Oklahoma were capable of accommodating in a year. Data compiled by the U.S. Public Health Service National Center for Health Statistics provided information about how often people see their doctor. While this varied widely by sex, color, family income, geographic location, area of residence (urban or rural) marital status and age, the average for all persons of all ages was then 4.3 visits per year.

Population figures by Oklahoma county, distributed by age, permitted the visit demand to be determined by simple calculation. Statistics about the way physicians practiced in the early 1970s were available in a publication called *1972 Reference Data on the Profile of Medical Practice*, published by the American Medical Association. This listed the average number of office visits doctors accommodated per week, how many weeks per year they worked, and how these numbers varied by specialty—general practice, surgery, pediatrics, etc.—and by census division—New England, West North Central, Mountain, Pacific and the other five. By counting the number of practicing physicians in each county and noting their specialty, the capability of those doctors to meet the demand for medical service in their area could be compared. For example: in 1972, the 4,145 people in Cimarron County would demand a total of 17,965 office visits per year. Two general practitioners, each seeing 161 patients a week and working 48.9 weeks a year could see 15,746 patients in a year. The service deficit was 2,219 visits, the equivalent of one quarter of a doctor. This meant the two doctors in the county had to work a little harder than average or some patients had to travel out of the county for care.

In the area which includes Ottowa, Delaware and Craig Counties, in the opposite corner of Oklahoma, the 62,289 people there required 277,543 office visits. The 49 doctors could furnish 287,119 visits, 9,576 more than the average demand. This was the equivalent of 1.22 physicians more than the demand justified. By extrapolating on the basis of anticipated population increases as well as the additional supply of doctors being educated at O.U., the balance for 1985 was determined.

The study, published in June, 1973, reached these conclusions:

1. There are enough physicians in Oklahoma now (1973) to serve adequately every person in the state.

2. In fact, there is a surplus of 443 doctors in Oklahoma now (1973).

3. In 1985, there will be a surplus of 1,207 doctors in Oklahoma.

4. Physicians have found it increasingly difficult to practice modern medicine by themselves in the small towns and rural areas of Oklahoma. Consequently, these communities and areas are underserved medically despite the surplus of professional capacity to render health care in Oklahoma.

5. Expanding the O.U. College of Medicine and/or establishing a college of osteopathy in Tulsa to educate more physicians will NOT solve the problem of providing physician care to people in small towns and rural areas WHERE THEY LIVE. Educating more physicians in Oklahoma will merely increase the cost of medical service to patients and taxpayers. Many people have the idea that doctors operate in a free market. They do not. The study showed that in the Pacific, Mountain and New England states where the ratio of physicians to population was the highest, fees were also significantly above average. When physicians see fewer patients, they tend to charge each patient more. In a free and open market, increased competition tends to depress prices.

6. Oklahoma already enrolls 1.2 percent of the first year medical students in the U.S. (148 of 12,361 freshman students in 1972). This means that, because Oklahoma's population represents 1.2 percent of the national population, the O.U. College of Medicine is now producing its proportional share of physicians. There has been a 41 percent increase in the size of the entering class since 1966 (from 105 to 148 students).

7. There are more than enough general hospital beds in Oklahoma.

8. The presence of a modern hospital in a small community will not necessarily assure that physicians will locate there.

9. More than a third of O.U. Medical College graduates take their post-doctoral training (internship and residency) outside of Oklahoma. This occurs because the opportunities for post-graduate education in Oklahoma are deficient in number and attractiveness. Physicians have a tendency to go into practice where they receive their last post-graduate training.

10. Merely graduating more physicians in Oklahoma will not assure adequate distribution of health services throughout Oklahoma. Therefore, a different system of delivering health care to people in small towns and rural areas should be developed and implemented. The system suggested is the *Time-Availability System* proposed by William G. Anlyan, M.D., Vice President for Health Affairs, Duke University, for approval by the Association of American Medical Colleges (AAMC) on October 30, 1971. This system recommended: self or "buddy" care to take care of dire emergencies within 0 to 15 minutes of need. This

kind of emergency care should be taught in every junior and senior high school; rescue squads of trained allied health personnel within 15 to 30 minutes of need. For non-emergency care, nurse practitioners to render preventive care, operate screening clinics and treat lesser illnesses; primary medical care rendered by groups of 8 to 10 physicians within one hour of need. Such services would include obstetrics and minor surgery; standard secondary specialty care within two hours of need; and tertiary subspecialty care in a university hospital or its equivalent within five hours of need.

Hardy's study went on to indicate how the health personnel appropriate to this system could be educated and deployed. Finally, a summary of recommendations outlined the action which should be taken by the appropriate leaders, organizations, agencies and institutions in Oklahoma:

1. Adopt the principles of the Time-Availability Health Care Delivery System for Oklahoma.

2. Limit the size of the entering class in the O.U. College of Medicine to the current level of 148.

3. Abandon plans for the establishment of a college of medicine and a college of osteopathy in Tulsa.

4. Expand opportunities in Oklahoma for postgraduate medical training, particularly in regional centers in Oklahoma. Relate these expanded opportunities to the need for various medical specialists throughout the state.

5. Expand the Physicians Associate Program in the O.U. College of Health.

6. Expand or redirect nursing education programs in Oklahoma as indicated in order to educate more family nurse practitioners.

7. Encourage the concept of "branching" as a way to bring periodic physician services to people outside of the regional centers. Branching is the provision of health services by an established hospital or clinic at locations remote from its base.

8. Improve emergency medical services throughout Oklahoma.

9. Expand the health education programs in Oklahoma public schools on all levels, kindergarten through high school, with particular emphasis on first aid at the junior high and high school levels.[25]

Dr. John Schilling talked about the need for doctors in Oklahoma:

Let's say 600 to 750 people need one doctor, in Oklahoma you'd come out needing four or five thousand doctors. [In 1982, there were 4,776 M.D.s and D.O.s in

Governor Hall, astute politician. (Oklahoma Observer)

the state.] If you just educate what you need and the practicing life of a physician is 30 to 35 years, you'd need a graduating class of roughly 150. I've always felt an area should educate the equivalent of their needs.

One of the reasons I left Oklahoma was this very thing. Governor Hall made a political speech and said, "We need 50 doctors in southeast Oklahoma and we need 50 more out in the northwest corner of the state. That's a hundred doctors, so by golly, we're going to set up a new medical school that will train a hundred doctors *a year* to take care of it." It was a politcal gambit! In essence, he was going to train *3,000* doctors for those areas!

The University of Washington, where Dr. Schilling went, serves the four state area of Washington, Alaska, Montana and Idaho (WAMI) with a population of seven million. The medical school has an entering class of 175. Oklahoma, with a population of three million, graduated 268 physicians in 1983.[26]

With Dr. Eliel gone, the Foundation's study report on the need for physicians in Oklahoma could not be delivered to the vice-president who requested it. On July 6, 1973, it was presented to the executive committee of the Oklahoma Health Sciences Foundation of which both the acting provost of the OUHSC and the chancellor of the State Regents for Higher Education were members. E.T. Dunlap said he regretted the study had not been available two years before. Although the foundation executive who did the study recommended it be circulated to state legislators, Dr.

Bill Brown, the acting provost, said "The way this information is transmitted to the legislature should be thought out carefully and the study should be circulated selectively." The Foundation accepted the study report with appreciation. It never got to the legislature.[27]

Of course, this report placed the chancellor in an awkward position. Even if he agreed with it, which he did not say, it was not politically appropriate for him to champion it. Dr. Dunlap said the conclusion of the Booz, Allen report was:

There is not just now justification for a full-dress medical school in Tulsa. However, there is need for attention to medical education in the growing metropolitan area of Tulsa and there are clinical facilities that should be used. Over here [in Oklahoma City] they said we can't expand the input class because of limited facilities for clinical experience. The recommendation was, and the [state] regents concurred, that the University of Oklahoma College of Medicine would establish an upper level clinical operation to utilize those hospitals over in Tulsa and enlarge the class, eventually to 200, and send 50 a year to Tulsa for the last two years of medical school.

Frankly, with inept leadership after Jim Dennis left, we couldn't get the school of medicine to do that. We provided $100 thousand in consulting money, each year for two years, and they sat on their can and didn't do a damn thing toward concrete development [of the branch]. In 1971, Finis Smith came to me and said, "We're tired of waiting. You folks agreed in 1968 to develop a clinical program in Tulsa." Well, the legislative council made a study in 1971. Bill Willis and Jim Hamilton got into it and they came back to the legislature in 1972 with the recommendation there be a program of medical education in Tulsa. The bills to establish the Tulsa branch and the college of osteopathy became law on the tenth of March.

Finis and Bill called me up to their office and said, "We're going to introduce two bills [to organize these schools] and we want you to draft them for us." I said, "If you boys know what you want, why…fine. If you're going to do it, we'll be glad to be helpful," which was always my policy. Whether I agreed with them or not, I worked *with* the legislature. I learned a long time ago, you can't go off and cry-baby because tomorrow you're going to come back and beg them for something else.[28]

Senator Hamilton gave his reasons for insisting on these two new medical schools:

We were very disturbed because we were only graduating about 110 students from the medical school. Being from a rural area, I was more cognizant of the lack of medical facilities, medical doctors. We had only three

James Hamilton, D-Poteau, on the floor of the Senate. (Oklahoma Observer)

counties in Oklahoma that met the national average of doctors per population ratio—Oklahoma, Tulsa and, I believe Enid [Garfield County]. We had 74 counties that had an inadequate number of doctors. That's when we initiated the doctor studies and that lay the basis for increased funding at the University of Oklahoma and to open the additional campus at Tulsa.

That's exactly why we did it. We wanted to get them out into the rural areas. We pay taxes in the rural areas and we felt that people paying taxes there were just as entitled to good medical treatment as those who lived in Oklahoma City, Tulsa or Enid. One of the bases for opening the two schools in Tulsa was they didn't have the [clinical] facilities in Oklahoma City to increase the number of students needed at that time.[29]

Jim Hamilton even changed the bill Dr. Dunlap had drafted to read that the State Regents would establish, maintain and operate a college of osteopathy in Tulsa. He wanted to be sure it got started right and under this direct order, Chancellor Dunlap had little choice but to comply. He promised the legislators that 20 months from the fall of 1973, the State Regents would open the school of osteopathy; and they did.

The OHSF study showed that the number of physicians then in Oklahoma was more than ample to meet the demand for health service and only 61 physicians would have to be enticed into less populated areas of the state to solve the doctor distribution problem. It appeared the two new colleges of medicine in Tulsa would needlessly cost Oklahoma taxpayers at least $50 million over the next decade. Bob Hardy commented:

> Predictably, my study report went over like a pregnant pole-vaulter with the Tulsa Chamber of Commerce. They even had an "expert" pick it apart to show that its methods were statistically poor and its conclusions were invalid. About a year later, though, another health planner independently devised and used this same method to determine the need for doctors and reported it in the literature, so it must not have been completely irrational.

Not all Tulsans approved the idea of creating new medical schools there. William A. Bell, an attorney and a trustee of the Oklahoma Medical Research Foundation, called the decision "great political wisdom":

> At that time, the studies indicated that Oklahoma, at the very best, didn't have the teaching material nor the resources to really have two med schools. Even to put the upper division in Tulsa for the clinical programs, we were going to stretch our resources; funding, patients and so on. So the legislature comes along and, for political reasons, authorizes *two* med schools. Instead of recognizing we have limited resources in medical education, the legislature had now allowed three med schools where at best we could support two. We talk about what we've done with federal funds to build this health sciences center in Oklahoma City, but we have not faced the reality of funding it correctly from state sources.[30]

Robert E.L. Richardson agreed:

> I suggested to Governor Hall that we might not have sufficient funds to have one, excellent college of medicine and therefore we shouldn't open a college of medicine in Tulsa. Also, looking back at the Carnegie study [which recommended establishment of a school of medicine in Tulsa], my attitude was there was going to be an oversupply of M.D.s and I think that's happening or it will. And I suggested they *certainly* should not open both an M.D. college and a college of osteopathic medicine in Tulsa. In that same conversation, I said the two schools [allopathic and osteopathic medicine], ought to be joined as they did in California. The governor said, "That's the type of thing we might do *after* I'm reelected."[31]

Frosty Troy, publisher of the *Oklahoma Observer* and a watcher of the political scene for 30 years, had this to say:

> I thought the branch of the medical school was a serious mistake. Number one, we didn't need it and, number two, it was just to take care of some hospital rivalries between Tulsa and Oklahoma City. We really couldn't afford it. [But] I was very much for the osteopathic facility. I thought it *really* fit a need. The plain truth is, the medical profession has made *no* attempt at all, until recent years, to provide any care in rural and small-town Oklahoma. Fact is, a lot of those guys can't get out of medical school fast enough to get into one of those comfortable suburbs in one of the larger communities. I don't go to osteopathic physicians, but they are the only consistent medical treatment rural Oklahoma has and I can show that to you on a map. I can put the little red pins where they are. Maybe it was because they were already there. But all I know is that if you went to Wilburton, or Kiowa or Sallisaw or most of the smaller communities, people were being treated by osteopathic physicians. Now even they are starting to get out of that a little bit.[32]

Dean William E. Brown also asked the question, "How much is enough health manpower?" He knew Oklahoma needed more dentists but he wanted the statistics to support this position and his application for capital funding from the Health Professions Educational Assistance Program.

In March, 1974, the Oklahoma Health Sciences Foundation completed a study covering dentistry, a study similar to the previous year's survey of the need for physicians. Again, the difference between the *demand* for dental services and the *need* for dental health care was stressed. Everybody needs dental health services but many people do not seek them because they may not understand the importance of or have any interest in taking care of their teeth. Some do not go because there is no dentist nearby and they will not take the time and trouble to go where dentists are available. For others, dental care is on the bottom of their spending priority list.

The demand thus varies widely with age, sex, color, education, socioeconomic status, residence, geographic region and other factors. In 1974, according to the National Center for Health Statistics of the U.S. Public Health Service, demand ranged from seven-tenths of one visit to the dentist per year for non-white persons to 2.5 visits per year for members of families with $15 thousand or more annual income. Less than half of the American people saw their dentist, if indeed they had one, once a year.

In 1974, Oklahoma had 1,025 practicing dentists, more than half of whom were located in the metropolitan areas of the state's two largest cities. There were 109 specialists, three-quarters of whom were in Oklahoma City and Tulsa. Comparing per capita visits to

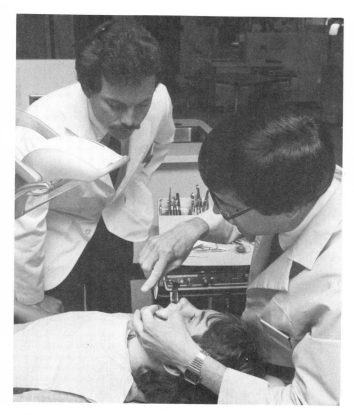

There was little question Oklahoma needed a dental college. (University of Oklahoma)

Governor David Boren. (University of Oklahoma)

the dentist's office with the capability of these 1,025 Oklahoma dentists to see and treat patients, the state had a deficit of at least 253 dentists, depending on how it was calculated. When Oklahoma's population was divided by white and non-white and national estimates of the demand for dental visits were classified according to color and applied, the Oklahoma dentist shortfall rose to 276.

The ratio of dentists to population in Oklahoma was 42 per 100,000 compared with the national average of 59.4 dentists per 100,000 people. The difference from state to state was extensive, ranging from 27 in Mississippi to 81 in New York. Oklahoma ranked 39th among the states.

The study estimated that to satisfy the true *need* for dental care in Oklahoma would require 1,109 additional dentists, more than twice the number then in practice. By projecting the output of the new dental school and the growth of the state's population, it looked as though the supply of dentists would grow to meet the *demand* for dental care by 1988, a matter of 15 years. On the other hand, assuming no advances in care and prophylactic methods and no increase in the use of dental assistants and hygienists,

the study estimated it would take *142 years* to educate enough dentists to satisfy completely the *need* for dental care in Oklahoma. The decision to establish a college of dentistry in Oklahoma appeared eminently appropriate.[33]

When David Boren ran for governor in 1974, he used a new broom as the symbol of the approach he would take if elected. On July 20 that year, he charged that "old guard politics has left our medical center gravely threatened." Two of his pledges in a five-point plan toward "solving the medical center crisis" were: a state appropriation to create 50 new residency positions in hospitals. He said the state was short this number per graduating class which caused doctors to leave the state for post-doctoral training and remain elsewhere; and an expansion of rural medical scholarships by providing smaller communities with grants to attract medical personnel.

Finally, there appeared to be a shift in the approach to solving the physician shortage problem. Finally, there was a glimmer of recognition that producing more doctors in Oklahoma did not get them into the small towns and the ghettos where they were needed most. Candidate Boren achieved this insight in an interesting way. About the time Hardy had completed his physician manpower study in 1973 which indicated Oklahoma already had more than enough doctors, Dr. Tom Lynn did a private study for Dean Bob Bird which, he said, "indicated the establishment of additional resources for undergraduate students was not appropriate. What we ought to be doing was establishing more residency positions." Tom Lynn continued: "He [Boren] first heard that in a speech I

Evangelist Oral Roberts, spiritual leader of millions of people who listen and watch on radio and television. (Oral Roberts Evangelistic Association)

gave to the Oklahoma Academy of Family Practice, where he and I were speakers on the same program."[34]

David Boren remembered his campaign promises. He had been governor only a few months when, on April 26, 1975, he announced that agreement had been reached with the State Regents to fully fund the operational budget requests of the medical school. He also pointed out, "One of the real problems is that we have been graduating more people from our medical schools each year than we have residencies in Oklahoma. This has been a tragic mistake, particularly for rural Oklahoma...." He went on to say the immediate goal was to create 50 more residencies in the state. Lynn was one of the ideation authors of the legislation which established the Oklahoma Physician Manpower Training Commission that year.

The fifth point in Governor Boren's plan to rescue the Medical Center was to provide the medical head "full authority over all medical center functions subject to review only by the university president and regents." With a strong provost on board, it now appeared the proposed functional relationship between the Norman campus and the OUHSC, advocated by Hollomon and reiterated by Dumas, had been discarded. Back to the days of Dennis! The controversy had come full circle.[35]

On April 28, 1975, Oral Roberts University in Tulsa announced a plan to get into professional education including law, nursing, dentistry and medicine. This generated a lot of conversation about the need for more such programs, although ORU said it was focusing on national needs and the missionary field. Despite these disclaimers, Governor Boren decided to take "a harder look" at building a new facility for the Tulsa branch of the O.U. College of Medicine. It now appeared that Tulsa, which had struggled so desperately to get one medical school, was about to have three.[36]

CHAPTER 31

DREAMS COMING TRUE—
DREAMS GONE AWRY: 1970-1975

Nancy Davies and Dan Macer at the dedication of the VA Hospital research wing on April 4, 1972. (OHSF Collection)

The radiology addition. (OHSF Collection)

On August 21, 1970, The Veterans Administration Hospital announced a $2 million research addition to be located at its northeast corner. This three-story, 30,000 square foot laboratory building would expand the V.A. scientific investigation program and allow the space in the hospital then being used for research to be converted to patient care. During the early 1970s, the federal government was struggling to keep up with the demand for care in the nation's 166 Veterans Administration hospitals. A waiting list of 6,300 patients had built up, although four of every ten applicants for admission were being rejected. This increased patient load reflected the growth in veterans rolls resulting from the Vietnam war, plus the fact that World War II veterans were growing older and needed more health services. Also, V.A. hospital operating budgets were too tight to permit full utilization of all the facilities the government had.

Dan Macer reported that outpatient visits at the Oklahoma City unit had quadrupled since 1962, from 25,000 to 100,000 a year. Fortunately, the research addition, which was completed and dedicated on April 4, 1972, freed 5,000 square feet of space in the main building for patient care. But Macer could see that would not meet even the current demands, to say nothing of the future, so he had already started planning another addition to the hospital. The proposed 30,000 square foot expansion would provide needed outpatient clinic space and permit conversion of 46 beds to psychiatric service. Also, he planned 120 extended care beds in coordination with the university. The package was expected to cost $19.4 million. As previously mentioned, these ideas expanded significantly two years later with the advent of the federal state sharing concept.[1]

Across 13th Street at University Hospital, the addition to radiology came about because the department had accumulated enough private patient fee income to pay for it. Functionally, it satisfied the immediate needs of the radiology department but it was hardly an architectural triumph. It looked like a massive brick carbuncle obstructing the main entrance to the university clinics. The project was well along by the time the campus architect arrived in Oklahoma and it made Arthur Tuttle realize that there were two levels of development occurring on the Medical Center campus, the expedient and the long range:

> This was an ill-conceived building, built "quick and dirty" and to hell with anything else. It was unfortunate esthetically, functionally and operationally; a good example of short-range development to serve an immediate purpose at the expense of a good, long-term solution. At the same time, the radiology department in the new University Hospital was under construction.[2]

A major, central shared facility started April 16, 1971, with the dedication of the site of the $4 million steam and chilled water plant at 8th and Laird. Originally, the Oklahoma Health Sciences Foundation expected to become the general administrative office for

Leonard Eliel (left) and members of the O.U. Development Authority at the dedication of the site. (Oklahoma Journal)

the campus and the operator of the proposed central, shared facilities. However, in the course of obtaining tax-exempt (501-c-3) status from the Internal Revenue Service, the Foundation was told it could not operate such facilities on a permanent basis. The tax exemption was essential because the Foundation was supported by contributions which would not have been forthcoming had they not been tax deductible. For this reason, the Foundation recommended that the university develop the steam and chilled water plant. O.U. appeared to be the logical entity to do this because it was the first institution which would need heating and cooling for its new buildings. Arthur Tuttle talked about the situation:

> One of the ideas in [the university's portion of] the health center development that couldn't quite come off was that some entity other than the university was going to have certain functions…steam and chilled water, for example. I recall some of the agonizing that went on when finally the O.U. Foundation took over the responsibility for building the steam and chilled water plant. My feeling is that you look at where you're trying to go, not the means to get there. I felt the university could reach its ends several different ways.[3]

The university did not have the money to build the steam plant and was reluctant to ask the State Regents for permission to sell revenue bonds. It was the attitude of the State Regents that if O.U. needed a building, the State of Oklahoma would appropriate funds. But the university was pressured because it had two buildings under construction and no way to heat or cool them. Boyd Gunning, head of the O.U. Foun-

dation, the university's fundraising organization, became interested in the problem. Tuttle continued:

> A lot of people do not appreciate the fact that the O.U. Foundation ultimately built the first phase of the steam and chilled water plant. It was not until the big, second phase came into being that the university became the direct owner of the property. The O.U. Development Authority and the O.U. Foundation funded the project and were taking the risks, taking the heat until the $16 million bond issue was sold that refinanced the original bond issue. At that point, the university took it over but before that, there was a little entity, the O.U. Development Authority, sitting there owning and operating a steam and chilled water plant and being responsible for collecting funds from everybody [it served], including the University of Oklahoma, to pay the debt service.[4]

On May 14, 1971, Colin MacLeod, M.D., world-class research scientist and new president of the Oklahoma Medical Research Foundation, conducted dedication ceremonies honoring John Rogers, Tulsa attorney and state civic leader for whom the Foundation's new office building at 15th Street and Phillips Avenue was named. For years, Mr. Rogers had been a trustee of the Foundation and had helped it become established and financed. The space in this five-story building was assigned to OMRF administrative and service functions but the Foundation had more room than it could use, so it rented areas to the Oklahoma Heart Association, the university Medical Center administration and the Oklahoma Health Sciences Foundation. Office accommodations in the Oklahoma Health Center were then very limited because most of the major new buildings were still under construction or on the drawing boards.[5]

Less than nine months later, February 7, 1972, after 14 years of service, Reece McGee, the executive vice president of the Oklahoma Medical Research Foundation, abruptly resigned. Harvey Everest, a member of the board, speculated this caused quite a strain on the president. On the following Saturday, Colin MacLeod died of a heart attack in London, England, at age 62, leaving the foundation suddenly leaderless. Reece McGee observed, "Colin MacLeod understood administration. He knew it was a necessary evil in order to produce good science. He was an excellent scientist himself, known throughout the country and, at the time he died, he was trying to recruit some excellent young researchers from all over the country. Harvey Everest agreed, "Colin MacLeod was truly a great scientist and a great find for us. His tragic death

232

Dr. Colin MacLeod and Harvey Everest. (Oklahoma Medical Research Foundation)

COTPA co-chairman James Tolbert III. (James Tolbert III)

set us back quite a bit. With him gone, that's when I assumed charge of the foundation for a short while."[6]

As planning for expanded campus parking facilities went forward, it took eight months after bids were received for the Central Oklahoma Transportation and Parking Authority to get the lot at 13th Street and Phillips Avenue surfaced and in operation. This first temporary unit in the parking system had 388 spaces and by the end of the first week in March, 1971, all but 30 of the 260 spaces for lease had been snapped up at a monthly rate of $10. The 128 spaces for visitors were pulling in about 100 parkers a day. The charge was 50 cents for up to 12 hours. Toby Akkola, COTPA director, called it "an instant success," which may have been a slight exaggeration but it did mean the principle of centralized administration of a parking system for the Oklahoma Health Center was now under demonstration and the prognosis for the parking blanket idea was positive, indeed. Architects Shaw and Shaw had designed the first two units of the parking blanket, a 363-space module for the State Health Department and a thousand spaces in another location to serve the university. COTPA chairman Earl Sneed said this first phase would cost $4.83 million.[7]

Unfortunately, this optimistic future was short-lived. Nine months later, the plan for a centrally operated parking system in the Oklahoma Health Center ran into a political squall, capsized and swifty sank. James Tolbert III, the co-chairman of the Central Oklahoma Transportation and Parking Authority, recounted the events:

The principles that were at issue in the beginning had to do with whether the health sciences community—employees, institutions and, to a lesser extent, visitors—could be expected to pay for their parking to the degree required to pay for the parking structures. We started out by putting in some surface lots as a basic matter of accommodating the community to what the future was all about and to provide income to the university and COTPA to compensate for the planning costs to get the system off the ground. The issues were: was it right to charge and was it economic to charge, given the wage scale of a lot of "entry-level" employees who were out there? Then there were the questions of ownership and COTPA's involvement on state property. Those were intertwined with the conflicts of goals and needs between the university, the health department and some of the other institutions in the OHC which were in different stages of their evolution and their understanding of what they were about.

I'm not sure I can put my finger on the ultimate problem that led us to the governor's mansion. Maybe I blocked that out because I got so angry. I think the critical issue was the matter of turf between the governor, the [State] Board of Affairs, the university and the health department, primarily. Secondly, if there were politics, the fact that COTPA was going to control financing ar-

These pedestrian walkways were dead-ended for more than a decade. (Oklahoma City Chamber of Commerce)

rangements and the awarding of construction contracts was an unstated issue. Finally, there was a truly felt concern whether the state and the state-related institutions out there should be providing a potential stream of income to a trust that would benefit the city. There were all kinds of advantages to the city [because the project] provided substantial Urban Renewal [local, non-cash grants-in-aid] credits at a time they were needed badly. [Locally-financed public improvements earned credits toward Urban Renewal matching requirements which could then release more federal funding.] This made the state uncomfortable about helping the city.

Senator Berrong was opposed to the city being involved in a state project and he was essentially opposed to pay parking. We had a meeting with the governor [David Hall] and thought we had resolved all of the issues. Senator Berrong was harassing us throughout the meeting. Then we went back some days later and found out it was as though we hadn't even had the first meeting.

That was during the time Mr. Rader and his organization were beginning to penetrate the Health Sciences Center and there was probably opposition from some elements there. I was terribly frustrated by all that because I thought it was such a nifty idea and I thought we had it down to the wire, ready to go. The ownership of the structures, when fully amortized, would have reverted to the agency on whose land they were built.[8]

Bids on the first two units of the parking system had been taken on June 25 and there was an August 26, 1972, deadline for awarding the construction contract. COTPA had waited for more than two weeks for word from Governor Hall's aide, attorney Robert E. Lee Richardson, as to whether or not it should proceed but the word never came and the deadline passed. Sneed told the governor in a letter, "We do not believe there is any opportunity to revive those bids."

Shaw and Shaw had invested $135 thousand in de-

signing and drawing plans for the parking system. Dr. George Cross, president of the Oklahoma Health Sciences Foundation, said this delay caused $1 million in urgently needed street improvements to be suspended and $2 million in other federally funded improvements "to come to a sudden stop." Sneed even offered to proceed with the building of the parking structure for the state health department and turn it over at COTPA's cost to the entity designated by Governor Hall. But the double walkways at the second floor level, designed to connect the building with the proposed garage, were destined to lead nowhere for the next 10 and a half years.[9]

Along with the unstated issue of COTPA controlling the financing and the award of construction contracts for the parking system was the unstated suspicion that Earl Sneed and Jim Tolbert stood to gain financially from the project. This was totally unfounded. All they were trying to do was perform a needed public service. Jim Tolbert explained Earl Sneed's feelings:

He was cut up about it. He had a lot of pride in what we were doing at COTPA and he had a lot of pride in his own ability to work out good things with public entities. He took it personally that we lost this project. It made so much sense to him and yet he had been unable to prevent the outcome. His reputation as a successful facilitator was damaged.

More than that, he and I both felt very strongly that we were providing a much needed service and we were doing it in a manner that was going to enhance the whole project physically. That was the waste. We all knew eventually the structures would be built, they would end up costing more and they wouldn't be done right because it wouldn't be a comprehensive, consolidated, managed system, to say nothing of the esthetics. It looks tacky, and it's a damned shame![10]

The OHSF executive found this untimely abortion of the original OHC plan hard to accept and attempted to salvage the parking program by suggesting a different sponsor for the system. Hardy reasoned that if the legislature and the state's chief executive did not want a local organization operating on state property, the University of Oklahoma, a creature of the state, ought to be acceptable. After all, the O.U. Development Authority and the O.U. Foundation had assumed responsibility for the construction and operation of the steam and chilled water plant which would also serve the entire, multi-institutional campus.

On September 28, 1972, at a meeting of the O.U. Regents Health Sciences Center committee in the Faculty House, Hardy advanced this idea. What he

Earl Sneed and Mayor Latting enter a new COTPA bus in August, 1974. Director Toby Akkola is immediately behind Sneed. (The Oklahoman)

did not appreciate was the intensifying pressure Dr. Sharp was getting from his regents and the legislature to do something about the management problems on the Oklahoma City campus. The budget shortfall, the furor caused by the suggestion that Children's Hospital be shut down and the mounting discontent of legislative leaders with the whole situation gave the president of the university more problems than he could say grace over. Dr. Sharp gave the Foundation planner the courtesy of hearing his ideas but reacted immediately. "Hardy," he said, shaking his head, "that's just like straightening the deck chairs while the Titanic is sinking!"

Oklahoma City Mayor Patience Latting, a member of the COTPA board, said:

> We were disappointed, frankly, and it was somewhat of a surprise to us. It seemed to us, with COTPA'S experience in operating the other parking facilities in the city, it was a natural thing. COTPA was doing quite well and we never defaulted on any bonds issued to build parking garages in Oklahoma City. I think it would have been cheaper in the long run for the health center and for the patients and others using it.[11]

So the parking blanket plan stayed on the bottom, lost and layered over by many fathoms of political and territorial conflict, never to rise again. While it looked very much as though the Oklahoma Health Center plan were coming unglued, all was not gloom, as Dr. Bill Brown recounted:

> The money for the Dental Clinical Sciences Building came through [in September, 1972] but it was after the second try. The first time through, the Feds placed a moratorium on all funding and recycled things, in part to add the environmental protection statement [requirements] to all grant applications to be sure the community was being managed appropriately. That delayed us about a year. And the biomedical sciences building was in the same boat. [John R. "Jack" Sokatch, Professor of Microbiology, was chairman of the planning committee which had been working on this project since 1969.]
>
> A number of us went to Washington to talk with the staff about what to do, what our chances [of funding] were, so we could develop a strategy. In fact, at that time, we had three applications in: the library, biomedical sciences and this dental building. The staff said, "Fellers, if you're lucky, you might get one of them funded, but if you think you are going to get more than that, you guys are out of your minds!" So we came back— Bob Bird, Arthur Tuttle and I—and we made a commitment. We'd scrub the library for that cycle; we knew we couldn't get that. But we decided we'd go full ahead to get these two buildings in tandem. Very interesting! I was on the N.I.H. review committee for dental facilities and I guess if I'd had my selfish hat working, I'd have fought for the dental building and to hell with biomedical sciences. But, very honestly, Bob Bird and I were very close.... I had great respect for that man. And I thought, "One without the other isn't really worthwhile doing." So we scrapped all the way for the two of them![12]

Arthur Tuttle said the federal government wanted the university to say which application should be funded first but O.U. refused. Both buildings were critical to the university's academic program in the health sciences. Dr. Brown continued:

> The two buildings were funded to the full amount that we had requested. It was a calculated risk but there was a big payoff. These two buildings received about 16.5 million federal dollars to match with [$5.5 million in] HERO bond money. The total federal dollars available for the entire country that year was $90 million so we got a heck of a percentage of the money in that cycle.[13]

The very next year, however, the university promptly experienced the effect of the Nixon administration's

Everett Tower: the new University Hospital. (University of Oklahoma)

determination to hold down spending. Dr. David Steen, associate dean of the College of Health, related the event:

In January, 1973, after the November in which Nixon was elected for a second term, he took all of the money out of health facilities in the United States. The money for the construction of the college of health was appropriated but he told the director of the Office of Management and Budget [OMB] not to spend it. We had just gotten notice from Washington that our application had been approved and we were due to be funded. We had a party at my house, the architects Murray, Jones and Murray came down from Tulsa and we celebrated, prematurely![14]

As Dean Schottstaedt said:

That sort of thing was not unheard of but it changed all of our plans. It looked as though we were going to have to continue operating in these small, cottage-style arrangements forever, which didn't work nearly as well as one would like because of physical separation of the departments. We had no place we could get all the faculty together in one room.

Actually, I expected it to be simply a matter of waiting and some day we would have a new building for the school. The planning had gone on for a long time, it seemed to be well accepted by the planning group on the campus and it had been approved in Washington.[15]

The new Everett Tower essentially had been completed since September 1, 1972. It had been patientless for more than a year while the financial and political storms whirled around the university. With the transfer of University Hospital to a new board, chaired by Dr. Don H. O'Donoghue, the turbulence

had subsided but the funding problems were yet to be solved. On October 30, 1973, Governor Hall called for immediate action to open the new 214-bed facility by the first of 1974. He said, "I am prepared to propose to the legislature the necessary millions of dollars increase in the budget for University Hospital." He did not say how much it would cost and conceded the hospital would operate at a deficit at the start, estimating it could be "anything from $800 thousand to $2 million for the first year." Hall said, "When we finally achieve total utilization of all beds, we will have had a 50 percent increase in the number of beds and at the same time [will have] achieved an actual reduction of 20 percent in total cost per patient day."[16]

Although Dr. O'Donoghue was chairman of the new board of the adult hospital, he had opposed the idea of removing it from the control of the university:

I didn't like it at all. They set up a nine-man board of trustees for University Hospital and insisted I be chairman. We spent many months deciding who owned what because the bill [transferring the hospital] said everything important to or in use by University Hospital should belong to the board. We had a pretty strenuous several months getting this exchange made. Our problem was we didn't have much eyeball to eyeball confrontation—it was usually done by correspondence. We argued over such things as parking space...essentially everything.

The board met every Sunday for weeks and weeks, months and months, until the wives all revolted and we decided to meet some other time. There were no personality problems as far as the members of the board were concerned. Our funds were very limited and those first couple of years we spent a lot of time getting a deficiency appropriation every year. There was a big argument again about whether this was a charity hospital for Oklahoma County or it was a state hospital for education.

I still thought it would have been better if the university teaching hospitals were run by the university. I think it was a mistake to separate them.[17]

The Cost of Living Council (CLC), which then controlled the charges hospitals could levy, ruled in Washington on October 29, 1973, that University Hospital could raise its rates 23 percent and that Children's Memorial Hospital was entitled to the status of a new facility and was not bound by past rates subject to CLC controls. Dr. O'Donoghue said it was less than half the hospital wanted but the 23 percent hike was expected to generate $2 million a year in additional revenue. Although this new rate increased reimbursement to $130 per patient day, hospital costs were running $170 a day.

Finally, on January 4, 1974, the Mark R. Everett Building of the University Hospital and Clinics was dedicated in a morning ceremony featuring an address by Governor Hall. Later that month, a House subcommittee approved a $612 thousand supplemental appropriation, described by Representative Hannah Atkins as a "bare bones figure," to cover the additional expense of operating the Everett Tower until June 30. Administrator Jeptha Dalston told the subcommittee the hospital board already had reduced services drastically to stay within the current year's budget.[18]

Dr. Dalston commented on the Everett Tower and the fact that it was just "half a hospital":

> I was there when we were planning it, with Bob Terrill, Jim Rice [associate administrator] and the architectural firm [Frankfurt, Short, Emery and McKinley]. I thought it was basically a sound design. The kitchen was far too big for what we had but not for what we were going to have. There was a logic about the design which made sense. As we tried to bend that to fit our immediate situation, that was very difficult to do, with half a hospital and an old building. Our main problem was how to make it work for the near term.
>
> The whole situation was politicized in a classic sense. When that happens, logic flies out the window. The legislators and other figures were making extreme criticisms of the most incredulous sort. I recall one of the senators criticizing our Amscar [automated supply cart] system and there was a caricature in the *Daily Oklahoman* about this machine bursting into an operating room while they were trying to do surgery. People believed that; it became ludicrous and resulted, I think, in contempt for the place. I resented this politicization but, on the other hand, I had to deal with it and I felt it would do no good to be a Don Quixote flailing against windmills. It was unfortunate that the whole place got laid open and the political forces could then dip in and pick it apart.[19]

In the meantime, the competition for the decommissioned Moon Junior High School at 11th Street and Lindsay Avenue increased. Presbyterian Hospital wanted it because it was across 11th Street from the east portion of their property and Stanton Young could foresee need for additional land in the future, even though the new hospital was not yet open. The university was already out of space for a number of its support functions. Finally, the Oklahoma City Board of Education decided to lease the building to the university for $35 thousand a year for up to five years

"Moon Base One." (OHSF Collection)

beginning July 1, 1974. If the university continued to lease for the full period, the deed to the building would be theirs at no extra cost.

The 1968 Oklahoma Health Center plan called for centralized receiving, storage and maintenance facilities in the vicinity of the steam and chilled water plant on 8th Street. But sharing of centralized facilities, as originally conceived, was not working so the university seized this opportunity to get 79,350 square feet of building and a city block of land at a bargain price. Raymond Crews, who had become director of operations, estimated such a building would cost over a million dollars. Security, personnel, financial services and the campus-wide Centrex telephone system eventually joined the physical plant department in the remodeled high school, dubbed Moon Base One. A wooded swale at the northeast corner of the building was preserved because it was the site of historic Payne's Camp.

While the legislators anted up the money for the linear accelerator which the University Hospital requested, they refused to spend less than that amount ($1.6 million) for a parking garage to keep clients and 300 workers of the State Department of Health out of the weather. Getting to work from the unimproved lot west of the building was a real challenge because in rainy weather the sloping lot became a bog of slippery, gooey mud. Security personnel were often drafted to push cars out of parking places and keep them from sliding into each other. Senator Herschal Crow of Altus said the legislature had plenty of money to complete the parking structure to conform with the original plan. But Senator Ed Berrong, who seemed determined to block this project, on March 20, 1975, offered an amendment to substitute a $300,000 appropriation to build a surface parking lot. The effort to keep the Oklahoma Health Center from

Lunchtime at Payne's camp. The historic marker reads: "Payne Boomer Campsite. In April 1884, on the Cedar Springs site, David Payne established the central boomer camp among those established from the Deep Fork creek to the North Canadian. For five years, he had led those who sought the opening of the unassigned lands. Their efforts hastened the land opening of 1889. University of Oklahoma Health Sciences Center and Oklahoma Heritage Association, 1976." (OHSF Collection)

becoming an endless mass of automobiles was again thwarted. Senator Crow summed it up for the legislative committee, "The whole thing out there is a fiasco."[20]

While many facets of the Oklahoma Health Center project were not going according to plan, the campus was beginning to take shape. The entire street system in and around the OHC was being revamped by the Urban Renewal Authority and the State Highway Department. Phillips Avenue, 10th and 11th Streets had been widened and resurfaced, replacing the narrow streets of this once-residential area. In ceremonies on June 15, 1974, Oklahoma City Mayor Patience Latting dedicated Lottie Avenue, the east boundary of the campus, which had been widened into a divided boulevard from 4th Street to 13th Street. Similar improvement of Stonewall Avenue was scheduled to begin promptly, and Lincoln Boulevard, with three traffic lanes in each direction, was replacing Durland Street as the west boundary of the campus. Lincoln Boulevard, a part of the state highway system, was programmed for improvement south to 4th Street.

Along with these projects, the university had completed acquisition of the residential area between Everest and Lottie avenues, 12th and 9th streets, and had cleared it for development of 300 townhouses for students. In the first part of the 1970s, the trend was for college students to move out of dormitories into apartments off the campus. As a result, one Oklahoma college was having difficulty paying the indebtedness on dormitories it had recently built. For this reason, O.U. decided not to build the units planned for the OUHSC, but a market analysis showed that it was then feasible for private enterprise to develop 100 apartment units.

Had the casual passer-by not been influenced or distracted by the political turmoil surrounding the OHC, as reported almost daily in the newspapers, he would have been favorably impressed by the hum of construction activity on the campus and the changing face of the land. The progress was both obvious and significant. To paraphrase *Desiderata*, "And whether or not it was clear to some of the leaders, no doubt the Oklahoma Health Center was unfolding as it should."

CHAPTER 32
PRESBYTERIAN HOSPITAL: 1970-1974

The last house and oil derrick on the Presbyterian Hospital site. (OHSF Collection)

In September, 1970, Presbyterian Hospital officials signed an agreement to buy 24 acres of land from the Oklahoma City Urban Renewal Authority. This L-shaped parcel between Durland Avenue (now Lincoln Boulevard) and Phillips Avenue was expected to cost 21 to 30 cents a square foot or $218 thousand to $312 thousand. The modest price was the "written-down" cost after federal funding through the urban renewal program. The site extended to 10th Street and included the land now owned by the Oklahoma Eye Foundation.[1]

Jack Shrode, Presbyterian Hospital administrator, said construction of the new $23 million hospital was scheduled to start in 1971 and they were working on methods to finance it. One approach was a local fund drive, although this was expected to realize only a small portion of the needed money. Because the Chamber of Commerce effort to interest the city and/or the county in financing private hospitals had not met with success, it looked as though most of the capital funds would have to be borrowed. For a while, there was a contest to see whether Mercy or Presbyterian, faced with identical funding problems, would be permitted to solicit funds first. On September 29, 1970, the Appeals Review Board of Greater Oklahoma City gave the green light to Presbyterian for a campaign to start in May of 1971. Mercy's $2 million drive was approved for the following spring. The Oklahoma-Arkansas Synod of the Presbyterian Church approved a half million dollar fundraising campaign for the new

Episcopalian and O.U. Foundation director Lee Teague found time to help the Presbyterian Hospital. (University of Oklahoma)

hospital on October 5. Stanton L. Young, Presbyterian Hospital board chairman and an elder in Westminster Presbyterian Church, said the church had approved a $100 thousand contribution to the hospital building fund three days before. Three months later, The Right Reverend Chilton Powell, Episcopal Bishop of Oklahoma, announced a quarter of a million dollar New Year's gift to establish a geriatric wing in the new Presbyterian Hospital. The money was bequeathed to the church by Ena M. Cochran of Okmulgee, Oklahoma, the entire estate she had inherited from her brother, Judge A.D. Cochran. Lee Teague, director of the O.U. Foundation at the Medical Center and an active Episcopal layman who helped arrange the gift, said, "It is in the true spirit of ecumenism that the Episcopalians of Oklahoma show through this gift their cooperation with the Presbyterian Hospital in a way that will be helpful and meaningful to all people of the state." Jack Shrode was also a dedicated Episcopalian who later became active in the ministry.[2]

While Stanton Young and the trustees of Presbyterian were trying to figure out how to acquire $23

Jack W. Shrode…modern Moses. (Presbyterian Hospital)

Oncologist Ted Clemens became chief of staff at the new hospital. (Presbyterian Hospital)

million to finance their new, 400-bed hospital, their architects, Benham, Blair and Affilates and their consultant, Dr. Louis J. Block of Silver Spring, Maryland, had created its design. It utilized the idea of interstitial space which Lester Gorsline advocated to build in flexibility for future use of space. This was the first use of this concept in Oklahoma.

In early 1974, the administration of the Presbyterian Hospital changed. Jack Shrode had been administrator since 1952, when the institution was called Wesley Hospital and was owned by the Oklahoma City Clinic. He was replaced by Harry Neer, one of the team which did the financial feasibility study for the new hospital. Like Moses, Jack Shrode had led his people for a long time but never got into "the promised land." He gave these reasons:

> Our consulting CPA [certified public accountant], Bill Bardwell [of the Oklahoma City office of Wolf and Company] and my old cohort there, Marion Pickett, the hospital accountant…the three of us worked very close together toward preparing all the financial projections [for the new hospital]. Of course, Booz, Allen and Hamilton just gave us status. That's what we bought from them. Their projections were purely and simply *our* projections. They lifted them up and put them under cover of Booz, Allen and Hamilton. That's the way most consultants work. They fed back to us what we wanted. Much of the legwork was done by our own people. Not many people know that. We needed them, of course. The bond people had never heard of Bardwell, Pickett

and Shrode. They had our history which became part of the [bond] prospectus, but that was it.

> There were some younger physicians and one of the older physicians in the Oklahoma City Clinic who felt I had spent my time. After that many years, there are those who feel you've worn out your time and have done all you can do. I precipitated some of it by saying I intended to retire when we got the hospital open and operating. I was a very conservative individual and I still am. I would not have developed the hospital the way it did. I'm strictly a hospital-minded person, not a developer or promoter.

> Harry and I overlapped for a couple or three months. I became the first president of the new, corporate-type organization for the Presbyterian Hospital and Harry was brought on board as executive vice president.[3]

Dr. Ted Clemens related the feeling of some medical staff members about the administrator:

> Some people in the Oklahoma City Clinic thought Jack was not capable of running a larger hospital. There were physicians who were not in the Oklahoma City Clinic who were negative about Jack because he had developed into the kind of guy that if they went to him wanting something, his answer was no. He ran off several members of the staff.

> He was certainly nice to Bill [Hughes] and me. After we decided to leave the Oklahoma City Clinic [in 1970] and made the announcement, we went to Jack to make sure we could still be on the staff and have admitting privileges as we always had. Jack was very nice to us and assured us that we could.[4]

Presbyterian was looking for leadership which was

240

November 21, 1972 was a snowy day for breaking ground at the Presbyterian Hospital site. Stanton Young is at the podium. (OHSF Collection)

Fifty-foot-long girders hang over the edge of the Presbyterian Hospital's steel skeleton. (The Oklahoman)

President Harry Neer and Internist Bill Hughes converse in Harry's office. (Presbyterian Hospital)

a bit more aggressive. Harry Neer said that when he arrived:

> Jack moved out and over to the annex. His job turned out to be finishing up the equipment listings for the new hospital and he stayed on until March. I started part time in October, 1973, but I was still doing assignments for Booz, Allen so I was in and out of town. I wasn't full-time until after Thanksgiving.
>
> I didn't even know Jack was going to be here. That was the biggest surprise of my life. When I accepted the position, title didn't mean anything. I was interested in reporting to the board and programming Presbyterian Hospital.[5]

As the new Presbyterian Hospital rose at the corner of Lincoln Boulevard and 13th Street, Manhattan Construction Company of Muskogee, Oklahoma, the contractor, ran into some unexpected trouble. On August 10, 1973, two steel workers were killed and another was seriously injured when three floors of the steel framing collapsed under heavy winds. The workers were part of a crew stringing guy wires to brace new steel girders recently set in place to outline the fifth, sixth and seventh floors at the southeast corner of the bed tower. All three men were trapped under several tons of steel beams balanced on the edge of the fifth floor frame. Jim Ullmer, a field superintendent for Allied Steel Construction Company said the collapse was caused more by the bad timing of nature than by human error. "You put the steel up and partially bolt it in. Then you moor it with guy lines. It's normal construction procedure, but who would have predicted that wind would come up just then?"[6]

Just a year later, another construction site collapse

241

The Presbyterian Hospital is at 13th and Lincoln Boulevard. (OHSF Collection)

happened, this time in the 960-car, $2.6 million Presbyterian parking garage east of the hospital. Three huge double T-bars crashed to the ground two stories below about six P.M. on August 6, 1974. No one was injured but a construction worker at the site said the falling beams "sounded like an earthquake." The cause of the collapse was not immediately determined.[7]

By December, 1974, the new $37 million Presbyterian Hospital was complete. The huge, earth-tone building blended well into the Oklahoma landscape. William "Bill" Hughes, M.D., an internist on the medical staff, jokingly asked, "When are they going to mount the guns in those turrets out front?" He was no doubt referring to its fortress-like appearance, but campus architect Arthur Tuttle was impressed. "Presbyterian Hospital was a forward-thinking, outstanding design and the Benham group has every reason to be pleased with what they have produced. It is basically good design which has a lot of capability for expansion."[8]

On Saturday, November 30, 1974, a small army of construction workers, technicians, doctors and nurses toiled almost around the clock applying finishing touches within the building so 78 patients could be transferred from the old hospital on Sunday morning. It took three hours, beginning at 7 A.M., for a motorcade of twelve ambulances and emergency vans to move them into the new building. The 195-bed, 1913 vintage facility at 12th and Harvey had been running an average daily census of 140 patients. With 240 of the 408 beds in the new hospital open, Presbyterian Hospital had ample room to grow. New patients were admitted that afternoon.[9]

When Harry Neer and his employees moved into the building, though, they had more space than they knew what to do with:

Our biggest problem was staff—both employees and managers. In one month, we went from 500 employees to 800 because of the size of this facility. In a very small hospital with a close-knit organization, we could manage with 500 but when we got spread out in this big place, we had to add people. We had just about every

242

There was slushy snow on the ground as the patients were moved from the old hospital to the new one. (Presbyterian Hospital)

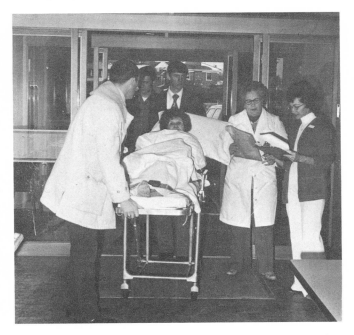

A patient is checked against the census list as she is rolled into the front door. (Presbyterian Hospital)

kind of problem plus we didn't have the managers. Trying to accommodate to the technological changes in this hospital almost "did in" the people of 20, 25, 30 years experience at "old Pres." They just couldn't handle it.

I think the worst problem we faced was lack of leadership throughout the hospital. We were putting in all

The lobby. (Presbyterian Hospital)

these new programs; for example, we didn't have a heart station or basic EEG [electroencephalography] at the old hospital...no special procedures except angiography and cardiac cath[eterization]. The equipment we had was anywhere from 10 to 15 years old so here we were, starting with new equipment nobody had ever used. I'd say the first year was catastrophic from that standpoint. We didn't have the skills [or] the capabilities, and we went through a lot of people during that period.

We were weak in some areas of general management, too. Basically there was John Turner and Dennis McGrath and myself, and I was out much of the time in rural Oklahoma and around the city talking with physicians. Financial services was a one-man shop. Everything was done by hand in accounting and the expansion almost did that department in. What we didn't know was that Marion Pickett had everything in his head! He'd been there so long and he did quite well in the basic things like getting out the bills and aging the accounts, but when he died [in October, 1978], everything went to pot, totally. The systems were non existent; it was all Marion.

Harry Neer explained the reason for the approach the Presbyterian Hospital leaders believed they were compelled to take:

For the first five years, we put all our time and money and energies into building clinical services. What Mercy Hospital did was tighten their belt and let the population grow to them. Therefore, with physicians coming onto their staff in a slow process, they didn't experience the big losses we did. On the other hand, we had to act quickly. Being in the central city with a census that had been declining for 10 straight years, having a somewhat aging medical staff and not having a full-service hos-

243

pital at the old place, we had to go out and get the technology and manpower to build the environment to a tertiary level so we could attract physicians. And we had to do it in a hurry. We couldn't wait for the population to grow because there was no population [around our hospital] *to* grow. We had to build our networks around the state so physicians out there would be able to refer patients to physicians on our staff. We went into internal medicine and the subspecialties because that was the need at the time. The surgical specialties were already pretty well overdone. Our thought was to build partnerships with physicians; if they did well, we'd do well.

We wanted to be a tertiary care hospital on the cutting edge of medicine. Being in the Health Center, connected with the university and having a teaching program is an advantage for the kind of hospital we are.[10]

A tertiary hospital, which accommodates the more complicated, less frequently occurring medical problems, must have a broad medical service area from which to draw. Harry Neer and Presbyterian Hospital personnel had been busy developing contacts with physicians throughout the state. One important service to the local doctors in 13 outlying communities was remote coronary monitoring, developed at Presbyterian Hospital with the assistance of the Regional Medical Program. A heart attack victim could be placed on an EKG monitor in a small hospital in, say, Hobart and his condition watched by special nurses in a central station at Presbyterian Hospital, a hundred miles away. This was possible by telecommunicating the electrocardiogram to the Presbyterian monitor via leased telephone lines. Then, if the patient's condition worsened and swift action was required, the specialists—cardiologists or nurses— could call Hobart instantly over a direct telephone line between the two hospitals and alert the nurse and/or the doctor in Hobart, advising them what to do. Thus, the expertise available in a large, teaching hospital was provided to 13 small communities around the state and patients could get state-of-the-art coronary care without leaving their hometown. Later, the Presbyterian Hospital system grew to serve 22 remote hospitals, the largest coronary monitoring network in the country.

THE EYE INSTITUTE: 1973-1975

At the July 6, 1973, meeting of the Oklahoma Health Sciences Foundation Executive Committee, Chairman Dean McGee suggested the time had come for the foundation to reduce its role in coordinating the development of the health campus. There were many reasons, most of which stemmed from the recent unrest at the university. Both Richardson and Dumas had criticized the foundation's role as an "outside planner." Governor Hall had resigned from the OHSF on May 2, 1973, saying the goals of the foundation "may conflict at times with the interests of the OUHSC and state government in Oklahoma." Financial support [in the form of Hardy's salary] had been withdrawn by the university. The University Hospital had a new governing board and Children's Hospital had already been taken over by Lloyd Rader, so there was little likelihood either would welcome planning and coordination assistance from the foundation.[1]

This turned out to be a correct supposition. A few months later, Greggory Harmon, planning director for the Central Oklahoma Areawide Health Planning Organization (AHPO), wrote to Mr. Rader pointing up AHPO's responsibility to review and comment on proposed health programs affecting the area. Senator George Miller of Ada shot off a blistering 12-page reply to Harmon, criticizing the ability and efforts of the agency and stating in unequivocal terms that improvement of Children's Hospital was mandated by the legislature, it would be done by the state and they did not need any help from AHPO or anybody else. To be sure, Harmon had raised hackles by reminding Mr. Rader of AHPO policy which said: "The construction of specialty hospitals or expansion of present ones should not be given encouragement. Consideration should be given to providing in general hospitals any additional facilities that might be needed for such specialties."

He also asked a lot of tough planning questions such as: is the long-range plan for the hospital generated by the Oklahoma Health Sciences Foundation and which called for a short-term acute, general hospital—and to include an adult tower, a children's tower and a psychiatric tower, and eventually a rehabilitation tower—to be officially scrapped? If the plan is not scrapped, why is the Children's Memorial Hos-

AHPO director Greggory Harmon headed health planning for the central Oklahoma area. (The Oklahoman)

pital developing separately? If it is to be scrapped, what long-range plan is being developed to replace it? If no new plan is being developed, how will the Medical Center know where it is headed? Why is Children's Memorial Hospital adding space and undergoing major renovation when it may not be used as a general hospital in a few years? In particular, why is a new kitchen being added when a completely new kitchen with equipment sits a few hundred feet away [in the new University Hospital] with a lighted, enclosed tunnel connecting the two buildings?

Senator Miller said such questions "should be taken up directly with the elected representatives of the State of Oklahoma and not with an appointed department head who is appropriately carrying out the provisions of a State statute." While he accused Harmon of trying to place government officials on the defensive, his letter very effectively put AHPO in that very position.

According to William Bross, director of the Community Council of Central Oklahoma, of which AHPO was a division, identical letters were received from several other state legislators, including Representative Wiley Sparkman. Senator Miller later became an assistant to Mr. Rader.[2]

That exchange confirmed the speculation that

AHPO was part of the Community Council of Central Oklahoma which was dedicated to meeting the social needs of greater Oklahoma City. Executive director Bill Bross also worked with other private, voluntary agencies. (The Oklahoman)

DISRS would follow an independent course and help from the Oklahoma Health Sciences Foundation would not be requested. Furthermore, the foundation was not included on the committee to pursue planning for the OUHSC in the fiscal year just starting, federal money for construction was declining or being impounded and the future of the colleges of public health, allied health professions and nursing was in doubt. In addition, Jack Dumas's criticism of the planning which brought Presbyterian Hospital to the campus had reduced communication among the institutions and diminished the prospect of sharing central facilities, a concept most institutions found difficult to accept under the best of circumstances.

It now seemed that multiple crises, political intervention, investigations, consultant studies and shifting hospital sponsorship had divided the once-cohesive group of campus institutions, sheltered by the foundation's umbrella, into two sections. If the foundation continued as representative of non-state institutions, it appeared that competition, isolation and conflict would result. Because the foundation apparently had come to the end of its useful life, Hardy could see no point in staying. Following the Dennis pattern, he was ready to accept a position assisting the development of Area Health Education Centers for the University of Arkansas College of Medicine. But the members of the executive committee did not see it that way.

They decided the foundation should strengthen itself with the new people becoming involved with the state hospitals and continue its role as coordinator. Hardy announced his resignation on July 6, 1973, but was urged to stay on.

Two months later, in September, 1973, Governor Hall appointed a Health Sciences Center Planning and Advisory Committee, representing state institutions, with federal and private institutions as advisors. This group took over most of the functions previously handled by the umbrella foundation, so the OHSF was effectively sidelined. Thus, the two state hospitals and the process of planning coordination were all under new management. Because the foundation had decided to remain active, it faced the decision about its future role.[3]

Ever since the mid-1960s, the Oklahoma Eye Foundation, which had been organized by Dr. Dick Clay, the Oklahoma City ophthalmologist, had been trying to create an eye institute for the Southwest, but it had been a difficult struggle. As a private practitioner promoting a teaching institute, Dr. Clay occupied a unique position, somewhere between "the town and the gown." Also, he came from a family of optometrists, a semi-professional group which historically had been at odds with the physician eye specialists. As Dr. Clay described it, he had a foot in each camp. He commented about the early attitude of the town doctors toward the idea of an eye institute:

> They followed Tullos Coston's lead at first and he wasn't in favor of it. The reason was, I think, because of his interest in St. Anthony Hospital and their eye department [which] he had worked to get going over there. So the first meeting we had where I presented this idea, Tullos and three or four of the people who followed his lead said, "Oh, I don't think we need that sort of thing."
>
> After we got to the point of getting the charter, they said they wouldn't have any objection to it and signed the charter. But it was not enthusiastic support by the people who worked at St. Anthony's.[4]

Dr. Coston was the head of the department of ophthalmology at the O.U. School of Medicine before it had a full time professor in this specialty. For six years, Dr. Clay led the crusade for an eye institute but enjoyed only limited support from his professional colleagues. While it was by no means certain this institute would ever be developed, it was included in the 1968 Oklahoma Health Center Development Plan.

Dr. Coston, who had come to Oklahoma from Johns Hopkins in 1936, was considered the dean of

Tullos Coston, veteran ophthalmologist, began practice in Oklahoma in 1936. (University of Oklahoma)

ophthalmologists in the state. He gave the reason the project had stalled, "Nobody would give any money!" Then, Dean McGee suffered a serious eye problem and everything changed, as Dr. Coston related:

He came to see me with a detached retina and I explained we would operate at St. Anthony Hospital. We did so on January 29, 1971. The next day, while I was dressing his eye, he asked me where I was trained and where Dr. Acers, who assisted me with the operation, was trained. I told him we were both trained at the Wilmer Institute at Johns Hopkins [Hospital in Baltimore]. He said, "Do we have that kind of training here?" and I said, "No, we train ophthalmologists here but we don't have an institute." I explained to him there was a tremendous difference in the number [of ophthalmologists] on the staff and the experiences the residents would have and that it is an institution for research…finding new cures and reasons for eye diseases. I said we had wanted one in Oklahoma, [and we had] had a foundation for some years. Then he asked why it never happened and I told him.

The next morning, Dean said, "Back to that eye institute. You know, that just might be arranged." He did not go any further at that moment but obviously, that was his decision. He donated the first money but he wanted others to join him and they have. He's been very generous ever since, as he is with so many philanthropic things that he does.[5]

Dr. Clay was delighted. "Mr. McGee was such a prominent person that his support attracted other people. It was the first thing he had ever lent his name to." As Mr. McGee said, "I hoped we could develop a really first class, quality eye institute to serve this middle part of the country." With McGee's backing, Dr. Coston was assured the eye institute would become a reality and prepared to step down as the chairman of the department at the medical school. It was planned the institute would be a privately funded facility affiliated with the university and be the headquarters for the department, similar to the relationship of the Department of Dermatology to the College of Medicine. Dean Tom Lynn was apprehensive about this arrangement but an affiliation agreement was worked out. Dr. Thomas E. Acers was appointed chairman of ophthalmology on October 4, 1972. McGee was not on the search committee but he observed, "They interviewed a number of people from around the country and finally decided they had the best one right at home." The 39-year-old Acers also became the director of the eye institute which was named for its initial benefactor, Dean A. McGee.[6]

The institute was in the planning stage with Benham, Blair and Affiliates as architects. The coordination of planning for state facilities in the Oklahoma Health Center had been taken over by Governor Hall, so it appeared the appropriate role for the OHSF was to help launch this newest institution proposed for the health campus. At the next meeting of the Foundation's Executive Committee on February 11, 1974, the members again discussed the future of the OHSF. Hardy had already helped to develop the program and budget for the eye institute and construction of the building was scheduled to begin at mid-year. Stanton Young, who was heavily involved in funding and organizing the eye institute, suggested the Foundation continue this assistance as well as provide liaison with local and state health groups and civic organizations, including the Central Oklahoma Areawide Health Planning Organization, the Regional Medical Program, the Capitol-Medical Center Improvement and Zoning Commission, of which Hardy was a member, the Urban Renewal Authority and the Chamber of Commerce. The Executive Committee expressly vowed "not to get into any cross-purposes" with the governor's committee, advising that group only on the request of Governor Hall. He never asked.[7]

Originally, the eye institute was planned to share a one-acre site at 11th Street and Phillips Avenue with a proposed cardiovascular institute. When Mr. McGee looked at the site, his reaction was that "It's too small."

He was right. There was not enough space to accommodate the institute, the parking it needed and the expansion which might some day be required. Arrangements were made with Presbyterian Hospital to purchase the five and one-half acre site bounded by 11th Street, Lincoln Boulevard, Lindsay Avenue and 10th Street. Mr. McGee always insisted on a model of any building proposed for the Kerr-McGee Corporation and he required the same for the eye institute so there would be no question the site would be adequate.

Dr. Tullos Coston remembered one of the early planning sessions:

> We had the two [Oklahoma City] bankers, Jack Conn [of Fidelity] and Chuck Vose [of First National] at the meeting. Stanton Young, E.K. Gaylord, Dean McGee and the others on the board [of the Oklahoma Eye Foundation] were all there. It was determined we had certain funds, enough to build a basement and two floors. That was sufficient for the time and a resolution was passed. Then I spoke up and said, "Now that will last us about two years! This is going to expand rapidly." Well, they all looked a bit startled at that and I said, "Why not shell in some floors for future expansion, even if we have to borrow the money?" Well, the two bankers got out their pencils and their note pads and started figuring. I never will forget that scene; it's as clear as if I had a movie of it. I was sitting between Dean McGee and E.K. Gaylord. Stanton says, "Dean, what do you think of that?" and he said, "I think that's a wise thing to do." Well, it went around the table and the two bankers said, "That'll be much cheaper if we're going to need it…to shell it in at present interest rates than to build on top of it later."

> But one thing I couldn't get over was to build a tunnel from the parking lot to the basement so patients wouldn't have to walk up the steps [to the main floor entrance]. It would have cost $30,000 and they said, "Well, now, that's added and we'd just better not do that." Later, Dean McGee came out here and saw all those old folks and people half-seeing, trying to get up those steps, holding onto the rail and he said, "We've got to do [something about] this." When we did do it [in 1982] it cost over $110,000![8]

Subsequent expansion of the Dean A. McGee Eye Institute proved Tullos Coston to be an ophthalmologist with vision. In November, 1983, less than eight years after it opened, the McGee Eye Institute launched a $2.4 million fundraising campaign so the third floor, the last of three shelled-in levels, could be completed. If this rate of growth portends the future, there will be a twin building expanding the Eye In-

Dean and Dorothea McGee sign the "eye-beam." (Dean A. McGee Eye Institute)

stitute to the south before the turn of the century. Mr. McGee was both foresighted and conservative. He made no little plans, yet he knew how to manage resources from day to day, allowing time to integrate each forward step. The steady growth of the Kerr-McGee Corporation was a demonstration of his management philosophy. Because he recognized the importance of an adequate site, the Dean A. McGee Eye Institute will have space in which to expand when the fullness of time has come.

On a cool, drizzly day in October, 1974, the 22nd, the Oklahoma Eye Foundation celebrated the start of construction of the Dean A. McGee Eye Institute (M.E.I.). As 400 guests filed into the new, unoccupied Presbyterian Hospital, they were invited to sign their names on a 24-foot steel I-beam which was to be set in place later in the ceremony. At a catered luncheon held in the dining room of the hospital, across 11th Street from the construction site, John M. Houchin, former chairman of Phillips Petroleum Company of Bartlesville, Oklahoma, and president of the eye foundation, said the institute was the result of a decade of work and planning. The Lions Club of Oklahoma, which had always been interested in sight preservation, had raised more than $350,000 to provide scientific equipment and furnishings for the institute, support which came about through the effort of Dr. Clay. The Lions Eye Bank, which collected human corneas for transplant, was planned to be housed in the new building. During the construction celebration, it was too rainy for the crowd to go outside and watch the first structural beam being lifted

Oil derricks dotted the landscape in 1974 as construction began on the Eye Institute. The Greater Shiloh Baptist Church at 10th and Lindsay is in the background. (Dean A. McGee Eye Institute)

Architect Frank Rees was then with Benham, Blair and Affiliates. (OHSF Collection)

and riveted into place, but each visitor received a small, engraved "eye-beam" as a memento of the occasion.

For a short period, it looked as though the eye institute would not bear the name of its original benefactor. Tom Acers said:

Somehow word was delivered to me that the governor (Hall) had stated "that as long as he was governor there would not be an eye institute named for Mr. McGee on the Medical Center campus!" Parenthetically, he had often referred to my friends supporting the eye institute as the "downtown Mafia." When I got word of this I was shocked. I had discussed the plans for the institute with the governor on several occasions and he had always seemed so positive. Besides that, I had already spent my own money for stationery!

Now comes one of the advantages of being a true Okie. After a few weeks, I said to myself, "To hell with this! I'm going to straighten all this out." I called the governor and told him of this "rumor" and he, too, was truly shocked. He immediately called Mr. McGee and told him that this was an absolute untruth and he personally thought the M.E.I. was a vital project and would have his total support. So much for rumors![9]

Frank Rees was the principal architect on this project for Benham, Blair and Affiliates:

We were building a tunnel between Presbyterian and the eye institute, a tunnel that would not only carry patients and staff but would carry a continuation of the steam and chilled water system [to serve the MEI]. We had to build the tunnel low enough so that a possible

underpass at what was then 11th Street could go under Lincoln Boulevard. I received a call one day from the contractor who was very concerned that nothing seemed to be where it appeared on our drawings. We had designed the tunnel to miss a manhole and avoid a lot of trouble for him, but [as he started the project] he was going right through the manhole and was going to have a lot of expenses he hadn't planned on. We agreed if he entered Presbyterian and the eye institute where we told him and made the tunnel deep enough, he could make it a bit longer and go around the manhole.

So he did that and we thought the problem was solved until three weeks later when I received a call from the Manhattan Construction Company which was building the eye institute. They told us the drawings for the stair going from the parking lot up to the main entry level weren't right. The stairs were actually 12 feet longer than we had shown on the drawings. So we had an outside survey firm check it and it seems the eye institute was built 12 feet 8 inches west of where it was supposed to be, which caused all of the trouble with the tunnel. This happened because the construction company took a measurement from the wrong pin and their field engineer located the building in the wrong place. The county surveyor apparently didn't check it very closely. The stair had to be redesigned because it was a little bit too expensive to move the building![10]

Thirteen months after the beam-setting ceremonies at the Dean A. McGee Eye Institute, the first two floors of the building were ready for occupancy. Dr. Tom Acers had recruited C.P. "Pat"

Not every OHC institution had an oil well in its front yard. This one was eventually plugged and abandoned. (OHSF Collection)

Wilkinson, M.D., a retinal specialist, and Hal Balyeat, M.D., a corneal expert then in private practice. He also asked Dr. Coston to join the institute

staff but the former chief of ophthalmology was reluctant at first and said to Dr. Acers:

"I don't know that it's proper for the former chairman to be right there with the present chairman. I want you to think about this carefully." He said, "I don't have to think about it. I not only want you there, I need your consultation at times and I'd appreciate it if you'd come. Furthermore, we get along well and there can't be any conflict between the two of us." There hasn't been and it's worked that way. I have been happy with the arrangements.[11]

Dr. Acers was understandably pleased. After all of the planning and work:

The institute *did* occur and we *did* manage to recruit people who were willing to ask "how?" and "why?" They were willing and anxious to be involved in a multidisciplinary environment where they could provide patient care, be involved in research and participate in medical education. They were unique people and they still are and we're still recruiting this type of dedication.

Dean McGee speaks at the Institute's opening celebration. Enjoying the proceedings are Tom Acers and Tullos Coston, far left, then Bill Thurman, Stanton Young, Paul Sharp, Bob Hardy, Marty Johnson and Edward Gaylord. (OHSF Collection)

Eleventh Street changes its name. Stanton L. Young smiles as Dean McGee holds up the new sign and Paul Sharp applauds. (Daily Oklahoman)

What so many people don't know is that all of our staff physicians "give" 50 percent of their income back to the institute for operational expenses. Besides that, they agree to spend at least 20 percent of their time in research and educational efforts. Yes, these people do exist.[12]

The fact that none of the M.E.I. medical staff has departed during the first eight years not only reflects the care with which they were selected and Dr. Acer's leadership but also shows these ophthalmologists have the best of all worlds. They do not have to hassle any administrative or money details, they enjoy ample personal income and they can teach or do research or both. Who would *want* to leave that kind of situation?

On a sunny Friday, December 5, 1975, the Dean A. McGee Eye Institute was dedicated. As part of the ceremony, the four-block portion of 11th Street which is within the Oklahoma Health Center was renamed Stanton L. Young Boulevard in honor of the man who had contributed so much of his time and energy to launch both the new Presbyterian Hospital and the McGee Eye Institute. The institute opened for service on the following Monday.

Because Hardy had helped plan, equip and organize the administrative affairs of the Eye Institute, he was assigned as its first administrator, on loan from the Oklahoma Health Sciences Foundation. He set up the organization to resemble a hospital, where the administrator reports direct to the board of trustees. However, the director, Tom Acers, in charge of professional services, also reported to the board, so it was another of those two-headed organizations similar to the OMRF when Dr. Eliel was there. Hardy commented:

It didn't work! An eye institute, I came to realize, doesn't work like a hospital. As a single-specialty group practice, the doctors coming onto the staff were used to having full charge of their office and the eye institute was their new office. And unlike the hospital, where physicians come and go, the eye institute staff was there essentially all day. So the potential for conflict was built in...by me!

At one of the dinner meetings about the time the Institute opened, Mr. McGee took me aside and said, "Now don't let the doctors run away with this operation." He knew we would probably run a deficit the first few years but he wanted to contain costs insofar as practical.

251

PART FOUR

THE GOOD TIMES: 1976-1982

CHAPTER 34
THE TEACHING HOSPITALS: 1976-1982

The expansion of Children's Hospital was moving rapidly. By mid 1976, the remodeling of the old building was well along, a Child Study Center had been built in what was once a triangular park at Stonewall and 13th Street and the nursing tower to be named for veteran pediatrician George H. Garrison was nearing completion. Frosty Troy, editor of the *Oklahoma Observer*, had these comments:

When they transferred it to Lloyd Rader, he went hog-ass crazy! As a lot of people do the first time they get around the medical mystique, suddenly Lloyd Rader, who had busied himself with juvenile delinquents, the mentally, physically and emotionally deficient, the economically needy...suddenly he went up on the mountain with the doctors from Nichols Hills. It was an experience of a lifetime for him. The amazing thing was to watch his personality change; his entire approach to government and politics changed during that time.

We were not only building Jim Dennis's dream, we were also building quite a political empire in that medical complex. And that happens when you have almost unlimited resources. I was bothered by what I saw as a tragic decline in the real concerns of social welfare in this state. Suddenly, we didn't have enough money to do both. The choice for Lloyd Rader was not even close.... It was, "Give it to the hospitals." For example: we reached a point where we had virtually lost accreditation for Paul's Valley State School [for the mentally retarded]. It was a terrible problem. It was crowded and we didn't have the professional help and that's what most people thought they were paying their two cents state sales tax for. But every dollar they [the hospitals] said they needed...when Halverstadt said, "Boo," Lloyd Rader said, "How much?" and over it came.

The Children's Hospital is better than I ever thought we'd have in Oklahoma and I'm proud we've got it but I am just astonished at the *way* we got it. I'm astonished that we let vital social programs get in trouble—and we've got some serious trouble—simply because we started packing all that money over there. The management was poor. You've heard of little kids playing "doctor" and "nurse"? Suddenly, Lloyd Rader started playing "hospital."

And that's all he ever talked about. Most of his working days I ever knew anything about were involved in that complex. And that's sad; that's not what the people of Oklahoma employed him to do. And we didn't have

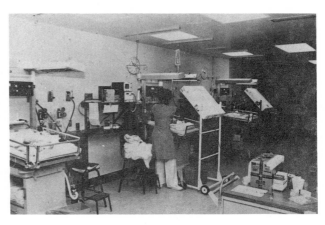

The neonatal nursery in Children's Memorial Hospital. (University of Oklahoma)

a governor with the guts to pull his leash. We didn't have legislative leadership with guts enough to draw the line.[1]

While Mr. Rader was generous with the Children's Hospital, he was not so in awe of the physicians that he let them do as they pleased. He observed that, "You had as many managers as you had department heads. Each one of them was running his own kingdom. There was no uniformity between them." He went on to tell about an incident in which the hospital's first neonatologist had upset the director of nursing because he refused to use standard hand-washing and sterile technique in the neonatal nursery:

I couldn't understand the damn doctor wouldn't want to be sterile. I listened to the doctor and Mrs. Jones argue. I couldn't see anything unreasonable about it [the procedure Mrs. Jones thought was appropriate]. Reminded me of that old country story—the guy said, "Didn't your mama teach you to wash your hands after you pee?" and he said, "Hell, no, my mama taught me not to pee on my hands!"

I thought there's just about as much sense this damn doctor sittin' there telling this nurse he wasn't going to do it. I said, "Doctor, I don't believe that's an unreasonable request." He said, "*I* am the neonatologist. There's no damn nurse tells *me* what to do." I said, "I'm going to tell you something, my friend. I am going to adopt that rule— now! That's what you're going to do if you stay at this hospital." "Well," he said, "we'll see about that." I said, "By God, you're fired! Right now!" He said, "You can't do that." I said, "I just told you that you're fired and if you don't get your ass out of this office, I'm going

255

The man in charge. (Department of Human Services)

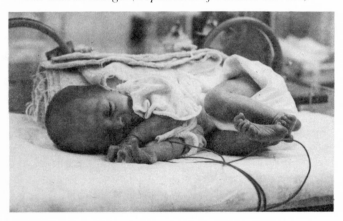

This tiny newcomer is in an Isolette. (University of Oklahoma)

to see if I'm horse enough to...." We never did have any more trouble after that[2]

When Bruce Perry arrived at University Hospital in September, 1975, the cost of operation was $36 million a year, of which $9 million came from the legislature. Said another way, collections covered 66 percent of costs, not too much different from the 70 percent during Bob Terrill's administration. Perry explained their objective:

> ...was to get to 80 percent self-sufficiency. We didn't think we could do better than that with the kind of programs we had, with the amount of money going toward medical education and with the emergency room and the medically indigent people coming into the hospital. Also, the Medicaid reimbursement system did not pay after

[a patient had been in the hospital] 10 days. And, of course, we had no control over the patient mix.

Clearly, our role was *not* to be a hospital for the indigent patients in the state of Oklahoma. We rewrote the admission statement, emphasizing patient care, caring for all persons who needed the services provided there, but it was *not* to be the general, routine service hospital for anybody, no matter what their financial class was. I *never* perceived the hospital as having the indigent care role. That role was imposed upon it because it was a state public hospital in Oklahoma County. Neither of the two big counties [Oklahoma or Tulsa] in the state have county or city hospitals. And the Tulsa delegation in the legislature did not want to support University Hospital because they saw it as the indigent care hospital for Oklahoma County. Rural legislators did not want to support it because they didn't want any money that could go to their counties to go to University Hospital. The Oklahoma County delegation felt very sensitive about advocating support for the care of local indigent patients so they had to call it a teaching hospital. It was a tremendous political problem. From that standpoint, as far as I was concerned, the hospital's biggest problem was that it never had a constituency.

Very interestingly, if you go back in history and look at Children's Hospital, you would expect that there would have been a constituency for it, the only children's hospital in the state. And yet, until it went under Mr. Rader's administration, it *had* no constituency. When it went into the welfare department, its constituency was one Lloyd E. Rader! You need to give the man credit for that. He was the constituency for it, he had the money to do something with it, and he did it!

I would characterize Lloyd Rader as a benevolent J. Edgar Hoover, a benevolent dictator for what he thought was the good of the people and the state. He used the power he had developed over the years to make that good occur, whether it was good or not. I did not always agree with his methods. I saw him intimidate people; I saw him get other people to lobby against bills that would threaten the welfare department. He'd say, "Boys, you know if this happens there won't be enough money to pay you doctors, or pay hospitals, or nursing homes. I just want you to know that if you boys don't get out there and help, you're going to be in a little bit of trouble and I'm not going to have any control over it. I'm just a good old state employee and I don't tell the legislature or the governor what to do."

In that sense, he was a tyrant but he did all those things for what he believed was the benefit of the people of the State of Oklahoma. Over the years, he developed a tremendous power base by helping people. He had enough on enough people so he could pretty much do what he wanted. He always found a way to show that legally or economically, he was *required* to do the things he thought should be done. There was never any choice. He *always* did the only thing that could be done. He was a master at creating situations so he could only make the choice in one way…his way.[3]

Mike McEwen had joined the University Hospital as public relations director in March, 1978. His job was to improve the image of the hospital with the public at large and with the legislature:

> We had a very clear mission at that time. The legislature had bought a program which Bruce Perry had developed called the "Self Sufficiency Program." The legislature said, "We will provide the funding to cover indigent care and legitimate educational costs, but the hospital needs to generate the maximum amount of revenue and get the maximum number of private, paying patients so it can help become self sufficient." So, we were trying to make the hospital into a business like operation. When I came in 1978, progress was just beginning to be made, both in image and "bottom line."

Whether or not the ability of the University Hospital medical staff to perform sex change operations added to the luster of the hospital's image is debatable, but during the late 1970s, Oklahoma City became the sex change capital of the world! Mike McEwen continued:

> Christine Jorgenson, the first well-publicized sex change patient, done by Swedish doctors in the 1950s, was in our hospital for something, I don't know exactly what. She was living in California and had come here for care. She was one of the more unusual challenges I had as P.R. director. You don't want the news media to find out about it and sensationalize it, for her sake or the hospital's. That was one advantage of having been a reporter for a long time before I got on the other side of the fence; I could get cooperation from my friends. We had a couple of discreet releases. She told me she didn't want to be bothered so that's the way I handled it. She wasn't.
>
> This was the premier facility for gender dysphoria patients. Two of the physicians in Oklahoma City who were on our staff have international reputations. They are among the best in the world. A lot of people laugh about sex change operations but I had a pretty objective view. Personally, I find it impossible to identify with the need for it but I talked with a number of the patients who felt a sex change was right for them. Another aspect of it, completely ignored, is that there is a large number of people who have disfigurations or dysfunctions of the genitalia that require corrective surgery for which you use the same techniques that you would for a sex change operation. You can imagine what a personal strain it would be to have such a problem and not

have access to the surgical talent, facilities and other services necessary to repair it. In the summer of 1980, those procedures were eliminated but, oddly enough, University Hospital could legitimately claim, by number of procedures and quality of work to be the *best facility in the world* for sex change operations. And I couldn't say anything about it because of the problem of adverse public relations![4]

Meanwhile, the other state teaching hospital continued to expand. George H. Garrison, M.D., was 78 when the new Oklahoma Children's Memorial Hospital (OCMH) wing named for him was dedicated on April 27, 1977. Designed by Hudgens, Thompson, Ball (now HTB, Inc.), the Garrison Tower was built, as the congressional delegation had specified, on the west of the original children's hospital building. During the ceremonies, the esteemed pediatrician observed, "Children are the nicest people we know! We are dedicating a children's hospital for their benefit, for research, the study of illnesses and the acquisition of knowledge which will be useful for future generations not only to the children of Oklahoma but to the nation as well." Nine months later, the $7,314,736 Nicholson Tower addition to the hospital, named for pediatrician Ben H. Nicholson, was completed, providing 48 intermediate term beds and accommodating 56 tiny patients in the general nurseries.[5]

Bruce Perry had been busily pursuing a plan for development of University Hospital which he described as an offspring of the Federal-State Sharing Program:

> It also sprang from the original Dennis plan. It was clear University Hospital needed to be a self-contained institution as much as possible, with sharing agreements with various organizations. We did a development program that looked at the roles of the hospital over time, what programs were necessary to meet those roles and the facilities necessary to develop those programs. The high priorities were: signficantly improved ambulatory care and emergency facilities, all modern inpatient beds— we still had 100 plus beds in the "C" wing of the old hospital—and sufficient support in capital equipment and personnel to meet those programs. We were looking at "centers of excellence," trying to develop things that would enhance the teaching program and the reputations of the university and University Hospital. This way, you get the "halo effect" of having five or six superior programs so people would say, "If they're *that* good on that one, they must be good in other things."
>
> We presented this program to the legislature and *proved*, as much as you can prove anything in this business, that after the hospital was expanded, it would cost

(Department of Human Services)

Governor George Nigh. (Oklahoma Observer)

less in inflated dollars to manage [the single, expanded Everett Tower of] University Hospital than it did then [operating both Old Main and Everett Tower]. [Senator] Al Terrill's Health Oversight Committee was very excited and I think there was general support in the legislature, but we could never sell it to Governor Boren's office. David Boren never placed the priority on it that I thought was necessary. Unless the governor's office really supports a capital appropriation, you ain't gonna get it! So the plan never got off the ground until the hospital was transferred.[6]

When George Nigh became governor in 1979, the priority given University Hospital rose rapidly. The new governor said:

I had long been disappointed in University Hospital. I thought it was a shame and almost a disgrace the very low level at which the state funded the program. Frankly, my mother died there, so I spent a great deal of time in the old hospital. They had a dialysis machine and she had to come in very often. I can remember as the students came around, she'd say she wanted part of the royalties of any book they were going to write about her.

The governor smiled and continued:

But I became very depressed. They gave her good treatment, they were nice people and they did the best they could but the facilities were terrible, just a disgrace. I made a personal commitment at that time that if I could ever have an influence on that hospital, I would. When I became governor, saw what had been done to the Children's Hospital, the outstanding improvements and the example it had become across the country, I went to Lloyd Rader and asked him if he could do the same thing at the University Hospital. I wanted the finest teaching facility possible and if it could be outstanding in the country, that's what I wanted. He said he could do it, he had the people and at that time he had the funds. The money was earmarked for his department.

Simultaneously—and I think this is important—we changed the name of the welfare agency. Under the constitution, it's welfare, but it really bothers me that we provide such excellent services in so many ways that are *not* "welfare." To make people say they are going to the welfare department or they got a welfare check or they're being treated by a welfare worker bothers me because it is a *care* program. So I recommended to the legislature and we passed legislation changing the name to the Department of Human Services (DHS), an agency that provides for people.

This was all part of a master plan because I wanted one of the finest medical facilities in the country there. But it was a great political struggle to transfer the University Hospital. The opposition— his critics in the legislature and the public—didn't want Lloyd Rader to have another facility. My wife [Donna] finally came up with the best idea. I was having difficulty convincing the legislature. She said, "What you need to do is take them on

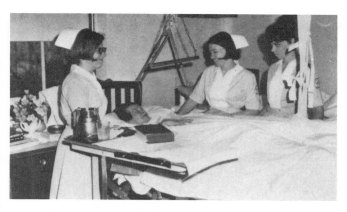

Student nurses attend a bedfast patient in Old Main in the late 1960s. (University of Oklahoma)

a tour of the [old] University Hospital and follow that up by a tour of the Children's Hospital to see the "before" and "after." So we had a big legislative tour and that's when the opposition melted; when they found out what could be done under Rader's leadership.

Mr. Rader didn't want University Hospital. He never once asked for it; he said he really didn't want it but that I was the governor and if I wanted him to have it, he would administer it to the best of his ability. I told him I was going to give it to him.

I wanted the capital improvement program done by the end of my term [December 31, 1982]. It wasn't something I wanted to run for reelection on because, frankly, it doesn't get you any votes. I was concerned that no one else would have the dedication I did to the project. I wanted it in place, so if I were not governor, it would be done. Frankly, when I started the program, I wasn't sure I was going to run for reelection. I am the first one who ever was successful at it.[7]

From Bruce Perry's vantage point, some of the events and motivations which resulted in the transfer of University Hospital appeared this way:

I had a very good relationship with Governor Boren's office although I didn't agree with him very often. We never disagreed publicly and I was not viewed as a political liability. Almost from the beginning, though, I had a very poor relationship with Governor Nigh's staff and to this day, I try to think back why and I really don't know.

We were still pushing for the dollars for the physical additions and the first year he was governor, Nigh spent personal time listening to me and the needs of University Hospital. And we got some money, a better operating account but no capital funds. In the midst of that, there was a strong feeling [among the medical staff] we needed a new coronary intensive care unit but we couldn't get the money from the legislature. In fact, I was told in no uncertain terms by the governor's office

that it wasn't necessary. So, undaunted as I have been from time to time, we made a deal with the University of Oklahoma—Bill Thurman. The university wanted it…badly. They had no cardiology section, which was one of the centers of excellence we had in mind. The deal was that the university would lend University Hospital the money; then the following year, we would increase the master physician reimbursement contract by that amount and pay them back. Well, the governor's office knew we were doing it [the construction], they knew we didn't have the money and they wanted to know *how* we were doing it. So they put us in a position of prohibiting our paying the money back to the university. It got to be a really big, political, smelly issue. Not a very pleasant situation!

At the same time, we were trying to get more capital dollars and the only way legislators who supported the plan saw to get the money for it was to take money away from the welfare department. All of these things together made the transfer come about. Mr. Rader saw it as a way to have more control over the university than he had at that time. I don't think it was his idea to have University Hospital but once the idea was brought up, he really wanted it. The hospital was a political liability to the governor's office, the University had the problem of getting reimbursed, the legislature didn't want to be frustrated by not being able to fund capital improvements at the hospital and saw the welfare department as the way to do this. Another thing the transfer did was free up $12 or $13 million in hospital operating funds the governor could spend somewhere else. The welfare department now absorbed all of the indigent care and all the losses of the hospital. So it freed up money for roads, or prisons, or teachers. Politically, it was the thing to do.

Representative Bill Willis commented:

When the time came, I was the House author of the bill to transfer University Hospital to him. I had a little bit of a fight out on the floor to get that bill passed because the cry was—and I suspected it was true—the Department [of Human Services] could not afford to finance the operation of that institution and carry on all its other functions, too. But I was so desperate to see a hospital built down there, I shrugged off and answered arguments by [saying], "Yes, he has the money to do it with," when in fact, I felt myself it might lead to problems later on.

Of course, he talked to me many times. I *knew* he wanted it, but he didn't make that real obvious to the general membership. But he didn't discourage it; if he had, it wouldn't have happened. In fact, I wouldn't have handled it myself but, yes, he *wanted* the hospital.

Representative Hannah Atkins, the wife of a physician, had a special interest in medical services at the University. (The Oklahoman)

Even though her district was Norman, Representative Cleta Deatherage also looked out for the interests of the university's Oklahoma City campus. (University of Oklahoma)

Asked if Lloyd Rader was truly the most powerful person in the state of Oklahoma, Willis replied:

> Well, I would say, possibly so, because he used his power in such a way that members of the legislature were pleased to go along with any suggestions he had to make. He constantly consulted the legislature. He didn't do things just on his own initiative.[8]

State Representative Hannah Atkins had a major interest in University Hospital which was the principal source of medical service to patients within her predominently black district in Oklahoma City:

> We had tried it under the university and that was frought with tremendous problems because it was too academic and remote. Their budget problems were immense, also. It got tangled up in the [state] regents process and couldn't get enough money.
>
> I don't think it was given a fair chance under a separate board. There was a good board of very dedicated people but they were all new to the concept. They didn't know health, they didn't know budgeting, they didn't know the politics of financing a new state institution. This was during a period [1973-1980] of change of leadership in the hospital; Bruce came on. Before they could establish themselves, along came "the great Godfather" to offer and insist on taking it under his wing. At that time, there was plenty of sales tax money coming in and they could devour any institution that wanted to come under [them]—gobble them up—and so they did.
>
> Mr. Rader liked institutions which broadened his base of power. Here was an institution in financial difficulty, partly because of lack of the legislature's confidence in its leadership and administration. Bruce had learned to lobby the [legislative] leadership and he got along with some of them but there was still not adequate

funding. It was a mediocre hospital because it had been kind of a stepchild, getting leftovers. The old hospital was in terrible physical condition. The staffing was not adequate and to do the kinds of things that needed to be done would have required a great infusion of money all at one time. Bruce got quite a bit but not really what was needed. The legislature had to supply the money; it was a separate appropriation.

> The history of Mr. Rader's administration through the years was to offer to rescue any ailing institution…to build an empire. This was another opportunity and Mr. Rader did lobby for it. He came to committee meetings, he did go to the governor to ask for it. He did come to the legislature, individually and before committee meetings, to ask for that hospital. Governor Nigh came to committee meetings to make a plea that we transfer it.
>
> I was opposed to it. I spoke against it in committee meetings and on the floor of the House. I opposed it because I felt better administration could be effected if it were governed separately.

Another state representative opposed to the transfer was Cleta Deatherage, Democrat of Norman, who was regarded as the legislator who looked out for the interests of the university. Her opposition was based on philosophical grounds:

> I had felt for a long time, instead of transferring functions of state government to the source of revenue, which is the sales tax earmarked for the Department of Human Services, the legislature more appropriately should have transferred funds to the functions of government. Part of the reason was, by taking these functions to Mr.

260

Rader, he would say, "You don't have to worry about it any more." The legislature didn't have to grapple with it anymore because it was *his* money—it wasn't state money, it wasn't appropriated. I've always thought that was just a *terrible* way to conduct the public's business. It wasn't Mr. Rader's money, it wasn't the department's money, it was *public* money! I strongly believe the sales tax money should be unearmarked. At least, it's appropriated now and that we can thank Speaker [Dan] Draper for.

In one sense, I admire Mr. Rader's political style because he was able to get all that done. I was not a supporter, at the outset, of transferring University Hospital. I don't think the Children's Hospital transfer which occurred under Governor Hall was necessarily the best idea. Again, it was a question of transferring the problem to the money.[9]

In September, 1979, at which time the decision to transfer University Hospital to Mr. Rader was considered firm and had only to be passed by the legislature, Bruce Perry bailed out—or did he? He protested:

That's an incorrect perception! I did *not* bail out. I know, everybody thought that. I think the fact that the ownership of the hospital was changing precipitated the decision but it was not the major catalyst. University Hospital was constrained as to what it could pay me as chief executive officer. When Jep left, he was earning like $30 thousand a year and went to Michigan for probably more than twice that. When I came for $36 thousand, it was a cut from what I had been making.

So I began consulting for Presbyterian Hospital and IHP [the profit-making division of the hospital, the title of which is the initials of Presbyterian Hospital, Incorporated written backwards, a.k.a., Innovative Health Programs]. The board agreed I could spend a certain number of days every year this way and I had a consulting agreement with IHP. I'd already been doing that for about a year and a half. In the meantime, Harry Neer had been working his backside off for the survival of Presbyterian Hospital; 1977 and '78 were the really bad years.

The word about the welfare department started to leak out in July, 1979. In September, the governor told me they were going to do it. Mr. Rader called me on the phone and said he really didn't want it "but don't worry about it, you've got a job." "It may not be as chief executive of University Hospital," he assured me, "but you've got a job and there won't be any cut in salary." The joke around the hospital was that I'd be the highest paid director of welfare that Beaver County had ever seen!

Clearly, I could not have survived within that system. I'd have had the salary and a desk someplace, but I would not have been doing what I wanted to be doing. The handwriting was on the wall. It was time to get out. In that sense, perhaps the perception [that I bailed out] was correct.[10]

When Harry Neer heard about the impending transfer of University Hospital, he asked Bruce to become president of IHP and Perry joined the Presbyterian organization on January 1, 1980, exactly six months before the transfer took effect.

When the proposed transfer of University Hospital to DHS was placed in the form of a legislative bill, it included the land on which this facility rested—and a little bit more. On this transaction hangs an interesting tale about which most of the Oklahoma public is totally, and blissfully, unaware. Tom Tucker, legal counsel to Mr. Rader, began the story:

The O.U. Research Building [on 13th Street] was structurally a part of the old hospital, a wing off the "A" corridor of Old Main. [Actually, it was a separate, free-standing building connected only by a glassed-in passageway at the first floor level.] In any event, it was my feeling at the time, and I suppose it was this feeling that determined events, it was not desirable to have another entity own a building or a chunk of land that would be important for long-term reconfiguration of the hospital—looking 30 years, 50 years down the line. The desirable thing was that it be transferred, become a part of the hospital, but that it be given back [to the university]. We ultimately gave the [O.U.] regents a lease, without cost, on the structure for what was estimated to be the life of the laboratories. I think it was a very good resolution because they use the building now, free of charge, as though they owned it. In the year 2000, the lease will be up but could be renewed.[11]

Apparently, the regents did not realize what was happening to them. While they had received a legal description of the land, the metes and bounds of the tract which DHS proposed to take over had not been clearly explained. Tucker laughed and continued:

I sent them a copy of the [legislative] bill. They should have been more alert! You can't really say we straightened out the boundaries; it was a little more drastic than that. We included in the transfer something that had not been included previously: Everett Drive, the street between the two hospitals. And we took the land immediately south of the hospital which functioned as the hospital parking. That had been built by bonds issued by the O.U. regents, who were extremely upset about the parking structure being taken and wanted it back. It was my feeling the hospital should have its own parking and this *was* hospital parking. Of course, at that point

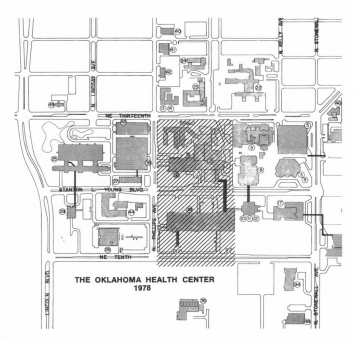

The properties (shown by crosshatching) acquired by DHS when it took over University Hospital extended well south of 10th Street. (OHSF Collection)

I was a [Human Services] department employee; it was the philosophy of the department that employees and visitors should park free. The university would charge money.

We put in the bill a provision for retiring the bonds by creating a trust fund in which we deposited four plus million dollars. The bonds, over their life, would have run more like $18 million, but the interest earned on the investment of our four plus million dollars would be adequate to make the payments on the bonds as they came due. So we did not pay off the bonds; we simply put in escrow the funds sufficient to do that. This means the regents still have outstanding the parking bonds on that structure but they are completely paid for, which gives them a triple-A rating, one of only a few AAA rating bond systems in the country.

The people who park there are basically the same people who parked there before—the medical faculty. This gets back to the dual character of things. Yes, those are faculty who park in the garage and have offices in the South Pavilion [the multi-level structure above the east end of the garage] but they are also the medical staff of the Oklahoma Memorial Hospital [as University Hospital was renamed].[12]

Representative Deatherage tried to get the university to commit itself about the transfer of the hospital:

I talked with the dean of the medical school, the president of the university, "You all are the people directly affected. I have a sense this isn't the right thing to do but I need to know from you whether you think this is a good thing or a bad thing." There was a sort of hem hawing and, "We really don't want to say anything." Finally, I got a resolution from the University Board of Regents, unanimously endorsing the transfer. At that point, I said, "Well, I'm not going to fight it. If they're for it...."

But I have to tell you, there were some interesting things that happened. I asked the question in the House Rules Committee, "Does this legal description transferring the hospital match the legal description in the 1973 legislation that established control of this property by the hospital trustees?" The answer was no; in fact, the bill included other university property. I got them to hold the bill over and talked with people on the main campus where the legal counsel and the president are. Ultimately, the people in the Health Sciences Center have to rely on some of the decision-makers on the Norman campus. I said, "Look, they're getting ready to transfer property that belongs to the university, that does *not* belong to University Hospital." Their response on every occasion was they were hesitant, they didn't want to fight with Mr. Rader or they didn't know what it meant. I finally said, "If you guys don't know what you want to do, then I'm certainly not going to try to save you from yourselves." So I said to heck with it.

I did talk with David Walters, Bill Thurman's assistant. They were intimidated about having any kind of fight with Mr. Rader. Dr. Thurman and Dr. Halverstadt's loyalties were to Mr. Rader and one of them went to the regents to get them to pass the resolution in support of the transfer. There were those dollars in the back of their mind. They thought that was the only way to get the money and they were probably right. There's no question a lot of DHS dollars went into that hospital.

At the time we were getting ready to vote on the hospital transfer, I was the last person the governor called. He had already talked to everybody else before he talked to me. That was the only time since George Nigh has been governor I've ever known him to call people about a bill. He just doesn't do that. But this was the only way he could balance the budget that year and still cut taxes.

I finally realized I couldn't vote against it if the university wasn't going to be against it. The governor called me on Friday and said, "You're the last one I've called. I already have the votes. I'm only calling you as a courtesy." So I said, "You can mark me down. I'm not going to fight with you about it anymore."

The next night, Saturday, I was at home at six o'clock and I got a call from Mr. Rader, asking me about a couple in my district for whom I had written a letter of recommendation several years earlier. They wanted to adopt a child and their social worker told them they

Regent Dee Replogle was less than pleased. (University of Oklahoma)

needed a letter from a legislator. Mr. Rader said, "Sissy! That couple—they still want a baby?" I said, "Well, I don't know, Mr. Rader, I haven't talked with them about it in two years." He said, "You call 'em and tell 'em if they still want the baby, go pick it up, nine o'clock Monday morning. Got 'em a little girl." He didn't bring up anything about the hospital. He said, "Just want to be friends with you. Want you to know we're doing everything we can to try to help you."

Let me tell you, there is no feeling in the world like being able to call someone and say, "Do you still want a baby? This is The Stork!"

Cleta laughed merrily and continued:

They were ecstatic. And the funny thing was, she'd never been able to get pregnant, but after they'd adopted this baby, within a couple of years she even got pregnant.

I always referred to that child as the "University Hospital baby." Mr. Rader didn't know I'd already told the governor I was going to vote for it. What you need to remember is that it wasn't a question of whether he had the votes. He didn't want any opposition, any debate, any amendments. At the same time, he never said one word to me that was improper. I find that system for placement of babies to be somewhat unusual but there was nothing improper, illegal or unethical. It was just curious timing…highly coincidental![13]

When attorney Dee Replogle, the chairman of the O.U. Regents Health Sciences Center Committee, was asked about this land transaction, he inquired:

You mean the act of piracy? Our reaction was: we were outraged! We were repeatedly assured at various points in time that this was a mistake and would be corrected by various people, ranging from Mr. Rader on down. Obviously, we were limited in what we could do. We were extremely dependent on the teaching hospitals and the ability of the university to fulfill its educational mission depended on a good working relationship with them. Mr. Rader had made a number of statements about his desire to upgrade those hospitals and turn them into the type of facilities which all of us wanted to see. They could never be adequately funded through the university because of the State Regents. Regardless of what they were telling people, they were requiring the University of Oklahoma to use educational dollars to subsidize the operation of those hospitals. That meant we were going to be short on both ends. We had hoped the hospitals would be placed directly under the legislature where they would receive appropriations from the legislature but they looked on the acquisition of those hospitals by Mr. Rader as perhaps the only means of providing adequate funding for them.

We were also admonished by the governor's office not to get involved in turf battles. So it was one of those situations where, yeah, our land was being pirated off from us and it was taken under circumstances that, I think, did not speak well of those who took it. We saw some great displays of not the finest side of human nature, I might add. But we were in a position that, from the standpoint of the best interest of the university, we didn't feel like we could really do too much about it. The circumstances under which it was initially explained to us—presented to the board—left a lot to be desired from the standpoint of ethics on the part of Mr. Rader and some others. Initially, we were absolutely not aware of what was being done.[14]

Associate Provost David Walters believed that Mr. Rader's ultimate victory was "a very impressive display of his power in the legislature." "After it was all over," he observed, "I think the regents felt they were lucky to have kept what they had." He went on:

It was a vicious struggle behind the scenes from the time we discovered major portions of our property were included in the transfer until the bill ultimately passed; the regents were on the verge of going public and raising Cain about it. Lloyd, through a series of masterful strokes, managed to keep these guys quiet until the bill became a reality, constantly pledging he would "make it right." Once the bill was passed and signed, his negotiating posture changed dramatically.[15]

Representative Deatherage continued the story:

This is a fascinating thing that happened. I had raised

Details of the land struggle were described by Associate Provost David Walters. (University of Oklahoma)

a lot of questions [about the transfer] so Mr. Rader said, "You come down. I want to show you what we've done at Children's and what we can do at University Hospital for the kinds of things you're concerned about." In other words, I'm going to make you feel better about all this. I had been worried about the women's clinic and the provision of obstetrical/gynecological services which were very limited. So I went down there in July [1980] just after the first of the fiscal year. In a conference room, Mr. Rader was showing me a map of the Health Sciences Center and he said, "We're having a fight with the university regents and their legal counsel over property down here." It was the commercial space [now called the South Pavilion and used for clinical faculty offices] and parking garage. He said, "They don't know whether they want us to have control over this or what." I said, "In the bill, it transferred that property to you. What do *they* have to say about it any longer?" So he said, "That's right! They really *don't* have anything to say about it. They don't understand that." I started laughing. This was exactly what I'd tried to say to them and here they were, now suddenly figuring out they'd lost control of this property. Mr. Rader went down there and changed the locks on that building *that night.* He called me two days later and said, "Sissy! I took your advice," and when I said, "What advice?" he said, "Well, we just went down there and took it over. You said it was O.K." That's how he'd always do things. He'd be very careful what you said to him because he would [then] say, "I had legislative approval."

It was quite a little scene there for a few days. It threw the university officials into a dither. I remember a meet-

ing; [President] Banowsky called me into his office. They were distressed because they'd lost this space and the research building. I was absolutely in awe! I said, "I don't understand this. I've been trying to talk to you people about this for three or four months and you all acted as though it didn't make any difference." I'd held up the bill to get the information from them to amend out those parcels of property they didn't want transferred. I think we could have made the case. I think I could have gotten the votes.[16]

Rader not only locked the doors on the proposed commercial space but moved the university out promptly. According to Walters, the university had included the 30,000 square feet of space in the parking structure to start the first student union-type facility in the center of the campus. Mr. Rader had "told us not to worry, that we could proceed with those plans." The university had advertised for leases for a barber shop, gift shop and book store and had entered into a construction contract to finish out the space. Walters continued:

I was called one morning by Tom Tucker after the bill was passed that the decision had been made that DISRS really needed that space. We were using only the downstairs area as a vending warehouse. We had soft drinks and all the vending machine supplies there. I asked, "Do I have a week?" and he said no. "Do I have a day?" and he said, "No, the trucks will be there at noon and you need to find a location by noon."

So Gary Smith [Director of Administration and Finance] and I very frantically began looking for warehouse space. By noon, we had no alternative storage space but by noon, sure enough, two semi-trucks with DISRS on the side showed up with a swarm of 40 or 50 people. They backed up to the dock and began loading the warehouse contents onto the trucks and asked us where we wanted to put it. We wound up putting it onto a parking lot where it was guarded until we could dissipate it into other storage areas around the campus which took two or three days.

Gary and I went over that evening because they were still going fast and furious to get it empty. They were destroying a large amount of the merchandise as they were trying to move it. Fork trucks rammed pallet trucks full of [cans of] pop, and it was running all over. We got quite irritated but left and went back to my office.

Mr. Rader then called us. It was one of his classic telephone calls in which he went through this long justification as to why he had to do what he had to do. There must have been 10 people on other phone lines. He'd say, "Isn't that right, Tom?" and you'd hear Tucker on the other line say yes. He'd say, "I'm a servant of the people and the people's representatives are telling me

Two additional levels were built on the South Pavilion in 1981 to house the clinical staff of Oklahoma Memorial Hospital. (Oklahoma City Chamber of Commerce)

to do thus and so. Isn't that right, Representative Deatherage?" and you'd hear her say, "Yes, that's right."

He didn't ever recall telling us we could proceed with the leases. He seemed to imply that the university was trespassing and that we were trying to build "these ice cream stores" and he needed it for things that were really important, much higher priority. The governor and the legislature were telling him they wanted him to do a five-year project in three [years] and to do that he needed to take over that space and convert it to interim facilities for physicians so he could get on with the expansion of University Hospital.

It all made perfect sense but we, unfortunately, had crawled way out on a limb with leases and construction contracts which we proceeded to buy back at great expense to the university. We wound up spending probably $50 thousand to get ourselves out of them. Everybody was afraid of irritating the "cash cow," but on the other hand, they were very concerned about the oppressive tyranny that took over.[17]

Mike McEwen was concerned about the transfer, too:

At that time, key legislative committee people were very carefully monitoring what was going on at the hospital. Bruce had appeared frequently at committee meetings and given them up-to-date reports on what was happening. As long as the legislature saw improvement, they were happy. It was a period of continually improving legislative oversight.

At the end of the last (1979) legislative session, when they were getting into the appropriation bills, Representative Don Davis, chairman of the appropriations committee, said words to the effect, "Look, Bruce Perry and his boys tell us this is what they need. They've been straight with us the last couple of years; they're doing what we told them to do. Let's give them the money." That was an absolute turnaround which had not happened prior to that time. The credibility did develop.

I was pessimistic about the future of the University Hospital based on my own personal disappointment with the fact that I had been part of a movement to build the hospital [into an efficiently operating organization], we were apparently succeeding and it was frustrating to see that momentum lost. I was certain that under the control of the Department of Human Services, the basic thrust toward effective management and administration would be lost. There would be a surfeit of funds, there would be a tremendous surge in building, probably not well planned. I also knew there would probably be a lot of money spent that was not spent efficiently but spent to ameliorate the concerns, fears or animosities of the physicians or the university.

I don't think Governor Nigh fully understood all the implications of building the institution, what the costs would be, what the impact on health care and education would be. He saw the problems of University Hospital and he saw the solution—let it be funded out of this tremendous resource we have available in Human Services. I don't think anybody involved in the transfer decision thought it was going to end up having the economic impact on DHS that it had. *I* thought it was going to, as did a lot of my friends who knew the University Hospital and DHS, but we weren't in a position to do anything about it. I don't think they had any idea of the amount of money that was going to be eaten up. I believe Mr. Rader felt impetus to build that institution as rapidly as possible. He built it in a "fast track" style of construction that was not good economic sense. Now that doesn't mean it wasn't excellent political sense. Basically he had a couple of years to get things done and if it had stretched out any longer, it wouldn't have happened.

If you look at the money spent at University Hospital for the two year period prior to the transfer and the two year period after... [operating] budgets more than doubled. And I know they didn't double the service. The money did not buy care. It was not money well spent, from an economic standpoint. Now, politically...![18]

Mark Allen Everett was picked by Lloyd Rader to be the chief of staff at the adult hospital. He explained why he was chosen:

If you look at the ones running the hospitals, Thurman, Halverstadt and myself, those are three people in whom

Mr. Rader had personal confidence. It was very important that the hospital head be able to deal with the director because things were done personally in those days. Any important decision was made by the director, not at any other level. That's the exclusive reason because otherwise there would be no reason to appoint a dermatologist as the effective administrative officer of the hospital.

He was a czar, basically, and there would be no point in having the director of the hospital someone to whom he would not speak. And there were a lot of them. He did not allow many physicians access to his person.

Dr. Everett observed that "the organization of the Oklahoma Teaching Hospitals is almost Byzantine."[19]

That Oklahoma Observer of politics and self-professed government critic, Frosty Troy, was not reserved in his comments:

In the long range view of Oklahoma, I think the transfer of those two hospitals was one of the most fatal fiscal errors this state ever made. The only time I've ever heard George Nigh admit making a mistake— I know him, we grew up together in McAlester—was the transfer of the teaching hospital to the State Department of Public Welfare. The theory was really simple. The idea was to get them under the welfare umbrella. But, number one, we were on a collision course with the downturn in the economy, number two, with Reaganomics, and number three, we had extremely poor management at those hospitals after the transfer; at least, I thought so. It was, "Oh, my God, look at the bucks! Do what you please and go."

They were poorly managed and when the belt-tightening came…and it had to come [because] we were living in a very false fiscal atmosphere in Oklahoma. At the same time, those clowns over at the State Capitol were cutting taxes as hard and as fast as they could. If we were going to finance those hospitals, we should have done it adequately and the teaching hospitals certainly should have stayed a part of the University of Oklahoma.

I've heard George Nigh since say of his first term, the only thing [about which] he really thought he made a mistake was that transfer, that precipitously. Lloyd Rader just swallowed that whole complex— whole. And the attendant waste…!

He wouldn't take any advice and if you think anyone was around advising him, you guess again. Now you could snow him a little bit, but after he'd had a good night's sleep, forget it! If he did not have to make a decision that day, he'd sleep right through your snow. He's sharp. Don't sell him short![20]

Frosty emitted a low whistle to punctuate his evaluation of Mr. Rader.

In February, 1981, the Department of Human Services opened the new emergency medicine and trauma center at Oklahoma Memorial Hospital with the capacity to accommodate 50,000 patients a year. It also completed a 400-car garage to serve the adult hospital and a 1,400-car garage on the west side of Stonewall just across the street from Oklahoma Children's Memorial Hospital. The Don H. O'Donoghue Rehabilitation Institute, the third unit of the Oklahoma Teaching Hospitals (OTH) as they were now identified, was dedicated on March 6, 1981. It provided 120 beds for both adults and children who needed rehabilitation services, that is, accident victims, stroke patients, paraplegics, patients with birth defects, burn patients and the like.

Mr. Rader further expanded the department's capacity to take care of children. He completely remodeled Culbertson Grade School, built in 1919, to create a shelter for abused and neglected children and renamed it the Pauline E. Mayer Children's Center. The Mayer Annex, on Lottie, was built as a group home in which teenage mothers could be taught how to take care of their babies. A major addition to the Child Study Center was completed in April, 1981, which meant more services could be given to children with neurological and developmental disorders.

Mr. Rader could demolished buildings as fast as he built them. "When they transferred the adult hospital, if I hadn't "fast-tracked" it, we never could have built it [the three level addition atop Everett Tower]. And if I hadn't torn these buildings down…had some more fights with the doctors…." The story behind the demolition of Old Main was recounted by Representative Cleta Deatherage:

Someone asked me one day at a news conference about an order of [U.S. District] Judge [Luther] Bohanon's having to do with a psychiatric hospital for [state] prisoners and if we had to have such a facility in Oklahoma City, where would it be? I said that was an impossible question to answer. First of all, he hadn't ordered such a thing and second, if he did, I did not know how much it would cost or where it would be. They asked, "What are some possibilities?" and I said, "Obviously, the first thing we'd do would be to look at any state property we had, state facilities that might be suitable. It's possible after we build the new University Hospital, perhaps some of the old quarters might be suitable." I mentioned a couple of other different possibilities.

I heard from people who were close to Mr. Rader [who said when] he heard that, he decided he didn't want any damn prison facility right there next to his brand new hospital and said, referring to me personally, if I was going to put a bunch of prisoners there, then he was

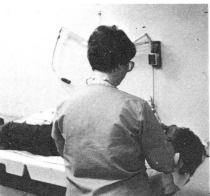
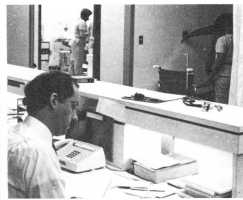

Scenes at the entrance and inside the Emergency Medicine and Trauma Center in Oklahoma Memorial Hospital. (Oklahoma City Chamber of Commerce)

The new Children's Hospital expanded until it was considerably longer than Presbyterian. A new addition was under construction west of Garrison Tower in 1985. (University of Oklahoma)

"Dr. Don" addresses the crowd at the dedication of the $12 million Rehabilitation Institute named for him. (University of Oklahoma)

The Child Study Center expanded, too. (Oklahoma City Chamber of Commerce)

going to fix that—get the order to tear it down. But that would never have been my first choice, anyway. I have been sort of the Health Sciences Center legislator for a number of years. For a long time [since Bryce Baggett], we've had a hard time getting the local delegation to feel that it was theirs.

The answer to that [reporter's] question was completely off the top of my head. In the final analysis, I don't know that I would have supported anything like that—putting prisoners over there. The funny thing about that [situation] was, Mr. Rader would get it in his mind something was going to happen and that's how he'd make decisions. And he wasted no time getting something done about it.[21]

267

Dr. Sol Papper, chief of medicine. (University of Oklahoma)

The "headache ball" slams into Old Main. (Department of Human Services)

Representative Bill Willis told how Mr. Rader went about it:

> He came to see me one day, said he was getting quite a bit of pressure to house prisoners [in Old Main]. He said, "I don't want to ruin the hospital and that's what it would do." I went down there with him and looked it over. He said, "I'd like to tear it down." and I said, "*Tear it down!*" That was on about a Wednesday—maybe a little earlier in the week. When my wife and I started home on Thursday afternoon, there was a wrecker there, tearing that building down. He sure didn't waste any time.[22]

Mr. Rader went on with the story:

> In those old buildings, they had some of the finest quarters [offices]. They [the clinical faculty] were all broke, but they'd furnished these fancy offices and they didn't want to give 'em up. So they just kept horsin' and stallin'. Dr. Sol Papper [Solomon Papper, M.D., Chairman of Medicine]—he's a pretty good fellow, Papper is—I told him, "Now, Pap, y'all get ready to move." We'd brought a crane in and I had occasion to go over there for something and saw the foreman hadn't made any effort to get moving. I said, "Bill, when are you going to start on that building? I'm tired of this bullshit. Where's that crane?" "Well," he said, "the ball's not attached to the cable." They had to bring it two blocks so I said, "Bill, you be over there with that damn thing at three o'clock and we'll start tearing it down." They [the doctors] all had their cars parked out there but that was the only way I could see it could be done. So about 10 minutes

The old hospital is almost gone. (University of Oklahoma)

after three, we hit the first lick! We'd warned them, "Move your cars!"[23]

Lloyd Rader chortled as he thought about the incident. He meant what he said.

DHS attorney Tom Tucker had the opportunity to observe Mr. Rader's administrative style for many years and had these comments:

> Mr. Rader viewed himself as running the entire agency personally, both the traditional Department of Welfare and the hospitals. In the hospital complex, I'm confident he felt he made all the decisions. In fact, though,

268

there was such an appearance because of the extraordinary detail with which he dealt with things. There have always been sub-units in the agency which just quietly and inconspicuously went about doing their business without ever coming to his attention so that large parts of the Department of Human Services ran without reference to the director and I'm sure parts of the hospitals did the same thing.

Mr. Rader had the reputation in state government of being an administrator *extraordinaire*...the finest administrator in state government if not in the country. In my assessment, Mr. Rader was a wretched administrator. He maintained the appearance of success through vast sums of money, great power and the ability to do things quickly, however inefficiently. He totally wrecked the systems that were really pretty good in the adult hospital when it was transferred using the approach that his financial officer in the welfare department knew how to take care of all these things and they should do it his way. So the private, computerized systems were just scrapped. Mr. Rader didn't look at them, didn't want to hear about them, made everybody in that hospital suspect as having resisted the transfer. The hospital has probably been less effectively run since it was transferred to us than it has ever been in its history.

On the other side of the coin: with that extraordinary power and financial resource he had, as well as individual autonomy within state government, he was able to spend somewhere between $200 and $250 million out of current operating funds for capital improvements in the center which could not otherwise have been done. So the trade-off was; the adult hospital was completed in a pretty good fashion; Children's was built in a very inefficient, rambling, disorganized way, but nevertheless, we have large, completed, well-equipped facilities which probably, but for Mr. Rader, could not have been done.[24]

The 1968 OHC Development Plan showed a helicopter pad on the campus across Stonewall Avenue from the Oklahoma State Department of Health building. It was one of the few elements of the plan which were actually located almost precisely where shown. Called "Love Field" after Bruce Love, Director of Operations for the University, who had birddogged the project to completion, it had an elevation of 1237 feet above sea level. It was dedicated and placed in service on May 31, 1979.

However, Med-Evac army helicopters based at Fort Sill at Lawton, Oklahoma, were still using the helipad south of the governor's mansion when they ferried patients from distant points in Oklahoma to the Health Center. This did not help George Nigh's repose, as he related:

Helipad atop Children's Hospital. (Department of Human Services)

I'm extremely proud of the Mediflight program. I'm personally proud of it because it's an idea I read about in some other state. There again, my personal experience played a vital role. We moved into the mansion [in 1979] and were awakened almost every night by helicopters landing. They brought people in from all over the state but the only place they could land to get people to the hospital was at the mansion. Some ambulance would have to come over, they'd get them out of the helicopter, put them into the ambulance, get them over to the hospital, put them on a stretcher and then take them up several stories. The helicopters flew right over the mansion and I became aware people were being jostled around blocks from where they were to be treated. So, once again, I personally went to Lloyd Rader and said I would like a helipad on top of a building. Speaker [Carl] Albert had a heart attack and they lifted him by helicopter and brought him to Oklahoma City. They attribute the success in saving his life in large part to that. So Mediflight was born out of a personal experience.[25]

Why Medi-Evac helicopters continued to use the pad adjacent to the governor's mansion when there was a landing pad on the campus after May 31, 1979, is not clear. There was no helicopter service based in the Oklahoma Health Center which could pick up patients from over the state. Mr. Rader contracted for

269

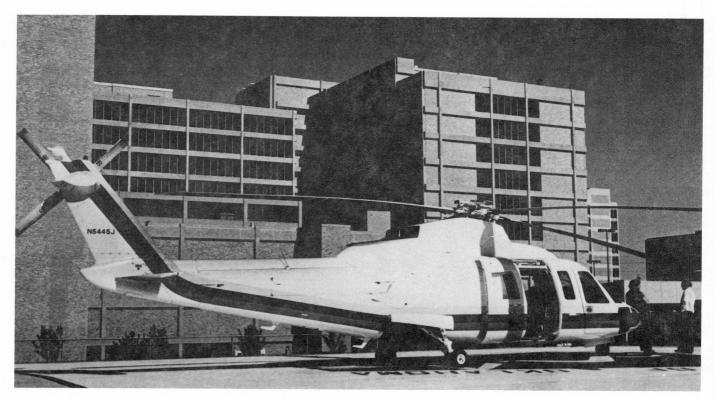

The third pad built in the OHC is adjacent to the trauma center at Oklahoma Memorial Hospital. (Oklahoma City Chamber of Commerce)

Presbyterian Hospital's helipad is outside its emergency room. (Presbyterian Hospital)

a helicopter and Mediflight began operation in October, 1980, from Love Field. Then he built a pad on the top of the Garrison Tower of Children's Hospital and operated the service from there beginning in No-

vember, 1982. Also in 1982, a third helipad was built adjacent to the emergency entrance to Oklahoma Memorial Hospital, on the former site of Old Main. In 1984, Presbyterian Hospital built a helipad outside its emergency suite so there are now four landing places in the Oklahoma Health Center and Governor Nigh sleeps peacefully through the night.

In the fall of 1982, Lloyd Rader announced he would retire at the end of the year. Governor Nigh appointed former Governor and Senator Henry Bellmon as interim head of the Department of Human Services. This was an excellent choice because Bellmon had 12 years experience in the Senate of the United States, working with the federal programs from whence much of the DHS money came and he had also been the ranking minority member of the Senate Budget Committee. He said he would serve only until a permanent director could be appointed. On October 4, Bellmon joined DHS as associate director so he could work with Rader for the last three months of the director's career.

CHAPTER 35
SHARING SCUTTLED: 1977

Garrison Tower, the new, seven-story, 190-bed wing of Oklahoma Children's Memorial Hospital, included a burn center and a 47-bed neonatal intensive care unit where critically ill newborn were treated. With this new bed tower in place, the Oklahoma Children's Memorial Hospital was ready to tie into the planned concourse building for maximum sharing with the V.A. Hospital, the University of Oklahoma College of Medicine and the University Hospital and Clinics. But something had gone wrong. Architect-planner Bob Douglass explained:

> We were very close. We weren't so naive we didn't know there might be legal problems. We brought in the legal counsel for the V.A. as well as the university's legal representatives, lawyers from Mr. Rader's shop and we had those people working out a concept they thought would be consistent with laws and mandates they all operated under. It got as far as Washington, where the general counsel for the V.A. Central Office came up with a contrary opinion. He said it was not legally possible for the V.A. to cooperate in the construction of a facility for use by others. If they had somehow had blinders on and built it too big and allowed others to come in and use it, that would have been more legal than to work out a cooperative agreement to build the facility [for joint use]. So that's where it hung up.[1]

Dan Macer had worked since early 1974 to get all of the institutions in agreement with the concept of federal-state sharing and to line up the political and financial support needed. Lloyd Rader, Bill Thurman, Paul Sharp, Bruce Perry and John Chase, M.D., former director of the Oklahoma City V.A. Hospital and then the Chief Medical Director of the Veterans Administration in Washington, all had placed their stamp of approval on the idea. The concept had the blessings of Hayden H. Donahue, M.D., and the other members of the Oklahoma Health Planning Commission. Stanton Young endorsed the plan on September 19, 1974, because he could see the value of a patient/pedestrian bridge over Phillips linking Presbyterian Hospital with the other inpatient institutions on the campus. Many times, pediatric patients had to be transferred from Presbyterian to Children's.[2]

Governor Hall favored the idea and Senator Bellmon, senior minority member of the Senate Appro-

Dan Macer and VA Chief of Staff Walter Whitcomb talk about the ill-fated Federal-State Sharing project. (Dan Macer)

priations Committee, actively and enthusiastically supported the V.A.'s request for $30 million for new construction. The project was expected to cost $35.5 million, of which the state's share was $5.5 million. It looked as though everything was lined up until the V.A.'s legal counsel made his decision. Bob Douglass continued:

> Governor Hall had a lot of vision and influence in the beginning and when we presented the concept to the legislature, several of the legislators who spoke to us afterwards said—I don't know whether it was true or tongue-in-cheek—it was the first time in living memory the Oklahoma legislature had ever voted unanimously for anything! So the logic and the political support were in confluence then. There was no hang-up until it got to Washington and the general counsel said we couldn't do it because of this technicality.
>
> Senator Bellmon said, "We'll fix that. We'll change the law." But Governor Boren decided not to follow through on his earlier commitment to provide a modest amount of funding [$500 thousand for planning] to allow the concept to go forward. That sunk it![3]

Dan Macer disagreed. The state share of planning money was half a million dollars of which Governor Boren had authorized $200 thousand "for additional consultant services to further implement the project." This money came through the State Regents for Higher Education and was released by Chancellor Dunlap at the request of Dr. Sharp on April 19, 1977.[4] Douglass continued:

> In my time frame, it may be more fair to say he simply procrastinated. Funds had been authorized but were not provided. But I think there was another player who influenced Governor Boren. It was never clear to me what his agenda was or why he took the position he did but Dr. Thurman targeted the scuttling of this idea, particularly the "loaded" bridge [a corridor with clinics and other health facilities on each side] and the ambulatory care center connection with the V.A. because he had another idea he liked better, whatever that was. His aggressive campaign against it started after we had completed our report [February, 1975] and it looked as if things still might go forward if Senator Bellmon could solve the legal problem.
>
> The people who were trying to get this sharing concept to gel had worked out a carefully united front and so long as that united front was visible, Senator Bellmon felt comfortable in tackling the legal and legislative problems. But when Dr. Thurman backed away and started trying to torpedo the concept and it was clear the university was no longer committed to it, we lost the united front and it cratered.[5]

Something or someone had influenced Governor Boren. Minutes of the Human Services Mini-Cabinet of April 25, 1977 listed follow-up actions including:

> After a discussion of planning needs in the Health Sciences Center Complex and proposed use of $200,000 available for further study, the Governor stated that he did not want the money to be used for anything that would be duplicative of earlier planning or that would commit the state to future indebtedness. He further indicated he considered it to be fiscally infeasible to consider the full Concourse concept at this time [the state could not afford the high cost involved], and that a more simple physical connection should be built. Dr. Thurman assured the Governor and Representative Atkins that the Douglass study and all prior studies and planning would be examined. Appropriate recommendations would then be made to the Regents and through the Regents to the Governor, on how best to spend the money.[6]

Bob Douglass continued:

> The two ambulatory care centers did not come to-

Dr. John "Jack" Chase, former director of the Oklahoma City Veterans Administration Hospital, was head of the Department of Medicine and Surgery at the Central Office in Washington, D.C. (The Oklahoman)

gether. That was the big gap, the heart and soul of it! If you put it into the context of the two concepts around which the whole plan was built, centralization and connection, we got connection; we didn't get centralization.[7]

There was opposition to the plan from other quarters, as Dr. John Chase related:

> The V.A. worked very hard on the federal-state sharing plan and I don't know all the reasons it did not work. It was a step which was so far from the usual, there were lots of people in the government who were not prepared to take that risk. But it made real sense. One of the basic hang-ups was the idea of the Veterans Administration constructing a shared facility on somebody else's territory but it was beyond that: how would it be operated?; how could the federal government assure itself it was getting a fair shake in terms of a return on its investment?; how would the dollars flow when physicians were practicing medicine in a federal installation but charging patients who were not federal beneficiaries? These were the kinds of complexities I think were the obstruction to final approval. The V.A. has been involved in comparable suggestions over the years and they did not work out, either.[8]

Dan Macer talked about still other resistance:

> There was opposition by the American Legion, the Veterans of Foreign Wars and the D.A.V. [Disabled American Veterans]. They thought this would be the first step toward abolishing the V.A. system because the plan envisioned what they termed a "federal hospital." Part of the concourse would have called for the closing of the Air Force Hospital at Tinker [Air Force Base]. Also, it would have been in a position to care for all entitlees of the federal government for various reasons. Their fear was that veterans' services would be diluted

The bridge over 13th Street. (OHSF Collection)

and if that happened, pretty soon we'd be speaking of federal hospitals, not Veterans Administration hospitals.

They exercised that objection politically. Although V.A. Administrator Johnson and Chief Medical Director Jim Musser disagreed, these veterans organizations took the position they could never endorse the reelection of people in Oklahoma who signed off on this plan.[9]

Apparently, they made their point clear to Governor Hall who, according to Dan Macer, withdrew his visible, public support. However, Bob Douglass said:

I think representatives of those groups did say that to him and later, when it did not get implemented, they felt like that was the reason. But to the best of my knowledge—and I've been in contact with Governor Hall since—he never wavered in his support for the idea. He was enthusiastic about it until the last.[10]

Dan Macer found this turn of events both "startling and depressing." Governor Hall's term was ending and the veterans groups influence was not as important on the state level as it was nationally. Macer was hopeful the project would get back on the track but, he explained:

With a new administrator and a new medical director at the V.A. Central Office, the people working for them tried to nit-pick the program. They felt they would look good to the service [veterans] organizations if they found ways not to do it. [In addition, any sharing was a threat to the Veterans Administration employees' territory and authority.] It was political! Dr. Chase *did* support the project but the architectural and construction programs were not under his jurisdiction.

I guess I didn't give up the idea until the architectural plans were drawn and the contract was let to build it [the addition to the V.A. Hospital] on the other side of the [13th] street.[11]

Looking back at this ill-fated attempt at maximum federal-state sharing, Bob Douglass observed:

There was a heirarchy of sharing that worked. The things

Because inter-institutional architectural coordination disappeared after 1973, the bridges over OHC streets took many forms. This one connects OMH and OCMH. Below it is the black glass pedestrianway from the VA Medical Center. (OHSF Collection)

The "Santa Fe Superchief" between Children's and O'Donoghue. (OHSF Collection)

This bridge between the Biomedical Sciences and Basic Sciences buildings was built by the University. (OHSF Collection)

This one also spans Stanton L. Young Boulevard between the South Pavilion and OMH. (OHSF Collection)

"Sharing Is Everything"

Not everyone agreed....(Oklahoma City Chamber of Commerce).

that had relatively no medical significance and things that had relatively low cost and therefore didn't matter very much, were shared. The things that had to do with high cost, high tech, high expertise in medical care were not shared.[12]

The early Oklahoma Health Center sharing effort and the federal state sharing project both tried to centralize activities and share buildings. Neither worked in that fashion but there was a sharing of programs in which services for the patients of one institution were performed in other campus institutions. The V.A./University of Oklahoma relationship is the best example. Where there were 140 shared services before the federal-state sharing project, there are now 22 major shared services and over 200 sub-categories. As Dan Macer said:

> There has been a considerable growth in sharing which may not appear in the physical arrangement but would not have existed had we not tried to get some type of physical connection. It resulted from the studies that were done.[13]

The pedestrian bridge over 13th Street connecting the three hospitals was installed as a part of the V.A. construction project and was opened in 1984, a full decade after the concept was first put forward. Despite the abortive outcome, the federal-state sharing project holds a special place in Bob Douglass's heart:

Dan Macer and his committee took a chance when they hired me to do this work because it was the first consulting work I'd ever been hired to do. From that beginning of my firm, we have specialized in planning of university medical centers, we are now the fourth largest hospital consulting firm in the country and have worked in 40 states and 10 foreign countries. So this is the most important project there ever was or ever will be in my life. I'm thrilled to see as much as there is; I'd be more thrilled if we had gotten more done. But in my view of the world, it is a monument to Dan Macer.

You can look at the Oklahoma Health Center through polarized glass. You look at it one way and it is wonderful to see what an incredible lot has been accomplished. I don't know of any places in the country that compare with it in terms of convenience and the ability to do a really unified job of teaching medical students and caring for people. Then you turn the glass the other way and, because of my experience, I can't help seeing all of the opportunities that were missed to do something absolutely smashing. But it's all there and the bottom line is: it's pretty wonderful that that much has been done![11]

CHAPTER 36
THE UNIVERSITY: 1976-1982

William G. Thurman, M.D., pediatrician, crisis administrator. (University of Oklahoma)

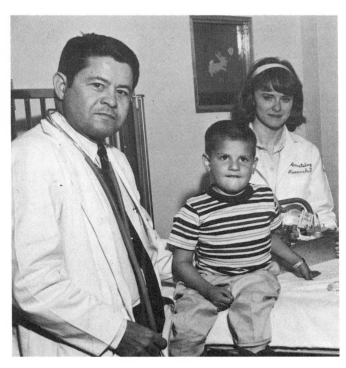

Chairman of Pediatrics Pete Riley with one of his young patients in Children's Hospital. (University of Oklahoma)

Provost Bill Thurman saw the major problems of the University of Oklahoma Health Sciences Center as money, image and deadwood. Concerning the alleged latter, there were several versions of the process by which Pete Riley was deposed from his position as chairman of pediatrics. Dr. Thurman said:

> I had to fight Lloyd Rader about that because Pete was Lloyd's boy. They got cross-wise after that happened. When I was going to make a major decision that related to [Oklahoma] Children's [Memorial Hospital—OCMH or CMH], I would always tell Lloyd about it so it wouldn't come off the wall at him. I told him I had to replace Pete as chief of pediatrics. He was opposed to it because Pete had been the architect of the Children's Hospital and had worked closely with Lloyd making sure the legislature and the regents both approved the transfer of CMH from the university to the Department of Public Welfare rather than to an independent board as University Hospital had.
>
> Pete had taken Lloyd Rader all over the United States to look at children's hospitals so Lloyd would have a better perspective of what to build and what to do. In many ways, their's was a father/son relationship. Lloyd didn't

like the fact that I was going to have to replace Pete. He understood the reasons but I can't say he supported it with enthusiasm but he did nothing to make it harder for me to do.[1]

This was the way it looked to Dr. Riley:

> I resigned January 1, 1976. Dr. Thurman denied to me he was responsible for asking me to resign and in fact, wrote me a letter to that effect. He said it was a decision of the dean. In my opinion, he's told so many different versions of things, he doesn't remember what's correct. He said he was backing the dean but he denied initiating it. Tom Lynn was the acting dean at that time and I don't believe the acting dean would have done that.[2]

Provost Thurman talked about the chief of medicine:

> Jim Hammarsten was not really deadwood. Jim was an active, involved teacher but he was not an administrator and a leader. The department of medicine is the guts of any medical school. They are responsible for

275

physical diagnosis, they are responsible for the largest chunk of the curriculum and you've *got* to have both an administrator and a leader in medicine. He was no Stewart Wolf!

Jim's the happiest man in the world right now. I talked with him in the airport at Denver. It's taken a while for him to get over his bitterness about my requesting his resignation; that's a euphemistic term for firing. He said, "I didn't like it then, I don't like it now but it was the right decision."

There were others, some of them not so graphic. Hammarsten just happened to be the most visible.[3]

James F. "Jim" Hammarsten, M.D., had been chief of the department of medicine since Dr. Wolf went to the Oklahoma Medical Research Foundation in 1967, almost 10 years. He said:

I never talked to Bill Thurman in any airport in Denver and I don't agree with what he said. I think I was treated in a crummy fashion. My original plan was to stay on another two years, at the most, as chairman and then stay in Oklahoma.

I submitted my resignation at his request in April, 1977, and left the chairmanship on June 30. I went on sabbatical and returned in February, 1978, but before leaving I already had things arranged [to become professor] at the University of Washington. As for leadership, the fact they named a lectureship after me, they named the Oklahoma Thoracic Society meeting after me and they named the conference room over at the V.A. after me.... I think that says something. After Thurman arrived, I got no salary increase one year and I got a salary reduction one year.

Asked if the provost was trying to squeeze him out, Hammarsten replied, "Sure, he was." The former chief of medicine went on:

Paul Sharp told me he got dozens of letters about that episode. I think if a vote of the faculty had been taken, things would have been different. I had a good track record in research. I set up the program at the V.A. Hospital, plus a pulmonary program going there, which is one of the best in the country. I would hope I'd be remembered at Oklahoma for the things I did, not for what Thurman did to me.[4]

One of the others was Jim Woods, who had been at O.U. since 1968. He was a professor of physiology but his job was the operation of the basic science educational facility, the BSEB:

My experience started at Hopkins [Johns Hopkins University] in 1957 when we put together a new basic science building there. I was recruited by Jim Dennis. I was on sabbatical during 1975 when Thurman arrived

Dr. Jim Woods talking with student Jean Dorsey in 1969. (OHSF Collection)

and got back in January, 1976. I made an appointment to see Bill Thurman and he told me he did not intend to have, during his watch, any senior faculty members doing administrative jobs. I quote him: "I can hire an MBA [master of business administration] who can do your job and pay him less." So I had quite a long discussion with Thurman about the role of senior faculty in administering the campus. He was quite adamant, you know. "Senior faculty are not going to be the administrators on this campus while I'm here!"

Here was a difference of philosophy and he was in charge but I thought then and I think now that any person who thinks that the senior faculty shouldn't be involved in the administration of the medical campus is goddam well crazy! I would classify a full professor of pediatrics [Thurman's academic rank] as senior faculty. Certainly would.

My replacement was the guy who'd been my assistant. Curiously enough, do you know who's running that place now? My former secretary. To my knowledge, this is the only place in the country where the doctorate-level teaching faculty were moved out of administrative positions.[5]

Dr. Woods left in December, 1976 to go to the University of Arkansas Medical Center in Little Rock and do once more for Dr. Jim Dennis what he had done at O.U.

David Walters, M.B.A., worked closely with Dr. Thurman as associate provost of the OUHSC. In his opinion:

Bill was a real motivator. To some extent, he was a real intimidator and he could be very irascible if he wanted to be. The fun part about working for him [was that] he was a builder and a developer who could get things moving. His problem was he had people who were either terribly loyal to him or did not care to work with him. In a large, complicated organization, you really need to cut more the middle of the road and move the organi-

*Yale's main street has not changed much over the years.
(OHSF Collection)*

zation along. Bill was good for the campus during a period of time which it needed to grow.

The formation and use of committees was disdained…not his management style. We looked critically at the Norman campus as being too bureaucratized, having too many committees and moving too slowly, whereas the Health Sciences Center was a new campus without all that committee structure. Bill regaled in that by making all the decisions and moved things along. He was most unpopular, I guess, among faculty ranks who traditionally feel, in a higher education setting, *they* should run the campus.[6]

In early February, 1976, and after two years, the "Yale Experiment" came to an end, broken up on the twin shoals of financial insufficiency and lack of local acceptance. Bill Stanhope told the story of this attempt to take medical care to the people in the tiny [population 1,239] town of Yale, Oklahoma, 20 miles east of Stillwater. The most famous son of Yale was Olympic athlete Jim Thorpe:

We had a graduate [of the physicians associate program], Fred Olenberger, who was working with a pediatrician in Stillwater named Ed Schissler. The people of Yale were concerned that they hadn't had a doctor in a long time. The leaders of the community approached Dr. Schissler, asked him if he wouldn't find a way to come to Yale and practice on a once-a-week basis. He then approached us and we worked with the State Board of Medical Examiners to set up an experimental study, looking at the economic utility of "satellite practice," where a PA would be remote from the supervising physicians on a day-to-day basis.

The experiment was a success in that it gave us a lot of information. It was a failure in that the Yale clinic couldn't make ends meet. It lost $14,000 in two years. It failed for a couple of reasons. First of all, there was the recurring problem with Medicare/Medicaid. Secondly, the quality of medicine which was practiced by the Schissler/Olenberger combination was a quantum level different than the quality of medicine practiced in two neighboring towns, Cushing and Drumright. In those towns, patients could go to the community doctors and get injections of whatever they wanted on demand…antibiotics, vitamins, etc., [merely by saying], "Give me a shot, Doc." The brand of medicine Schissler and Olenberger practiced was much, much different and the word got around the community that "Fred wouldn't give me a shot!" We could not break through educationally to convince people that *not* giving shots on demand was better quality medicine. We never could publicize that because in the mid-1970s it was too explosive an issue. We could not say the quality of medical care was so much better and the people could not adapt to it. Instead, we said it was an economic failure; the clinic could not support itself.

Looking at the literature and all the other satellite clinics in the country, there has yet to be more than a very small handful which have ever worked out economically, even in the most remote areas. The Medicare/Medicaid barrier [these programs would not reimburse independently-based PAs for the services they rendered] is certainly a very big part of it because there is such a high percentage of older people in the smaller communities.

I think in some *really* remote areas of the country, isolated by distance or terrain, the independently based PA service, as Yale had, is feasible. There is a PA out in the Havasu branch of the Grand Canyon taking care of the Papago Indians. But in more populated areas, people don't use solo practitioners, be they physicians or PA's, in a small community for anything but a "Band-Aid practice." Their trade patterns are toward larger communities where there is full service. Just as there is full service for their automobiles and their household mechanical things, there is full [medical] service for people. I think the Anlyan "Time-Availability" model is a much more realistic and viable way to get health care to people.

The theory of distributing physicians into every hamlet in the state is poppycock! If you talk to the solo docs in the small towns, they'll tell you it's not economically feasible for them to stay there. The reimbursement for ambulatory, office-based care is not very high. We have a procedure-oriented, specialty-oriented reimbursement system in America. Secondly, patients today are sophisticated enough to know that if they're really bad sick, they sort themselves out and go to the bigger communites where there is a full range of specialists.

I really think we have been guilty of perpetrating a myth—the idea of having a doctor in every hamlet. I would guess it would take an established community of at least 2500 with a "draw" of two or three times that to make a clinic viable. I have a hypothesis: a community that can't support a McDonald's [fast food restaurant] won't support a medical practice. McDonald's has some very strict population and traffic requirements before they'll issue a franchise. And if you think about it, it takes a helluva lot more sophistication and technology to practice medicine than it does to run a McDonald's hamburger stand. Medicare/Medicaid still does not reimburse the independently based PA. We were never able to muster enough support on the national level to push this through generically. What we did get pushed through was a compromise: the Rural Health Clinics Practice Act of 1977, a federal act which will reimburse designated rural clinics for 100 percent of charges on Medicare and Medicaid. That was done to create a pull-demand situation for redistribution of [professional] people into rural primary care. Rader was the power broker for that [legislation] but he never would allow any of those rural health clinics to be established in the state of Oklahoma.

We got the law passed—in fact, two of my staff worked very hard on that law—but we never could get the State of Oklahoma to agree to set up any rural health clinics. First of all, they had to receive the blessing of Lloyd E. Rader which he steadfastly refused to extend. I have no idea why.[7]

The O.U. College of Pharmacy had been on the Norman campus since 1893, preceding the O.U. College of Medicine by 17 years. Pharmacy was not included in the 1968 Oklahoma Health Center Development Plan because it was assumed that school would stay on the main campus although Dr. Dennis and others recognized it as a time-honored and integral part of the healing professions. Rodney Ice, Ph.D., dean of the College from 1976 until 1983, talked about the decision to move:

In the spring of 1976, there was great debate whether or not the school *should* move. I preferred the school go to the Health Sciences Center, which was the faculty position at that time. There was a trend which took place over the past decade and is still going on toward orienting the pharmacist to the patient and that requires patients— clinical training. Years ago, we dispensed drugs and didn't even tell the patient what the name of the product was. Prescriptions were written in Latin and kept secretive. We now feel we have an educated consumer and the more they know, the better off they're going to be. So we are teaching our students to work directly with patients. The student needs to interact with the patient.

The idea of keeping pharmacy at Norman was based on the budget situation. The State of Oklahoma budgets by the number of students and basically, where the

College of Pharmacy Dean Rodney Ice. (University of Oklahoma)

students are located, that's where the budget goes. The other big disadvantage about moving to the Health Sciences Center was we were going to have to move into temporary facilities for an unknown period of time. There was great question about whether or not funding could be found for a new pharmacy building. The facilities at Norman were outmoded but we were all together down there in one building, not scattered over seven buildings. There was also the consideration that we had a medicinal chemistry department and the library at the Norman campus was far better from a chemistry standpoint than the library at the Health Sciences Center, which emphasizes the clinical sciences.[8]

In mid-1976, the College of Pharmacy moved to Oklahoma City and Dean Ice, who took over in August, immediately began to experience some of the disadvantages of "camping out" in the houses on 15th Street:

When you are scattered out in seven different buildings, you're somewhat of a step-child. You are not part of the "main line" of the Health Center. A lot of people don't know you exist. Students have to walk to every class or to see faculty, no matter how inclement the weather. Faculty are dispersed in other buildings to do their research. It's hard to bring everybody together. It's hard to have unity of purpose when you are so broadly scattered.

We had labs wherever we could find space. The "shared facilities" area of the biomedical sciences building was turned over to pharmacy for research. In addition, we

The new chancellor, succeeding E.T. Dunlap, was Dr. Joe Leone. (Oklahoma City Chamber of Commerce)

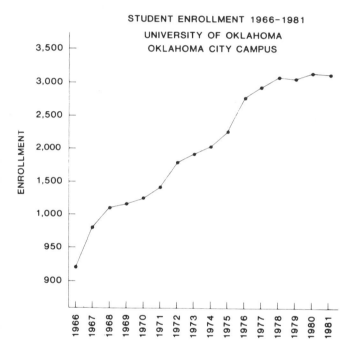

STUDENT ENROLLMENT 1966–1981
UNIVERSITY OF OKLAHOMA
OKLAHOMA CITY CAMPUS

Student enrollment at the O.U. Health Sciences Center did not begin to plateau until 1978 when it topped 3,000. (Oklahoma City Chamber of Commerce)

had scattered laboratories throughout the basic science education building.[9]

As 1982 began, Joe Leone, Ph.D., succeeded Dr. E.T. Dunlap as chancellor of the State Regents for Higher Education. During the years Dr. Dunlap headed the State Regents program, enrollment in health sciences educational programs at O.U. had more than tripled, climbing from 920 students in 1966 to 3127 in 1981. (Two years later, in the fall of 1983, that total had increased to 3,236 including 229 med-

Dean of Medicine Charles McCall confers with Dr. Virginia Nunn, Associate Dean for Academic and Student Affairs. (University of Oklahoma)

ical students and house staff in Tulsa and 82 military personnel enrolled in the physicians associate program and scattered about the country in military bases.) Dentistry, public health, dental hygiene and the physicians associate program were all started during this period. Clayton Rich, M.D., who arrived June 1, 1980, the sixth provost at the OUHSC since Dr. Dennis, was enthusiastic about the future, noting that concentration had shifted from constructing buildings to building excellence into the educational programs. The former dean of the School of Medicine at Stanford University said, "Top flight clinical experience, real progress in teaching and high grade research programs are here and are improving, made possible by the fine accomplishments of the past. We now have the potential of becoming a truly outstanding academic health care center in the Southwest."[10]

The mission which Jim Dennis undertook in 1964 was accomplished— almost. By this time, half of the faculty and 41 percent of the students in the seven colleges on campus were in the College of Medicine. The percentage of women entering the profession was approaching 30 percent and the College of Medicine was trying to recruit more Indians, blacks and Hispanics. The college was accepting 176 students each year. Charles McCall, M.D., who became dean in February, 1982, 13 months after the departure of Tom Lynn, outlined the challenge facing the medical student.

Students must have solid grounding in the biomedical

Life as a medical student is not a total grind, as this picture from the 1980 College of Medicine Gridiron attests. (University of Oklahoma)

sciences if they are to become good doctors. Today's scientific advances are mind boggling and the student must be able to use these scientific tools. In addition, the physician must be able to deliver today's technology in a sensitive, caring fashion, viewing the patient as a whole human being instead of a diseased body part. When the doctor becomes skilled in the science of medicine, he must also learn to *manage* ilness as it affects his patient pyschologically, physically, mentally, socially...not an easy task!"[11]

The major problem which kept the dental profession busy was the behavior of people. Only 50 percent of Americans went to their dentist even *once* a year, let alone twice as had long been advocated. Most people did not do what they knew they should, that is, brush and floss their teeth with religious regularity. Only 25 percent of the population was receiving comprehensive, continuing dental care.

Fluoridation of water and fissure sealants applied to the biting surfaces of the teeth were, however, improving the nation's dental health, particularly in children, but as yet there was no miracle cure for caries, such as a vaccine, on the horizon. Dean William E. Brown noted that the focus of dentistry was shifting from the young people to the old people, where attention to periodontal (gum) disease and tooth fractures is required. He said, "The challenge to the dental profession is more a matter of motivating than educating the public."

In 1982, the college accepted 72 students in dentistry and 24 in dental hygiene. Meanwhile, due to the cost of dental education, still quite modest in Oklahoma compared to the nationwide average, plus proliferating opportunities in other scientific pursuits, the student applicant pool was shrinking. It dropped from 2.4 applicants for every place in 1975 to 1.4 per position in 1982. The percentage of women entering dentistry was approaching 25 percent and getting larger but the applications from minority groups was not increasing. About this time, Oklahoma looked like the land of opportunity not only for people who worked in the oil patch but to health professionals as well. Dr. Brown said that in these boom times there had been more dentists moving into Oklahoma than the college graduated.[12]

In nursing, the light at the end of the 40-year-long nurse shortage tunnel was getting brighter. This was true in central Oklahoma because salaries were higher than any other place in the country except the San Francisco Bay Area, according to Dean Gloria Smith. Despite this pleasant trend, fewer high school graduates were choosing nursing as a career. As in the other health professions, the size of the applicant pool had declined. In nursing it dropped to 1.4 candidates per entering class position. The mix was changing, too, probably as a result of higher salaries. Fifteen percent of the entering class were men.

The role of the University of Oklahoma College of Nursing remained primarily that of educating educators to provide faculty for the 15 associate degree programs and other baccalaureate level college programs in the state. In 1982, there were 130 students in the master's program and half of those were expected to become nurse educators. The college was also organizing a Ph.D. program to educate the future leaders of the profession who would be capable of heading up colleges of nursing or administering service departments in large, teaching hospitals.[13]

For every physician/leader, there were 16 other professionals on the health care team. The task of the College of Allied Health was to educate these people who work with the doctor. At the University of Oklahoma, these health professionals included dietitians, cytotechnologists, medical technologists, occupational therapists, radiographers, radiation therapists, nuclear medicine technologists, ultrasonographers, communication disorder specialists and medical librarians. Dean Philip E. Smith, who retired in mid-1982 after 12 years as head of the college, said that flexibility was the keyword for their 10 separate programs which had to adjust rapidly to the need for and interest in these professions. All of these educational tracks led to the baccalaureate degree except communication disorders which was on the graduate level and medical library science which involved an internship for graduates who had acquired a masters degree elsewhere.[14]

Pharmacy had an important protagonist in the personage of the governor of Oklahoma. George Nigh said, "I thought it was a disgrace. If we'd become professional, why would we not have a professional pharmacy school? So, once again, we started our efforts and I'm very proud of that." The governor's efforts involved getting a legislative appropriation to construct a modern college building on the Oklahoma Health Center campus at Stonewall and Stanton Young Boulevard. The $7.5 million structure, begun in the spring of 1982, was designed to accommodate classes of 72 professional students and 25 graduate students in the master's and doctoral programs.

Many people think all pharmacy college graduates go to work filling prescriptions at the corner drug store. Not so. Fully a third of the O.U. graduates entered hospital practice and 15 percent were going into manufacturing, pharmaceutical education, research and other specialties. Salaries had risen with the times, too, with graduates of the five-year baccalaureate program starting around $23 thousand a year and Ph.D.s in pharmaceutical science or Pharm.D.s with two or three years post doctoral experience commanding salaries in the $35 to $40 thousand range. Also, contrary to the notion that only men do well in the hard sciences, half of the students in the College of Pharmacy were women.

Although everybody was complaining about the high cost of health care, and with adequate reason, pharmacy was the bargain branch of the health sciences. It took only seven cents of the health care dollar for drugs. With the exception of public health, pharmacy was more cost effective than any other area of medical care.[15]

Experts graduating in the four major disciplines of the O.U. College of Public Health were essentially invisible to the people they served. They dealt with unseen hazards and their accomplishments were not apparent to those whom they protected. Only their failures were easy to spot. When epidemics happened, everybody knew, but their unsung triumphs in the prevention of disease usually passed unnoticed. However, these experts in environmental health, biostatistics and epidemiology, social sciences and health behavior and health administration did more for the general health of the people than any other single branch in the entire field.

Peter Levin, Ph.D., arrived at the University of

Dr. Peter Levin as he began his brief tenure as Dean of the College of Public Health. (University of Oklahoma)

Oklahoma as the new dean in January, 1982. At that time there were 24 faculty members and his goal was to expand this group to 40 or 45 and increase the research component of the college. Also, there was growing recognition among physicians, nurses, technicians, administrators and other health professionals that, in order to do their own job better, they needed to know more about the general parameters of public health. Thus, the College of Public Health was expanding its degree-granting continuing education program.[16]

The seventh college at the OUHSC was actually a part of the Graduate College on the Norman campus, where Kenneth Hoving, Ph.D., was dean. In Oklahoma City, Ralph Daniels, Ph.D., served as the associate dean. In 1982, there were 604 students enrolled and they were also distributed among the other colleges this way:

Basic Medical Sciences	140
Dentistry	2
Public Health	241
Allied Health	87
Nursing	116
Pharmacy	18

Almost a quarter of the total was in the basic medical sciences. For example: students who pursued a graduate degree in microbiology might go into research or perhaps teach this discipline to medical and dental students. All public health disciplines were on the graduate level. O.U. ranked fourth in the number of students compared with graduate colleges in other health sciences centers in the country. In 1982, renowned OUHSC Graduate College alumni included Dr. Edward N. Brandt, Assistant Secretary for Health, U.S. Department of Health and Human Services; Dr. Joseph Exendine, Deputy Director, Indian Health Service and Dr. Shannon Lucid, one of the first female astronauts.[17]

On July 22, 1982, the president of the University of Oklahoma, Dr. William Banowsky, announced he would resign to become president of the Los Angeles Area Chamber of Commerce effective September 1. He said, "I have been homesick for Southern California. Having been away these four years, I see clearly that this five-county chamber territory is America's most exciting place in our time." He called his new position "a great challenge and one of the most compelling service opportunities in the country today."

During his short tenure, Dr. Banowsky completed what the regents called a "staggering" list of accomplishments. Since 1978, there had been a 102 percent increase in state appropriations to the university, a 45 percent increase in faculty and staff salaries, and over $125 million in capital improvements, the most notable of which was a new library. There was also an increase in faculty of 140 positions, plus four endowed chairs and five endowed professorships.

Bill Banowsky represented a departure from the type of prexy who formerly had led the University of Oklahoma. Previous presidents had been chosen because of their scholarly backgrounds and achievements. As Banowsky explained, "I had the disadvantage in becoming president of the university of being opposed by many who thought I lacked in that area. I think once I was on the job, that was no longer seen as a shortcoming."

Banowsky was a fundraiser *par excellence*, a leader who could inspire loyalty, pride and generosity. Under his leadership, the assets of the O.U. Foundation rose from $18 million to more than $45 million. When he departed, he was in the midst of his largest fundraising project ever—a $65 million energy research center on the Norman campus. Despite the fact that half of a $30 million gift from Dallas oil man and alumnus, Bill Saxon, would probably have to be written off because of the donor's growing financial difficulties, it appeared the energy center would be built.

But Dr. Banowsky was not quite as homesick for

President William Banowsky. (University of Oklahoma)

Southern California as he had thought. He explained his very brief stay:

> It was a Mulligan! Golfers understand this. A Mulligan is when you tee one up and you hit it over the fence, into the railroad tracks, it bounces once and goes into the dump. You're out of bounds, so you say, "Mulligan!" and your congenial golfing friends let you tee up another one and hit it free of charge.
>
> So that was a Mulligan. It was just one of those experiences I felt uneasy about when I was making that decision. It was clear when I made it I was not going to be comfortable with it. I've just been grateful to have been given the chance to come back and serve these additional two years.[18]

With the growth of the O.U. Health Sciences Center, the bureaucracy which Stewart Wolf had talked about expanded and the good old days of informal procedures, close personal ties, tight communication lines and other hallmarks of a small organization disappeared. With them, some of the romance and joy of working in a group of modest size also vanished. Wayne Beal, Associate Director of Operations, who had been with the university more than 32 years commented:

> The biggest change I've seen—and I realize you can't run a place this size with a "down home" atmosphere— but the thing that disappoints me most is it's gotten so big, so complex that we no longer have intimate personal contacts with department heads. Then, we were small enough that everybody knew everybody. When I

Wayne Beal watched the growth of the Medical Center over three decades. (University of Oklahoma)

This picture of Jeanie Taller Marshall was taken when she was secretary for the Oklahoma Health Sciences Foundation. (OHSF Collection)

came here, there were 900 people on the payroll—total—from the administrators down to the janitors. In the university alone we have 2630 and I don't know how many are in the hospital. I liked the close-knit, know everybody, small town atmosphere.

We have become so complex, we are administering ourselves to death! There are so many layers of administration that you're absolutely frustrated. You can't get anything done. As a department head, you know what you're responsible for and you know what to do but you can't just go ahead and do it. You have to go through a whole bunch of people to get approval to do something you were hired to do.

Take parking for example. You can't make decisions on parking. It has to go from myself up to Bruce [Love] to Gary [Smith] and finally to the provost to make a decision. That's dumb! Why do we have someone to manage parking? Let the provost make all the decisions and we can save all kinds of money. We've got so many administrators, there's nobody around to do the work.[19]

Jeanie Taller Marshall was secretary for the Oklahoma Health Sciences Foundation for more than five years, later joining the university as a computer programmer. Her feeling about the bureaucracy was just as strong but she had a different view of it:

The provost goes out and gets the money, deals with the legislators and the president and like that, but the middle managers see to the day-to-day operations. Their tenure is much longer; some have been out there for a very long time and will continue to stay until they retire,

probably. If the individual happens to be a talented, innovative person, it can be very good for the university. But I don't think the university tends to attract and keep those kinds of people. That's one of the big problems they have.

I don't think they've gotten enough guidance from the top level middle management. There are people in the university who have a vested interest in things not getting a lot better. They wouldn't have the power they have now if the university were well managed. Anyone who has control over money, accounts of any sort, has real, definite power. If they don't have to account to someone else for that money, that's a form of power. There are all sorts of people in the university who have all sorts of accounts [which they can spend for their department]. Some of that money is being unwisely spent; not necessarily for the good of the university as a whole.[20]

On the professional level, even though facilities within the O.U. Health Sciences Center had expanded greatly, space was still a problem and the university did not appear to be in a position to provide for the graduate program in radiological physics, as Gale Adams, Ph.D., explained:

My views are clouded by my personal needs. We were turned down twice for training grants because they asked, how did we expect to get money if we had no space that was dedicated for a program? We get rooms for lectures, classes but that's not dedicated space. I have graduate students and no place for them to sit; a simple

Gale Adams, Vernon Scott and Clayton Rich enjoy the "attitude adjustment hour" at the Faculty House. (University of Oklahoma)

thing like a desk and a chair for them to do their studying on campus. A lot of our things involve computers; I have no place to put a computer terminal except in hospital space. They come and use hospital space and I'm sure if the hospital knew it, they'd throw us out.

I told the dean of the graduate college, "It would be awfully nice if we had space for some of our graduate students." Other people had told me, "Well, if you get some grants, we'll give you some space." It's a vicious circle and Ralph Daniels said it's clear the university has to break that circle. The trouble is the graduate dean controls no money and no space. It's a very poor situation if the people of Oklahoma really want graduate education to be a part of the mission here.

I've heard every chief executive officer, every year, get up and say, in one fashion or another, "Things are a little tight this year. It's going to be better next year." Period! The financing of radiology has improved very little over the years—very little, indeed.[21]

Of course, no university can hope to satisfy the needs and wants of every faculty member and every employee. The O.U. Health Sciences Center was growing and with that growth, acquiring the characteristics of a large organization. But the outlook was encouragingly positive. The legislature had recognized the importance of this campus and provided more money for state programs. There were no acute crises and no investigators or consultants nosing about the Oklahoma Health Center looking for crises. The good times had returned. But just as storms blow out, calm seas inevitably get rough again. How long would the smooth sailing last?

CHAPTER 37
PRIVATE INSTITUTIONS: 1976-1981

By the last week in 1976, it was abundantly obvious the two-headed administration of the Dean A. McGee Eye Institute was not working. In the process of holding to an austere, start-up budget, Bob Hardy effectively had alienated the medical staff:

We had a $50,000 deficit in 1976, not too bad for the first year. The doctors were understandably upset when they asked for things which I decided the institute could not afford. The operation was growing and there were supplies and additional services as well as new equipment they felt were reasonable requests. Had they still been in their private offices, they would not have had to contend with an administrator who questioned every expenditure. When they put in a requisition, they expected it to be honored. One of the physicians said to me, "It doesn't make that much difference how much we spend; the board [of trustees] will get the money."

But that wasn't the policy I understood Mr. McGee had in mind and it became increasing apparent that an impasse was rapidly approaching. At lunch the week after Christmas, Stanton Young, one of the institute trustees and chairman of the Operations Committee of the board, asked me what I thought could be done to ease the situation. I told him it was time for me to leave. A day or so later, he and I repeated that idea to Mr. McGee. Gentle leader that he was, Mr. McGee understood immediately and expressed his appreciation for the contribution I had made to the institute. We agreed I should return to the Foundation at the end of February, 1977.

Tom Acers and I got along well and I believe he understood the necessity for fiscal constraint, but he had to support his colleagues. It was a lot easier to hire administrators than to recruit outstanding ophthalmologists. The M.E.I. was in a critical stage of development and a satisfied medical staff was essential. Tom Acers did exactly the right thing.

Of course, I was pretty stubborn; some people would say, and have said, passive-aggressive. I either had to run the business affairs of the institute or get out and let someone else do it.

Later, when Mr. McGee talked about the situation, he was unruffled. "I think it was just a question of the thing settling down. The doctors hadn't worked in that kind of environment before. I think time would have solved it." This pointed up Mr. McGee's continuing involvement. As Dr. Clay said, "He just didn't give the money and get out of the way. He has been

The Oklahoma City Clinic, across 12th Street from Presbyterian Hospital, looked like this in 1967. (OHSF Collection)

an important influence in the board meetings and dynamic in his leadership."[1]

During those first years of operation, there was not total enthusiasm among the other eye specialists in Oklahoma City and the state, as Dr. Clay recalled:

For the first two or three years, I would get calls from [ophthalmologists] in town and out of town. "What in the world are you supporting the eye institute for? They're taking all our surgery!" They were pretty unhappy then but I have not received a call now for two or three years. I think their attitude has improved because of the Monday morning "grand rounds" conferences [at the institute]. Some of the town doctors attend. Also, the MEI sponsors a one-day spring meeting and good men [from over the country] come to lecture.

Nobody cares if the MEI takes the intraocular infections, the cultures, the corneal research cases, the kerato-refractive surgery and the trauma cases, but what they *do* object to are the lens implant and the cataract cases the institute handles.[2]

The Oklahoma City Clinic was the first group practice established in the State of Oklahoma. When John W. "Jack" Records, M.D., senior obstetrician/gynecologist with the clinic, was asked if he had been apprehensive about moving "to the other side of the tracks," he quickly replied:

Yes! And I wasn't the only one. There was a difference of opinion about the projected move at the time the lay board of Presbyterian announced they planned to go ahead with a hospital on the Medical Center campus. There was no foot-dragging or delay by the clinic once it became understood what the mission of the hospital was to be and what could be accomplished in regard to helping out with the teaching program. Of course, the doctors in the clinic had always been interested in that, anyway.

But the problem was; the clinic was, if you'll pardon the French, in a hell of a mess financially. To build a new building, which turned out to be over a $5 million investment, in a short period of time was just impossible. We were in bad shape and, strange as it may seem, we didn't realize what bad shape we were in. This goes back to the philosophy some of the doctors had about the business side of medicine. I was the eighth doctor in the Oklahoma City Clinic when I came here in 1939. We really didn't think much about money. Rather dutifully every month, we went over the expenses and the income with the administrator, deciding whether we should buy equipment, or insurance, various things like this. But there were very few doctors who really understood the financial side of medicine. There *were* a few, fortunately.

When we converted from a partnership to a foundation early in the 1960s, we were broke! We were the kind of doctors who rarely insisted on anybody paying their bill. Our collections were very lackadaisical. A patient would have to be very determined to pay at the time of service. The usual tendency was to say to them, "Oh, don't worry about that. We'll send you a bill." [Now, signs at the clinic reception desks note that payment is *expected* at the time the service is rendered.] There was no way, at the rate we were going, that we could establish the credit necessary to build a building.

Once we understood the mission of the Presbyterian Hospital, the clinic decided, with reservations and with some who were not too happy about it, to move and build a new building. It was with that decision the clinic began to realize it was going to have to shape up its administrative situation. After the hospital moved, we got here as soon as we could.[3]

In mid-July, 1978, the 50 physicians in the Oklahoma City Clinic moved into their new, two-story, red brick building at 10th and Phillips. While almost everything on campus was again going swimmingly, Presbyterian Hospital was struggling against the financial currents which often beset a newly enlarged institution. Harry Neer reminisced:

During the first several years, we did nothing with computers, nothing with financial services. We could barely do what we were doing, financially and otherwise, so those things were left alone. We just hoped we could get through but it came almost to a tragedy for us when Marion Pickett died in October, 1978 [the 29th]. At one time we owed vendors as much as nine months and I'd

The Oklahoma City Clinic, 1984. (Oklahoma City Chamber of Commerce)

say, technically, we were bankrupt. We kept the doors open, we paid our employees, had a few bounced checks but we were able to get from one week to the next that way. Our accounts receivable jumped to 129 days—we are at 55 days today—and even though we were starting to do better financially, the accounts receivable went to pot. Later, in 1980, we had to refinance the hospital.[4]

About the same time the Oklahoma City Clinic was opening its new building on the health campus, the eight physicians who made up the Oklahoma Allergy Clinic were trying to decide whether or not they should follow suit. Similarly, the Oklahoma Allergy Clinic was a private, free standing group practice with a strong commitment to the university. Robert S. "Bob" Ellis, M.D., said all the members of his group had been encouraged—expected, really—to become members of the faculty of the medical school. "All of us except Jim Wells, who heads the division of allergy [in the Department of Internal Medicine] and is half-time with us and half-time with the Medical Center, are strictly volunteer faculty. It just so happens we give the medical school enough help they don't need a full-time allergist to carry on a good teaching program." For a long time, the clinic was located on 10th Street across from St. Anthony Hospital. Dr. Ellis continued:

In the early 1970s, I began to think about a new location for the clinic. It was pretty obvious to me and most of my colleagues that the best place for us to be located would be at the Medical Center. When the Oklahoma Health Center plan was developed [1968], I don't think we had considered moving. We were pretty well located in the Pasteur Building at that time…five or six physicians and adequate space.

Dr. Bob Ellis thought moving the Oklahoma Allergy Clinic to the Oklahoma Health Center was the right idea. (University of Oklahoma)

The decision to move was made in 1978 and initially, it wasn't unanimous. There were two doctors who voted against the move but the majority, six out of eight, ruled. I had talked with Mark Allen Everett, Tom Acers and Hal Balyeat who had considerable private practice at the Center and security problems, which worried some people, seemed to be insignificant from the start. We had a lot of comment from town folks [physicians] who had trained there in the 1930s and '40s and couldn't understand anybody moving back. A lot of people, especially doctor's wives, said, "What are y'all moving out there for?" but I don't think they had been out there in 15 years![5]

Despite the vigorous public relations efforts of most of the Oklahoma Health Center institutions, the entire campus as a cohesive health care center was not recognized in the way the Texas Medical Center was known. This is the reason, even as late as 1983, Dr. Rainey Williams called it the "best kept secret in Oklahoma". In early 1977, the Oklahoma Health Center Public Relations Council had its unofficial, highly informal beginning. Joe Flowers, who headed media information for the university, thought it would help if the P.R. people in all of the campus institutions got together once in a while, if only to talk and drink beer at the Faculty House. Some of the members were quite reluctant to do more than that, but Joe pushed the idea of producing a fancy brochure which described the total campus so people would understand what held this loose consortium together and what health services each institution provided. On October 3, 1977, a proposal was made and accepted, with April 1, 1978 the target date for completing this brochure.

In the interim, Presbyterian and University Hospitals outlined a full-blown public information program to promote the Oklahoma Health Center. Karen Waddell, assistant to the president of Presbyterian, Bob Nichols, who had switched from consumer advocate and joined the health care establishment as the director of planning and development and Michael T. "Mike" McEwen, the director of community and media services, both at University Hospital, outlined a three-year, high visibility, statewide media campaign that would cost $405,225.

The first thing suggested in this plan was to change the name of the campus to the Oklahoma Medical Center to overcome the confusion between the Oklahoma Health Center and the O.U. Health Sciences Center. The ultimate goal was "to firmly establish a reputation for the Oklahoma Medical Center as an outstanding, regional, tertiary health care center pioneering in many areas of health care."[6]

When Harry Neer presented this plan to the chairman of the Oklahoma Health Sciences Foundation Executive Committee, Mr. McGee favored a low key, more personalized, less expensive approach and asked Gloria Bremkamp, by this time an independent consultant, to develop the elements of what she called an out-state awareness development program. At the OHSF meeting on December 15, 1978, she presented her ideas, a program which was designed to convey the message that the Oklahoma Health Center was a place where special health services were provided by 8,500 "Friends...when you need them most." Ms. Bremkamp estimated the program would cost $60,000 a year plus the cost of the large OHC brochure.

The name of the Center was not changed and the $63,000 provided by the institutions financed an information program which was carried out by Robert Hardy during the ensuing 30 or more months. He made 250 presentations to hospital medical staffs and civic clubs throughout Oklahoma, conducted three tours of the campus for selected visitors from various parts of the state, presenting the OHC message to 7,175 people. To be sure, this was a small percentage of the three million population but all of these people were opinion-makers in their community. On the other hand, it was practically impossible to measure the results or to determine whether or not this information program had really increased the awareness of the Oklahoma Health Center among the average Oklahoma citizens who might

The new building as it opened on campus. (University of Oklahoma)

some day need to use it. It was not intended as a marketing program but merely a way to let people know how their tax money had been spent.

When the program came up for renewal in 1982, the OHC institution directors decided not to finance its continuation. The reasons varied but it was probably because the institutions were so successful in their advancement their directors no longer saw any need to publicize the Oklahoma Health Center as a coordinated, multi-institutional complex. Thus, the Foundation's role changed once more.

The Oklahoma City Clinic, meanwhile, was contemplating the idea of establishing the second health maintenance organization in Oklahoma. The clinic was one of only two group practice organizations in the state which appeared capable of initiating an HMO when Hardy studied the subject nine years earlier. In late 1980, Prudential Insurance Company was getting into the HMO business and, recognizing the potential of the Oklahoma City Clinic, approached Wayne Coventon, its executive director. Suddenly, the clinic was faced with

a dilemma; should it or should it not consider this idea? The advantage of an HMO was a ready source of referrals to the many specialists who composed this group practice. However, the offsetting disadvantage was that primary physicians then referring to the clinic might construe this action as competition and stop sending their patients to Oklahoma City Clinic doctors for specialty care. Dr. Jack Records explained the real reason this proposal ultimately was rejected:

The county society and the state medical association *told* us to reject it. They thought it was too big a threat; it would be developing a monopoly in the practice of medicine. They immediately threatened to inform all of the doctors in the state that we were probably going to take on this HMO deal and advise them to stop referring patients to us. This was, of course, crucial at that time [because] it was right after we'd moved into this [new] building...signed a big mortgage.

I'm not too surprised [that Pru-Care, as Prudential's HMO was called, developed independently in Oklahoma City] because Prudential announced they had set

288

Dr. Jack Records, one of first members of the Oklahoma City Clinic group practice. (Oklahoma City Clinic)

The OSMA office in Oklahoma City. (OHSF Collection)

PruCare did not hesitate to advertise its new HMO. (OHSF Collection)

aside a fund of, I think, $2.5 million to start an HMO. [Actually, the figure was $5.5 million, according to Dr. LeRoy Carpenter.] I knew they'd be able to get doctors to work under this sort of arrangement. I haven't been too surprised about their success so far because they've treated their consultants right. I've had some of their patients. Most doctors, if they're treated right and are paid for their services in accordance to what they usually charge, are going to be satisfied.

In essence, [Pru-Care has been successful] although the organized medical community opposed starting it, and particularly opposed our starting an HMO because they knew we had a running start, so to speak, in organization. The regular medical profession has really encouraged and fostered [the idea] once it got started. The physicians would have made it very difficult for them if the society and the state association had continued to threaten—like they threatened the Oklahoma City Clinic—their own members who were beginning to engage with the HMO. But they didn't.

Pru-Care apparently found enough physicians who did not care whether or not they belonged to the county medical society or the state association. Dr. Records agreed. "That's obvious, and as far as Prudential was concerned, it was just strictly a business proposition." By 1984, Pru-Care had enrolled 27,000 people in the Oklahoma City group and two other HMOs were getting started in the capital city.[7]

Both the Oklahoma City Clinic and the Oklahoma Allergy Clinic were long-established group practices and well ahead of a trend which was gathering momentum. The Dean A. McGee Eye Institute and the Dermatology Clinic are examples of single-specialty groups practices within the Oklahoma Health Center. With the advent of health maintenance organizations in the early 1970s, the organization of physicians into practice groups gained favor. Some doctors were not offended by the idea of working in an HMO for a salary. Other forms of professional organization were appearing as alternatives to the fee-for-service, private enterprise, solo practice model which had been the traditional way to deliver physician services.

CHAPTER 38

THE CENTRAL EXPRESSWAY: 1977-1982

With the Dean A. McGee Eye Institute under way and Hardy separated from that assignment, the Executive Committee had to decide what the new role of the Oklahoma Health Sciences Foundation should be. At the April 13, 1977, meeting, Chairman Dean McGee suggested that, having experienced a period of quiescence, the Foundation should once more become active in supporting the development of the total Health Center. The committee was particularly concerned about the deteriorating area on the west flank of the campus, between Lincoln Boulevard and the Santa Fe Railroad, from 13th Street south. The long-awaited Central Expressway was planned to come through this neighborhood somewhere but even the State Highway Department did not know which of four suggested routes would be chosen. The Urban Renewal Authority had commissioned Gruen Associates, urban planners and consultants, to devise a broad-brush scheme for the redevelopment of this area as well as others in the vicinity of the downtown business district. The plan was published in February, 1975, but by that time, federal money for such projects was no longer available so the neighborhood continued to decline. There had been many beautiful and some quite expensive homes in the area but the original owners had long since moved and the current owners did not want to invest the money to maintain their rental property if it was just going to be swept away to make room for I-235. The *uncertainty* of the area's future had caused the neighborhood to go down hill steadily for almost two decades.[1]

One of the original homeowners was the family of Harvey Everest who lived on 10th Street east of Geary between 1899 and 1915, well before the University Hospital was built:

> I remember that the Rolater Hospital [at 4th and Stiles] was about the only hospital in town except the little St. Anthony Hospital 'way out in the country over west. J.B. Rolater was a recognized surgeon in Oklahoma City and, according to my relatives who had used him on occasion, he was not much of a surgeon. He didn't keep his tools very sharp or very clean but he had a tremendous practice.[2]

The uncertainty that worried the homeowners in 1977 also worried the Foundation. By this time, the capital investment in the Oklahoma Health Center was well over $200 million and constantly increasing. Dean McGee, Stanton Young and other OHSF trustees could envision uncontrolled and undesirable redevelopment once the area turned around. Its proximity to the downtown business district, the Health Center and the State Capitol gave it unexcelled location. Only the uncertainty of Central Expressway plans and it location in the northeast quadrant of the city kept opportunists from snatching up desirable plots of ground at giveaway prices and putting in less than desirable activities, those the Foundation felt would not complement the health campus. There was apprehension that N.E. 10th Street would become another May Avenue, with used car lots, fast food restaurants and assorted strip commercial enterprises.

In early 1977, Mr. McGee had suggested to Governor Boren the area between Lincoln Boulevard and the Central Expressway should be made into a park. The State Department of Tourism and Recreation was already working on plans for the area from the Capitol south to 13th Street and the governor was enthusiastic about the idea of a park. Mr. McGee then suggested to the Executive Committee that the Foundation buy some properties in this area in strategic locations to prevent new development "until the governor gets it turned into a park." Stanton Young reminded the committee that in the past, the Oklahoma City Chamber of Commerce had taken the initiative, borrowed people's credit and had never lost any money on property so acquired for community purposes. The selling price had always been sufficient to cover the interest. Over the next year, the Foundation purchased 45 parcels of land scattered in 28 blocks between Central and Lincoln Boulevard, 13th and 4th Streets.

Five years earlier, Bob Hardy had written to President Paul Sharp suggesting that the university purchase all of the land west of Lincoln Boulevard to the Santa Fe tracks between 13th and 8th Streets. This would have given space for the creation of a diversified campus, not only for the expansion of the Health Sciences Center but for such colleges as law, architecture, political science and social work, those disciplines which are actively pursued in a large metropolis such as Oklahoma City. Dr. Sharp said:

That was a marvelous idea and it was not at all alien to our thinking. The concept of developing at the heart of Oklahoma City an "urban university", because that's really what it is, I thought was a really first-rate idea. There were two or three things: one, of course, was finance. We were trying to survive. But deeper than that was the consistent opposition to any move like that on the part of the chancellor and, I assume, the State Regents. We were even forbidden at that time to use space in the Health Sciences Center for activities of the Norman campus along those lines that could have been translated to the urban community and taught right there. But we were impinging upon the assigned and allotted functions of other institutions such as Central State [University]. This did not make sense to me. That was a modest proposal but we could never get approval for it, let alone establish a center.

The whole question of educational outreach was never really solved while I was president. I think now the new chancellor is working on it and I assume there will be a resolution to the turf questions which inevitably arise. I was impressed that we were sitting next door to Oklahoma City and did very little with respect to what I thought were the great opportunities of an urban university. I came down here with lots of ideas but I quickly discovered there was no damn money to do anything with. We were struggling to stay alive, to keep our heads above water. That doesn't leave you with very many pleasant recollections of the dreams you have about being able to do things. In fact it was just the reverse. We were cutting back, retrenching.

I think, also, a great many people got so discouraged on the Health Sciences Center campus and in Norman, year after year, of not having enough money to mount these programs they saw had educational urgency and social need that many of them left—just left. Other major universities were doing these things and there was a steady and unhappy exodus that quietly continued until Oklahoma had the reputation of being a good place to start. Happily, the last four years have somewhat closed those gaps but we need to remind ourselves always that four years isn't enough. It's going to take fifty to a hundred years to catch up with the range and depth of educational achievements and services of major universities in the public realm...North Carolina and Texas in the South, Michigan, Wisconsin and Minnesota, in fact, the whole Big Ten. Berkeley [University of California] is still regarded in just about every poll at the top of the list with respect to public universities.[3]

After a decade of searching for the best way to bring auto traffic from the populous northwest quadrant

Monty Murphy, experienced highway planner in the Oklahoma Department of Transportation. (Monty Murphy)

of the city into the central business district, real progress was being made on the proposed Central Expressway. In 1972, Oklahoma City had appointed a committee headed by Frank C. Love, president of Kerr-McGee, to figure out how to connect the Broadway Extension into the downtown area and Interstates I-40 and I-35. Monty Murphy, Assistant Director for Planning and Research, explained:

The Love Committee called on the [State Highway] Department to take a look at some alignments through that area. The old alignment visualized in the OCARTS study was probably no longer valid. I took some aerials and laid out some different lines for the Central Expressway. I gave them some rough, off-the-cuff [cost] estimates and I believe we supplied some traffic volumes. They liked what they saw and thought it was feasible to get something in that corridor.

Then they explored funding, looking at a toll facility, at county financing and a combination of city-county funding...also a bond proposal. Of course, we were getting into the inflation problem and the costs kept going up. They finally decided because of the high cost, the only thing they could come up with was to somehow get it on the interstate system [with 90 percent federal funding]. A delegation went to Washington—Mayor Latting, Frank Love, our director Truman Branscom, Barry Johnson with Urban Renewal—and met with the [Oklahoma] congressional delegation. Congress had set mileage limitations on the interstate system but it just happened Seattle or one of the big cities in Washington had some problems with one of their urban routes and they gave up five miles of interstate, saying they'd never be able to build it. On May 13, 1976, as a result of that trip and a very active congressional delegation, Oklahoma was assigned that interstate mileage for the Central Expressway, as I-235, connecting the interchange at the Broadway Extension and what is I-44 now, the old I-240.

One of the requirements for any federal aid project, including an interstate highway, is an environmental impact statement [EIS]. That became law in 1969. We knew we were going to have "people problems" with the neighborhoods and minorities, the whole ball of wax we get into when trying to build an urban freeway. We hired Gruen Associates, [consultants] out of California, to do the environmental impact statement. We had more citizen participation in the early planning and preparation of the EIS than we had on *all* of the combination highway projects that we had ever done before! We had neighborhood representatives from all along the route, we had a committee of businesses located along the route, the Chamber [of Commerce] and other technical people being involved. We committed ourselves to death in the planning of that [environmental impact statement].

The minority neighborhoods south of 23rd Street expressed some concern over the project and we tried to answer all those concerns but, in hindsight, perhaps we didn't. We got the draft [of the EIS] approved and we were close to having the final approved with practically no problem when a lady named Kay Ahaus, who lives in northwest Oklahoma City and had been one of the opponents of our west by-pass project up there, had no involvement in the Central Expressway whatsoever, wrote a letter to Patricia Harris, Secretary of HUD [Department of Housing and Urban Development]. She expressed concern about this highway project going through a minority neighborhood. Mrs. Ahaus, a white lady, was a very strong proponent of mass transit and public transportation. She didn't like highways. Her letter started the whole chain of events that got us into the mitigation plan.

Pat Harris wrote to the Secretary of Transportation. The civil rights director for the Secretary of Transportation was a white lady named Ellen Feingold who, on May 7, 1979, found the Oklahoma Department of Transportation [ODOT—as the State Highway Department had been renamed] in non-compliance with Title VI of the Civil Rights Act of 1964.[1]

Julia Brown was a young, attractive and articulate black attorney. As a child, she lived at 312 N. Byers, a block west of what had been Durland and is now Lincoln Boulevard. When she finished law school at

Circuit riding attorney Julia Brown. (Harrison-Walnut Redevelopment Corporation)

the University of Oklahoma, she went to work for legal aid in Oklahoma County. As she explained:

At least 50 percent of what the lawyer did was help communities organize and develop. That fit into my plans perfectly because I'd always been involved in community activities since I was a little girl. I started doing what is commonly known as "circuit riding", going to outreach areas to give legal advice to people. One of those areas was the Bethlehem Center at 6th and Kelley, run by the Neighborhood Services Organization. Alvah Boyd was working there and in the process of going to such meetings as the Coalition of Neighborhood Associations, we ran into Henrietta B. Foster who had organized the 3rd Street Neighborhood Association back in the very early 1960s. She was quite concerned about the deterioration of the neighborhood, the fact there was no kind of housing rehab, that people couldn't get home improvement loans, most everyone had lost their insurance benefits, lack of code enforcement, lots of fire hazards and people not keeping the weeds cut on vacant lots they owned—that sort of thing. So we orgaized around those concerns.

About five us sat around in Henrietta's living room one evening casting about for a name for the group. There was nothing significant about the intersection of Harrison and Walnut; they just happened to be two of the prominent streets in that whole area. We incorporated the Harrison-Walnut Neighborhood Association in August, 1975.

There were two civil rights complaints filed. We initially filed a complaint against the Lincoln-Byers con-

The original northeast neighborhood organizer, Henrietta B. Foster. (Henrietta B. Foster Center)

Alvah Boyd succeeded Julia Brown as chairperson of the Harrison-Walnut Redevelopment Corporation.

nector [the extension of Lincoln Boulevard from 4th to Reno Street]. That got what is commonly referred to as "the deep six." It just vanished on some heap of papers on somebody's desk in Washington. At that time there were three projects on the drawing board. The third one was a Lottie extension which was going to cut through Washington Park and tie up with the other two at Reno [Street]. It seemed to us there was no reason to have *three* arterials bisecting the same neighborhood within 10 blocks of one another, all carrying traffic in the same direction.

It was our contention federal regulations had not been followed in the Lincoln-Byers connector. ODOT had not allowed people in the Harrison-Walnut area to have any real input in selecting the location of that road and that was even more true of the Central Expressway. Well, we got bulldozed pretty much, we were ignored, nobody cared and nobody responded. But we didn't go away. We kept nipping at their heels. They went on and finished the Lincoln-Byers connector in 1979.

When the public hearings on the route of the Central Expressway came along...federal regulations call for two separate hearings, one on location and one on the design of the roadway. Under very extraordinary circumstances, if the State can show they're going to suffer some sort of hardship if they are not allowed to combine those hearings, they can have them together. In this case, they

had the two hearings together but they had not made any kind of showing to the feds that there was some reason to expedite the process and have them together. That was our first complaint. It wasn't adequately advertised but we found out about it and took about 200 people to the meeting. When we got to the Jim Thorpe building, the scheduled public hearing was in a conference room that would seat 14 people! We tried to get them to postpone it but they said, "Oh, no, we'll move it to the Wildlife Conservation building auditorium." Everybody moved over there and ODOT had some maps with them but they didn't have engineers who could answer the questions people had. It was obvious they weren't expecting anybody to show up.

The meeting turned into a real ugly kind of situation. I recall that Alvah [Boyd] and I were publicly castigated by Goree James, [a black minister] who was [city] councilman at that time. In effect, we were made to feel like we were criminals for being young. He said we were being guided by mysterious "crosstown interests," people outside the neighborhood, and he said people should not listen to us because they were only going to be hurt.

For years, we told people we were not trying to stop the highway but nobody believed it. We had enough sense to realize that if the highway did not come through, there was not going to be any funding to rehabilitate the neighborhood. Somehow, people always missed the message. We just felt the people who stood to lose the most by it should not be prevented from benefitting by it, too. The folks who were going to be left on both sides of the highway should not be forgotten in the process. The Central Expressway would literally divide the

While Councilman Goree James was critical of Brown and Boyd early on, he later became the redevelopment corporation's chief supporter. (Harrison-Walnut Redevelopment Corporation)

neighborhood and things needed to be done to rehabilitate the area after the highway came through. It was kind of a new theory, not only in Oklahoma but in the rest of the country. Historically, there had been concern only for those directly in the path of the highway who were going to be relocated.

So we filed a complaint to the U.S. Department of Transportation (USDOT). Time passed and we weren't hearing anything. We wrote a couple of follow-up letters and we knew somebody got them because we got the green [receipt] cards back. They were acting as if they [our complaint and letters] didn't exist.

A friend of Henrietta's by the name of Kay Ahaus, who lived near Lake Hefner, was, along about the same time, fighting I-240. When we went to the very first public hearing back in 1976, we had talked with about a dozen other neighborhood associations around Oklahoma City. For the first time, we had a coalition of neighborhood associations and we all agreed we had a common enemy and that was the Oklahoma Department of Transportation. The same kind of things they were doing over here were going on out there. They [Kay Ahaus and her group] came to be called the Lake Hefner Alliance, trying to preserve the area around the lake from the highway. We agreed that when that kind of thing was going on in one neighborhood, it behooved the other neighborhoods to come to the support of the neighborhood where the spectre loomed. At our hearing, seven other neighborhood associations from all over Oklahoma City came to voice their support for our position. Kay's neighborhood was one of those.

She called Henrietta to find out about the progress of our complaint. At one time, at a national conference, Kay had met Patricia Harris so she decided to write to her to see if maybe she knew somebody who could pull a string to bring our complaint to the fore. The HUD building is located directly across the street from the U.S. Department of Transportation.

Now we get to the irony! Pat got Kay's letter and had somebody hand-carry it across the street to Ellen Feingold. Somehow our complaint had never filtered down from the Secretary's office to Feingold. The trickle-down theory did not work even then! [Julia laughed merrily.] It still doesn't work. There are too many sponges in between!

On the very morning Pat Harris sent the letter over to Feingold, Dick Ward and Monty Murphy and all the folks from ODOT were in Washington, sitting down with the Secretary of Transportation, Ellen Feingold and the others. The feds were getting ready to sign off on the agreement to let ODOT have 90 percent federal money, indicating the environmental impact statement was just fine, there were no historical preservation sites in the way, there were no complaints from residents. Then, in walks this person from across the street with the complaint! If we had planned it, we could not have timed it any better. So the feds said, "Wait a minute, wait a minute. We've got to investigate this. We can't sign off on anything."

So they responded to Kay's letter because Henrietta's letter had vanished from the face of the earth. They never found it. So the complaint came to be known, not Foster vs. ODOT, but Ahaus vs. ODOT.[5]

After this complaint had shut down everything, at least for the time being, was Julia Brown confident of ultimate success?

Oh, no! I suppose you could say we had stopped the wheels but it was like putting a piece of wood into a cog; you know it will hold for a few minutes but the pressure's going to snap it and they'll roll right along. I figured it would be pretty much the same thing here but that did not mean we should not put forth our best effort to have justice done for the folks who were going to be impacted by the highway. I never let on to Henrietta or anyone else in the group I thought it was not going to be successful.[6]

Monty Murphy did not then think, nor does he now think, there was any civil rights problem and he advised his director that ODOT should file a lawsuit and fight it through the courts. He believed there was no discrimination by the Department:

The letter cited ODOT because the project took a disproportionate number of minority homes. Mrs. Feingold had sent a black investigator named Davis down here who interviewed people in our department, the consultant, and people in the Harrison-Walnut Neighborhood Association. When he spoke with us after those interviews, he said there was absolutely no problem, that the department had done a better job on this project than any he'd ever seen and he thought the people in the black community were simply jockeying for political position. He said we probably wouldn't hear anything about it.[7]

Obviously, it did not turn out that way. R.A. "Dick" Ward, ODOT director-chief engineer, was not ready to go to court because he believed this would delay the entire process an unreasonable length of time. Murphy said he would have made the same judgment not knowing what they were getting into and observed that "it probably drug out almost as long, anyway." He continued:

We ended up with a so-called mitigation plan that was developed jointly by Mrs. Feingold, a commmittee here and our department to try to address the things that had been brought up, primarily by Harrison Walnut. There was a four- or five-page list of concerns, many of which did not even deal with the highway itself [as well as] things that could legally and reasonably be done under a highway project at that time. The primary concerns, more than anything else, seemed to be how we were going to acquire the right-of-way, under what rules and regulations, how much people were going to be paid, where they were going to be relocated and the benefits and also, would the people be allowed to build new homes in the neighborhood and stay where they were.[8]

Thus began an extended process which first produced a "conciliation agreement" which said that "it is in the best interests of the Federal government, the State of Oklahoma, and the residents of Oklahoma City to achieve voluntary compliance with Title VI." At that time, Stanton L. Young was the State Highway Commissioner from District 5, the Oklahoma City area. The Chamber of Commerce, represented by Paul Strasbaugh, became active in a Central Expressway Advisory Committee which first met on May 25, 1979, at the Oklahoma Department of Transportation. The development of the central business district of Oklahoma City long had been a priority goal of the Chamber and getting people in and out of downtown, particularly from the northwest suburbs, was vital to the achievement of that goal. A mitigation plan committee was formed which included Julia Brown, Monty

Murphy, Robert Hardy and a dozen or so others. Hardy was later removed because he did not live in the affected neighborhood although he did live in Lincoln Terrace, closer than some of those on the committee. He was designated a "resource person" because he represented the Oklahoma Health Center and he attended the meetings regularly.

The conciliation agreement between ODOT and USDOT, "in the matter of Ahaus vs. ODOT," was developed to define the issues and lay the ground rules. It described the elements of the mitigation plan, including relocation and impact alleviation. It also described the players and the steps of the process by which they agreed to arrive at the mitigation plan. Ellen Feingold and R.A. Ward signed this document on October 30, 1979.[9]

All of these events were extremely important to the future of the Oklahoma Health Center because they created a legal and formal method for redevelopment of the west and south flanks of the campus, gave the process substance so it could later qualify for funding, and helped assure ultimate development of the Central Expressway, thereby greatly improving access to the Oklahoma Health Center. This meant the rapidly deteriorating area between the Health Center and downtown Oklahoma City would be turned around. It meant a portion of this space could be designated for health related facilities as well as housing and other developments complementary to the campus. Moreover, it meant the land purchases by the Oklahoma Health Sciences Foundation west of Lincoln Boulevard turned out not to be needed.

The mitigation plan committee adopted the Central Expressway (I-235) Mitigation Plan on April 17, 1980, fulfilling Julia Brown's hope that things would work out notwithstanding her unexpressed apprehension they would not. But it was a long, drawn-out struggle, an experience she would long remember:

ODOT was the direct enemy but everybody was an enemy. That may have been paranoia but it's sort of like the saying, "If you're not part of the solution, then you're part of the problem." Nobody would help us and we thought of the city's participation, all these years, in literally bringing this neighborhood to its knees as a very direct, purposeful kind of participation. In 1975, we still had streets in the area that were not paved! Of course, after we filed the complaint and a couple of years later, when the feds decided we were right, everybody wanted to help, including the city. They got the streets paved, put in curbs and got street signs up, started code en-

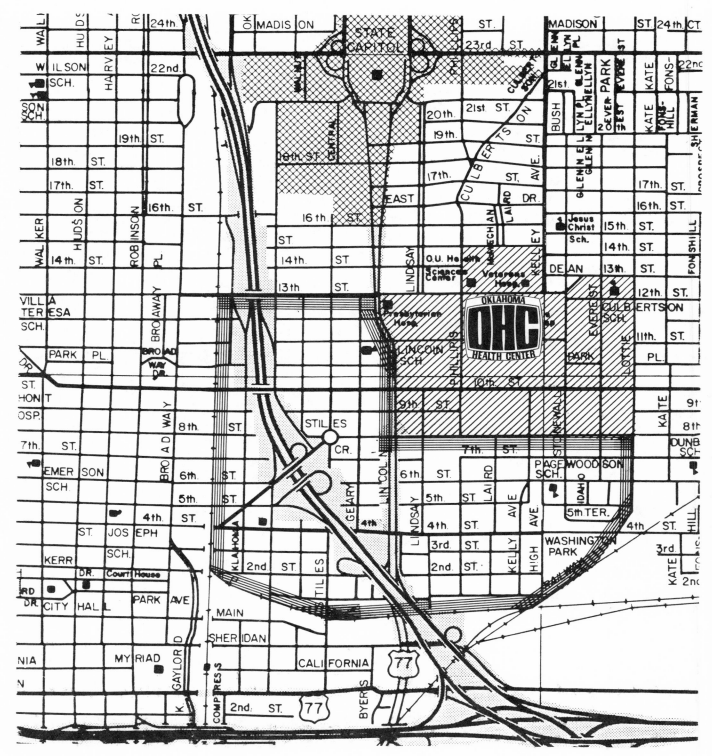

Map shows the route of the Central Expressway. The L-shaped area south and west of the Oklahoma Health Center is the Harrison-Walnut neighborhood. (Oklahoma City Chamber of Commerce)

forcement, made people cut their weeds, all kinds of things.

The biggest problem was ODOT's absolute refusal to cooperate. They, I think, took it as a personal attack on their integrity, their professionalism. The biggest obstacle to moving ahead at all, throughout the entire mitigation process, was Monty Murphy. I imagine that engineers who came out of college in the 1950s and early '60s really didn't have any training in human relations. Their business was not people; their business was formulas and equations, building roads and highways.[10]

Tiana Zaffuto, assistant city manager, represented Oklahoma City in the mitigation process. Julia continued:

When the process first started, Tiana was director of Neighborhood Development Conservation Centers (NDCC), so we had known her before we got to the Central Expressway mitigation thing. We'd had a home repair project and, I might add, we didn't get along at that point. We were bitter enemies. [Julia laughed.] We didn't become good buddies until much later. She and I are going to write a book about that. [More laughs.]

The mitigation plan was approved by Ellen Feingold subject to seven conditions which ODOT was expected to fulfill. Dick Ward, the ODOT director, responded and final agreement was reached on August 8, 1980. Julia Brown was quite satisfied with the outcome and commented:

It was a long and tedious process but it was very educational for us and a very necessary process. It did one thing: it did not bring us any closer to ODOT because they literally had to be dragged, kicking and screaming, every step of the way, but it brought us very close to the city. We developed a very good relationship with Tiana and the [city's] planning folks. We came to understand what they did and they came to understand a lot about us. So as a result, the heart of the mitigation plan is the neighborhood.[11]

What the neighborhood wanted, and got, were these principles and objectives included in the plan: 1. A better economic and racial mix in the area. 2. Repopulation from 1196 households to 2300 households or about 5,500 people. 3. Participation of the neighborhood in the planning of its redevelopment. This is where the "neighborhood non-profit vehicle" fit, the organization now called the Harrison-Walnut Redevelopment Corporation. 4. A specific plan describing land use. 5. Assembly of land for reuse through the Oklahoma City Urban Renewal Authority which has the right of eminent domain. 6. Elimination of dis-

crimination in the granting of loans and insurance coverage to people in the neighorhood, a practice known as "red-lining." 7. Provision of low and moderate income housing opportunities. 8. Provision of relocation assistance for displaced residents. 9. Opportunity for displaced residents to relocate in other sections of the Harrison-Walnut neighborhood.

Possibly because Robert Hardy had served as a "resource person" throughout the mitigation process, possibly because the Oklahoma Health Sciences Foundation was a major property owner in the neighborhood, but more likely because the group wanted communication with their neighbor, the Oklahoma Health Center, he was named to the Harrison-Walnut Redevelopment Corporation board of directors. This "neighborhood non-profit vehicle" was formed in September, 1980. Its first action was to select as consultants the American City Corporation, the planning division of the Rouse Corporation, which had planned and built the "new town"of Columbia, Maryland, which now has 60,000 residents, and the "festival marketplaces" at Fanueil Hall in Boston, Massachusetts, and Harborplace on the Baltimore, Maryland, waterfront. Their job was to put together a scheme for the 130 city block, L-shaped area west and south of the Oklahoma Health Center.

Fourteen months and uncounted meetings later, the consultants produced a development program and strategy for the Harrison-Walnut neighborhood. Briefly, it provided for 702 new housing units—single family, townhouses, duplexes, apartments, 752,000 square feet of office space, a 216,500 square foot hotel and conference center, 102,000 square feet of shopping center/commercial space, 70,000 square feet of light industrial construction, 3,700 parking spaces and more than half a million square feet of parks and greenways. This was in addition to three projects already planned for the area and accepted as "givens" when the American City consultants began their work. These were the 136 Chaparral Townhouses, the Oklahoma Blood Institute and the headquarters building for Pan Oklahoma Cable Television. American Medical International (AMI), which owned Doctors General Hospital at 13th and Robinson had picked out a site along Lincoln Boulevard between 8th and 5th Streets and this project was included although AMI's plans were highly tentative when the American City Corporation program and strategy for Harrison-Walnut was published in December, 1981.[12]

Health institutions tend to cluster and as the Oklahoma Health Center grew, it attracted other organi-

Urban planner David Bisbee. (Harrison-Walnut Redevelopment Corporation)

zations in the field. The Oklahoma Blood Institute (OBI) wanted to relocate from its small building at N.W. 13th Street and Classen Drive to a site in the Oklahoma Health Center, but the university would not relinquish the land on which the OBI had cast its eye. Wanting to be near the campus, the blood institute purchased a site on the west side of Lincoln Boulevard, the block also bounded by 9th Street, Geary Avenue and 10th Street. Most of this land had been a city park so little relocation of residents was required. On January 21, 1982, the blood institute held a "groundbreaking" luncheon at the Skirvin Plaza Hotel at which Sylvan N. Goldman, prominent Oklahoma City philanthropist and major donor ($1.5 million) spoke about the acute need for this new facility. Construction of the $6 million building began soon thereafter.

In mid-April, 1982, David W. Bisbee, a 31-year-old urban planner from Des Moines, Iowa, started work as executive director of the Harrison-Walnut Redevelopment Corporation. With the broad-brush plan for the area completed, the next step was to refine the plan and get it approved by four layers of government, namely the Capitol-Medical Center Improvement and Zoning Commission, the Oklahoma City Urban Renewal Authority, the City Planning Commission and finally, the City Council. In the interim, it was Bisbee's job to solicit proposals from developers throughout the country. Of the $130 million

which the redevelopment of the neighborhood was expected to cost, $100 million was proposed to be funded by private investment.

In 1977, the Oklahoma Health Sciences Foundation trustees had recognized that the Oklahoma Health Center could not remain a sparkling and expensive island in a sea of deterioration. It was only a matter of time until the value of the campus environs would be recognized. The foundation was concerned about *how* redevelopment would occur because the trustees knew it would have a dramatic impact on the future of the OHC.

Similarly, Dean Krakel and his board were perturbed about development around the National Cowboy Hall of Fame and Western Heritage Center which they considered inappropriate. When Dr. Frank Cox proposed building more than a hundred townhouses on Eastern Avenue within sight of the Cowboy Hall of Fame on the Northeast Expressway, Dean Krakel was appalled and immediately threatened to get the shrine moved to another western state. In fact, the governor of Colorado was quite eager to get it. In order to placate Krakel and prevent this major Oklahoma City attraction from moving westward, Governor Nigh proposed conversion of the area adjacent to the museum and along the Northeast Expressway from Lincoln Boulevard to I-35 into Cowboy Hall of Fame Park. Frank Cox continued the story:

I don't look at myself as a developer—I really don't. My goal wasn't to get into the business of apartments to make money. Six or eight years ago, Mayor Latting appointed a committee of a hundred to plan for the growth of Oklahoma City through the year 2000 and she asked me to serve.

The consultants said there would be very little development in the northeast quadrant and that's when I really got pissed off. I could see all the wealth of the black community going down the tube if that occurred. I said, "I just don't believe that's true!" So I got a group of people together and asked them to petition the city council and the mayor to set up a special study of the northeast quadrant. And that's how that happened.

One of the conclusions of the first [city-wide] study was that the lack of development in the northeast quadrant would be the result of developers not wanting to put dollars into a dead area. And I said, "That's bullshit! We've got streets in, utilities in, all the things developers should want and a lot of deteriorated property. Now, why wouldn't a developer want to come over here?" I was talking to a developer out in the Nichols Hills area and he said, "I wouldn't put money over there. What are you going to do—pass legislation to *make* me put my

The National Cowboy Hall of Fame and Western Heritage Center surrounds a reflecting pool atop Persimmon Hill. (OHSF Collection)

money over there?" I said, "Hell, no. I'll do it myself!" That's how it came about. My goal was to demonstrate that people *would* redevelop the northeast quadrant.

Dr. Cox said it was one hell of an adventure story. He sighed and continued:

I was going to put in 118 units there on Eastern when along comes Dean Krakel and our good friend who owns the newspaper. I don't believe, by any stretch of the imagination, that Dean Krakel was acting as his own agent at all times. That man could not have caused to happen what did happen if he didn't have the backing of the newspaper. What their goals are, I don't know.

The complaint was that development was going to occur "very close" to the Cowboy Hall of Fame, a little bit less than a mile from its front door. It was on top of the hill about a half mile south of [U.S.] 66 [I 44]. As the crow flies, it's not near the Cowboy Hall of Fame. I frankly believe it was an attempt to acquire that land, for some reason or other. It certainly would not have influenced the development of the area or the value of the Cowboy Hall of Fame—at all!

I think the Section VIII part was used as a rallying point. [Section VIII is a U.S. Department of Housing and Urban Development (HUD) requirement that a portion of the development (in this case, 20 percent) be made available to low and moderate income people whose rent would be subsidized by a federal housing program.] It just scared people to death and I suffered as a result of that. It made me look like an old slum landlord and Chaparral had never been conceived in that manner.

When the thing was hot and heavy, I was interviewed by a white, female news reporter for televison. When I explained to her what Section VIII meant, one of her aside comments was, "Why, hell, *I* qualify for Section

VIII!" She was a divorcee with one child and she made something like $15,000 a year. Once she understood, that was the end of the story. It never did get on the air.

The Oklahoma City Chamber of Commerce then got involved, arranging for the acquisition of the four-block site bounded by 13th Street, Stiles, 11th and Walnut in the Harrison-Walnut neighborhood as an alternative to the location on Eastern Avenue. Asked if the new site would achieve the demonstration goal Dr. Cox originally had in mind, he said:

Not really. There's going to be a lot more different kinds of activities in Harrison-Walnut, as opposed to *really* being in the black community where I was going to be in the first place. My goal was to demonstrate that a first class housing project could be developed in the northeast quadrant and would be new, successful and good. In the present Harrison Walnut scheme, there are all kinds of people fighting for the opportunity to redevelop. If Chaparral were not in the area, I still think that redevelopment would occur, maybe not as swiftly. When Chaparral goes on board, I think a lot of other things are going to fall into place. Harrison-Walnut will go ahead because of its location, the plan to connect downtown Oklahoma City with the health science center and connect that with the state capitol.

The value of Chaparral is diluted because it's *really* not in the black community. My purpose was to say to the financial world out there that the black community has a value, too, and its value is on the same level as if you develop in Quail Creek [a predominantly white neighborhood of expensive, single family homes on the far northwest side of Oklahoma City].[13]

In the spring of 1982, the Oklahoma City Urban Renewal Authority was completing the purchase of the land in the new Chaparral site. Five of the lots were condemned and acquired from the Oklahoma Health Sciences Foundation. While the land package was being put together with little difficulty, financing was another matter and more than a year would go by before that arrangment could be completed.

Less than five months later, however, on September 3, 1982, the Harrison-Walnut Redevelopment Corporation received seven proposals from developers interested in projects in the neighborhood. Frank Cox had been right in his appraisal of the future potential of the area. Totaling almost $50 million, proposals came from two non-profit organizations, two housing developers and three groups interested in office buildings and retail commercial facilities. Other characteristics of the developer "mix" were that two were based outside of Oklahoma City and three were minority developers. The proposals included:

Presbyterian Hospital—Two office buildings and a parking garage (In addition, the hospital planned a 200-room hotel on the OHC campus.)

Park Place Associates—100 townhouses

Renaissance Developers—Medical/professional office bldg

Royal Office Products—Office supply store and restaurant

American Heart Association—Oklahoma Chapter headquarters

ESD Associates—Office and commercial retail

Lincoln Property Company—600 apartment units, 2 office buildings

CHAPTER 39

FROM SHORTAGE TO SURPLUS: 1980

Graduates of the University of Oklahoma College of Medicine. How long should these lines be? (University of Oklahoma)

For several years, a committee organized at the request of the U.S. Department of Health and Human Services (HHS), formerly the Department of Health, Education and Welfare (HEW), had studied the impact of the dramatic increase in the number and capacity of U.S. medical schools. The charge to the Graduate Medical Education National Advisory Committee (GMENAC) was "to advise the Secretary on the number of physicians required in each specialty to bring the supply and requirements into balance, methods to improve the geographic distribution of physicians and mechanisms to finance graduate medical education." The suspicion that perhaps the federal government had again responded "too late...with too much" was beginning to invade the HHS consciousness.

GMENAC, headed by Alvin R. Tarlov, M.D., professor of medicine at the University of Chicago, brought together 11 other M.D.s, a D.O., two nurses, a hospital administrator, an economist, an insurance expert and an attorney to study the physician manpower situation. It was becoming obvious that America did not have the right kinds of physicians in the right places and there was the distinct possibility of an impending oversupply.

By the time the GMENAC report was submitted on

September 30, 1980, to Secretary Patricia Harris, who had moved from HUD to HHS, the committee had quantified these imbalances and forecast what appeared to some an alarming surplus of doctors by 1990 if there were no changes in the system. One of the great leaps forward this committee accomplished was to quantify the *need* for physician services by figuring out how many doctors of what specialty were required to manage the volume of reported illness in the United States. As it turned out, this figure was an average of 191.4 physicians per 100,000 population, a ratio previously unknown. Of course, the fact the population *needs* this number of physicians per 100,000 people does not mean that the people of America will *demand*, and pay for, enough care to keep that many doctors fully occupied. On the other hand, because 85 percent of the people in America had insurance coverage to pay part or all of their health bills, there was some over-use of the system. Another element involved in this ratio was the number of non-physicians who provided services which doctors also perform, health professionals such as nurse practitioners, physicians assistants (or physicians associates as they are known in Oklahoma), nurse midwives and nurse anesthetists. In any event, the GMENAC study departed from the traditional method of using the national average ratio of doctors to people, a method which included no standard of need.

The committee reached these conclusions based on the assumption that current trends would continue:

* In 1990, there will be 70,000 more physicians than required to provide physician services. Said another way, there will be 536,000 doctors to meet the health service requirements that could be handled by 466,000 doctors.
* There will be shortages in some specialties and surpluses in others in 1990. Actually, all specialties were forecast to be in surplus except several pediatric sub-specialties (such as pediatric endocrinology), general and child psychiatry, emergency medicine, preventive medicine and anesthesiology. Curiously, a projected surplus of 28,150 general and specialized surgeons were expected to face a 1,550-person shortage of the physician specialists needed to put their patients to sleep.

This table gives some impression of the magnitude of anticipated oversupply in various specialties:

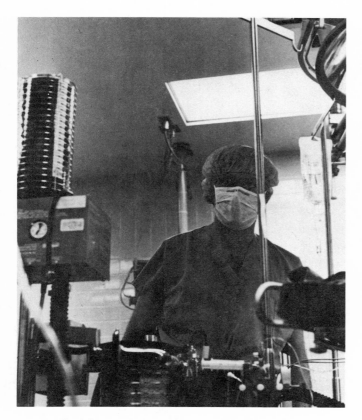

Anesthesiologists…a rare shortage in a projected surplus of medical specialists. (University of Oklahoma)

Specialty	Surplus	Percentage Oversupply
General Pediatrics	7,500	25%
General Internal Medicine	3,550	5%
Cardiology	7,150	95%
Pulmonary Diseases	3,350	93%
Obstetrics and Gynecology	10,450	44%
Orthopedic Surgery	5,000	33%
Plastic Surgery	1,700	44%
General Surgery	11,800	50%
Neurosurgery	2,450	92%
Urology	1,650	21%
Pathology	3,350	25%
Radiology	9,800	54%

The GMENAC Report further speculated that if the trends current in 1980 continued until the year 2,000, the physician surplus would total 145,000.

* The requirements for non-physician health care providers should be integrated into physician manpower planning. The committee recognized that people like nurse practitioners, physicians assistants, nurse midwives and nurse anesthetists do some of the things doctors do and at the then rate of training, the supply of the first three would double by 1990.

* Mechanisms to achieve a more favorable geo-graphic distribution of physicians are needed. This problem had already been faced in Oklahoma by the establishment of the Physician Manpower Training Commission in 1975.

These conclusions are only four of a dozen the GMENAC group listed. It also made 40 recommendations to overcome the problems it foresaw. Some of the most important steps it advocated were:

* Cut the size of the classes entering medical schools by 17 percent relative to the 1980-1981 class. Do not open any more medical schools, allopathic or osteopathic.

* Severely restrict the number of foreign medical school graduates (FMGs) entering the U.S. The committee estimated there would be 4,100 FMGs coming into the country each year by 1983.

* GMENAC did not specify how residencies and fellowship opportunities should be increased or decreased, assuming the numbers would speak to each institution. It did, however, recommend that first year trainees not be increased or decreased more than 20 percent by 1986 compared to 1979 in order not to disrupt the graduate medical education system.

* Encourage graduates to enter primary care or those specialties where a shortage of physicians is expected.

* Conduct extensive research to determine the relative efficacy of medical services provided by non-physicians and physicians. Cease all incentives to expand the capacity and number of optometric and podiatric schools.

* Encourage medical students to select a location for practice in underserved rural and urban areas.[1]

While the GMENAC report did not impress all of the educators in the country's medical schools, it inspired the Tulsa County Medical Society to recognize the potential problems in that area of Oklahoma. A committee, headed by John R. Alexander, M.D., studied medical education in Oklahoma, particularly the period since 1966 when Tulsa began to explore the possiblity of having a medical school. Jack Spears, the executive director of the organization, talked about the conclusions of the committee report which came out in November, 1981:

This study was directed toward certain problems. It says, in effect, that for the Tulsa schools, we feel the entering classes should be held at their present levels. We would hopefully like to see use of the [University of Oklahoma] Tulsa Medical College outpatient clinics for treatment of indigent patients. Also, residency training programs, unless very carefully justified, should continue at their present level.

There has never been any consideration or advocacy in the Tulsa County Medical Society of developing the

The administration building of the Tulsa Medical College, or "Tulsa Branch" as it is called at OUHSC. (University of Oklahoma)

Tulsa Medical College as a four-year program. It may take place some day, but our whole emphasis at this time is maintaining it as a two-year [clinical] college.[2]

Mr. Spears was asked if, 10 years previously, the Society had any idea Tulsa would wind up with three medical schools. He laughed and answered:

Of course not! That was never even thought of. At the time we started, we were thinking of developing an M.D.-type school and as the project began to mature, the osteopathic profession made a proposal for an osteopathic college and that came to fruition at virtually the same time as the Tulsa Medical College. Oral Roberts University [ORU] was just in the formulation stages as a general college. In those early days, there just wasn't any ORU and we did not think it would subsequently develop its own school of medicine.

I'm sure that a good segment of the Tulsa medical profession feels that we do not need to educate as many doctors as are coming out of these three schools. These things are in development, in transition. The Oral Roberts school has long advocated it is educating physicians to participate in their own ministries and they are *not* educating physicians to serve the population of Tulsa County, or for that matter, Oklahoma. Whether that proves to be true, we don't know. We are just at the point

where, in a few months, they'll graduate their first class [mid-1983].

Nationally, we are into a situation where the development of many new medical schools during the past 10 years and increased sizes of classes [in established medical schools] has led to such numbers of doctors graduating, there is what many call a *glut* of physicians. We feel we are reaching saturation points in Tulsa. In 1982, our society received applications of 120 new physicians, an incredible number, the highest we've ever had. Of course, this is not a net figure; our loss was 30 or 35, but what you're talking about is a 10 or 12 percent increase, just in a single year.[3]

Complicating this national situation was the so-called "patient shortage". In an October, 1981 article in *Private Practice* magazine, Harry Schwartz pointed out that visits to doctor's offices, both M.D. and D.O., had held constant at about one billion a year in the United states since 1970. The figures, in millions, are:

1970	1975	1976	1977	1978	1979	1980
927	1,056	1,041	1,020	1,017	1,022	1,036

If this trend continues through the 1980s, physicians will be averaging about 1,600 patient visits a year at the end of the decade. In 1970, each of the 350,000 doctors saw an average of 3,000 patients a year.[4]

The City of Faith. Oral Roberts was the model for the gigantic praying hands. The 777-bed hospital building is on the right. (OHSF Collection)

CHAPTER 40
MORE BUILDINGS: 1976-1982

The Dental Clinical Sciences Building presents an interesting design. (Oklahoma City Chamber of Commerce)

The Dental Clinical Sciences Building was dedicated on April 25, 1976. When Dean William E. Brown was planning the curriculum, he envisioned the objective of the college this way:

> Basically, we wanted to provide a dental education program that would produce a well-rounded, general dentist who had many, perhaps even most of the skills that were the domain of the specialist 25 years ago. Let's face it; our program is not that different from many other dental schools today. A well-rounded generalist could be comfortable going to a smaller community where he did not have to rely on a battery of specialists. Our graduates do not do the big oral surgery things; they don't do major orthodontics but they will do most of everything else.
>
> We started with clinical activities early on, instead of two years basic science and then two years of clinical science. We felt we should move into the clinical sciences even in the first year. In fact, within the first week or two, our students are in the clinics, exposed to a bit about dentistry.

One of the major differences between medical and dental education is that we have four years to produce a "product" that is eligible for licensure and ready to go out into the world and manage patients. Medicine has those four years plus, on the average, another four years to prepare physicians. So our curriculum is considerably more intense, much more information stacked into a small amount of time. The fourth year comes as close to a residency as we can provide. There is no residency requirement in dentistry, except in Delaware, so it does create some problems in terms of intensity and crowding of the dental curriculum. And it's getting worse instead of better because of the volumes of new information coming down the pike.[1]

The $11 million, 10-story Biomedical Sciences Building also opened in 1976 on October 22nd. It was designed primarily to accommodate the offices and research laboratories of the basic science faculty but it had adjacent areas for clinicians to do research related to the basic scientific disciplines. The first floor was designated as a "joint science area" so multidisciplinary research projects could be carried out. The second floor centralized the animal facilities, with cages for mice, hamsters, rats, cats, rabbits, dogs, primates and an occasional goat or calf. There were special areas to house animals with contagious disease and isolate those on which radioactive experiments were being performed. There was a large operative area where nine surgical procedures could be performed simultaneously. The animal quarters had a separate air supply and ventilating system so none of the offensive odors escaped to the other floors of the building. On other medical school campuses, the reeking stench of the animal quarters not infrequently permeates the entire building where biomedical research is done.

The office of the medical school dean, four teaching laboratories and a lecture hall for the Graduate College were located on the third floor. Ph.D. candidates who aspire to teach or become researchers enroll in the Graduate College, now directed by Ralph Daniels, Ph.D., associate dean.

Each of the floors above were assigned to the several disciplines this way:

Four: Pathology

Five: Anatomy

Six: Physiology and Biophysics

The University's Biomedical Sciences Building houses the College of Medicine and its research facilities. (Oklahoma City Chamber of Commerce)

Seven: Pharmacology

Eight: Medicine, pediatrics and other clinical disciplines

Nine: Biochemistry

Ten: Microbiology and Immunology

There was an outboard corridor around each floor and a central, east west hallway bisecting the block of interior labs and offices.

Did *this* building work as designed? "Not exactly," according to Dr. Vernon Scott. The theories on which such designs are based tend to change and almost never coincide with the ideas of all those who use the building, even though the faculty on board during the design process is fully involved. Needs, people and ideas all change. For examples:

> * Dr. Scott said the first floor "joint science area" did not work as planned because the scientists "were not made to use it." Now it is "surge space," offered as needed to candidates for chairman positions in basic science disciplines. In mid-1983, there were several such vacancies and it had always been difficult to recruit chairman in the basic sciences. Dr. Scott said, "The reason is, the clinicians have more clout and they have always felt they had to have more money and we, as the basic scientists, are always 'sucking hind tit,' so to speak." This first-floor space was also used by College of Pharmacy

Dr. Jack Sokatch, left, with Sir Hans Kornberg, chairman of the biochemistry department of Cambridge University in England, who visited in 1980. (University of Oklahoma)

faculty until they could move into their own building in mid-1983.

> * The second floor animal surgical area was never used because scientists found it more convenient to take the smaller animals to their floor and operate on them in their own laboratories. Lazar Greenfield, a surgeon, envisioned a large volume of experimental surgery would be performed on dogs but when he departed in August, 1974, this did not happen.

> * The labs on the tenth floor are now used by clinicians for procedures which bear no relation to microbiology or immunology. Medical school faculty are very territory-minded. Once they have laid claim to space, it is very difficult for them to give it up or for the dean to pry it away from them. Dr. Scott quoted Bob Bird's observation on the subject, "They pissed around it so it's theirs!"[2]

When lay people tour this building, they have difficulty understanding what those white-coated, long-haired men [and some ladies] are doing in those laboratories, surrounded by curiously shaped glassware, strange instruments and talking to their colleagues in a language totally unintelligible to the average person. Science-speak! John R. "Jack" Sokatch, Ph.D., microbial biochemist, tried to explain his mission in everyday terms—what he was doing in his research lab:

> Let me think about this. Pretty esoteric! There is a disease called "maple syrup urine disease," a genetic disease which is very rare. The genetic lesion is known to occur in an enzyme which is called "branched chain keto acid dehydrogenase." We are not working with this enzyme in humans; we are studying it in bacteria. It is a

large, very complex enzyme and it is not well studied. We are using the bacterial system as a model for it. We've got the enzyme isolated and we're studying its regulation of activity and the genetics of the enzyme.

The disease is caused in humans when the enzyme is not there, a genetic deficiency. The babies pile up a keto acid in their blood and before you can do much for them, they get a lot of brain damage. They die very young…a few months. Pediatricians try to correct this deficiency with diet and they have some success but the only long-term hope is genetic engineering…recombinant DNA.

The life of the biomedical researcher is not all spent in the laboratory. In the late 1970s, support for research, whether federal or private, was becoming increasingly difficult to get. Only the researcher could obtain that support because only he could explain in an application for a grant what his research was expected to achieve. Dr. Sokatch continued:

Of the applications that are submitted and approved, roughly one in three—maybe less—one in four gets funded. I'd say 10 or 15 percent of my time is spent in "writing grants." That's going to drop off for me because I've got one grant that goes for five years. All I've got to do is write the annual reports and that's not too bad. But I serve on a national committee, a study sec-

tion that reviews grants. I spend at least three months a year, full-time, doing nothing but reviewing grant applications.

The thing this does for me…I get exposed to "cutting edge" research and I get to see it before it's published. That's the good news part. The bad news part is that it takes three months of the year, maybe longer. We review these proposals three times a year at meetings in Washington.[3]

By the time the College of Nursing Building was ready in July, 1977, the enrollment at OUHSC had grown to 335 master's and undergraduate level students. Gloria Smith believed the new four-story, 93,000 square-foot building, designed by Murray-Jones-Murray of Tulsa, changed the image of nursing in Oklahoma:

We have been very careful in projecting to nurses in this state that this building is a resource for *all* of nursing in Oklahoma. They take a great deal of pride in it and it certainly has been a boon to our ability to attract people. If we can get faculty candidates here and they begin to see what the resources are in this center, we have an easier time recruiting them. We have to cut through people's biases and misconceptions about Oklahoma and Oklahomans. Then, when they come to

The College of Nursing building, Dean Gloria Smith's pride and joy. (Oklahoma City Chamber of Commerce)

Dr. Robert E. Nordquist, director of research at the MEI, inspects a slide containing cancer tissue before examining it further under a light microscope. (Dean A. McGee Eye Institute)

The OUHSC library opened in the summer of 1978. (Oklahoma City Chamber of Commerce)

A student relaxes in a quiet corner of the library. (University of Oklahoma)

this center, they can't really believe it! It impresses them very, very much. And we capitalize on that. When any kind of nursing meeting is held anywhere near this campus, we make sure there's an opportunity [for visitors] to tour the facility.[4]

By the spring of 1978, the fourth and fifth shelled-in floors of the McGee Eye Institute had been completed, plus quarters for research animals. The fourth floor was dedicated to eye research, made possible by a $2 million gift by Mrs. Cora Snetcher. The administrative and teaching space on the fifth floor freed up more clinical area for the treatment of patients. This expansion, while not visible from the outside, was an important advance for ophthalmology and came just two and a half years after the institute opened.

The Oklahoma Medical Research Foundation held open house on June 11, 1978, in its newly expanded building. The former inpatient wing had been closed and remodeled for other purposes, and research patients were hospitalized at Presbyterian. A two-level, 20,000-square-foot wing had been added to the north, improving the library, animal facilities and research laboratories so the Foundation's investigations in cancer, hematology, nutrition and cardiovascular disease could grow.

Meanwhile, across campus, it took three weeks to move all the books and journals out of the old medical school building into the new OUHSC library at Stonewall Avenue and Stanton L. Young Boulevard. This four level facility, the academic heart of the campus, was in the geographic center of four (and later, five) of the seven colleges. The arrangement was similar to the 1968 campus plan but as time went on, the

Visitors inspect the autopsy area of the State Medical Examiner's Office, 1978. (University of Oklahoma)

The 1,100 car garage is flanked on either side by surface parking lots. In the background is the South Pavilion and the Biomedical Sciences Building. (OHSF Collection)

Provost Bill Thurman makes a point to Paul Sharp and Mayor Latting at the groundbreaking ceremony for the parking structure.

university nucleus shifted to the north and east. The library building also housed the new office of the provost and his administrative staff who moved from one of the houses on 14th Street. The building was officially opened on August 20, 1978.

That same month, the 18,000 square foot State Medical Examiner's Office building opened, at least in part, at Stonewall Avenue and 8th Street. The morgue and autopsy areas were finished and placed in service. The responsibility of the state medical examiner was to investigate all deaths other than natural deaths which were attended by a physician for a known fatal disease. The bodies of people who died under mysterious circumstances or as a result of

homocide were autopsied to determine the exact cause of death.

The next month, September, 1978, construction began on an 1,100 space, $3.7 million parking structure for the university. Atop its east end was planned a 30,000-square-foot building to accomodate a new "Faculty House," a cafeteria, book store, campus store and travel agency. This multi-use section later became known as the South Pavilion. It was located south of Stanton L. Young Boulevard across from University Hospital and was acquired by the Department of Human Services when Mr. Rader took over University Hospital.

During 1980 and 1981, a second surge of construction in the Oklahoma Health Center changed the campus dramatically. In mid-1981, there was a veritable forest of construction cranes working on five different projects totalling $60 million. This, coupled with the $260 million of capital improvements in place meant the originally estimated $185 million OHC was reaching toward $320 million with yet another $62 million in projects on the drawing boards. Had the surge of inflation not occurred in the 1970s and early 1980s, the 1968 estimate of $185 million would probably have been quite accurate.

The university expanded the Dermatology Clinic building ($185 thousand) and the steam and chilled water plant ($1.46 million). In February, 1981, the Veterans Administration Medical Center began construction of a $34 million clinical addition. This was the proposed concourse-bridge building redesigned for the exclusive use of the V.A. and relocated on the north side of 13th Street. The outpatient space in the original hospital was built to accommodate 50,000 patient visits a year and by 1981, that number had exceeded 140,000, so there was no question about the need for expansion. The plan was to move the clinics out of the hospital into the new addition and remodel spaces thus freed in the old building for nursing services, dental clinic, research and administration. As a part of this project, more than a million dollars was invested in the original building to make it earthquake-resistant. During the 1970s, a V.A. hospital in California had been demolished by an earthquake and the Central V.A. Office wanted to forestall any such disaster in central Oklahoma which, unbeknownst to many, is also in an earthquake zone.

The mammoth clinical addition displaced the hospital's main parking area and although there were built into the structure 30 parking spaces for the cars of disabled veterans and for vans from state veterans homes, it complicated an already critical parking situation. The V.A. Central Office (and Congress) traditionally had given patient and employee parking a low priority, so as this project began, no solution to the problem was in sight. The people who lived in the houses on 15th Street north of the hospital began to rent their front yards as parking space and the street lost its once orderly appearance. But Walter Whitcomb, M.D., director of the Oklahoma City unit, expected to manage the problem eventually:

> Currently [1983], the V.A. has purchased the houses [on the south side of 15th Street between McMechan Parkway and Kelley Avenue contiguous with the hospital] and funds have been set aside to surface the area, providing between 280 and 300 spaces. We'll still be dependent on DHS space in the south part of the campus [between Lottie and Everest] for employee parking. We have made a request for a parking structure and we're beginning to think in terms of putting our need for additional research space and our parking problem together in the most cost-effective manner. We just don't have that thought through. We won't be fully accommodated until we have multi-level parking and we'd like to see it on the north and the east.
>
> We've been told that the mind of Congress is a bit different than it was years ago. They now seem to be not so hostile to the notion of funding parking structures. Thus far, only one has been approved in the system. If the V.A. won't do it, maybe somebody else would like to build a structure and charge for parking. We need to coordinate this planning with the foundation [OMRF] over here.[5]

On the other side of the campus, the new Presbyterian Hospital, which had seemed so cavernous to the staff and employees as they moved from the old plant, was already running out of space. In mid-1981, just seven years after it opened, the hospital was busily infilling two bays under the inpatient tower to provide new quarters for the pharmacy, the house staff and on-call physicians. It was also extending the podium to the east to accommodate an ambulatory surgery center, a cancer center, expand clinical laboratories and house the sleep disorders center. The project was estimated to cost $6 million for construction and another $3.5 million for equipment.

The Oklahoma Medical Research Foundation was also capturing needed space by enclosing the first level of its north research wing to create the Ben Wileman and Roy Lytle Learning Center, a half million dollar project which included a 143-seat auditorium.

The university had capital funds to renovate the old medical school building at 13th Street and Phillips so the modernized facility would fit the needs of the Colleges of Public Health and Allied Health, a $3 million investment. The 1969 preliminary planning analysis which proposed a new, separate building for these schools, had estimated its cost on the basis of 1972 prices for 155,575 net square feet and had come up with $8,287,000. While they did not enjoy new quarters designed specifically for their use, the two colleges found the remodeled building adequate and considerably less costly.

Finally, the legislature appropriated $3.3 million in each of its 1980 and 1981 sessions to build a parking garage for the State Health Department. This happened almost eight years after the concept of a COTPA-built and operated parking blanket sank out of sight. Construction started on an 800-space, four-story structure in the fall of 1981. Bids for the original 1972 model came in at $2,222 a space; the cost of the 1981 model was $8,100 a space, up 265 percent. Inflation had increased 120 percent during the same period. The consumer price index went from a base of 100 in 1967 to 125.7 in August, 1972 to 276.5 in August, 1981.[6]

Some of the construction which had been started in 1981 was completed in 1982: the Wileman and Lytle Learning Center at OMRF, the three-story addition to Oklahoma Memorial Hospital and the helipad atop Children's Hospital. The third helipad at the entrance to the OMH trauma center was placed in service. A three-level, $3.95 million addition on the west side of the Oklahoma City Clinic was begun in 1982.

Two floors were added to what Dr. Bill Thurman first called a "multi-use" building at the east end of the then University Hospital parking facility on Stan-

Construction of the State Health Department garage finally got under way in 1981. (OHSF Collection)

Construction on the east end of the Presbyterian Hospital podium. (Oklahoma City Chamber of Commerce.)

ton Young Boulevard at Phillips. It was renamed by DHS the Physicians and Education Building because its new purpose was to house the clinical departments of the medical school. It was later that it became the South Pavilion.

As 1981 ended and spring returned in 1982, the institutions in the Oklahoma Health Center were riding the crest. In fact, all of Oklahoma was in the midst of an economic boom led by the robust activity in the oil and gas business. Everybody had money, the state was collecting more taxes than ever before and a lot of people were flowing into Oklahoma looking for jobs because the unemployment rate in the state was down to 3.7 percent in contrast to the nationwide average of 8.8 percent. On July 1, 1981, the state of Oklahoma had $326 million more than it needed to pay for everything and the governor was even embarrassed by the affluence Oklahoma enjoyed as he met with officials of other states that were sliding into recession.[7]

Much of the campus plan was nearing completion, expansion was the codeword, construction was moving apace, prospects for rebuilding the deteriorated area west of the campus were bright. In fact, the entire horizon was cloudless. Let the good times roll!

PART FIVE

CRISIS REVISITED: 1983-1984

CHAPTER 41

CRISIS...AGAIN! 1983

With such progress and prospects in 1982, what could possibly go wrong? It looked as though the future of the Oklahoma Health Center was at last secure. But a sudden squall in the financial world over the Independence Day weekend signalled more heavy weather to come. Federal regulators shut down Penn Square Bank in Oklahoma City because of its very large loan commitments to petroleum producers in an industry which was beginning to experience a downturn. Penn Square had made numerous energy-related loans to borrowers whose ability to repay was dependent on continued high prices of their product. But conservation efforts and a contracting economy had produced a glut of oil and gas. Prices were slipping, which meant many of the less well-financed energy companies were unable to keep up payments on the loans granted to them by Penn Square Bank. In the meantime, Penn Square had peddled the loans to Continental Illinois Bank and Trust Company of Chicago, Seattle-First National Bank and New York's Chase Manhattan Bank—more than $2 billion worth!

It later was charged that a few days prior to publication of the bank's condition, a number of large depositors were tipped off that the bank was about to close. Bank officials had to scramble for funds to pay them and to offset an increasing number of bad loans. As a result, the Federal Reserve had to pump $26 million into the bank to cover the cash shortage. On Friday, July 2, the news media reported the bank's troubles and scores of depositors removed their funds that day and the next. As Federal Reserve Chairman Paul Volcker said, they made the loans because "there was a run on the bank."

Thus, when the Federal Deposit Insurance Corporation (FDIC) took over Penn Square Bank on July 3, 1982, the closure had national reverberations. As *Business Week* reported on August 2, 1982, "When excesses of a small Oklahoma bank were compounded by the laxity of the giants, the mixture of management styles became explosive. Banking regulators concluded they had little choice but to risk the consequences of closing down Penn Square...." The FDIC could not merge it into a healthy bank, its usual practice, because at that point the potential losses were not

Penn Square Bank depositors line up to get their money. (The Oklahoman)

readily calculable. Two years later, in April, 1984, those losses totaled $1.2 billion and were expected to mount because more than half of the approximately $1 billion of Penn Square outstanding loans were nonperforming. It had become the costliest bank failure in U.S. history, exceeding by at least $100 million inflation adjusted dollars the previous record loss caused by the failure of the Bank of U.S. in New York in 1930.[1]

The immediate, direct effect on the Oklahoma Health Center was essentially nil but this highly-publicized event awakened many Oklahomans to the changes which were taking place in the oil patch. By fall, nationwide spending for oil and gas exploration, activity which had lit up the night sky clear across Oklahoma, was expected to total only $24 billion in 1982, down 25 percent from the previous year. Penn Square Bank had gone belly-up largely because it did not recognize the potential financial weakness of its energy-company borrowers. Because much of the state government's revenue was derived from wellhead taxes and from sales taxes growing as a result of the booming oil business, this slowdown was destined to affect higher education and health services financed by the state. When Governor Nigh said in his State of the State message to the legislature on January 4, 1983, that with careful management no new tax revenues would be required, few people in the legislature or at the university, the State Health Department or the Department of Human Services then realized how deep the ultimate budget cuts would have to be.[2]

Henry Bellmon became director of the Department of Human Services the first of January, 1983:

I don't want to sound like I'm critical and I hope it doesn't turn out to be that. Mr. Rader came to the welfare department back when it was a very small agency, had a fairly small budget and a small number of employees. He ran the agency as he had run his [contracting] business out in Hinton [Oklahoma]. He made most of the major decisions, in fact, I assume all of the decisions himself and, I think, in a very commendable, conservative, credible way. As time went on—and he was there for over 31 years—and the operation grew larger and larger and larger and the budget and the number of people got bigger, he never changed his system. He had a rather commendable capability of focusing his total energy on the most pressing problem of the moment. When the department took over the schools for the mentally retarded, he more or less concentrated on dealing with those new challenges and problems and let some other things drift.

He did the same thing with the hospital. Once the transfer had been made, Mr. Rader literally moved his office, or at least opened an office in the complex and spent most of his workday there, leaving the traditional DHS responsibilities to others, although he didn't actually delegate those responsibilities. The result of it was, he made the decisions in the teaching hospitals to the point of deciding who got what jobs, where the money would be spent and I suppose passed judgment on the architectural design—I don't know that.

Frosty Troy said he made *all* the decisions, "down to the color of the mop handles." Bellmon continued:

At the time I came down there, the people at the hospitals had the title but Mr. Rader had the authority and was making the decisions. He had gained or perhaps had always had the capability of making those decisions. I didn't have it and I didn't want that responsibility so one of the first things I did was to turn the operation over to Dr. Halverstadt who was the chief of staff and totally competent to run the place. When I first came in down there, there would be stacks of documents relating to the operation of the teaching hospitals that had to have the director's signature on them. We stopped that immediately. Those papers stayed in the office of the hospital chief of staff and he had to decide whether to buy equipment or hire or fire people…make the management decisions. [Before that, though,] I think Don will tell you Mr. Rader was in charge.

The sales tax receipts, plus collections were running

Lloyd Rader and Henry Bellmon. (Department of Human Services)

25 percent below projections. This started happening perhaps in September [1982] but I didn't have any voice in the decision-making when I was associate director. This began to happen but Mr. Rader didn't pay much attention to the developing crisis because he had some reserves he'd been carrying and he could deal with the problem without having to make any serious management changes.[3]

Bellmon said when he came along, they were rapidly using up all the resources they had and it was obvious by projecting the lines they were going to run out of money within 60 days. Some things had to be done immediately, not only at the hospitals but all across DHS, such things as ultimately closing down two of the juvenile schools. Bellmon put a freeze on hiring and reduced the payroll "something like a thousand…over 400 at the hospitals." "Dr. Halverstadt and I talked about the hospital situation," he continued, "and I think he'll agree he was not reluctant to make the changes that needed to be made down there. I think he will say he realized the operation was perhaps a little over-staffed." Most of the construction was stopped because it used a great deal of money in payroll and supplies. Mr. Rader had bought a lot of construction materials "so it was kind of a mixed bag but we felt we could stretch out construction." Dr. Halverstadt delayed the purchase of some equipment he thought he could get along without. Also, he delayed placing in service some of the beds they projected to be opened. In Bellmon's opinion, "Dr. Halverstadt was a very strong administrator and very supportive of the efforts the agency had to make to get its financial house in order."

Asked if he thought this reordering was accomplished during that period, Mr. Bellmon replied:

> Not completely but a good deal was done. One of the things was to start doing a better job of collecting for the services the hospital rendered. You'll have to check the record because my memory may not be totally accurate, but those collections had been running not too much above $50 million a year. Now they are running pretty close to $100 million, in the course of less than 12 months. Another thing was the enormous amount of inventory we were carrying in warehouses. We had some items [of which] we had many years supply on hand. It was rather poorly managed and Dr. Halverstadt rapidly cleaned up that operation.
>
> There were a great many problems, partially due to the preoccupation Mr. Rader had had with the construction phase and due to the fact the agency had not had financial problems. There was plenty of money to do whatever needed to be done. Because that all changed about the time I came there, we had to deal with the new realities.[4]

Collections were not as bad nor did they improve quite as much as Mr. Bellmon thought. Between FY 1982 and FY 1983, revenue from services to patients in the Oklahoma Teaching Hospitals went up $20 million, or 22 percent, from more than $93 million to almost $114 million. At the Oklahoma Memorial Hospital, formerly University Hospital, during the last two years Bruce Perry was there, patient revenues had risen to 93 percent of the cost of operation. In the following two years, that percentage dropped back to 78 percent because the cost of operation surged forward, as Mike McEwen had predicted it would. And it almost doubled, from $30 million in 1979 to $59 million in 1982. Twenty five percent more people [314 employees] were added, the available beds declined from 314 to 249 as a result of razing Old Main, and the cost per patient day jumped 108%, from $355.75 in 1979 to $739.03 in 1982.

Mr. Bellmon apparently saw the need for an abrupt turnaround. In a front page *Oklahoma City Times* story

on February 11, 1983, he said "the two teaching hospitals in years past have treated the state like a rich, foolish uncle. In plush times, they got everything they sought and operational costs went up 24 percent in 1981 and 17 percent in 1982." He said when he took over the agency, he attempted to discuss soaring budgets with hospital officials, "But you can't argue with people who don't speak the language."

Bellmon worked out a deal whereby the hospitals would receive the same share of the DHS budget—about 14 percent—as before. That pegged them at $60 million in state funds, a $10 million cut. "That brought about a change in the hospital attitude and they got very cost conscious," the former United States senator added. Halverstadt was so impressed by the newspaper article, he had it framed and hung on his office wall.[5]

But as Tom Tucker, DHS attorney pointed out, "The disaster of the earmarked sales tax is this: it is designed basically to support welfare programs. At the time in the economy you need the welfare program the most, when you go into a recession, that's the time the sales tax falls off. So we have the greatest amount of money when we need it the least and the least amount of money when we need it the most."[6]

Although Mr. Bellmon reduced the employee force in the teaching hospitals by 400 people, there was actually a net increase in full-time equivalent employees during the 1983 fiscal year. Two hundred and fifty five employees were added, increasing the number on the payroll to 3,989 or about 6.5 employees per bed, up 6.8 percent. Similarly, the cost of operation rose from $136 million in 1982 to $149 million during 1983, an increase of 9.4%. Interestingly, the revenues during 1983 were $173 million, including the $57.6 million from state funds, so there was an actual *surplus* for the year of $24 million.[7]

On May 23, 1983, Robert Fulton started as associate director of DHS and became director when Henry Bellmon left in mid-July. Dr. Halverstadt offered to resign his $108 thousand position, the highest paid state employee in Oklahoma. Frosty Troy said, "I'm not going to bug you or anybody else about Halverstadt. Everybody knows he's a good surgeon, O.K.? He had no business in an administrative position." In an editorial in the *Oklahoma Observer*, Troy urged DHS to let him go, saying "If any other agency head had spent his facilities into the trouble Halverstadt has, he'd be sent packing." The chief of staff also framed and hung this article on his wall.[8]

Gordon Deckert, chairman of psychiatry and be-

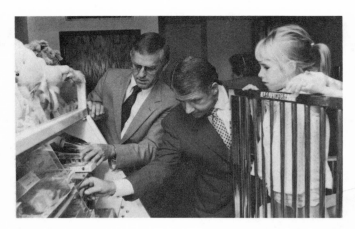

The new Director of Human Services, Robert Fulton (left), helps select a toy for one of the patients at Children's Memorial Hospital. (Department of Human Services)

Dr. Gordon Deckert…the second time around. (University of Oklahoma)

havioral sciences in the medical school, worried about the center's fiscal problems when he talked about them in May of 1983:

> We are *right* back where we were in 1972, with some very major differences. Now, it's the other way around. In 1972, it was, "The university isn't doing right by the hospitals. The problem is in the university and we need to get the hospitals out of the university. If they were managed right, we wouldn't have this financial problem." If you listen to the current legislative comment, the view is, "If there was decent management in the hospitals, there wouldn't be the evolving problem and the financial crisis there." The crisis is similar but now it's kind of a mirror image.
>
> There is a heirarchy of problems but *the* major problem in the health science center, in my judgment, is the schizophrenic messages that come to the OUHSC, especially to its teaching hospitals but also to its college of medicine. It is the schizophrenic way in which this state, the private sector as well as the public sector, views this operation. At one moment it says, "You must take care of the indigents but we really can't give you the necessary money to do that. That really should be possible within the money that's already given to the faculty through their salaries in the College of Medicine. It really ought to be possible to finance that through some sort of private practice." There has not been a clean, clear-cut decision to deal with this. It has simply been punted over and over. There are temporary solutions [such as] taking the problem to where the dollars temporarily seem to be, but there are long range problems to the very solutions that are created. The major problem is coming to a clear statement of what the function of these teaching hospitals is.[9]

Representative Cleta Deatherage also recognized this difficulty:

Cleta Deatherage. (Oklahoma Observer)

> The legislature can't decide from one day to the next what we want that facility to be. On Mondays, Wednesdays and Fridays, we want it to be a facility that is home to the homeless. And on Tuesdays, Thursdays and Saturdays, we want it to be a top-notch, blue ribbon, first-rate teaching facility. There has never been a concensus reached by the legislature as to the mission of the hospitals and what it is going to take to fund that mission. It's one thing for somebody to stand up and say, "This is the mission…" but you have to have a concensus that this *is* the mission and what it's going to take to fulfill this mission. That's the part that has never been established. I chaired the subcommittee that handled the University Hospital before it was transferred. It struggled badly from underfunding, partially because politically there was no constituency.[10]

Robert Fulton faced many tough questions at DHS, particularly about the Oklahoma Teaching Hospitals. (Department of Human Services)

Mr. Fulton was also concerned about the multiplicity of the teaching hospitals' roles:

It is sometimes forgotten that the OTH are a back-up referral center for major parts of Oklahoma, which is quite different from the mission of caring for indigent patients. The hospitals are a sophisticated, tertiary care center. Then you come to the third question, the indigent care, "public hospital" role. And there are two parts to it: how much of that indigent care is really needed for the teaching mission; that is, routine stuff—appendicitis—things every hospital in the state can do? Second, how much do we have to do because we are a citizen of the community and there is a problem of serving poor people?

The real question comes: do you try to ration that? Do you try to keep that portion of the care load that is not required for teaching from coming in? I don't know, really, if the state is ready to draw that line. I think it could be defined, almost department by department, based on historical information. The department of internal medicine, for example, gets most of its teaching [material] through the clinics and if you didn't have indigent care, you wouldn't have an adequate supply of patients.

I guess I'm becoming more convinced that doing that kind of definition is probably important. I worry a little about "throwing the baby out with the bathwater." I would not like to get in a position where we didn't have a pretty free hand to take people in and serve them. It's pretty clear, [though], there is quite a bit of concern about the

state treating poor people in this area more generously than in the Tulsa or Lawton areas.[11]

Despite the recurrence of the state funding crunch, the total Oklahoma Health Center and the neighborhood around it continued to improve. The Oklahoma City Clinic completed the $4 million addition on the west end of its building and occupied it in December, 1982. Cars began parking in the new State Health Department garage in late March, 1983. And the Central Expressway, which would some day move cars more expeditiously to and from the OHC, went under construction on June 6, 1983, starting at 36th and the Broadway Extension. This $160 million project, including land acquisition for right-of-way, had been in the planning stage for 18 years and was expected to be carrying traffic by Oklahoma City's Centennial Year, 1989. To Monty Murphy, this period did not seem excessive, even though it would be almost a quarter of a century between the conception and the completion of the Central Expressway:

As a part of the Oklahoma City Area Regional Transportation Study (OCARTS), which began in 1965, there was developed a freeway plan, supposedly for the year 1985, a 20-year plan. The Central Expressway was in the first part of the plan and wasn't one of the critical projects in the earlier stages. Any part of a [transportation] plan is developed as it becomes necessary to handle the traffic and as you get funding, which is one of the most important things. At that time, we received relatively small amounts of federal aid funds. Even if the route had been built in sections as money was available, it would have required all of the primary [highway] funds of the entire state, building just a couple of miles at a time. That's not only unreasonable; politically, it's unacceptable. You can't take all of your primary funds and put them on one project.[12]

On a hot morning in August, 1983, the 29th, Congressman Mickey Edwards, a Republican representing the Oklahoma City area, spoke briefly and later, along with Dr. Frank Cox, Julia Brown and a half dozen others, stuck a symbolic shovel in the Harrison-Walnut earth to mark the beginning of construction of the Chaparral Townhouses. This was the second project to get under way in the redevelopment of the neighborhood. The contractor expected to finish the 136 units in the autumn of 1984.

On the first of October, after months of planning and application preparation, it was announced that Presbyterian Hospital had received a grant of $4.5 million under the federal Urban Development Action Grant (UDAG) program. This would help fi-

Congressman Mickey Edwards and Dr. Frank Cox at the beginning of construction, Chaparral Townhouses. (Frank Cox)

nance the planned 200-room hotel at the northwest corner of the hospital, an 850-car garage along 11th Street west of Lincoln Boulevard and a medical office building north of the garage. The total cost of this project was expected to be $29.5 million. Actually, the federal "grant" of $4.5 million was a low interest loan which would be paid back to the local, not the national government and was expected to be earmarked for further improvements in the Harrison-Walnut area.

At the City Council meeting on October 11, 1983, a delegation of more than a hundred people in the Harrison-Walnut Neighborhood Association, headed by its president Gary Royal, showed up to protest the language pertaining to relocation benefits in the final H-W plan. There was much testimony on both sides but the council finally decided the residents would be amply protected as the plan was written and gave its final approval. Despite this demonstration, Julia Brown expressed her feeling there was a growing concensus and unity of purpose as planning for re-development went on. "That's going to gel even more after the folks are relocated from the first renewal project, from the Presbyterian area. The reason why it will is because other folks in the area will see the people are not being ripped off, that they are being dealt with fairly, and they will see we're *serious* about redeveloping the area. They'll see we're not just some fly-by-night people, trying to make a fast buck, who are going to disappear before sunrise."[13]

A few weeks later, the third H-W project was started on the east side of Lincoln Boulevard at 6th Street. This was the Pan Oklahoma Cable Television building, the headquarters to be leased to Cox Cable which bought the TV franchise from Pan Oklahoma to serve the northeast quadrant of Oklahoma City. In addition, still another group of developers sought a site for a bank and the Oklahoma Health Sciences Foundation optioned an acre parcel to them while their application for a charter was being processed. Lincoln National Bank was planned for the northwest corner of Lincoln and 10th. Also, the Oklahoma Department of Transportation was clearing the right-of-way it had purchased in the Harrison-Walnut area, including 11 parcels from the Foundation, so the land west of Lincoln Boulevard was becoming increasingly open. The old neighborhood was almost gone.

In the late summer and early fall of 1983, dedications came in bunches on the campus. On the first day of September the Veterans Administration Medical Center celebrated completion of its new addition west of the original building. Housed in this wing were the new outpatient clinics, clinical laboratories, radiology, pharmacy and other diagnostic and treatment services. New administrative space had also been added in front of the old building so the areas thus freed would permit remodeling of inpatient nursing units but the bed complement of 423 was not expected to change. The V.A. needed more research space and hoped later to build yet another floor on the new wing, move in the operating rooms and special care units and utilize vacated space in the old building for research laboratories.

On the hot afternoon of the dedication ceremonies, people were happy to get into the cool new clinical wing, but during an unseasonal cold snap in December, 1983, it was too cool for comfort. The building had been designed during the energy crunch when the federal government required thermostats to be set low during the winter months. The mechanical design of the new wing was such that it could not be heated above those maximum settings even though the regulations had been long rescinded. At year's end, the architects were scurrying about, trying to change the system and portable electric heaters were being used in examination rooms where patients had to take their clothes off.

Other than this problem and the adjustments necessary in any new building, the Clinical Wing, as it was

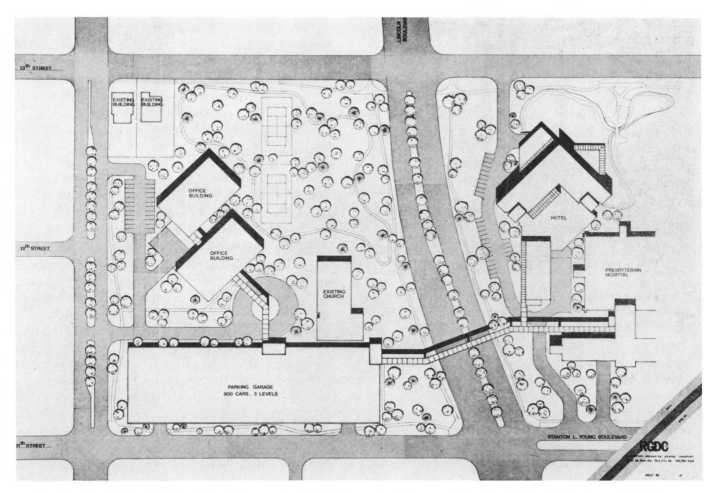

The site plan for Presbyterian Hospital expansion included new buildings on both sides of Lincoln Boulevard. (Oklahoma City Chamber of Commerce)

The first new building in Harrison-Walnut. (Oklahoma City Chamber of Commerce)

The Pan Oklahoma Cable TV Building went under construction in the fall of 1983. (Oklahoma City Chamber of Commerce)

321

The new Clinical Addition to the VA Medical Center. (Oklahoma City Chamber of Commerce)

Esther Pahlka holds the microphone while Dr. Fletcher Taylor speaks at the opening of OMRF's new facility for cardiovascular research. (OHSF Collection)

called, was a handsome improvement. Spacious, pleasantly appointed, and well arranged, it relieved much of the space pressure the V.A. had been experiencing for many years.

The Oklahoma Medical Research Foundation held open house at its new cardiovascular research building on September 24, 1983, after dedication speeches marked the occasion on the wind-swept, unfinished deck east of the laboratories on 15th Street. The building was designed to have a dual purpose. The west section opened that day contained laboratories for research in heart and blood vessel disease. The east section will some day be added to accomodate cancer research work.

Ten days later, Presbyterian Hospital kicked off the festivities which marked the opening of the Bob Hope Eye Surgery Center with a gala fundraising dinner at the Skirvin Plaza Hotel in downtown Oklahoma City. Eighty-year-old Bob Hope entertained an enthusiastic crowd which filled the ballroom. The next day, in an outdoor ceremony on October 5, America's favor-

Bob Hope holds March of Dimes Poster Child Helen Humphries at the dedication of the Bob Hope Eye Surgery Center. (Presbyterian Hospital)

(Oklahoma City Chamber of Commerce)

ite comedian dedicated the new surgical suite. Ophthalmic surgery was rapidly becoming an outpatient process as new methods became available. Three quarters of eye surgical procedures were capable of being done on a "day surgery" basis without admitting the patient to the hospital. Most of the McGee Eye Institute patients needing surgery were treated at Presbyterian Hospital.

The fourth dedication on the campus that fall occurred on November 20, 1983, when the $7.5 million, 70 thousand square foot home of the O.U. College of Pharmacy was officially opened. The major private donation to this building, $1.5 million, was made by the estate of Henry D. and Ida Mosier, an Edmond, Oklahoma couple for whom the building was named. Mr. Mosier was a 1912 graduate of the O.U. College of Pharmacy and had a pharmacy in the Guthrie area. He and Mrs. Mosier also established a very nice trust account to provide scholarships for needy pharmacy students. Dean Rodney Ice, Ph.D., who had resigned in May of that year, said:

We probably have the most modern college of pharmacy in the world, at least in the United States. If it isn't first rate, it's all my fault. I think the facilities are very good. I wrote up two separate grant applications to the federal government for a new college of pharmacy building in the late 1970s. Both times there was money authorized but not appropriated and we went through that process *twice*. That's one reason it took us seven years. By this time, our accreditation body was breathing right

down our neck. We had made promises.... We showed them our grant [applications], but "approved but not funded" doesn't help very much. At that point, we redirected our efforts because we saw the handwriting on the wall. There just wasn't going to be any more funds from federal sources to support health colleges as there had been in the early 1970s. We began developing an alumni and legislative rapport that would help us to bring the money through the legislature. By the time we went to the state, we could recite our proposal frontwards and backwards. We knew exactly what we needed; we had consolidated and reconsolidated a number of times. When we did get to the state legislature, we were able to move very fast.[14]

The state's financial situation was becoming more and more critical as 1983 wore on. The budget balancing amendment of the constitution did not permit the government to spend more than it took in. As sales tax revenues fell, further cutbacks were necessary in the Department of Human Services. Although Barton Boyle, M.B.A., had been appointed director of administration for the Oklahoma Teaching Hospitals just 12 months previously, his $80 thousand a year

About half of the graduates in pharmacy go into retail drug sales; the others find jobs in research, hospital pharmacy, drug manufacture, and other specialties. (University of Oklahoma)

job was abolished in August of 1983. When he came to look at the position in the spring of 1982, he said:

> I was very, very impressed! That collection of hospitals represents a real asset to the State of Oklahoma. The facilities in the Memorial Hospital and the O'Donoghue are just as good as they could be any place in the country. Then, unemployment in Oklahoma was 3.9 percent and in Ohio [Boyle came from Ohio State University] it was 12 percent on its way to 17 percent. Oklahoma was going to have a $400 million surplus while Ohio was a billion dollars in the red. I saw here the hospitals running 50 percent of their bed capacity [all of the available beds were not open] and saw between eight and nine employees per [occupied] bed which had to be almost twice as many as in any other hospital in the world! I saw basically a total absence of managerial systems and thought, "Here is an opportunity to put in place some very elementary systems that would produce tremendous results for the institutions." As a result of those systems, I thought people would be very glad I was here and that would make possible even more changes which were going to be needed because of what was going to happen to the health care system.

According to Boyle, Mr. Rader had a plan in his mind for the hospitals. That was to consolidate them, eliminate duplication and begin to run them as a unit, a very large hospital that has multiple facilities. What they were working toward for almost two years was to create a quasi-corporate structure, with the executive chief of staff, a director of administration, a chief financial officer and an executive director of nursing. At the time Boyle was interviewed, they had just spent $11 million in acquisition of replacement and new equipment for those hospitals so in addition to good

Barton Boyle, M.B.A., was director of administration at the Oklahoma Teaching Hospitals only one year. (Department of Human Services)

physical facilities, the equipment was up-to-date and the next year's budget looked to be greater than 1982's. Boyle saw it as a tremendous opportunity and, in August, 1982, set out to analyze where all the people were:

> We had 8 or 9 per occupied bed and the upper quartile in teaching hospitals was 5.5 to 6.5.... That's the top! Before we really got that assessment made, the state economy began to turn down and we were forced to go through a reduction in force. We laid off 250 or 260 people. Food service was heavy; there was cafeteria service in all three hospitals, 24 hours a day. Hospitals haven't been able to afford that for ages, so we made substantial cuts in personnel.
>
> The staffing continued to be very high and that had to be attributed to the operation of three hospitals, many providing the same services; therefore duplication, redundancy. That was the next thing I wanted to address, to move on to the consolidation of activities. By November of 1982, though, Mr. Rader was talking retirement. With all of the uncertainty and almost antagonism directed toward the hospitals, there wasn't the leadership strength or position to pursue that consolidation.

Mr. Rader's retirement created a major vacuum in direction. Boyle said the director was fortunate that monies were available and he made sure they were available by maximizing federal programs. His retirement brought forward people who had disagreed with his philosophy and with decisions he had made. Everything was put on hold and there began a major effort just to hold the place together. Rader's idea of consolidation was developed about the time University Hospital was brought in, but the hospitals had a history and tradition and they had their own constituents. Boyle observed, "There is a significant reluctance on the part of the people within them to see a consolidation occur. The troops don't want it... They see a loss of identity, authority, turf." He continued:

Two things are under way. A peer review process involving people from [similar institutions in] other states coming in and looking at OTH, reviewing financing, organizational structure, mission, objectives, efficiency, staffing. My prediction is they'll suggest a corporate office with a strong leadership role and unification of the three institutions. Another thing going on is a performance audit to be done by a "big eight" [accounting and management consulting] firm. And I would predict out of those two reviews there will be support for the plan I came here to implement.[15]

Dr. Halverstadt talked about the cutbacks which were made during the period Henry Bellmon was director of DHS:

My staff and I were the authors of those reductions, the net result of five months of active attempt to control the budget, reduce expenditures and try to move the hospital budget down to whatever minimum level of support could be attained and still try to keep from injuring the programs, both service and educational. Most of the credit for the accomplishments goes to the finance officer, Mr. Gene Kozikoski, an extraordinarily able guy.

Kozikoski was given responsibility of director of administration as well as finance when Barton Boyle was terminated. Dr. Halverstadt himself resigned in mid-November:

I'd prefer to say I did not resign; I retired. Resignation implies to me an adversarial position with respect to a job, an unhappiness with it, which has nothing to do with why I stepped aside. I retired solely and simply because I needed to stand back and catch my breath. I'd been working at this challenge for almost ten years. Most of what I set out to help put in place was in place, moving in the right direction and maturing. From my standpoint, it was the right time to step back, take a breath and get my battery recharged.[16]

Owen Rennert, M.D., a pediatrician, was appointed interim chief of staff while a search committee began the process of seeking a replacement to head the teaching hospitals.

On the last Monday in November, 1983, Governor George Nigh opened a special session of the Okla-

Senator Marvin York. (Marvin York)

homa legislature with the plea to preserve the state's progress in education, roadbuilding and other services by adopting his proposed $654 million tax package. After months of enduring the worsening financial situation and hoping to get by without raising taxes, the governor decided to call a special session to deal with the financial crisis. Although the 1984 session would begin in just 34 days, he wanted new revenue to begin flowing into the state coffers as quickly as possible. He proposed increasing the state sales tax from two cents to four cents, removing the sales tax exemption from beer and cigarettes and increasing the excise tax on strong beer from $10 to $14 a barrel. In addition, he called for a 4.42 cent a gallon increase in the gasoline tax, with one cent each going to the cities and counties, running the total state tax up to 11 cents. Governor Nigh warned that saying no to his proposal would be saying no to the Central Expressway and the West Bypass in Oklahoma City and hundreds of other highway projects.

The Oklahoma Publishing Company launched a vigorous campaign against any tax increase, running front page editorials, encouraging readers to defeat the efforts of the "tax hogs" at the state capitol by putting pressure on their senators and representatives. The paper listed each one's telephone number. Thus, the running battle between George Nigh and Edward L. Gaylord, editor and publisher of the *Oklahoman* and *Times*, flared anew. The *Oklahoman* ran a picture of a black cowboy hat which somebody had placed on the

Speaker Jim Barker. (Jim Barker)

podium in the House of Representatives just before the governor arrived to open the special session. Governor Nigh had campaigned for reelection using the "good guy-white hat" theme.

Apparently, the lawmakers got the message from their constitutents. The special session was halted abruptly when the House adjourned *sine die* at 10:15 A. M. on Wednesday, November 30, after it was unable to get an agreement with the Senate for a 10-day recess to work on $63 million in budget cuts. No date

was set to resume. An avalanche of telephone calls to House members ran 10 to 1 against boosting revenues.

Senator Marvin York, president pro tempore, said, "We are headed for financial disaster the likes of which we haven't seen in years." He added that he had warned the public for 11 months of the pending financial crisis and said if it had been addressed sooner, it could have been handled much more cheaply. "Oklahoma must deal with the reality of a 16 percent budget cut."[17]

The governor reported that November tax collections, used for December spending, were running 26 percent, or $36 million, below the amount needed. House Speaker Jim Barker said committees would start to work immediately with plans for cutting spending. On December 14, 1983, President William Banowsky transmitted the bad news to the University Board of Regents. The $125 million state shortfall meant O.U. had to cut operations by 7.4 percent or $8 million in the remaining six months of the fiscal year, $5 million from the Norman campus and $3 million from the OUHSC. The University chose to furlough employees one day each month, beginning in December, a practice calculated to save $1,946,000 or about a fourth of the needed savings.

On this somber note, 1983 became history. It was almost as though the state entities in the Oklahoma Health Center were destined to run into a major financial hurricane every 11 years. Were the university, the Oklahoma Teaching Hospitals and the State Health Department organizations strong enough to weather this latest tempest?

CHAPTER 42
SURVIVAL: 1984

Clayton Rich, M.D., Provost. (University of Oklahoma)

As the Orwellian year of 1984 began, Big Brother was out of money— at least in Oklahoma. The recession had penetrated the Great Southwest and Oklahoma Health Center institutions dependent on state tax revenue were in trouble. The provost of the OUHSC, Dr. Clayton Rich, was worried:

In 1981 and 1982, it looked as if this campus was really on the move toward developing fine quality educational programs at the national level. The budget cutbacks have hurt that [progress] and the real question now is whether we're going to have a delay in that development or all of that opportunity is going to be lost. And that is a significant question.

In the late 1970s, when the educational system in Oklahoma was getting very substantial funding increases, this campus had budget increases that were just slightly above the rate of inflation and significantly below the average for the system as a whole. Salaries lagged the CPI [consumer price index] so that actual earnings dropped. Also, we lost almost $2 million in federal capitation grants as a result of a policy change and that money was not replaced. So that was a loss on top of rather meager increases in state support.

That all changed around in 1981 and 1982 and we were able to make up for some of the problems as well as make some very fine improvements in faculty devel-

opment. Unfortunately, about that time, the economy of the state failed and we had an absolute four percent cut in our budget last year [FY 1983]. We were able to deal with that, but this year [FY 1984] we are dealing with a second cut of an additional seven and a quarter percent. We are at a standstill and our faculty is becoming quite demoralized. Some are beginning to leave and more will if we can't stabilize our budget. So right now, we are very concerned about keeping the momentum of development in medicine and our other professional schools.[1]

The deanships in the colleges of nursing, pharmacy and public health, as well as the directorship in the department of pathology, were open. Search committees were ready to invite candidates to visit the OUHSC, but this process had been put on hold until some indication of the budget prospects for the next fiscal year were forthcoming from the legislature. The dean of the college of medicine, Charles McCall, M.D., agreed that it was "absolutely a critical time in the history of this college and this Center." He observed:

We have outstanding facilities, we've developed a core of outstanding faculty, we have leaders on a national scale. You can't retain that quality of physician-scientist when you don't know what the future is. We are trying to hold it together with the gains we've made, but the length of time until the state's economy picks up is critical. We'll be moving into a third year [of reduced resources] next year. In fact, the exodus had already started and the numbers will begin to rise exponentially if we are not able to give raises and expand programs.[2]

Although Lloyd Rader was no longer there and involved, he was concerned about the Health Sciences Center, a sentiment he expressed to Senator Marvin York and to House Speaker Jim Barker. "They're in more than trouble! They're going down the drain as fast as they can go. [The center] needs a little money and it needs management." He went on to say he liked the people out there but "the fact that you like somebody personally, that don't put any beans on the table, my friend." "This is a cold-blooded, funding proposition," he added, and pointed out. "The legislature must provide stable funding for the medical school, the dental school and the allied schools. Unless the medical staff unites in all three facilities [of the OTH] and presents their needs to the legislature, in two years you won't have a medical school. You'll have the Tulsa school, which will go into a four-year school, and Oral Roberts." Of course, Mr. Rader could not know that the ORU itself, including the City of Faith Hospital, would be caught in an economic crisis just six months later.[3]

On January 30, 1984, Governor Nigh signed legislation cutting state spending by $150 million for the current fiscal year ending June 30. It was the first action by the legislature since the 1984 session began. In the meantime, the solons were also trimming the tax package originally presented by the governor. Instead of a two cent increase in state sales tax, the legislature added a penny, increasing the tax to three cents. However, this one cent hike was temporary, authorized only until December 31, 1985—less than two years—during which time it was expected to generate $390 million. The bill was signed into law and became effective on February 15.[4]

About the same time, a 100-member Commission on the Reform of State Government, appointed by Governor Nigh on November 1, 1983, began its work. Headed by Walter Allison, a Bartlesville banker, the commission was asked to prepare specific long-range government reform recommendations by Novmber 1, 1984, so they could be included in the governor's budget package for 1985. While the governor and legislative leaders pledged support, they stopped short of offering any solid guarantee that any of the commission's recommendations would be implemented. Representative Cleta Deatherage was skeptical and for apparent good reason:

> Over the last four or five years in the political culture, we didn't have to do anything hard. But now we have to make hard decisions in order to keep the things we've got and to go forward and I'm not sure we're up to it—whether it's modernizing the machinery of state government or making choices, saying [for example] we can't have three state-funded medical schools. We have to make hard choices, just like a tough-nosed business person. We don't have any experience doing hard things and we're not particularly prone to raise strong political leaders in Oklahoma.
>
> We just keep asking [people to tell us what we ought to do] because we don't like what we hear. It's not so much we don't know what to do; it's that we don't want to do it. I don't think you can teach people enough about state government in a short period of time so they can give you good advice unless you are asking for specific information. We've paid for enough studies that are stacked in my files that if we just did what we know we

need to do—right now—we could make some major changes in modernizing state government. But that would require a commitment of resources to things that are not very sexy politically— like a whole new financial accounting system, which I worked on for several years. The Senate never could get particularly interested in it but we have documented it could save over $60 million a year in payroll costs alone! And that doesn't count purchasing, which is still done manually. We've got all the reports. All we need to do is *do it*.[5]

The studies of the Oklahoma Teaching Hospitals to which Barton Boyle referred were completed. On January 30, the performance audit by Ernst and Whinney (E & W), accounting and management consultants, went to the legislature, which had authorized this study and a general review of DHS the previous spring. The cost of both audits totaled a half million dollars, an indication of the lawmakers' concern. In addition to the Ernst and Whinney study of the OTH, a peer group from the University of Texas performed a limited review and made a report in November, 1983, and Arthur Young and Company reported findings regarding OTH's data systems, making three studies within a six-month period. Robert Fulton, DHS director, said, "I think the slowing down of the growth of overall expenditures at the hospitals and the decrease in the state subsidy came just in time. I think the reaction in the legislature would have been much more destructive to the future of the hospitals if we had let [those costs] go out of sight."

Briefly, the Ernst and Whinney report recommended improvement in planning, organization, information systems, and personnel policies. The consultants thought the Oklahoma Teaching Hospitals should better define, document and communicate its goals and objectives to people within and outside the institution, and develop a better planning process. The addition of experienced personnel to the administrative team was seen as essential. They recommended that the position of Executive Chief of Staff be split in two, adding a Chief Operating Officer (COO), the same position, then called Director of Administration, which had been eliminated six months previously.

E & W suggested that top DHS and OTH management challenge the effectiveness of the existing administrative team because people at the hospitals said more effective leadership and better management was needed. In addition, the consultants recommended an improved management information system and highly qualified people to run it. Moreover, they said personnel policies needed revision. Although OTH had higher starting salaries, other institutions in the area surpassed these pay scales in two years or so. Nursing personnel turnover, for example, was 26 percent in fiscal year 1982-1983 compared with a national average of 7 percent.

To implement these recommendations, Ernest and Whinney estimated an investment of $15 to $20 million a year would be needed, offset by probable savings in the range of $18.5 to $25.5 million a year as changes became effective. This meant a possible net savings of $3.5 to $5.5 million per year. Additionally, E & W urged DHS to act quickly because hospitals in the U.S. were at a critical stage as a result of new federal reimbursement methods, increased competition and greater resistance by consumers and employers to soaring health care costs.[6]

Meanwhile, a search committee appointed by DHS was looking for a new leader to head the Oklahoma Teaching Hospitals. Because it would take the better part of a year after Dr. Halverstadt retired to select his successor and for the new CEO to begin work, DHS contracted with George Kaludis Associates, a Nashville, Tennessee, consulting firm to provide interim management services. Mr. Fulton said, "They are strictly a 'bridge group,' helping Dr. Rennert in the short run. They supplied a chief operating officer and also some other management help." The consultants' fee, at $23,500 a month plus travel, could cost the department as much as $347 thousand.

On May 15, 1984, John Byrne, the administrator of Oklahoma Children's Memorial Hospital was asked by those consultants to resign. When he came in 1982, "It was a bit of a surprise to find out that administration was really fractioned around here. There wasn't a direct line except to Halverstadt or to Mr. Rader when he was still here. You really couldn't make your own decisions." Personnel, purchasing and supply, maintenance, nursing, admitting, dietary and the business office were all centralized functions over which the administrators in the three hospitals apparently had no jurisdiction. When asked what he could make decisions about, Byrne replied:

> Not much. There was a lot of paper work to sign. You had to sign off on all supplies and repair work. If you needed a light bulb changed, you had to make out a form and have it countersigned by the administrator before the maintenance people would change the bulb. Admitting is a separate function which does not report to me. Technically, I could not discipline an admitting employee if one of them made a goof or called a patient

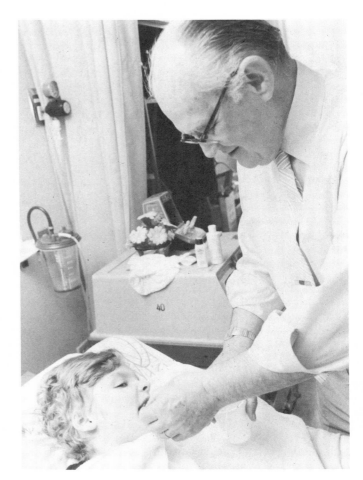

Administrator John Byrne…"shot down." (Department of Human Services)

a son of a bitch, which did happen on occasion. I had to go to a guy who is in the chain of command below me and ask him if he would discipline the employee who was impolite to a client.

I often felt like a eunuch because I was so limited in what I could do. Dr. Halverstadt kept saying to us, "Give us a little time and as we get organized, we are going to give the direction of the hospital back to the administrator and the medical director." He used to say he didn't want to make all those decisions; he wanted to get out from under all of that.

The morale started to slide right after I came here. When the Herman Smith people were here as consultants, they proposed that nursing be a separate unit altogether, free and distinct from the hospital, not reporting to the medical director or the administrator. Everybody from the ward clerk to the head nurse of the OTH is completely outside the realm of administration except that the head nurse reports to the executive chief of staff, now Dr. Rennert. Mr. Rader had used Herman Smith consultants since 1973. The major changes were made in nursing in 1982. A lot of the nurses had strong allegiance to Dorothy Jones, the former di-

Owen Rennert and Waiyee Chan had been studying copper metabolism since 1977. (University of Oklahoma)

rector of nursing. She was really a mother-figure to them and they related to her in many ways. At the same time, the criteria came down; no raises, no travel. That was about the time Bellmon came in.

There haven't been any raises and people are getting offers from other places. The anxiety level got higher and higher and now, on a scale of 10, I'd say the morale is about one or one and a half. There have been a lot of changes which have created a lot of anxiety and consternation among the medical staff and the department heads. When they [the consultant-managers] started having meetings to explain these changes to people, I think every department head in Children's Hospital ended up in my office, in tears or otherwise. I guess my mistake was, I came over and voiced all those concerns. That was probably why I was shot down. They finally said I didn't fit in with the management of the 1980s and 1990s.[7]

Dr. Rennert was quoted in the newspaper as saying, "When people don't work together in an optimal fashion, changes are necessary."[8]

Fulton talked further about the transition process:

E & W wanted some restructuring in the top management organization of the hospitals. We're going to work on that but not exactly the way they'd have done it if they were here to implement it. We advertised just for the chief executive officer. The search committee is reviewing candidates trained in medicine who have management experience and [those who are] lay administrators. We are getting a lot more applications in the second category. I'm hoping we can make a selection by the time the commission meets in May. [In mid-May, David Walters, a member of the commission and the search committee, said the field had been narrowed to about five candidates, only one of whom was a physician, and their visits to the OHC were just beginning. He estimated that a selection could not be made before July, 1984, and the person appointed to the position would not begin work until fall.] I think we should pick the top person and then adjust the organizational structure to take account of what we have. If we have a non-physician at the top, I suspect we'll still need a COO to do some things. But we'll also need a senior medical person in the structure. You do need a doctor, if not at the top, then very close to it.

Fulton thought the E & W report was so crammed with recommendations—240 or so—that there was a danger of getting bogged down trying to change too many things at once. His approach was to pick those "strategic management kinds of things" and make sure they took effective action on them. For example, the hospitals were described as critically underdeveloped in data management. The consultants said it was crucial to track costs, length of stay, dates of admission, charges, billings and a million other things which can be done by computers.

However, Fulton could see that a large, up-front investment of $12 to $20 million was unrealistic in the present climate. "We're just not going to have that kind of money," he said. "We are going to have to do the best we can without a big injection of money. We'll get some of those things done, but not quite with the speed and in the way Ernst and Whinney recommended." He added, "I think the state will find, over time, the investment in the audit was a good one."[9]

The addition of three floors to Oklahoma Memorial Hospital increased the capacity of the adult hospital to 438 beds. A process of moving into the new nursing units and remodeling the original ones began in early 1983 and was finished in the fall. By May, 1984, the hospital was operating 361 beds. Chief of staff Mark Everett said, "It is very unlikely additional beds will be opened until the state economy turns around. We could hire the nurses today—no problem." Everett continued:

In my view, the hospital must be placed on an effective, modern, cost accounting system and must be operated efficiently in order to survive, mainly because revenues [now] available from the sales tax will never permit the level of expenditure that was possible in the early 1970s. Priorities must be set and the hospital will have to operate as a prudent business.

The real problem is: will they [the OTH] be able to be operate efficiently enough to be a full, tertiary care teaching hospital and still care for the large numbers of indigents they presently do? There are many forces at work in this community around which the fundamental concept is that all indigent care will end up in these hospitals because indigent care is very expensive and unprofitable. This is a socio political problem, not a medical one. The county, the state, the legislature and the political and business leaders must make a decision as to the state's responsibility for indigent care—who's going to pay for it. If the decision is that these hospitals have that responsibility, then some other method of financing will have to be looked at. In my view, that would be a very unwise solution because we have built a very expensive facility designed to be a teaching hospital, not one designed to be an indigent care facility.[10]

After the state sales tax increase became law in mid-February, Governor Nigh immediately set about to lobby for a 3.42 cents per gallon increase in the state gasoline tax, down a penny from his original proposal. This would hike the tax to 10 cents a gallon. While it would not help Oklahoma Health Center institutions directly because this added revenue was earmarked for roads and bridges, it would decrease the pressure to fund transportation needs from the general revenues shared by higher education. Additionally, the gasoline tax would help assure completion of the Central Expressway which would one day serve the health campus. However, in Representative Bill Willis' opinion, there was never much doubt that the state would somehow find a dollar to match every nine dollars the federal government had already approved and allocated to this project.

In the legislature, Governor Nigh's gas tax proposal was reduced yet another penny a gallon and passed with an emergency clause so collection could begin as soon as the governor signed the bill on April 16. The measure was expected to pump an additional $48 million a year into road and bridge-building activities. Still, the taxing process was not finished, despite vigorous opposition by the local press. The third part of the governor's tax package involved additional levies on 3.2 percent beer, cigarettes and alcohol, the so-called "sin tax." It was calculated these increases would raise another $28 million for the state, $16 million of which would go to the Department of Human Services. The legislature passed this bill and Governor Nigh signed it on April 18, 1984.[11]

Would these state revenue improvements be sufficient to sustain the progress of the University of Oklahoma, particularly the OUHSC? President Banowsky did not think so:

The current budget crunch has been a *serious* blow, not only to the actual quality of the medical college and the other faculties here but perhaps even moreso to the intangible spirit and morale of the place. It's been a terrific setback. It comes after years of great progress when one of the things we were accomplishing was a sense of future....that it is inevitable that Oklahoma's time has come. Now, we have raised a serious question in the minds of a lot of people. Were those few years a mere abberation? Are we going back now to business as usual with a kind of mediocrity in Oklahoma? I think at this very moment, the jury is out, people are wondering and it is a very sensitive, serious time for the Health Sciences Center.

A turnaround will come, but we entered this thing in FY 1983 and FY 1984 is behind us, so that's two years. We are going into FY 1985; it's going to be flat, at best. Because this one cent sales tax is a year and a half proposition, it's going to go off in the middle of FY 1986, which at this date is projected to be an even more difficult year than FY 1985. That's four long, hard years...down and then flat. In the forseeable future, through FY 1986, there's no improvement. That's unfortunate.[12]

While the Oklahoma economy was gradually recovering, it was Representative Bill Willis' view that:

We shirked our responsibility when we made the sales tax a temporary thing. We postponed making a decision about the future direction of Oklahoma. We voted to hold things still at a lower level than we have had in the past when all it would have taken was a little more political courage to make it a permanent tax. That is not to say we are not going to have to raise taxes in other sectors because the increase in the sales tax is not a total cure, by any means.

[The level of government services] depends almost entirely on the oil business. I can't see enough economic growth in Oklahoma in the near term, at least, that would sustain us at a level of the more progressive states. We just don't have the industry here to do it. The price of oil is going to determine our future and that's a sad situation.

Mr. Willis commented on the propensity of the legislature to spend all of the available money every year. The idea of setting aside a $63 million contingency fund for the lean years was rejected by a vote of the people at the previous election. Apparently, the legislature has the authority to appropriate money into a contingency fund anyway but he explained why that probably would not happen. "You see, we have a revolving membership and the experience of those [who were here] in the past doesn't carry over to the new members. You can tell them how it was, but they didn't experience it. [When times get better], we'll have new members here, all of the pressure groups will be calling for more money, the legislature will respond, and we'll spend it all!"[13]

CHAPTER 43

THE DOCTOR QUESTION: 1984

If Dr. James L. Dennis's statement, "Health care is trained people at work," was correct, the success of his dream was not in the creation of the Oklahoma Health Center but in the improvement of health care achieved by the health manpower the OHC produced. The supply and distribution of physicians in the state was at least one measurement of the return on the public investment in the health campus. For such improvement in health care to be effective, there had to be enough doctors readily accessible to the people who needed them.

Whether or not in 1984 there was a surplus of physicians in Oklahoma was a matter of some debate. Whether or not there would be a surplus of doctors in the years beyond, as projected by Hardy's demand study and the GMENAC report, was also a matter of conjecture and opinion. Dr. Tom Lynn said:

I believe the philosophy of the GMENAC report. You can probably find some numbers to quibble with, some things they didn't take into consideration, [such as] the influence of women, the numbers of women entering medicine and how many hours a day or week they're going to practice. Also, the influence of new technology, allied health professionals, things like that. In a general sort of way, yes, I believe there will be a surplus of physicians and in fact already is a surplus of physicians.

I bought Hardy's study in 1973, pretty well agreed with it. I did a private study with Bob Bird which indicated that the establishment of additional educational resources for undergraduate students wasn't appropriate and what we ought to be doing was establishing residency positions.

The doctors in private practice see the Health Sciences Center physician faculty increasingly in competition with them from the standpoint of doing the sophisticated procedures. That competition is increasing but I think most of the physicians...the ones who count...still feel the practice of medicine in Oklahoma City is better off for having the medical school here.[1]

C.S. Lewis, Jr., M.D., et al, writing in the *Oklahoma State Medical Association Journal* in 1983, concluded:

How many physicians are enough and how many are too many is not an easy question to answer. The GMENAC report indicated that the ideal physician-population ratio in the United States would be 191 physicians per 100,000 population. This is assuming that all physicians would continue to produce the same amount of care as before. Current trends among younger physicians indicate that the productivity per physician is decreasing. The Carnegie report in 1970 indicated that more than 200 physicians per 100,000 population is too many.

It would appear that the projected figures for Oklahoma of 181 physicians per 100,000 population by 1990 is a satisfactory target.

STATE & NATIONAL PHYSICIAN:POPULATION RATIO

USA

	Active Physicians M.D. — D.O.	Population	Physicians per 100,000 population
1960	259,000	185,370,000	140
1970	323,200	204,878,000	157
1980	447,470	226,504,825	197
1990	536,000	244,000,000	220

Oklahoma

1960	2,392	2,328,284	103
1970	2,923	2,559,463	114
1980	4,238	3,025,290	140
1990	6,508	3,575,893	182

If the current trends continue, the ratio of DO physicians to MD physicians in Oklahoma will increase significantly. In 1982 approximately 13% of the physicians in the state of Oklahoma were DOs. If the current class sizes continue another decade or two, approximately 30% of practicing physicians in Oklahoma will be DOs.

The steps taken by the state legislature of Oklahoma, the State Regents for Higher Education, and the medical education institutions of Oklahoma have been successful in increasing the number of physicians practicing in Oklahoma in total and in rural areas and these projections appear to be "on target" to meet the needs of the state of Oklahoma in 1990. The need for an increased number of physicians in the United States was recognized in 1959 and its implications for Oklahoma pointed out in 1969. Programs were implemented to increase the number of graduates by expanding the class size at the University of Oklahoma Health Sciences Center, and the formation of the University of Oklahoma Tulsa Medical College and the Oklahoma College of Osteopathic Medicine and Surgery. The Oklahoma Physician Manpower Training Commission programs to increase postgraduate medical education opportunities in Oklahoma and its scholarship programs have been accompanied by a significant increase in the num-

OSMA *executive director David Bickham. (Oklahoma State Medical Association)*

ber of physicians in communities of all sizes in Oklahoma including small rural communities. The projected physician-population ratio in Oklahoma in 1990 of 181 physicians per 100,000 population appears to be a satisfactory goal compared with the national goal of 191 physicians per 100,000 population. The current programs and class sizes of the medical schools should be continued at their present size.[2]

In November, 1981, the Study Committee on Medical Education of the Tulsa County Medical Society recommended, "The total size of the entering classes of medical schools in Oklahoma should not be increased above their present levels." The committee further suggested continuing study of physician manpower, particularly as to the "impact of the number of graduates on physician manpower requirements in Tulsa County." The Society elected 108 new members in 1982 and 70 in 1983. There was a net gain of 36 members in 1983 bringing the total membership in active practice to 858. While the committee recommended "Oklahoma's manpower needs in relation to the size of entering classes at the Tulsa medical schools should be evaluated at the end of two years, or in 1983," this had not been accomplished by the end of March, 1984.[3]

Contrary to Dr. Lewis's idea that the medical education system in Oklahoma was "on target," the Oklahoma State Medical Association (OSMA) was more than a little worried about the increasing supply of doctors in the state. David Bickham, executive director of the Association, said:

There has been a growing concern for the past 10 years [since 1974] that's become more acute in the past five years. Because of the increasing number of graduates, plus the influx of foreign medical graduates [FMGs] into the state, Oklahoma was fast becoming saturated with physicians. We'd been talking about it a long time, so two years ago [1982] we established a committee to get started [on this problem]. The deans of all the medical schools are on our committee, including Oral Roberts and the osteopathic school.

I'm still not convinced we *do* have an abundance of physicians. By the end of the next decade, if we continue in the same way we're going today, then I would probably agree we have too many. But there are a number of things which take me to this position. Number one, I don't have telephone calls from physicians saying they're having a difficult time establishing their practice. We *do* have larger numbers of physicians, particularly specialists, who are moving out of the metropolitan areas into the regional and rural areas. We don't have any hard evidence that physicians are having a hard time making a living.

Things are different in other states, though. The things people in Oregon were talking about 10 years ago are the things we're talking about today. Now, Oregon really *does* have a problem, an oversupply of physicians and some of their members are having a very difficult time making a living. The president of the AMA [Frank Jirka, M.D.] said when he first got started in organized medicine 20 years ago, when he planned to leave town, he'd have to search for somebody to cover his practice and they'd all bitch and groan. Now, he gets telephone calls from his urology colleagues who say they'd be glad to cover for him when he's out of town and, if necessary, they'd even come over to his office. That's an indication of how things have changed.[4]

Another indication of the competition in other cities was highlighted in a March 13, 1984 *Wall Street Journal* article headlined "Ads for Plastic Surgery Stir Medical Feud." By investing in a $100 thousand-a-year television ad campaign, a Milwaukee, Wisconsin plastic surgeon and his three partners in the Clinic for Cosmetic Surgery doubled referrals, increased operations 58 percent and generated a list of 110 people waiting for consultation. Their colleagues in the American Society of Plastic and Reconstructive Surgery were outraged, maintaining, "Plastic surgery should be sought out, not sold." But it was apparent the Clinic had taken the GMENAC forecast seriously:

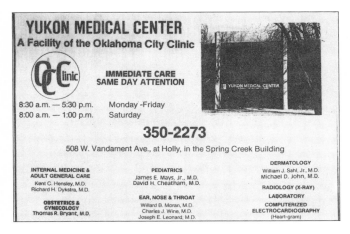

YUKON MEDICAL CENTER
A Facility of the Oklahoma City Clinic

OC Clinic

IMMEDIATE CARE
SAME DAY ATTENTION

8:30 a.m. — 5:30 p.m.   Monday -Friday
8:00 a.m. — 1:00 p.m.   Saturday

350-2273

508 W. Vandament Ave., at Holly, in the Spring Creek Building

INTERNAL MEDICINE &
ADULT GENERAL CARE
Kent C. Hensley, M.D.
Richard H. Dykstra, M.D.

OBSTETRICS &
GYNECOLOGY
Thomas R. Bryant, M.D.

PEDIATRICS
James E. Mays, Jr., M.D.
David H. Cheatham, M.D.

EAR, NOSE & THROAT
Willard B. Moran, M.D.
Charles J. Wine, M.D.
Joseph E. Leonard, M.D.

DERMATOLOGY
William J. Sahl, Jr., M.D.
Michael D. John, M.D.

RADIOLOGY (X-RAY)
LABORATORY
COMPUTERIZED
ELECTROCARDIOGRAPHY
(Heart-gram)

One of the ads for the new Yukon branch of the Oklahoma City Clinic. (Oklahoma City Clinic)

by 1990, there will be 45 percent more plastic surgeons than are needed.

However, the competition was not confined to other areas of the country. The Oklahoma City Clinic, which operated a branch in Edmond and Midwest City, employed a director of marketing in 1982. Randy Mindrup's job was to assess the needs of people in the community, determine the feasibility of the Oklahoma City Clinic providing services, and then tell people how to obtain those services. In 1984, when the clinic opened another branch in Yukon, Oklahoma, with an internist and an ob/gyn specialist, large display ads in the *Daily Oklahoman/Times* announced they were seeing patients. The doctors' pictures were shown, the clinic telephone number was prominently displayed and the availability of "immediate care" was featured in bold, capital letters. During the year, the Oklahoma City Clinic was building a new facility for its branch in Midwest City and Wayne Coventon, executive director, said it may establish additional outlying clinics if community need becomes apparent.[5]

David Bickham continued:

I think there is a conceived attitude among Oklahoma physicians. The competition is keener, there's no question about it. We've seen expansion of the osteopathic profession in this state in unusual proportions. In certain areas, up around Enid, for example, where they didn't used to have a problem with osteopaths, they now have a problem. They have osteopathic specialists in Enid and the rural osteopaths are referring patients to their colleagues where they used to refer to the M.D.s.

The number of FMGs is having an impact on the private physicians' practice. We were permitting FMGs to come into this country for post doctoral training and issuing them a visa with no time limit. A lot of them went for American citizenship. Now, though, under a law

passed in 1978, they're issued just a two-year visa and are returning home.

One of the most hotly debated issues in American medicine today is the American who attends a foreign medical school. Some of these are non-accredited, proprietary schools in Granada and elsewhere. By and large, these are students who could not get into American schools. Obviously, then, they want to come home [when they complete their medical education], so it's a real serious problem and I don't know how we are going to deal with it.

Our committee came to the conclusion we should reduce the entering classes of all the medical schools in the state—public and private, M.D. and D.O.—by 15 percent. That reduction would be evaluated each year. [With the annual production at 268 graduates, the output would thus decrease by about 40.] There was considerable debate about recommending a 10 percent reduction annually for five years but that idea was not approved by the board of trustees. [This would have reduced the number of graduates by 108 to 160.] We went to the State Regents for Higher Education which can affect all of the state-supported schools. That would then leave only Oral Roberts, which takes in about 40 students each year. The request for an enrollment study has been made to the Regents and been approved. They will appoint a multi discipline committee, I'm sure, but they won't have to go through the same data-gathering process that we went through [in order to verify the OSMA study and take action].[6]

Dr. Rainey Williams agreed with the GMENAC report:

...In the sense there are far too many people in the medical pipeline. I tend to think, regardless of the criticism of its methodology, its conclusions [are correct]; that there are or there are going to be too many physicians and the overage will become much worse.

We think...and John Schilling and I used to talk about this...that the state of Oklahoma needs six general surgeons per year to keep up the current ratio. So, we finish four chiefs in general surgery each year and every year at least one of those goes into thoracic surgery, which leaves three general surgeons [which must come] from other sources. My thought is that's not overproduction and we do not need to cut back.

I don't think there's any question there's increased competition and I'm told that, particularly in Tulsa, there's actually been a demonstrable decline in income level for general surgeons but I've not heard that about Oklahoma City. I still have a number of requests from physicians for general surgeons for very desirable communities in Oklahoma.

The supply of physicians is a matter of enormous concern to me and it is also a very sensitive issue. We are going to have to decrease the number of students

Chairman of Surgery Rainey Williams recommends closing one of the colleges of medicine in Oklahoma. (University of Oklahoma)

graduated from medical institutions in Oklahoma…and across the country. Basically, there are two ways to do it. One is reduce the class size in the several schools. Unfortunately, the legislature is going to equate that with reducing cost. If you just cut the number of students at all campuses 10 or 15 percent, you won't save any money at all. So I'm hoping somebody will lead in saying what we need to do is close institutions…and that *will* save money. It seems to me it is very rational and it's almost exactly the right numbers to close first the School of Osteopathy and perhaps follow that with the branch [Tulsa Medical College]. That'll save money![7]

Dean McCall took the opposite view about possible closing of the Tulsa Medical College:

I don't think there's any option that's going to happen. It does not deal with political reality. I think it is wrong to assume that if the Tulsa campus were closed, the money [spent there] would come to this campus.

The Tulsa College, as a clinical branch of the College of Medicine, is a *quality*, community-based, primary care-oriented institution which fulfills its mission as well as any clinical branch I know. As far as I'm concerned, what we do is use our resources effectively and efficiently and the only way this state loses is if it doesn't get quality physicians.

We are looking at all of the reports on manpower production; we are monitoring the distribution numbers and will continue to do so. We have joined with a special task force of the State Medical Association and

this faculty has recommended that the State Regents study the manpower needs of Oklahoma and make a recommendation state-wide. We are prepared to be a part of a pro rata reduction of the entering class as it comes out of that study.

There is an increase in the number of physicians in the state. In 1982, of 220 newly licensed physicians in the state, 70 were graduates of the University of Oklahoma and the others were from out-of-state. Many of those were U.S. citizen graduates of unaccredited [foreign] medical schools. Decreasing the class in the College of Medicine is only one factor. We are going to have to be looking at a change in demographics, the aging population, technology, the time spent delivering care…. It is so complex! It is an important problem and we need a clear strategy. We are monitoring it and we think this study (by the State Regents) is the right approach.[8]

Dr. James A. Merrill said in September, 1983:

I'm sure there is a surplus of doctors in the United States. There is a surplus of obstetricians in Oklahoma City. There probably isn't yet a surplus in the state but it's getting close.[9]

The GMENAC Report projected a surplus of 10,450 obstetrics and gynecology specialists by 1990 if no changes were made in the medical education system. Dr. Merrill commented on his approach:

While I was the chairman of the department, I was very careful not to increase the size of the house staff. We did look at the needs of the state and did, in fact, determine that the number of residents we were finishing each year was quite sufficient to meet those needs as near as we could determine. But I limited the size largely by certain patient populations I thought were necessary for teaching, mostly gynecology patients. The new chairman has, right off the bat, started to increase the size of the house staff and wants to increase it more. Young people tend to still believe that big is better and you have to go through the battles over a number of years to finally learn that's not necessarily so. That's what Stewart Wolf was talking about. He knew [that] a long time ago. Sometimes big is worse.[10]

The medical educators in the United States were caught in a dilemma. Few deans wanted to cut back the size of their program and almost none would volunteer to close down their school of medicine. Although many agreed with the trend shown in the GMENAC Report, they faced the risk of reduced financial support if they initated a cutback in the entering class. Yet they were aware that a surplus of doctors was not the entire answer to the dual prob-

Ralph Morgan headed the Physician Manpower Training Commission whose charge was to get doctors out into the small towns of Oklahoma. (Oklahoma Physician Manpower Training Commission)

lems of physician maldistribution and the rising cost of medical care. Dr. Mark Everett observed:

> Oklahoma definitely does not need three medical schools; that was purely political. There is probably not a surplus of doctors in Oklahoma at this moment but there undoubtedly will be within 10 years. There are many accurate conclusions in the GMENAC Report. The College of Medicine and its admission board has felt for the last three years, at least, that the size of the entering class should be reduced. It is quite clear that is a political, not a medical decision. The legislature sets the size of the medical school class. We have recommended a reduction to the State Regents for two years.
>
> The College of Medicine Branch was put in Tulsa as a counterbalance to the expansion of the osteopaths in that part of the state, which was an enormous threat to the physicians. Until you do something about *both* of those colleges, you can't do anything about either of them. It is not an issue of how many doctors [Oklahoma needs]; it is an issue of whether osteopaths or M.D.s are predominent in eastern Oklahoma. It is a *very* sensitive issue. The second issue is: the legislators like to have a big medical school class because they get less complaints about people who didn't get into medical school.[11]

The Physician Manpower Training Commission (PMTC) was created in 1975, well before there was local recognition that perhaps America was headed for a surplus of doctors. One purpose of PMTC was to support rotating interships for D.O.s and residencies for M.D.s. According to the Commission director, Ralph Morgan, D.O.s have post-doctoral training comparable to that which M.D.s had 20 or 30 years ago. Ninety percent of the D.O.s who graduate from the college in Tulsa take only a one-year internship, but most M.D.s now have at least a three-year residency. The Commission wanted to assure, through financial aid and encouragement, there would be enough post-doctoral positions in Oklahoma to accomodate the 268 M.D.s and D.O.s who graduate from Oklahoma medical colleges. This goal was achieved. Since the GMENAC Report was published, the number of M.D. residents in training in Oklahoma increased 22 percent, from 552 to 645. This better accommodated the Oklahoma graduates who were already in the pipeline, but of course it did nothing to mitigate the threatening nationwide surplus of doctors.[12]

In 1984, there was no real consensus about the supply of physicians. Whether or not people perceived a surplus of physicians depended on who they were, where they lived and what they expected insofar as health services were concerned.

Dr. Merrill was highly skeptical that the anticipated surplus of physicians would do much to improve the distribution of medical manpower:

> I have a feeling it's just going to be so dreadfully difficult to resolve the problem of maldistribution of doctors. I think before you see very many doctors leaving large, metropolitan areas, you're going to see them accept a lower income. I suppose they'll get to an income where they'll chuck it but I think they'll take a lower income for a considerable period of time before they go out into a small town where they'll be the only obstetrician…nobody to talk to. I don't think that's going to force a better distribution of doctors.[13]

But it was Representative Bill Willis's opinion that a surplus of physicians in Oklahoma was well nigh impossible:

> I would be opposed, myself, to a cutback in enrollment [in Oklahoma's medical schools]. A surplus of practicing physicians is a matter of judgment. In *my* judgment, we don't have a surplus. In fact, I couldn't foresee the day when we'd have a surplus.

When asked if he thought an increased supply of doctors would help control the cost of medical care, Willis replied:

> I certainly do. That's why I can't see a surplus. I think that a little competition might be a good thing. We have it in the other professions. Look at the legal profession.[14]

The migration of doctors into Oklahoma towns of

5,000 population or less during the 10 years between 1973 and 1982 was not overwhelming. Despite the Physician Manpower Training Commission's efforts to encourage doctors to practice in small communities, which it did by providing scholarships for medical students who would agree to practice in communities of 7,500 or less, the 531 Oklahoma communities of 5,000 or less had a *net* gain of only 44 doctors. Of these, 29 were D.O.s and 15 were M.D.s. There was an increase of 1702 licensed physicians in the state during that decade which meant that 2.6 percent of the gains were in towns of 5,000 or less. Al Donnell, who had become administrator of the Duncan Regional Hospital, was speaking of the PMTC when he said:

> They really haven't helped us at all. We're getting a lot of foreign medical graduates. We can't get U.S. medical school graduates to come to Duncan…. Their wives won't come or whatever…and we're having a terrible time in Waurika. They helped an internist finish his residency last spring, got him all the way through medical school. He came down there, stayed six months and bought his way out…went to the V.A. in Oklahoma City.
>
> I'm convinced of this as sure as I'm sittin' here: we can help make Waurika successful. It has 6,000 people, just 22 miles south, a nice, 35-bed hospital. We can help them get some doctors who will work here and work there, let the hospital keep its autonomy and help them with their services. I think that's the only way small hospitals can survive.[15]

As Donald "Don" Phelps, administrator of the Jefferson County Hospital reported, Waurika had experienced great difficulty recruiting physicians. The one D.O. sponsored by PMTC stayed three years and moved to Montana but none of the four M.D.s, to which the community contributed about $10 thousand each, practiced in Waurika long enough to complete their commitment. They will pay back their loans but that does not solve the problem of staffing the hospital. Despite offers of free rent for a year in a clinic building adjacent to the hospital, Waurika could not attract the number of primary physicians Don Phelps believes the community needs.[16]

Frosty Troy, as a lay observer, was favorably impressed by the PMTC program:

> One of the reasons the M.D. figures [M.D.s practicing in smaller communities] started coming up was because the legislature adopted a new loan program wherein they would actually put students through med school if they would then go into practice in rural Oklahoma. Some of the communities, four or five of them, also

adopted medical students, saying, "If you'll go, we'll pay your way through." I know one young man who did that, went back to a small town and loves it there. He otherwise was not going to do that.[17]

While physicians were not thronging to the rural areas, the stick of increased competition and the carrot of state scholarships were having their influence. As of November 1, 1983, 147 students had been enrolled in the Rural Scholarship Program; 54 physicians had returned to a rural community (defined by PMTC as 7,500 or fewer people) to render obligated service; and 25 scholarship recipients were repaying loans in lieu of their obligated service.

PMTC also had a scholarship matching program so leaders in rural Oklahoma communities up to 10 thousand population would have an incentive to help attract physicians. If the community paid up to $5 thousand a year to a medical student, the state would match that amount. The student had to agree to practice in that community one year for every $10 thousand he or she received, with a minimum obligation for two years before any loan forgiveness was granted. In this program, as of November 1, 1983, 90 individuals had enrolled, 38 were honoring their obligated service commitment and 16 were repaying loans in lieu of obligated service.[18]

It is highly doubtful that 92 doctors would have settled in rural communities without the financial incentives of the PMTC scholarship program. Whether this result was worth the investment of $1,136,340 in tax money, $12,351 per doctor, was a matter of opinion. The tuition medical students paid in 1983 covered only 7.14 percent of the cost of their education so by the time they graduated, each had already been subsidized by $104 thousand. In view of this large subsidy of the medical student's education by the taxpaying public, some saw this as "socializing the cost and privatizing the profit" of the medical profession.[19] The president of the university, William S. Banowsky, Ph.D., lamented the kind of encouragement students get to enter medicine:

> Frankly, one of the problems in the society is that the best and brightest of our students tend to be encouraged by teachers and others to go into medicine based frequently on materialistic rewards. We get away from the traditional view of medicine as one of the helping professions. You know, the four helping professions, traditionally, were the ministry, teaching, law and medicine. You can hardly convince any American that lawyers are in a helping profession but that's what they started out to be. We're training 33 thousand new law-

"And Not Enough of You Know Who!" (The Oklahoman)

President Bill Banowsky buttonholes the governor. (University of Oklahoma)

yers a year in the United States of America. We're the most litigious society in the history of the world, with everybody suing everybody else and one has to ask whether or not we're overdoing it. I suspect that we are.

School teachers, and I sympathize with their predicament, are so under-appreciated that they've unionized almost as fiercely as truckers. They give up something in doing that. I hate to see this great calling of healer lose that spirit of altruism. I guess the preachers are next and many of those on television seem to be doing pretty well as fundraisers.

But it's related to this whole question of how many [physicians] you train. If we were training them as servants, as healers, as people who went out to help wherever they could, with only a secondary concern for material reward, then one has to ask whether in fact we can train too many. If on the other hand, we're training them to live in the best neighborhoods, in our biggest cities, to drive the nicest cars, and have the most creative tax shelters for the highest incomes, then a state institution like this one, supported by the taxpayers, needs to ask, "What kind of a bargain is it for this handful of people who finally get to be admitted into this medical college?" I'm not sure the taxpayers are fully aware of how much they subsidize medical students. I think we ought to be highly responsive to real-world conditions—the number of people we train in this medical college and how we train them. The university needs to tailor its programs to the market for its graduates and I think we're slow getting there.[20]

The Physician Manpower Training Commission is subject to periodic review under the "sunset law" which requires that state agencies justify their activities in order to qualify for further funding. The next such review of PMTC is scheduled for 1988. It was Ralph Morgan's personal opinion that the distribution of physicians in the state would be so improved by that time that the scholarship program would no longer be necessary.[21]

Certainly the emphasis on educating primary care physicians had increased dramatically since Dr. Lienke began with three family practice residents in 1968. In 1984, 15 percent of the post-doctoral training positions were in family practice and 43 percent were in other primary care disciplines including internal medicine, pediatrics and obstetrics/gynecology, so these four specialties composed 58 percent of the residencies offered by the University of Oklahoma. All of the internships offered by the College of Osteopathy prepared the D.O.s for primary care.

What effect the production of physician manpower will have on the distribution and cost of medical care may not be known for several years until the profession and the population adjust to new ratios of supply.

CHAPTER 44
THE COST QUESTION: 1984

"Terrible," Dean Chrislip answered when asked about how the high cost of health care made him feel. As a layman linked to the development of the Oklahoma Health Center, Chrislip had been a long-time observer of the trends in health services. He explained what he was doing to hold down his personal medical cost:

I'm trying my best to take a page out of Mr. [E.K.] Gaylord's book. When he got to be about 65 and the doctors kept telling him all these terrible things, he started reading up himself and decided maybe he could take care of himself if he looked after the way he ordered his life, the way he ate, the way he exercised and the way he slept. [Mr. Gaylord was 101 years old when he died.] I've just got to stay away from these guys [physicians] if I can.

I don't know where we went wrong but in the overall concept we probably went wrong in Medicare and Medicaid and the administration thereof. I must say I was delighted to see [Henry] Bellmon get interested in DHS because we had gone overboard on some of the things we were doing. I'm really baffled by it; it's beyond my ability to imagine how we can do something about it. I think a lot of the costs that are out of control relate to elective things. It may be that people were not being properly served but now they are being overly served.[1]

Mr. Bellmon was in a position to do something about the cost of care at DHS and the Oklahoma Teaching Hospitals. He wanted to contain the cost of hospitalizing Medicaid patients, a cost which had spiraled upward 350 percent between 1974 and 1982:

We filed a plan with the federal government that limits the cost escalation of health care delivery in the state so far as DHS reimbursement is concerned. It was challenged in the court. Prior to that time, the cost to DHS of health services for our clients was going up almost at the rate of 20 percent a year, which is six or seven times the rate of current inflation.

I was on the board of a hospital before I came to DHS and our costs were going up 28 percent a year. When we had a meeting of the board, I would call it to the administrator's attention. "Look, you keep letting costs rise at this rate [and] you're going to drive our customers away." His answer was that his costs were not paid by the customers but by the third-party payors; the customers don't know and they really don't care. Well,

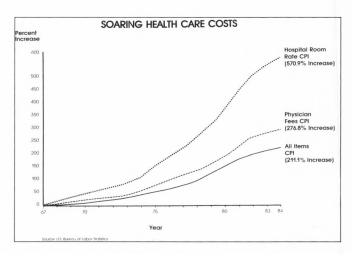

(U.S. Bureau of Labor Statistics)

that is not true. The customers *do* know. It's reflected in the insurance rate they pay and certainly, DHS knows.

We couldn't afford to allow that kind of loose management to continue. The system must become more efficiently managed and people in charge of operations are going to have to become cost-conscious. I think it is one of the most pressing problems we face for our citizens.[2]

In 1984, many people in America believed that health care costs were indeed out of control when 10.5 percent of the gross national product went to pay for health services. The situation had developed during a period of 55 years. In 1929, Dr. Justin Kimball at Baylor University Medical School in Dallas, Texas, got the notion that insurance protection against the cost of being sick might be a pretty good idea. After all, nobody could forecast who would become ill and when that happened, the doctor and hospital bills were often an unexpected and burdensome expense. With insurance, people could pay a little at a time and if they did get sick, they would be protected. The good doctor told a group of school teachers that in exchange for periodic payments, up front, the Baylor University Hospital would provide whatever hospital care they should happen to need. Thus, Blue Cross hospital insurance and later, Blue Shield medical protection began and the whole system of payment for health care changed.[3]

People who bought health insurance no longer worried about the cost of being sick. It was like fire insurance—with one important difference. Not everybody's house burns down but, sooner or later, everybody gets sick and needs health care. What was labeled and generally thought of as insurance was really the *prepayment* of the cost of inevitable illness. Of course, some people enjoy brimming good health and others need to use the health care system frequently so, in that respect, health coverage had the characteristic of true insurance.

With the financial worry removed from illness, the incentive to get the most for each health care dollar vanished. While the consumer forgot about how much health care cost, the provider quickly capitalized on that lapse of memory. As more and more people obtained insurance, hospitals and doctors, paid on a fee-for-service basis, had little reason to limit services. The insurors, also known as "third parties," did not greatly concern themselves with the amount of the fee charged for each service because they merely passed the increases along to their policyholders in the form of higher premiums. In the early days of prepayment, the cost of health care was not significant. Even by the early 1950s, hospital bills averaged less than $25 a day.

The health insurance idea appeared so beneficial that the politicians thought everybody should have this protection and, as previously described, there were great efforts to pass national health insurance. While these were unsuccessful, health insurance for retired people—Medicare—did become effective in July, 1966. Increasingly, the elements essential for runaway costs came together. For the patient, health care became a desirable, indeed, an essential service for which the bill was already paid. Often the insurance premium was paid by the employer or government, which meant the patient had no out-of-pocket expense. For the hospital, the system meant each institution could buy the latest and best in technology and personnel and pass the costs along to the third parties. For the physician, assured payment meant he did not have to limit the services he provided his patients and thus he could enhance their prognosis and his own reputation. In addition, by gradually increasing the fees charged insurance companies and government for each service, the doctor could improve his personal income. What could be better?

In the interim, as medical technology and professional expertise improved, health care became an increasingly desirable commodity. It came to be regarded as a right, rather than a privilege. Sick people expected physicians to cure them and with increasing frequency, applied medical science was able to do just

that. Renal dialysis, CAT scans, organ transplants, cardiac bypass surgery, antibiotics, vaccines, grafts, radiation therapy, artificial joints...the whole array of diagnostic and treatment services became absolutely marvelous—and absolutely, marvelously expensive. About the time Jim Dennis arrived in Oklahoma, Americans were spending $41.7 billion a year on health care, 6.5 percent of the gross national product, or an average of $211 a person. In 1982, public and private expenditures for health care had ballooned to $322.4 billion a year, 10.5 percent of the GNP or $1,365 per person. Two years later, in 1984, America was spending a billion dollars a day on health care. In 1985, Oklahomans were expected to spend, or have spent for them by government, an average of $1,842 per person per year. The Oklahoma Health Planning Commission forecast that the annual per capita figure for health services in the Sooner state would jump to $3,000 by the year 1990.[4]

Were the people of America getting their money's worth? It is quite impossible to place a monetary value on health so the answer to that question remains a personal judgment. For whatever reasons, there was no question that Americans as a group were getting healthier and living longer. Deaths from the number one killer, heart disease, had fallen 25 percent since 1970. The cure rate of cancer in children had advanced from essentially zero to 50 percent. Life expectancy had reached an average of 74.5 years in 1982—70.8 years for men and 78.2 years for women.[5]

The system of retrospective reimbursement of the charges made by hospitals for services to inpatients remained in place for more than half a century. Every facet of the system, including the Hill-Burton hospital construction program, stimulated the growth of hospitals on the theory that bigger is better. But the growth of costs did not fit that theory. In 1935, the consumer price index (CPI: 1967 = 100) for all items was 41.1 but the price index for a hospital room was 12.8. In early 1983, the general CPI stood at 293.2—that is, prices had almost tripled since 1967—but the price index for a room in the hospital had exploded to 604.1. With the advent of Medicare in 1966, hospital charges became a leading rather than a trailing indicator and have continued to be ever since. In 1982, health care costs rose 11.9 percent, triple the rise in the CPI.[6]

The former dean of the college of medicine gave his views:

People have been laying the [rising] cost of health care

at the feet of the health care providers and I think it is a partnership with the consumers. If health care consumers didn't keep coming around saying, "Gee, I'm willing to pay for this and that…,"the providers wouldn't cost so much money. The consumer has decided to pay for it through his employer or the national debt which is now, how many trillion? What he doesn't feel like he's paying for…he's going to have "the Cadillac."

I'm convinced that, if you weight completeness of diagnosis on a scale of zero to a hundred, for 50 bucks, a doctor can do a history and physical in his office and get to 92 or 93 on that scale. But to go the next three or four notches, to 95, 96, 97 percent confidence in the diagnosis, [would cost] another 500 bucks. It's that last bit of confidence that's costing all this money.

Dr. Lynn emphasized that because physicians cannot make the diagnosis 100 percent of the time, they practice defensive medicine to protect themselves against possible malpractice litigation. Every doctor can see himself in front of a jury, being examined by an astonished prosecuting attorney, "Do you mean, Doctor, you did an operation on this girl *without* getting a serum 'whatever' level?"[7]

Quite suddenly, the system of paying for hospital care made another abrupt change. Fearing the Social Security system was going broke, the Congress, in April 1983, amended the retirement program in various ways but it also introduced "prospective pricing"into the Medicare program. Briefly, in this new method of paying hospitals, the federal govenment said, "We shall pay the hospital a specific amount of money for each patient, an amount based on his illness, not on the length of time he stays in the hospital or how many tests and treatments he receives. If the hospital can take care of the patient's spell of illness for less than the amount we think it ought to cost, the hospital can keep the difference."

Illnesses were classified into 467 diagnosis-related groups (DRGs) and hospitals were reimbursed on the average cost of treating patients with these medical problems in nine regions in the country. For example, if the government's price for a simple appendectomy was $1,781, as it was in one New Jersey hospital in 1983 where the system had been operating for a while, hospitals with higher costs lost money. Thus, the government built into the new prospective pricing system the incentive for hospitals and their medical staffs to become cost-conscious, efficient and cost-effective. The motivation was turned around 180 degrees. Medicare introduced this system gradually beginning October 1, 1983.[8]

Other third parties were having the same problem of rising costs and were casting about for a better system than raising premiums every year. Once the federal government had installed the DRG reimbursement for Medicare, it did not take long for Blue Cross and Blue Shield of Oklahoma, the state's largest medical insurance company, to announce a major overhaul of its method of reimbursing hospitals, effective January 1, 1984. Called the Fixed Allowance Incentive Reimbursement plan (F.A.I.R.), it was based on the DRG system of the federal government. Blue Cross noted the wide variation in the charges made by Oklahoma hospitals for the same diagnoses. Examples: for a routine tonsillectomy, they ranged from $676 to $1,897, for pneumonia from $1,550 to $2,910, and for an appendectomy from $1,400 to $2,190. Blue Cross recognized the difference in charges due to the size and location of hospitals and divided Oklahoma institutions into four categories on this basis. Most of the hospitals in the state agreed to cooperate with the new Blue Cross system but there were exceptions, such as St. Joseph Regional Medical Center in Ponca City. Gregory Guntley, the administrator, said Blue Cross officials "implied that if we weren't interested in the plan, we weren't interested in cost controls." "We thought it was a marketing gimmick," he continued. "Why should we give Blue Cross a privileged position?" The Duncan Regional Medical Center, where Al Donnell was administrator, also declined to align itself with the new Blue Cross plan. How long these hospitals could hold out against the trend was not clear, however, because other third-parties, the commercial insurance companies, were also seeking to place a similar ceiling on the amount they would reimburse for a particular diagnosis.[9]

And there were other pressures as well. Because much of the health benefits tab was being picked up by business and industry as an employee fringe benefit, employers were beginning to recognize that a dollar saved in health benefits was a dollar added to their net profit—the "bottom line." So businesses began to form coalitions, such as the Washington (D.C.) Business Group on Health, to work together in an effort to reduce this expense. Earlier, union-negotiated health care fringe benefits were not too meaningful because they did not represent a large percentage of the cost of doing business. But by 1983, the Chrysler Corporation estimated that health benefits added $600 to the cost of each new car and truck, up from $75 a vehicle in 1970. Then it was just 31 cents an hour, a figure which ballooned to $3.30 an hour a dozen years later. At Chrysler, the $373 million annual health insurance bill for employees, retirees and their dependents worked out to more than $6,000 per active employee. Employers were justifiably worried that health care costs were out of control.[10]

The first Corporate Health Care Cost Containment Conference, sponsored by *Business Week* magazine, was held in Washington, D.C., in March, 1982. Business and industry approached the problem five ways. They tried to influence national legislation which would inject more market competition into the health services industry. The prospective pricing system adopted by Medicare accomplished one step in that direction. Employers set up procedures to review elective surgery and other treatments recommended for their employees to determine if they were really necessary. Some businesses chose to self-insure, particularly those with younger employees in non-hazardous industries, because their use of the health care system was less than the average. Industries also negotiated with doctor groups to get lower medical service charges for their employees. When such discount contracts were effected, the group practice was called a "preferred provider organization," a PPO. Companies did not require that their employees use the designated PPO but would not pay rates higher than those charged by the doctor groups which offered discounts. The employee was responsible for any charges beyond these approved rates.

A number of companies, Sentry Insurance, Xerox and Control Data, to name only three, saw the wisdom of encouraging preventive health care, fitness and healthful living among their employees. They developed workplace health programs including fitness centers, counseling and referral services and self-help, educational programs. All of these measures helped ease the cost of health benefits by keeping their employees healthy, reducing absenteeism and increasing productivity. Former mayor Patience Latting applauded this approach. "I am a strong proponent of preventive medicine and physical fitness. I don't know how long governments or business can pay medical benefits to cover cancer which has certainly been contributed to by the fact the employee smoked." The svelte Ms Latting, who jogged or played tennis almost daily, had a formula to avoid overeating and the obesity which can result therefrom. Her rule was, "Eat a good breakfast, as much as you want; give half of your lunch to a friend; and give all of your dinner to an enemy!"[11]

James L. "Jay" Henry was administrator of Baptist Medical Center for a quarter of a century. (Baptist Medical Center)

University of Oklahoma President Banowsky had similar convictions:

I think the medical profession generally has been woefully lacking in its emphasis on preventive medicine. The American Medical Association has had to learn from others about nutrition [and] the benefits of aerobic exercise. In my own view, that's a sad commentary on a profession which is designed to treat disease rather than prevent disease. I'm glad to see that's changing and it needs to change more dramatically.

I think a fitness center should be part of the [proposed OUHSC] student center. Why shouldn't something as great as OUHSC not have the most attractive and encouraging program in exercise for these professionals who are working under great pressure? I go every year to have my annual check-up to the clinic of our fellow Oklahoman and graduate of this medical center, Dr. Kenneth Cooper. He has, in my view, been frequently under-appreciated by the medical community. [Dr. Cooper wrote a book on aerobic exercise in the late 1960s and was credited with kindling America's interest in fitness which began to develop at that time.][12]

This sentiment was echoed by the administrator of Oklahoma City's Baptist Medical Center, James L. "Jay" Henry:

We spend an awful lot of money on high technology and medical expertise to care for a select group of patients. We've used a lot of dollars to treat a small number of patients whereas fewer dollars have been used to drive the programs that emphasize preventative medicine, good health and the preservation of health. The university is not a leader in prevention. The college of medicine is the flagship of education and unless prevention is part of the physicians' thinking, I don't think it will ever get going. The cardiologists, more than any others, recognize and apply some of their own professional knowledge and skill in prevention. But most doctors don't advocate physical fitness themselves. Some of them still smoke, eat too much and don't exercise, which gives you some idea of the value they place on prevention.[13]

Dr. David Steen explained the lack of interest in preventive health care at the university:

> The history of the teaching of medicine is taking cases of illness and teaching students about disease. The rule is: in order to make the educational program work, you have to fill the hospital beds. [The term] "health center" is a misnomer.
>
> And you have to pay the bills. You can't make a living out of wellness. Medicare, Medicaid and other third parties don't reimburse the physician [for his] time in wellness or prevention programs.[14]

As insurance premiums for health services went up, employers shifted more of the financial responsibility to their employees by increasing the deductible and co-payments. The "deductible" is that amount each employee and dependent has to pay annually before the insurance company begins to reimburse the patient. This was traditionally $50 or $100 for each person covered, but in the mid-1980s, that requirement was raised by many employers to $300 or more. The "co payment" is the percentage of the bill for which the employee is responsible after the insurance company begins to pay. For example, some company plans paid 80 percent of the bill up to $1,500 and 100 percent thereafter. When this threshhold was raised to, say, $3,000, the premium could be held down or at least it would not increase as much as it otherwise would. These shifts also eased the costs borne by the employers and encouraged the employee to use the health care system judiciously.

As a result of this pressure and the depressed state of the Oklahoma economy, Presbyterian Hospital and other private institutions in the central Oklahoma area began to experience a decrease in occupancy. At Presbyterian, this decrease in patient load became so severe it necessitated the closing of 80 beds, 20 percent of the hospital's capacity. The average daily census had dropped in April, 1984, to 254 patients from a previous high of more than 300. Two hundred of the

1,700 jobs at the institution were scheduled for elimination over the six months following the mid-April, 1984, announcement of personnel cutbacks. Harry Neer expected the layoffs to be permanent because he saw the declining use of inpatient services as a definite trend. In a consolidation move two years before, 93 jobs had been eliminated. Presbyterian also expected to undergo a corporate reorganization which would result in the formation of a parent company. The trend in hospital management was to organize and operate profit-making subsidiaries and use the earnings from them to supplement the income of the non-profit hospital. Harry Neer questioned whether some of the hospitals that Presbyterian (IHP) managed would survive, especially in southeast Oklahoma. "Hugo was in the black last fiscal year and so far this fiscal year [as of October, 1983], they're in the red. It is [because of] the impact of DRGs; when that gets to 100 percent, I don't know how they're going to survive." The American Hospital Association estimated that perhaps 1,000 of the 7,000 non-federal, acute, general hospitals in America would close. Neer went on:

> If a community won't vote in local support [such as a sales tax] to make up for the losses in Medicare and Medicaid, those little hospitals are doomed. And it's going to be a shame. There are always arguments— are there too many hospitals, too many beds? For some of these communities, [though], it is more than medical care; it's the economy. Often, the biggest employer in these towns is the hospital. If it is true that a dollar is exchanged six times a year and is spent mostly in the community, [the hospital represents] a lot of their economy. I can show you at least three communities in Kansas that went down the tube when their hospital went down the tube. I think we're going to see the 120 or so hospitals in Oklahoma reduced markedly in the next two to five years unless we find a way to finance them.[15]

Less than a year later, the prediction Neer made in the autumn of 1983 began to appear accurate. Another small, IHP-managed hospital got into so much financial trouble it filed a bankruptcy petition on July 24, 1984. The Wetumka (Oklahoma) General Hospital, 34 beds, was unable to meet payments on a $1.675 million, 1978 revenue bond issue, sold to allow renovation and expansion of the building. A combination of events led to the declaration of bankruptcy. The oil boom of the early 1980s faded, one of the two staff physicians was killed in an automobile wreck in 1982, and the advent of prospective payment (DRGs) reduced reimbursement for Medicare patients. In addition, the Department of Human Services held the line on payment for the hospital care of welfare patients. Because "a high percentage of the hospital's patients exist below the poverty level," the income of the Wetumka General Hospital was further constrained. It was uncertain how long the hospital could continue to operate.[16]

Small hospitals were not the only ones affected. The City of Faith Medical Center, the teaching hospital for the Oral Roberts University medical school in Tulsa, was also caught in a fund squeeze in the spring of 1984, necessitating the dismissal of 244 of its 907 employees. Since the City of Faith opened in November of 1981 with 294 of its planned 777 bed capacity licensed, it had struggled to attract enough patients to survive. By July, 1982, its occupany rate was 11 percent. Two years later, although at peak times there had been as many as 100 patients in the hospital, the average daily occupancy was reputed to be only 70 patients, or 58 percent of the 120 beds in service. This low occupancy not only prompted personnel cutbacks but placed the university and the hospital in a "Catch-22." Oral Roberts said, "Unless the City of Faith has more patients for our students to work on when the accreditation team visits this fall, we will lose our accreditation." The Tulsa evangelist said the hospital would begin seeking indigent patients as well as those who could pay. Of course, this could only compound the hospital's financial problems, making it even more dependent on contributions to Roberts' worldwide ministries organization which, since January, 1984, had experienced a shortfall of $1 million a *month*.[17]

Prior to DRGs, neither employees nor physicians had to be particularly concerned about the cost of operation of the hospital. With prospective pricing, however, each department had to become cost efficient, which meant better management of people. Hospitals are labor intensive, with 55 to 60 percent of their budgets used to pay salaries and fringe benefits. Thus, the productivity of each employee became important in their survival.

Physicians had to watch how many laboratory tests, x-rays and treatments they ordered for their patients in view of the maximum payment established under the DRG system. Medicare inspectors visited hospitals monthly to check medical records and see that billings were made properly. Hospitals established computer systems which would report daily how much the service rendered each patient had cost and how much money was left for his care.

To add to the physicians' consternation, on October

"Oooh!—That Feels So Nice and Cold!" (The Oklahoman)

19, 1983, the House Ways and Means Committee voted to recommend a major change in the Medicare program under which physicians treating hospital patients would have to accept fees set by the government and could not bill patients for any additional amounts. By late February, 1984, the AMA was asking all U.S. doctors to voluntarily freeze their fees for a year in an effort to "help the nation's economy." Medical fees rose faster in 1983 than the all-items index of health care costs. However, some analysts thought this was a defensive move rather than helping the nation "get out of a recession," the recovery from which was already 14 months under way. They believed organized medicine was worried about government interference because the FY 1985 Reagan administration budget called for freezing Medicare reimbursements to doctors for one year, thereby saving $600 million in the projected $75.9 billion program. Dr. Stephen L. Hansen of San Luis Obispo, California said the voluntary freeze "resolution implies that we don't want other people telling doctors what to do when we can do it voluntarily." A March, 1984, survey of the 4,000 physicians in Oklahoma indicated that 95 percent of the 1,250 who responded said they would comply with the AMA's fee freeze request.[18]

But that was not all. The Congress was considering AVGs—ambulatory visit groups—to accompany DRGs. This form of regulation would place a ceiling on the charges physicians could levy for service to Medicare patients treated outside the hospital. According to Wayne Coventon, executive director of the Oklahoma City Clinic, "AVGs is the doctors' side of DRGs and the Congress will pass it just as soon as they think they have the political clout to survive it. We'll be placed on a budget for a grouping of diagnoses that are common to out-patient visits. We'll be paid "x" dollars for the diagnosis regardless of what services we have to provide." Coventon went on to say:

> The feedback we get is that concept is being tossed around in the various committee meetings now, [with the idea that] "once we get the hospitals economically handcuffed, then we need to start on the doctors." I think we could see that as early as late 1985, early 1986. It will be a political fight to see whether or not ambulatory visit groups get installed.
>
> We were just barely able to defeat the mandatory Medicare assignment rule this year. I think that has the potential to become the law and it would certainly change the practice of medicine. It could force physicians to determine, purely as an economic decision, whether they would treat Medicare patients. There are political and social ramifications [involved in] forcing physicians to take assignments. That could place the Medicare population into a limited access position.
>
> The government has already been successful in creating competition among physicians without really doing a whole lot. Just talking about it has created a significant amount of competition. The advent of HMOs, PPOs, and all the other forms you see for alternative health care financing systems has forced physicians to find some way to compete. Hypothetically, an association of doctors might choose, rather than take mandatory assignment on Medicare patients, to replace their current Medicare population with a PPO [preferred provider organization] population where they had a greater control over reimbursement. There are methods [for doctors] to get around that. If you're going to get 67 percent of your billed charges on a Medicare patient and 90 percent on an HMO patient, you might opt, economically, to take care of HMO patients.
>
> The ultimate goal of government is to create enough competition that there are winners and there are losers. The losers drop out and enter other occupations. If the law of supply and demand is allowed to function, the winners get to stay and the losers move on. I'm not concerned about competition; I just hope in our endeavor to compete, the patient doesn't lose. I don't think the style of medicine in terms of compassion and caring for the patient and the genuine interest physicians have in treating patients and helping them get back to good health or stay in good health is going to change. The structure in which that happens and the way it is financed will change drastically and rapidly.[19]

In late April, 1984, physicians in the metropolitan Oklahoma City area formed a new council to help them

Wayne Coventon, executive director of the Oklahoma City Clinic. (Oklahoma City Clinic)

negotiate health care contracts with insurance companies, industries and hospitals. Called the Central Oklahoma Council of Hospital Medical Staffs, the group was unique because it cut across hospital lines. It was established to review a proposed contract between physicians at St. Anthony Hospital and Blue Cross and Blue Shield of Oklahoma. The council members hired an attorney to represent them and individual doctors in contract negotiations with HMOs and other organizations which pay for medical professional services.[20]

Dr. Jack Records had mixed feelings about the changes looming on the horizon:

> I think there's no question that physicians' fees will be controlled. I think it's too bad that the medical profession has to give up its freedom to the government; that's what it amounts to. Once that sort of thing is started, it's just like Medicare. When Medicare came in and set all these fee schedules all over the country, the third party payors immediately picked up the same thing. We dance to the tune of the federal government in regard to reimbursement and this [AVGs] will just be tightening down even more.
>
> I think this is a direct consequence of the big companies that have to pay all these premiums for their employees finding that the cost of medical care is eating their lunch. Something has to be done about it and *they're* the people putting the pressure on the government, on Congress. It's not just your little old John Doe from the

boondocks; it's the corporations. And in that sense, I think it's a good thing. There *are* economies that can be effected.[21]

The Medicare prospective pricing system and business coalitions fighting the seemingly uncontrollable rise of health care costs were more effective that anyone had predicted. By April, 1984, just as the census of Presbyterian Hospital had declined, the number of days patients stayed in hospitals throughout the nation was also down 3 to 10 percent. Admissions had declined in many institutions.

Other pressures contributing to this trend included competition from new alternative health services, such as day-surgery centers. In Oklahoma on May 23, 1984, the state health planning commission, from which applicants proposing new health facilities were required to obtain a "certificate of need," approved construction of six new "surgicenters." Four were planned for the Oklahoma City area and were expected to cost about $5 million. Jack Boyd said the ambulatory surgery centers would place "additional competition into the the healthcare delivery system," saving the patient about 20 percent when compared to a hospital-based center, available in several area institutions. He did not explain why the hospitals could not reduce their charges and thus save the $5 million in capital costs.[22]

Al Donnell was convinced that someone at the state level had to set the standards for hospitals and other facilities:

> You can't let individual institutions make their own plans and do whatever they want. There is an intense competition, particularly in the urban centers, and it isn't healthy. I think there is a lot of unnecessary duplication of a lot of programs. There's no need for everybody to have a burn center, the best cardiology service.
>
> Somebody's got to be responsible for coordination of the things individual hospitals want to do and how they fit together. You can't have health services developing like fast food franchises…or failing like them.[23]

Thus, Oklahoma had a regulated system in which there was increasing competition. In addition to financial incentives for patients to stay out of the hospital, like larger insurance deductibles and co-payments, there were the lingering effects of the 1981-1982 recession, growing consumer sophistication about second surgical opinions and available outpatient services, as well as new medical technology which shortened hospital stays. The role of habit and custom was being re-examined: for example, the average hospital stay for the normal delivery of a maternity patient was three and a half days in Chicago but only 18 hours in Salt Lake City. Most hospital executives and healthcare economists agreed with Harry Neer that the decreasing use of inpatient hospital facilities was permanent.

All of these changes stimulated hospitals to scramble for new ways to cope. Some opted to get into the home health care business, previously the almost exclusive province of the Visiting Nurse Association (VNA). Group insurers and their client companies began to promote home health care as an important element in their cost containment strategies. By 1983, 53 percent of the companies queried offered some kind of home health care benefit. They found that getting the patient out of the hospital early could significantly trim outlays, even in routine cases. In long-term cases, of course, savings were outstanding. Connecticut General Life Insurance Company said, "It comes to an average [saving] of $1,000 per hospitalized employee." With the Medicaid per diem reimbursement rates in the Oklahoma Health Center running $474 at the Oklahoma Teaching Hospitals and $361 at Presbyterian Hospital, there was a clear incentive to move patients to a less expensive setting. Moreover, Harry Neer estimated that Medicaid covered only about half of Presbyterian's cost of treating patients eligible for such support.

Multihospital systems, such as Hospital Corporation of America, the nation's largest proprietary chain, saw preferred provider organizations (PPOs) as a way to regain market share which had steadily eroded through competition and declining patient days under Medicare's prospective payment system. One executive described the situation as "…kind of a panic out there that we've got to be doing these things…doing them yesterday." Hospitals were trying to capture large groups of patients by giving discounts to employers wanting to cut their healthcare costs. Hospital chains had the advantage of establishing PPO networks and offering services in several locations to multiple units of companies whose facilities were spread across the nation.

By mid-1984, the health care industry was well into a period of rapid change which appeared to portend relief for the cost-beleaguered consumer of its services. An industry which for years had been inoculated against the forces of the marketplace now was losing its immunity, with certainty and swiftness. As *Business Week* put it, "The health community was putting on a business suit."[24]

CHAPTER 45
DIRECTIONS: 1984

The capital expenditures in the Oklahoma Health Center since 1968 totaled well over $350 million and by 1984, the cost of operating all of the institutions on this health campus exceeded a half billion dollars a year. The number of employees had expanded to more than 11,500.

EMPLOYEES in the
OKLAHOMA HEALTH CENTER
June, 1984

Oklahoma Teaching Hospitals	4,500*
O.U. Health Sciences Center	2,629
Presbyterian Hospital	1,746
V.A. Medical Center	1,200
State Department of Health	725
Oklahoma Medical Research Foundtn	300
Oklahoma City Clinic	213
Oklahoma Allergy Clinic	92
McGee Eye Institute	75
Pauline Mayer Center	64
State Medical Examiner	27
TOTAL	11,571

*All numbers represent full-time equivalents

Was this initial and continuing investment of public and private money appropriate? Did the Oklahoma Health Center accomplish the Dennis dream of improved health care for the people of Oklahoma?

Like most large, multi-faceted projects, it had its successes and its failures. There is no question the supply of health manpower in Oklahoma, essential for the delivery of health care, was markedly improved. The nurse shortage was essentially over and other health professionals were generally available as needed. Indeed, the physician supply was probably in surplus and it appeared that the dentist supply, as predicted, would soon balance the demand for dental services if, perhaps, that had not already occurred. While the OHC was by no means the only source of health manpower in the state, it remained the major Oklahoma campus for education in the health sciences. Because all of the seven colleges were adequately housed, staffed and operated, it is appropriate to conclude the essential means had been developed toward the end of providing health care to people in all of Oklahoma. Of course, the cyclical downturns in

A pioneer in pioneer country. (OHSF Collection)

operational funding of the university delayed the achievement of that level of excellence for which educators constantly strive and the OUHSC was going through such a period in mid-1984. However, the elements needed to make significant future gains in the quality of teaching, research and service to patients were in place. This much had been accomplished.

The broader goal of *delivering* health services to every hamlet in every corner of Oklahoma remained unmet, at least in the fashion it was conceived two decades previously. The Wakita project, after its monumental struggles, was a signal success. But it was also an anomaly. For a town of 500 people, isolated in the north central wheat country, to enjoy the services of two physicians (Dr. Graves' daughter, Donella, completed the family medicine program at O.U. and joined him in 1983), a physicians associate, a dentist and a pharmacist was quite unusual. In addition, the people of Wakita and the farms surrounding it had a well staffed 49 bed nursing home/emergency hospital conveniently available.

When Dr. Graves arrived, he was the only doctor in all of Grant county and physicians were scarce in other areas of north central Oklahoma. In 1984, Dr. Graves was one of seven physicians in the county, three of whom were D.O.s. Two served Medford and there were three at Pond Creek. Three of the M.D.s were part time, so there was the equivalent of five full time doctors.

Dr. Graves observed, "There's not enough work now for a couple of [full-time] doctors [at Wakita]." A line graph on the back of Dr. Graves' office door, which

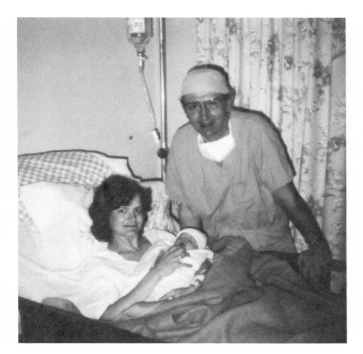

Dr. Don Graves, Wakita's doctor for 15 years, attends Connie Wolcott and her new baby, Lorna, born in 1982. (Don Graves)

The nursing home section of the Wakita Community Health Center. (OHSF Collection)

charted the number of patients seen each month since 1970, showed the direction of medical services there. Above the jagged, month-to-month fluctuations, an orange "average line" showed a rising curve until 1976 when patient visits peaked at 11,162 a year. Since then, the line sloped off gradually, leveling off in 1984 at approximately 6,000 annually.

While other small community hospitals were in financial trouble, the Wakita Community Health Center had the stable financial base provided by 42 nursing home beds which stayed full and for which there was a waiting list. In 1984, an eight-unit apartment complex was under construction at the east end of the building to accommodate people who could live independently but wanted medical services next door. The seven-bed hospital section maintained an average census of three. Dr. Graves commented on the doctor's life in Wakita:

> You always have to have a thick skin to live in a small town because, in general, people...[think] why would anybody who's any good come to a small town like this? It's quite depressing to have your neighbor go by your office on down to Enid for medical care.
>
> Wakita was supposed to be a demonstration project for small towns and as far as I know, nobody has ever followed it. I think it was a mistake for the university to give up this project. We were all sort of peeved at them

[because] they could have accomplished more [for rural health care].

> I would...include Wakita in the [university's] new family medicine [training] network so [medical students and] doctors could be introduced to a beautiful set-up [in a highly rural area]. It doesn't seem logical that all the small towns in the country should plan to give up their doctors and [depend] on the regional centers. We've proved the success [of this model]. If new students and residents were to rotate through it and see the satisfaction we have here, I think they would find it valid to consider, even in this modern day and age. Now, with costs snowballing, doctors should be encouraged to use a little more clinical judgment and less expensive technology.

Dr. Graves had found much satisfaction in the trust and confidence the people had in him. He said it was "the nucleus of real, old fashioned family doctor contacts that make it all worthwhile." He still made occasional house calls.[1]

Thus far, it appeared that Grant County was an exception to the general trend of doctor distribution. While the increasing supply of physicians had caused many doctors to move out to regional centers like Enid, expanded medical service in towns of 5,000 or less remained quite limited. The legislature's theory that if Oklahoma produced enough physicians, the cities would fill up with doctors and new graduates would be forced out into rural areas to practice, resulting in a trickle-down effect, had yet to be proven. To date, Bill Stanhope's observation appeared valid, "A town which is not big enough to support a McDonald's can't expect to get a doctor."[2]

Perhaps for some time, people in rural Oklahoma would have to travel to the doctor. Interestingly, residents of small towns tended to do that, anyway. Dan Fox, P.A., who succeeded Bill Stanhope as the director of the O.U. physicians associate program, related this experience:

About two years ago [1982], we tried placing a P.A. in Caddo, [a small town in Bryan County, 13 miles north of Durant, in south central Oklahoma]. He would work half a day in the clinic in Caddo and then go down to the main office in Durant [for the afternoon, seeing patients there]. Patients who lived in Caddo but bought their medicines in Durant, shopped in Durant, bought their groceries in Durant, would drive right past the clinic and see the P.A. in the Durant office. It was just their way of doing business.[3]

Originally, Bill Stanhope made great effort to place P.A.s in smaller communities on the theory they could augment the physician supply and, in the case of the Yale experiment, provide health care where there had been no physician. But graduates of the P.A. program in 1984 were headed in a different direction. Dan Fox explained:

In the current environment [of ample numbers of doctors], you have to question whether or not [we should] continue to train P.A.s. [We would need more P.A.s] if the environment would change where we would recognize that tasks can be delegated and the further down the [educational] scale they are delegated, the less they cost. But I don't see that changing.

I think the P.A. is living proof we have over-educated people in health services. For example: diagnosing and managing a common cold; normally, that is done by a physician in practices that don't have P.A.s and it is a horrible waste of his time. Most of the scientific studies have shown that P.A.s are technically competent to diagnose and treat 85 percent of the people who flow throught a primary physician's office. P.A.'s are on salary and receive about a fourth of the average family physician income.

The P.A. program reduced its entering class from 30 to 20 and, while graduates were still encouraged to go to less populated areas, the shift in 1984 was toward large institutions in metropolitan centers. Originally, P.A.s were trained by institutions, like Duke University and the Cleveland [Ohio] Clinic, which needed highly-skilled technicians to work there, for the V.A. and for other hospitals. Later, the thrust was to place them in rural areas because they had physician-like skills. Fox continued:

We are now seeing that come around 360 degrees whereby institutions affected by cutbacks in foreign medical graduates who filled permanent house staff slots are using P.A.s to do the day-to-day work. There are now some 21 post-graduate programs for P.A.s in surgery, emergency medicine and pediatrics, [special training needed by P.A.s who work in large institu-

tions]. The Veterans Administration is one of the biggest employers of P.A.s in the country and we are now seeing community hospitals use them in large numbers.

But our focus is still on primary care. If P.A.s are going to be an effective tool to reduce cost [of health care], we have to maintain that direction.[4]

In 1984, the direction of other educational programs and institutions in the Oklahoma Health Center had been formulated in response to changes in the health care delivery system. From the viewpoint of hematologist/oncologist Boyd Shook, medicine was headed for a wondrous future:

I think the business of doing surgery for metabolic disease will dwindle and disappear. I believe coronary by-passes will be by-passed because they are really not solving the problem. In the next five years, heart surgery will double because the by-pass is a very popular procedure, [but] beta-blockers and calcium channel antagonists probably will do just as well as surgery as they are utilized earlier in people's lives. Deaths due to heart disease are way down.

Exercise, fitness—they are important. How do you get rid of catecholamines—the chemicals that are produced by your "computer" to assist you in your daily fight? Once you get the catecholamines, they cause [heart] damage. You can get rid of them with [the drug] Inderal, by keeping your weight at a respectable place and by exercise. All of these influences have affected the incidence of heart disease during the past 15 years. It's very, very good—and will be more important by far than cardiovascular surgery in the next 10 years.

Cancer treatment will be vastly different in the very near future. Interferon is simply the first of a long series of immunological agents that will take over the care of cancer patients. The drug manufacturers, with the help of DNA alteration, are making very, very specific drugs that we didn't even dream of. In oncology, it is theoretically possible today to biopsy a suspected cancer lesion, say *your* histiocytic lymphoma, take enough of that tissue to culture it, subject it to recombinant DNA techniques, make an antibody specifically for Robert Hardy, give you back that antibody and that histiocytic lymphoma would disappear. This will some day become practical; we just need more money and more time. I think this will happen for the vast majority of cancers. There is no question that this is the explanation of spontaneous cancer remissions we see today; the body generates its own antibodies. We all have cancer every day in our bodies and we destroy it. A tenuous balance goes on between cell growth and cell control. Cell growth takes over when we have cancer, but if we can just whip it back down into place, then cell control factors will take over. In the next 15 years, super chemists as research people will develop "magic bullets" to treat disease and the physician will pull all this together in caring for patients.

Surgery will go by attrition. Where are all the people who used to spend all their time treating gonorrhea and syphilis? This used to constitute a third of the practitioners but penicillin changed all that. There are no t.b. [tuberculosis] docs anymore. Look at all the polio[myelitis] specialists there [once] were; they're gone.

I really believe we'll have a shakedown in the patterns of care. I think physicians will be more advisors than deliverers of care. The delivery of routine care is too expensive when the physician does it. I think nurses and nurse practitioners will do it; or we may develop a totally new breed of person as a physician-extender but not in the sense the P.A. is. Perhaps this new person, with a lesser educational background, will actually be doing most of the care and the physician will be looking at the data and making the decisions.[5]

Jolly West saw the future of psychiatry in the rapidly increasing application of basic biomedical and behavioral science to clinical practice. He said that psychiatry had lagged behind other specialties in becoming scientific but it is getting more scientific every day and it must be a part of a major center. He predicted that:

The other main thrust of the future of psychiatry between now and the end of the century is clearly going to be full rapprochement of psychiatry with the rest of scientific medicine. We are calling it "behavioral medicine" and it has to do, not only with the effect of psychiatric issues of mental, or psychological or psychosocial forces on physical illness, which is extremely important, but also the psychiatric complications and ramifications of people with organic disease. For example, 40 percent or more of people who have open heart surgery experience a clinical depression at some time afterward. That has to be cared for. We are now realizing that metabolic disorders have psychiatric symptoms or problems that have to be treated. The effects of life stress are important in producing physical disease but those physical diseases can be important in producing psychological, psychiatric complications.

The multi-institutional center such as the one developing in Oklahoma City is an ideal place for psychiatry to be getting involved with the problems of women who have just given birth to a child, with a kid who's in a total body cast and can't move for three months, with the problems of an old person who is confused and is called senile when it's really a psychological depression. Then there are the problems of the patient who comes back for a ninth operation and there seems to be one surgical

Oklahoman Ed Brandt, Assistant Secretary for Health, U. S. Department of Health and Human Services. (University of Oklahoma)

complication after another and nobody seems to understand why they don't heal up right.

All of these things are how psychiatry touches on the rest of medicine. In a modern center like the OHC, you can make those connections, you can teach the people involved, and you can do research on these joint problems.[6]

Taking a nationwide view, Dr. Edward N. Brandt, Jr., Assistant Secretary for Health, observed in 1983 that, for every 100 Americans, 75 visited a doctor at least once that year. Of that number, only 12 were sick enough to be hospitalized, and only one of them died before reaching his or her estimated life expectancy. But there was an enormous discrepancy between the number of people who went to the doctor [63 percent] and the number of people [less than 20 percent] who said—in a different context—that their health was not what it ought to be. When the National Center for Health Statistics inquired, most Americans— over 80 percent—said their health was "good" to "excellent."

While the definition of health as total physical, social, and mental well-being made a lot of sense intellectually, it presented a radical economic and social challenge to the health care system. Dr. Brandt said the nation needed to decide what it wanted "health" to mean and then agree on how it would be paid for. "I don't believe we can afford to continue much longer on this two-track system of wanting to crowd every-

351

thing possible under the health umbrella but getting cranky when the bills come due." Dr. Brandt also said the role of the individual should be further clarified and endowed with a good deal more responsibility than in the past; that is, in promoting his or her own health and preventing the occurrence of disease and disability.[7]

Turning to medical education, Rainey Williams, who was acting dean before Dr. McCall, talked about the ingredient necessary to achieve excellence in the O.U. College of Medicine:

> This is perhaps an old-fashioned view, but I don't think the medical school can be any better than the basic science departments. You can limp along and teach students but to have the kind of college of medicine we all want, the basic sciences have to be strengthened. They have been chronically under-financed and now with the reduction of federal funding, it's shameful. And, other than grants, they have no way of supporting themselves as the clinical departments do. One way or another, a good deal of money has to be expended in the basic sciences. And it is only money; we have some good people and we can get more, and we have beautiful physical facilities.
>
> As medical school administrators look around to see how they can increase [basic science] funding, they draw a bead on professional earnings [of the people in clinical medicine]. And we already support the basic sciences to some extent, but there is a point beyond which you're going to "kill the goose." I tend to think we could do a little more, but clinical folks work hard; furthermore, they're all good and they all have the option of making three or four times as much in practice. If the discrepancy between [private] practice and academic income gets too great, you're going to lose good people.[8]

Dr. McCall discussed his immediate problems as well as the long range outlook for the college of medicine:

> In times of shrinking support, the challenge is a matter of how to retain the gains we have made; how to keep in place the high calibre of individuals we have until [the economy improves and] we can move on. They all have multiple options and, should they leave, we would be a decade from regaining the position we now have because the word would spread that O.U. was not moving to the cutting edge of medicine.
>
> Long range, we've got to expand the corps of people we have in the biomedical science area, both basic and clinical. Some of the major advances I see coming in medicine will first develop at the basic science level. The bridge to the clinical sciences is in biochemistry, genetics, immunology, and biology.[9]

Christian Ramsey, M.D., took over the family med-

The head of family medicine, Dr. Christian Ramsey, came to O.U. from Texas. (University of Oklahoma)

icine program at the University of Oklahoma in February, 1982. He came from Texas with the expectation of building "the top, academic, family medicine department in the United States." In 1984, he believed he was ahead of schedule in many areas and commented that "there was a lot less obstacle to dealing with the personnel in the health center than any of us had expected there to be from what we had heard." He referred to previous attitudes of specialists toward family practitioners. Associate Provost David Walters explained how that came about:

> There were some horrendous political problems with the family medicine department which really encumbered that department for two or three years. It made no progress at all and, in fact, deteriorated completely. Then there was a turnaround, a breakdown of specialist bias against family medicine because we had a very fair and wise man by the name of G. Rainey Williams running the College of Medicine for a long, interim period [after Tom Lynn]. Here was a star specialist who said family medicine was a priority and had to be dealt with. So funding was allocated, a star chairman was brought in and all kinds of commitments were made. Rainey contributed significantly to that by taking the lead and getting his specialist brethren to back off.

In 1982, Ramsey had no idea the economy of Oklahoma was about to crash. "In fact, I was recruited with the promise of an $8 million building, limitless numbers of faculty and a whole variety of other things. If I had really had any inkling there was going to be an economic problem here, I would have insisted they appropriate the money [for the building] in the legislative session the year they recruited me rather than let the leadership talk me into waiting for a year. But I never looked back and I am delighted I am here." He described the program:

> Our most important goal is to teach family medicine to medical students. They need to learn the principles of how family systems interact with the major regulatory networks of the body and significantly influence the cause and the course of illness, rehabilitation, health promotion and all of those things.
>
> Our second purpose is to train enough family physicians to meet the needs of the state. We currently offer here, in Enid and Shawnee, 60 positions—36 on the main campus and 12 each in the two satellite locations. It is a three-year program leading to eligibility for certification by the American Board of Family Practice. Tulsa is not in our bailiwick. It is a separate department and has its own chairman.

Dr. Ramsey elected to reduce the number of family physicians being trained from around 100 to 60 because he believed O.U. did not have the resources to train the larger number. "We are just now getting to the point I can begin to ask 'how many physicians should we train?' Certainly, how many internists and pediatricians are trained and how much primary care is done by other people is going to influence how many family physicians we train." At mid-1984, he had established no specific objective as to the size of the educational program. He continued:

> G.P.s [general practitioners] went to patients' homes, cared for them and watched the comings and goings of their family members. It was a part of family medicine all along. Now for the first time, we are beginning scientifically to document the effect of one family type on the course of one illness versus another one and understand how we, as family physicians, use that information in making decisions about patients. We have reason to believe from our own work and the work of many people that the functioning of the family system is a major moderator of the susceptibility to disease. The third part of our program is a nationally recognized research program on family medicine in which we are actually teasing apart the family system's relationship to the nervous system and the endocrine system.
>
> We are looking at cellular effects of how the family system operates. We have documented now that the family system is a major contributor to prematurity and fetal malnutrition. Women who are in dysfunctional families tend to have smaller babies with a greater chance of their being premature than women who are in func-

tional families. For another example, we have found that dysfunctional families have a much higher attack rate of flu [influenza] than families that are highly functional. There really are changes in the immune system which render a [dysfunctional] family member more vulnerable to infection.[10]

The O.U. College of Dentistry was paying close attention to the market for its graduates and planning its future accordingly. According to Dean Brown:

> The numbers of dentists in the United States have increased enormously since the federal government got into the act in the mid-1960s; from 84 thousand in 1960 to almost 130 thousand dentists in 1983. The supply is plentiful and probably more than we need, at least in some parts of the country. Oklahoma has lagged behind national averages in terms of dentist to population ratios [U.S.: 1 to 1,740; Oklahoma: 1 to 2,340]. The applicant pool has dropped off enormously since 1974. Oklahoma, which was short of dentists for a long time, is not, in my opinion, particularly short of dentists today. During the latter part of the 1970s and through 1981, there was a great in-migration of dentists because there were lots of communities here that were not served. We were turning out fewer dentists [at O.U.] than the numbers coming into the state.
>
> Dental education is pulling back on enrollment, dropping nationwide from its peak of 6,000 in 1969 to 5,100-5,200 in 1983. We are talking about reducing class size here, from the current 72 down to 65. I don't think Oklahoma is going to consider eliminating this school [as the University of Washington in Seattle was contemplating in 1983]; I think we are here to stay.
>
> Our attrition rate has increased substantially in the last few years; we're only graduating roughly 60. We lose students evenly for personal and academic reasons. With the applicant pool diminishing, the bottom three or four or five students are not as skilled as they were a few years ago, so we are dealing with a different mix. We have taken more out-of-staters, too, because we have a commitment to the state to take 72 students. We have taken *every* qualified Oklahoma resident but that is not enough to fill a class of 72. We take a number of students from Utah; they have no dental school there. Most of them are Mormons and they have a very positive effect on our students and our educational system.[11]

Lorraine Singer, R.N., M.P.H., who joined the faculty of the O.U. College of Nursing in January, 1972, had been interim dean since Gloria Smith left in March, 1983:

> Before all of this financial cutback, we were really hoping we would be implementing a Ph.D. program in the fall of 1986. This might be delayed another year or so.

Lorraine Singer succeeded Gloria Smith as Dean of Nursing. (University of Oklahoma)

The State Regents would like to fully implement the Tulsa master's program [so that 40 percent of the students no longer have to take classes at OUHSC] before starting the Ph.D. program here. But we need additional space and more faculty in Tulsa so it gets back to money. I have to assume, with the state of the economy in Oklahoma, neither program will be funded right away.

For the college, our faculty has been involved in national and regional meetings, presenting papers. This started while Gloria was here but has [now] accelerated. Two books have been published by faculty authors and the third one is being printed now [January, 1984]. Those are monumental steps for this college of nursing. One of our faculty received a research grant and we have applied for another research project—a big "first" for this college. The faculty is very stable at this point.

Ms Singer talked about the effect of DRGs on the profession of nursing:

The predominant theme is that institutions are going to want the best educated, the best qualified nurses and many feel we'll be moving to more clinical specialists. They'll really want that expertise to assess the patient, plan the interventions and set up, say, home care because they'll want to get them out [of the hospital] faster. I see DRGs as an opportunity for nursing to really demonstrate what nurses can do.

On the other hand, some hospitals, particularly on the east coast, are eliminating RNs and bringing on lesser-prepared people. They want to cheapen their care but the majority feel you need the better prepared people because you can't afford to let the patient stay in the

bed two or three days and not make your interventions. I am aware of four hospitals in the metropolitan area that are looking to hire only baccalaureate-prepared nurses. Mercy [Hospital] has gone to all licensed personnel—LPN or RN—eliminating nurse aides.

For the first time in several years, the applicant pool for the school of nursing had gone up in 1983, with 260 aspirants for 150 places. The dean credited this to the economy, the job market, the increase in salaries and the nurse shortage, all of which made the profession more attractive as a career choice. It was her impression the nurse shortage was not over, but had settled down to "a more normal turnover." "If you look in the Sunday paper," she suggested, "there is still a fair number of ads for nurses."[12]

When Frances Waddle was asked what the nursing profession was striving for, she replied:

Control of practice. Physicians and hospital administrators in the health care bureaucracy now control nursing. As you see the patterns nurses are following, they are trying to move away from that institutional setting, [into] community health nursing, school nursing, occupational health or solo practice. They are fleeing some of the impositions of the employer-employee relationship, although they may get into one which is not any better. If you are a nurse in an elementary school, though, and you are the only one there, you're going to be pretty much autonomous.

Some hospitals are going into by-laws for nursing staff where they apply for and get clinical appointments. You hear lots of nurses talking about fee-for-service [payment] for nurses, but I'm not so sure they understand what they're talking about. I'm convinced the concept of fee for-service will never be extended to nurses and it will slowly but surely be withdrawn from other health care providers, including physicians. Nurses may in the future become private contractors, furnishing consulting services to nursing homes, DHS and other providers.[13]

In mid-1984, the dean of the College of Public Health, Peter J. Levin, Sc.D., was preparing to leave after only two and a half years. Recalling the history of the college, he said that when it started in 1967, it had the very unique focus on human ecology. This was a way of acquainting medical and other students with the greater totality of the person and relating this idea of the individual in his family, in his society and in his environment, which was quite a progressive concept at that time. The school really thrived as an intellectual entity from about 1967 to 1973. "Essentially, the school stopped being independent, which was the intellectual demise of what Schottstaedt had built up, and it stopped making progress."

When Levin came to the deanship in 1982, he said it was to a "very badly demoralized institution which had been officially separated from allied health but had not taken on an identity of its own." "My task," he continued, "was to try to get the faculty to reestablish themselves as a viable force in the Health Sciences Center and in public health in Oklahoma. I had a lot of things to turn around because it was a school which had turned in, instead of reaching out and building bridges to others." He went on to explain the progress since January, 1982:

> In two years, the research grants went up from $300 thousand to $1.5 million. I can say without any question that Clayton Rich backed his promises as to what he would do [to support the school]. We [planned to] add faculty, get money for laboratory equipment, encourage research and move out into the community doing projects. We bought the first laboratory equipment the college had obtained in ten years. You can't compete for federal grants in environmental health unless you have new equipment.

> We got in some exceptional young faculty, all of whom have gotten some sort of research funding and have started to publish. The role of the college has started to be reestablished with the health agencies. We are teaching the master of public health degree at the University Center at Tulsa, which is a big step forward. It is going to be very important for the state to have a more widely-educated work force in public health. That's the way you make progress.

> People already employed in public health are going to school part time, coming in at night to get a degree. This is a radical shift from 10 years ago when there was federal funding to support students to go to school during the day. We have had an 18 percent increase in enrollment since last year and the vast majority, in Tulsa and Oklahoma City, are part-time, employed students.

Dr. Levin expressed mixed feelings about the faculty tenure system at the University of Oklahoma. "In the financial vagaries of the State of Oklahoma, I don't think we could function without tenure because there is no stability in this environment. Here, tenure is an attraction because it means you are guaranteed to be left alone to do your work. In some universities, [eliminating tenure] would improve them because the competition and desire to be there is so keen; there is always somebody in line [for every faculty position], ready to come in." But he said that for somebody taking over a college, faced with a large number of people who have been on the faculty for years and who

Dean Lee Holder, College of Allied Health. (University of Oklahoma)

are tenured, it is very hard to install any kind of incentives to motivate behavior. "I think the leadership allowed a lot of 'third-ratism' here. I think it is the fault of what was expected by the university. I am astounded the College of Public Health was not disbanded."

Looking to the future of the college, Dr. Levin thought it would still have some difficulty. He said more young faculty should be added to the departments to maintain the momentum. "The new faculty really bring some zest to the school and, in the financial crunch, it doesn't look like they're going to be adding anybody here. You can't run a school where you have 25 faculty positions and 23 of them are essentially tenured. You constantly have to add new blood—junior faculty and research assistants." Dr. Levin resigned because "to start a new school of public health 'from scratch' [at the University of South Florida in Tampa] and hire a whole new faculty was a terrific opportunity I simply could not refuse."[14]

Very few of the disciplines in allied health are in independent practice; only audiologists, speech pathologists and, to a certain extent, physical therapists. Others are dependent on physicians who make referrals and hospital administrators who make the jobs available. Lee Holder, Ph.D., dean of the O.U. College of Allied Health, said the changes in the payment system, DRGs and the like, would influence demand for people in allied health. As a part of the health care delivery team, allied health professionals are influenced by everything that goes on in the field. Therefore, "we are foolish if we aren't very flexible in trying to meet those demands out there in the real world," Dr. Holder observed. He added:

In 1980, with the projected surplus of physicians, everyone was saying "Physicians are not going to call on allied health personnel to the same extent." However, the GMENAC report concentrated on physician surrogates—P.A.s, nurse practitioners and nurse midwives. So my conclusion was, the more surgeons there are, the more surgeries; hence, more demand for laboratory, x-ray, rehabilitation services, physical therapy and occupational therapy.

As a result of DRGs, the demand will still be there but the workplace is going to change. For example: we are already seeing the acute, general hospital rearranging and restaffing laboratory services. The typical hospital will probably hire the associate degree MLT, medical laboratory technician, instead of the baccalaureate-trained medical technologist. They are going to get the lowest trained personnel they can get by with—under adequate supervision.

The interesting implication is that the demand for the medical technologist will not decrease. For example, as a result of competition, more group practices are being set up which are starting to do their in house laboratory tests as an income source and because they don't want to refer patients out. There will be greater demands on us to prepare advanced level professionals for independent and interdependent practice and to supervise lesser-trained people. The physical therapist, for example, will be treating more people on an outpatient basis, in the home or in some alternative facility.

Eight percent of the people who make a living in health care are called physicians; two percent are dentists; three percent are pharmacists and 21 percent are nurses. Sixty percent are in those occupations or professions we call allied health. Where I see expansion is in graduate level programs. In physical therapy, for example, we are looking at a graduate program that may have a track in sports medicine and another in pediatrics. I see a graduate program in clinical dietetics. And we need better articulation with the junior colleges which are training the associate degree level people so medical technicians can become medical technologists at the baccalaureate level—a career ladder system.

There are no doubt two countervailing forces here. One is the marketplace that has to be as cost effective as possible. The temptation is to hire the lowest trained people possible which may affect the quality of care. The other is the natural tendency for a health occupation to become a health profession. People want their profession to become known, to become accredited and licensed, which assures quality but also keeps other

people out, thus forming an economic base. The current hot debate: the American Physical Therapy Association has declared that by 1990, the entry level for physical therapists will be a post-baccalaureate degree. We translate that "master's," some translate that "doctorate." The next step, of course, might be; if there is a school of pharmacy, why not have a school of physical therapy? As educators, some of us deans are not convinced that post-baccalaureate education is necessary at the entry level. So the debate goes on.

I believe the role of the O.U. College of Allied Health is to be the center of excellence for this state [which means] graduate education, continuing education and resources for consultation. We must grasp the hands of the junior colleges, vo-tech schools and other senior colleges which do the basic level education. They should be feeding into us and we should be supporting them.[15]

When H. Richard Shough, Ph.D., interim dean of the College of Pharmacy, joined the faculty in June of 1978, he was amazed at the lack of visibility of the campus. He lived in Edmond, Oklahoma, and when he cashed checks there, people would ask him where he worked. When he replied the Health Sciences Center, they would ask, "Where's that?" Or, if he said the University of Oklahoma, they would say, "Oh, you commute to Norman." People did not know the college of medicine was in the O.U. Health Sciences Center. People knew that Human Services was a major state agency and Lloyd Rader was located there and highly involved in it. People knew him but they still did not know the Oklahoma Health Center. They were confused by the entities on the campus.

Dr. Shough reported in June, 1984, that the search committee for the new dean to replace Dr. Ice had made its recommendations to the president of the university. Not a candidate himself, Dr. Shough hoped the new leader would be on board for the start of classes in September, 1984. He observed that the dramatic changes in the profession of pharmacy were already here but had not been recognized. One was the kinds of careers into which pharmacy graduates entered; hospital pharmacy, drug manufacturing and pharmaceutical research. Another was that the students in pharmacy, once an exclusively male profession, now represented the normal sexual distribution in the population—52 percent female and 48 percent male. Those changes, he said, were a reflection of some basic, underlying changes in drugs, therapy and the drug distribution system. He continued:

The things which have given rise to the change in pharmacy, medicine, all health professions are the basic so-

Dr. Richard Shough, interim dean when Dr. Ice left, was not a candidate for the position at the College of Pharmacy. (University of Oklahoma)

cio-economic changes of the last 25 years and certainly, the technological changes. If we want to be honest, *solid state electronics*! It's comparable to the wheel, to the industrial revolution, and it goes far beyond the computer. Telecommunications and fiber optics—these were obscure laboratory phenomena a few decades back that changed the shape of all health sciences, of our economy, of our society. Genetic engineering had not yet had that effect but will have a tremendous impact on drugs. I think we are now right in the midst of another therapeutic revolution. We will have new types of drugs we [previously] were just not able to prepare.

Pharmacy begins with developing new drugs. You will not see the medicinal chemist of the future with a lot of test tubes. Computers have opened up a whole new horizon of molecular manipulation. With computer simulations, we can study, right down to the molecular level, the shape and size of drugs. The way to picture how a drug works is the "lock and key theory," a theory which goes back more than a hundred years. Drugs are three-dimensional; the fact that they are submicroscopic does not change that. They've got shapes, like that coffee cup or that telephone, and they've got to fit with something to interact with it. They are really no different from the hormones and enzymes in our bodies; they are drugs, too. DNA is a double helix that is twisted; there is a possiblity of a right-handed twist or a left-handed twist. Take the drug epinephrine, or adrenaline: there is an "L" form and a "D" form; they are mirror images. Only one fits. It is like my right hand fits into my right glove, which

is my receptor, and my left hand fits into my left glove, but I can't switch gloves. That's the way drugs are.

The way we manipulated and developed drugs in the past was very gross. Antibiotics like penicillin are a good example: get soil samples, grow a microorganism, put it with other microorganisms and see if it inhibits their growth. It was very hit or miss; serendipity played the part. We pretend in our classrooms we did it rationally and by scientific investigation, [but] the most significant discoveries of man happened by *blind luck*! The important thing was that the guy who happened to be there was an open-minded person. And he didn't have to be a Ph.D. to see its significance.

Today, we can do things more rationally. The computer lets us study so many variables so rapidly, variables which would take a lifetime to study in the laboratory by trial and error. We are almost at the point today of observing individual molecules in the body.

We had very few drugs before the therapeutic revolution of the 1950s. Without many drugs and without electronic surgical techniques, physicians largely had [only] bedside manners. They were good diagnosticians but what tools did they have to cure with? Their success rates were bad. Most of the good drugs have come since the 1950s; antibiotics and hormones. Infectious diseases have been well controlled. In the biological field, immunology has been the revolution of the last couple of decades and it is closely tied to genetics.

The types of drugs we are going to see in the future will be peptide drugs. Chemists hate peptides because peptides don't make chemists look bright! They are hard to work with, hard to isolate from the body, hard to synthesize. Genetic engineering [now] lets us synthesize them. Interferon is a peptide [as are] growth hormones and the endorphines, the so-called "brain opium." We've known about peptides for many years but we have not been able to synthesize them well. They are very biologically active and the ones we identified first, like insulin, were in relatively large amounts in the glands and in the blood. The ones that are being identified now are the ones which are in trace amounts in the brain, like endorphines.

In his book, *Brave New World*, Aldous Huxley introduced *soma*, a "pleasure" drug, but I guess the first mind-altering drug was the apple in the Garden of Eden. The most notorious mind-altering drug in all cultures had been ethyl alcohol and, world around, perhaps the second has been caffeine. One property of endorphines is pain relief but certainly, mind-alteration is another. Pain is largely a perception, so if you relieve pain, you alter the patient's mind, his mental state. Pharmacy is involved with all areas of disease, mental and physical.

The problem with peptides is: they are rapidly metabolized by the body. You can't put Interferon in a capsule or a pill or an elixir as pharmacists have done [with drugs] for years. What is now happening is alternative dosage forms and delivery systems. With peptide drugs, this is a necessity because they are destroyed in the gut. They are metabolized on what is called "first pass." One pass of the drug through the body and it's gone, which means you have to deliver it locally. We would like to locally deliver every drug we use. Let's say we're using a steroid for inflammation of the knee. If you give a pill, the steroid is distributed throughout the whole body but the [only] place it is doing some good is in the knee; anything else is inconsequential or a side effect. All drugs have side effects and the more you can localize the action of the drug, the fewer side effects you get. With the newer drugs, it will be absolutely necessary to deliver them locally because otherwise they are not going to work. We have to synthesize these drugs and deliver them—almost firing molecules at molecules, almost like firing lasers. That's what I see in the future.

Dean Shough noted that the currently austere budget was an acute problem for the college but added that it was a normal, economic cycle. Of the three basic resources, facilities, budget and personnel, the budget was possibly the least of his problems. The most serious one was manpower. "It is a very, very competitive world out there [in which] to get good faculty. This is a fundamental problem because if you lose good faculty, it is expensive and very hard to replace them." One factor was the diversity of the field. There were at least 10 tracks in pharmacy which required specialists on the faculty.

Another challenge Shough cited was keeping up with rapid technological change. Because the generation time of computers was only six years, frequent replacement of expensive equipment to meet the educational and research mission of the college was a "nitty-gritty, daily problem."[16]

Provost Clayton Rich's challenge was to move the entire O.U. Health Sciences Center forward according to an Academic Plan compiled in 1983. A planning council had established the goals of the center, the plans to achieve those goals and described the general organization and administration which would carry out those plans. Part IV of the document was a facilities development plan. Dr. Rich commented:

The needs of the institution are well described and the State Regents for Higher Education have recommended a budget that would really meet our needs. Under these [economic] circumstances, of course, their recommendations are not being funded. We are waiting until we have enough money to upgrade some departments that need it and hoping we won't have to

demolish anything that has been built up with such care over the years.

What we'll do is stage it. As funds become available, we'll take one objective and get that completed and then another and eventually, I trust, we'll get there.[17]

President William S. Banowsky observed that:

The O.U. Health Sciences Center is one of the great developments in modern Oklahoma history. I can say that I would not have come to the University of Oklahoma in 1978 had it not been for the strength of the Health Sciences Center and what was happening here. It was a crucial part of my decision.

We have *one* university—we are not a biversity or a multiversity. All of the fundraising is designed to head up in one university office. The financial needs of the Health Sciences Center should be a major priority of the total university, of its central administration. We should have large perspectives and grand visions in these matters. We should do more fundraising here.

This campus desperately needs a point of "life focus," where students and faculty can gather, where there can be a common eating facility and a place for recreation and relaxation. The popularity of the faculty house, small as it is, is just a slight indication of what a terrific contribution a central facility of this kind would make. That is a priority in my mind for fund raising, as is a family practice center. We need to be training more family practitioners to be sending out into the less populated areas of the state. We have a fine leader in Dr. Christian Ramsey, but we need superior facilities. The third one is a brand new research building—laboratories and equipment for research. Obviously, the physical development here is breath-taking and we can be thankful it occurred when it did because the cost of everything now is astronomical.

In my view, this campus is as important to the University of Oklahoma as the Norman campus. I think we need these [teaching] hospitals back, for instance. We need for purposes of academic management, more integration and less bifurcation of activity. Currently, we're charged with the teaching mission and others are charged with the management and service mission. In my view, that makes it more difficult. If the entire responsibility were under our board of regents and the University of Oklahoma administration, it would be more dynamic and would be more effective from a management and academic point of view. As it is currently being operated, we are vulnerable to all kinds of disagreements, disputes, differences of vision and philosophy of operation. Any month or year, we could find ourselves in some difficulty.

Having said that, as president of the University of Oklahoma, I would not recommend that we take these

OUSHC students enjoy a spring day in front of the College of Health in 1984 but there was no point of "life focus" on the campus for both students and faculty. (OHSF Collection)

teaching hospitals back unless and until the state legislature would do two things: first of all, provide an absolute, guaranteed formula for funding them at a high quality level and, second, that funding formula would be separate and apart from the university's regular funding. If it came through the State Regents for Higher Education, it would always be a hunting ground for problems.

If these criteria could be met, Banowsky concluded, "then these hospitals should be under the University of Oklahoma Board of Regents and the whole program would operate more effectively." However, the president saw "absolutely no momentum to cause that to come about in the forseeable future." About a proposed plan for private enterprise to develop land leased from the University on Lincoln Boulevard between 8th and 10th Street, the president said, "I strongly favor this plan because I think this Health Sciences Center needs that critical mass of complementary facilities. We need the hotel

space, we need the continuing education and the convention-type facilities." For the time being, this plan was in abeyance until Presbyterian Hospital completed its hotel project.[18]

The Oklahoma Health Center institutions affiliating with the university were also looking ahead. Harvey Everest believed that Bill Thurman was one of only two true administrators in the history of the Oklahoma Medical Research Foundation. Thurman said that when he became president in October, 1979, it was obvious "the foundation was plateaued and did not yet know which way it was going to go for the next 15 or 20 years or what to do about it." "For that reason," he added, "it was an exciting challenge." It appeared that, with the exception of the brief period during which Colin MacLeod was in charge, OMRF had been on that plateau since Dr. Eliel had been asked to resign. However, evaluation of scientific progress over the period of OMRF's existence was difficult. Reagan Bradford, Ph.D., M.D., had been associated

Researcher and administrator Reagan Bradford. (Oklahoma Medical Research Foundation)

with the foundation since 1957, served in a senior scientific and administrative role after MacLeod's death until July 1, 1974 when Sam White, M.D., was appointed president. It was his opinion that:

> In science, if you have achieved the discovery of penicillin, [your progress] is pretty clear, but there are so very few of those. As a rule, scientists contribute pieces to a puzzle and quite often, an individual scientist's view of what is important is influenced by those things that attract him.
>
> I feel there has been meaningful and substantive progress in a majority of the [OMRF] research programs, on the average and over the years. There were periods during which OMRF made major contributions which influenced the thought and views of others in scientific areas, some of which had national and international impact. This was not in the sense of a single, spectacular discovery but rather influence on a trend or direction. To say how important those [were or] will be, is a value judgment. One of the best evidences of progress was the ability of major programs here to compete favorably for federal funding, even when the dollars got tighter and tighter.[19]

Dr. Thurman and the group at the foundation devised and implemented an incremental 10, 15 and 20 year plan, charting where OMRF was going and what it would need to get there. Thurman explained:

> The role of OMRF as a research foundation has now been defined. We have clearly determined its ultimate size on the basis of our ability to have the money to do things. We know the square footage [required] to fit that general program. I don't mean to say we know every scientist we'll have, but we have put into place a program that is modern and relates to the research thrust of the next 20 years. We have recruited both individual and group capabilities to meet that overall plan.
>
> I think we have reasonably well defined that the foundation will have a significant impact in the research of immunology related to human disease; across the board, better than almost any other research institute in the country. Some have tremendous programs in immunology and cancer. We'll never be that big, but Dr. Robert Good and his people are clearly on the cutting edge of that. Other people have strong programs in immunology and arthritis, but they don't have them in cancer. Others have them in heart disease but don't have them in the other two.
>
> We've built a base for immunology for cancer, arthritis and heart disease, across the board, to be studied here and in the hospital. That's where we'll go insofar as applying a very basic but rapidly developing research technique to those three major aspects of human disease. Our basic laboratory emphasis, non-specifically related to disease, will come into configuration with immunology.[20]

Across the campus at the McGee Eye Institute, Tom Acers had drafted, in 1981, a 10-year expansion program which would carry the MEI into the 1990's. When Dean McGee was asked if he had any doubts that the institution which bears his name would be successful, he replied, "No, not really." "The eye institute," he continued, "has met and exceeded my expectations. I hoped we could develop a really first class institute to serve this middle part of the country. A lot of other people were involved in making it a success. It really has turned out well."[21]

By June 1, 1984, the $2.4 million needed to complete the shelled-in third floor had been raised and completion of that project was targeted for December 6, 1985, the 10th anniversary of the institute. The plan was to place all support services, such as administration, accounting, optical shop, eye bank, and the like, on the third level so that the other levels could be used exclusively for patient services (1 and 2), research (4) and education (5).

Because McGee had insisted on a site large enough to accommodate future growth, the institute had space for a similar building to the south into which all research activities could be moved and expanded, "somewhere between 1990 and 1994," according to the director. Dr. Acers said, "There are probably more dramatic research findings in ophthalmology than in other [medical] specialties." He explained:

Much of the research we are doing now and probably in the future is clinically oriented. I would support Hopkins, Harvard and all of the old, legendary research centers [but] after research moves out of those basic science laboratories, the next stage should be done in the Dean A. McGee Eye Institute, Bascom-Palmer [Eye Institute in Miami, Florida] and similar institutions. Our bent is always going to be in the direction of clinical research even though basic and clinical research are hard to separate at times.

Unfortunately, most of the research now going on is not toward preventive measures; that is, the basic, underlying disease process. It's [focused] on better control which, of course, is very important. Sometime, we must make up our collective minds, nationally and internationally, to get down to basic research on the genesis of eye disease. We really don't know *why* the retinal vessels bleed in diabetes. We know how to handle it *after* they bleed. We can't prevent it in the first place. The same with glaucoma; we don't even know the cause. We are getting better at managing glaucoma [but] it may not be primarily an eye disease. It may have something to do with the central nervous system.

The concept of hyperthermia [heat] is being used now in various fields of cancer treatment and even though we were involved in developmental research of the "heat probe," we quickly changed direction. We realized it had much greater application in eye work in that heat can literally change the shape of the cornea. Dr. [J.J.] Rowsey and his corneal shaping group have developed that to a very sophisticated plane of research. They can virtually change the shape of the cornea any way they want to, which can *potentially* correct anything…myopia, farsightedness, astigmatism, corneal scarring— anything that misshapes the cornea.

Malignant melanoma is a fairly common cancer affecting the eye in adults. Until recently, there was no treatment; we simply removed the eye—pretty simplistic sort of thinking! But now, with the advent of proton beams—particulate matter radiation—we are treating some of them very successfully. That is an exciting new area. In this institute, we see, maybe, 15 or 20 [such patients] a year and send them to California for treatment. We'll have that [treatment] facility one of these days.

In the area of prevention, maybe within 10 years, we'll probably be able to control or prevent the development of cataracts. We need some more studies, but there are some real bright young people in this field. There is even one in Boston who is now involved in a clinical study of biochemically preventing cataract development. Obviously, it will take years to follow this clinical research study, [but if it is successful] that would be a dramatic breakthrough.[22]

In the late 1970s and early 1980s, the physicians at the Veterans Administration Medical Center saw lovely buildings being built and equipped across the street and the V.A. was behind in that building cycle. In 1984, the V.A. was being brought abreast of the quality of facilities elsewhere in the Oklahoma Health Center. "So now, I think," Director Walter Whitcomb observed, "the balance of the technology and the support between the institutions is once again more proximate as the state's economy has receded and there is a greater emphasis on accountability of the expenditure of funds for those sister institutions. The same goes for the V.A., so the balance, in a sense, is better now than it has been for many years." He said the emphasis was now on the quality of the individuals who provided care and education:

Our philosophy here is: how can we improve our management? How can we attract new talent into the health sciences center? We need to continue the emphasis on good people to create, to develop and to manage.

We have been so preoccupied with moving into our new $47 million ambulatory wing without jeopardizing patient care that it has consumed the time of the leadership. We still have to renovate our inpatient clinical units [in the original building] which will take at least another two years. However, I don't think this move has detrimentally affected our research activity or our inpatient care. The challenge is to build a management team that can create an environment in which creativity and excellence will thrive.

One of the long range strategies of the V. A. system was to expand the ability to reach out to eligible veterans. Beginning in mid-1984, the Oklahoma City unit expected to use a van to carry doctors to outlying state homes and communities to assess patients who may need long-term care. The catchment area around Lawton, Oklahoma, was underserved, so the V.A. Central Office proposed an outpatient facility there to make medical service more accessible to veterans. Asked if the future patient load of aging veterans was a "fiscal time bomb" similar to Social Security and Medicare, Whitcomb replied:

The V.A.'s chief medical director has said that if all of those veterans over 65 were to make their demands on the V.A. system, it would exceed the resources we anticipate. Our own demographic studies indicate the population over 65 in western Oklahoma will increase enormously by 1990. A qualifier is: we are actually seeing no more patients today [mid-1983] than we saw two years ago. That means these individuals are seeking their care elsewhere, for whatever reasons, in contrast to the situation 10 years ago. The distribution of health manpower has changed; some of the hospital facilities in smaller communities have been upgraded, so some patients seek care at home rather than drive long distances to the V.A. Medical Center in Oklahoma City. Our concern is: what is the deductible going to be on other third party sources of health care payment? What critical level will that deductible reach before the patient turns to the entitlement he holds with the V.A.? There are a lot of unknowns and we are trying to be prepared for either scenario. We probably tend to think we are going to have a lot more patients than a lot less. On the other hand, some of our staff think we may well be in competition [for patients] with the rest of the health care machinery in the state of Oklahoma.[23]

Dr. Whitcomb reported that in February, 1984, the V.A. began to experience an increase in its ambulatory patient load, possibly because of higher deductibles and DRGs, but no one could yet determine if that increase was a long-term trend.

The Oklahoma State Department of Health maintained a low profile because the actual work of the public health system of the state was done in the counties. Unless there was an epidemic, such as the outbreak of hepatitis which occurred in Marietta, Oklahoma, in 1983, the state department was not ordinarily in the public eye. The one exception was in environmental health, because most of the technical work in this area was done from the headquarters building in the Oklahoma Health Center.

Joan Leavitt, M.D., the Commissioner of Health, cited as a major achievement "the decentralization of our public health network out in the counties." She said she had:

> ...good administrators touching every county in the state. There are now 21 people out there running programs, seeing to the business of public health in Oklahoma. Kirk Mosley, at Enid, is one of them; each has several counties to supervise. We have 62 county health departments, and in the other 15 counties the administrator is responsible to see that what we have to be doing—sanitation or maternal and child health and the like—is going correctly. Our major problems at the moment have to do with maintaining health standards in nursing homes and boarding homes. As written, these are *minimum* standards, not necessarily what you and I would like to have.

Asked about the future, Dr. Leavitt admitted that her primary concern was the present:

Dr. Joan Leavitt, Commissioner of Health for the State of Oklahoma. (Oklahoma State Department of Health)

> Basically, what we have on our mind now is maintaining the services we already have with the current shortfall in dollars. We have been hit from both sides—federally and statewise. We are trying to stay afloat and so far we have been able to manage.[24]

Statistically, 1983 was the busiest year the Oklahoma City Clinic had ever experienced in terms of outpatient visits and admissions to the hospital. This outpatient visit trend continued in 1984 but there was an unexplained drop in hospital admissions during the first half of the year. Wayne Coventon speculated it was due to several reasons. The clinic's referring physicians out in the state were seeing fewer patients, due in part to the impact of the recession as people who were laid off no longer received health insurance benefits. Thus, there was a tendency for those physicians to treat as many patients as possible in their home community. Also, Coventon said there was much greater cost awareness among the 67 physicians in the Oklahoma City Clinic, who were now treating on an outpatient basis people they formerly would have hospitalized. He noted that the DRG limitations placed on hospitals had affected this decision-making process. Looking into the future, Conventon speculated that:

> ...the group could easily become a hundred physicians in our main and satellite facilities, based on the assessment of need. I can see the clinic involved in more satellites than we currently have. With the exception of a

few specialties, such as ophthalmology and psychiatry now being recruited, we feel very comfortable with the specialty composition we now have. We came to a mutual agreement with the McGee Eye Institute that we would add general ophthalmology, complementing both institutions.[25]

Despite the Herman Smith consultants conclusions that Presbyterian Hospital was located too far away to contribute to the university's educational program, it had become a major teaching affiliate. During fiscal year 1983, 56-fourth year and 74 third-year medical students rotated through clerkships there. There was an average complement of 21 resident physicians in family practice and nine other specialties working in the hospital. In addition, 34 students in nursing, 6 in physical therapy, 4 in occupational therapy and 8 hospital pharmacy students gained clinical experience at Presbyterian.

With a lower hospital census in 1984, Stanton L. Young, chairman of the board of trustees, forecast that:

We'll continue to develop services as a tertiary hospital. The emphasis will be on the development of centers of excellence where Presbyterian would be a regional if not a statewide resource, such as our gastroenterology institute. We now have people coming from all of the surrounding states because of this program. We will emphasize Presbyterian more as a clinical research hospital and less as a teaching hospital. If it were not for DRGs, I would see no contraction in the teaching program. The commitment is there but the new ways of reimbursing hospitals may require we reduce the extent of teaching. I see us playing the role of statewide referral hospital, particularly for certain areas, unique services such as the sleep disorders laboratory and sports medicine.

Mr. Young said he expected construction of the proposed hotel to begin by the end of 1984. Families that need to be close to patients in the hospitals would have priority. Patients coming for outpatient diagnostic tests and treatments would use the hotel. It would also serve patients who needed a few additional days of rest and recuperation after discharge from the hospital where they could have ready access to the staff and services of the Presbyterian Hospital. "Also," Young added, "we shall be testing the general public market for hotel services."

In 1984, Presbyterian had the highest nurse to patient ratio—one staff nurse per occupied bed—among private hospitals in the Oklahoma City metropolitan area. The chairman pointed out:

That's where our costs are, so if we are going to maintain that high level of nursing care, which we feel contributes to quality medical service, we have to have outside sources of revenue. In addition, we must become very efficient and have a level patient load. The number of admissions will have to increase as the number of hospital days per illness decreases.[26]

All of the institutions on the Oklahoma Health Center campus had their immediate problems but each had charted its course, fixed its heading and seemed to be moving in the right direction. As Dean McGee observed, "The physical plant is pretty well built and it's a question now of quality people making it work." There were many quality people on board and, despite the current financial trough and turbulence, the campus institutions were holding steady.[27]

The progress in the surrounding neighborhood was not readily apparent, but if the four-year planning period required for the OHC was an appropriate yardstick, the redevelopment of Harrison-Walnut was about on schedule. The three "givens," the blood institute, the Chaparral townhouses, and the Pan Oklahoma cable television building, were, respectively, in operation, about to open or nearing completion. The Presbyterian hotel, parking facility and office building were expected to go under construction by the first of 1985. Lincoln National Bank had obtained its charter and was planning a temporary facility at Tenth Street and Lincoln Boulevard until its permanent building could be readied. Construction of the first 260-unit phase of a six-phase, 1,500-unit, rental apartment complex, proposed by Property Company of America (previously Lincoln Property Company), was scheduled for 1985. HTB, Inc., the Oklahoma City architectural and engineering firm, proposed restoration of the Maywood Baptist Church building at Ninth Street and Stiles Avenue and expansion of that structure southward to Stiles Circle as its new corporate and design headquarters. Leonard Ball, one of the principals, said their firm was interested in historic preservation and blending the old with the new to create a pleasing and exciting environment.

Three of the original proposers were also moving forward in the planning phase of their projects for professional offices, specialized commercial and townhouses. In addition, a dozen new single family houses had been erected in the R-20 urban renewal area south of the OHC and a new day care center for 165 children had been approved for this part of Harrison-Walnut. Perhaps the elements of the "community of scholars" proposed for the campus would yet

Board Chairman Stanton L. Young presents a plaque to the popular comedian as the Bob Hope Eye Surgery Center opens. (Presbyterian Hospital)

develop in the neighborhood for the convenience of those who attended college or worked on campus and undoubtedly to the satisfaction of Dr. C.G. Gunn who opposed the idea of housing graduate students in campus compounds.

CHAPTER 46

THE OKLAHOMA HEALTH CENTER: TWENTY YEARS LATER

Transmutation of the Dennis dream into reality was not easy, as this two-decade chronicle of events attests. Nor were the results perfect. Some of the efforts to bring about these results were misdirected, politicized, and overly expensive but almost all were well intentioned. Despite numerous difficulties over the years, the Oklahoma Health Center was a remarkable achievement. Oklahoma now has a modern, academic, tertiary health care center which will serve its people for many years to come.

Several of the people who were deeply involved in the creation of this health campus offered their conclusions. Harry Neer:

> There has been disunity among the leadership on the campus at times, whether created by the legislature, by an acquisition, for whatever reasons. Over the next few years, I feel we'll see greater unity come about. It has been hard to work together to project this center as a unified campus. It has been extremely difficult to get together around a table because everybody was going in different directions—trying to survive.
>
> If we weren't worried about survival and only worried about success and we defined success as taking care of the people of Oklahoma, [we would recognize] there is enough business for all on this center. There is not enough business for all of the hospitals in Oklahoma and there is certainly not enough business for all of the hospitals in Oklahoma City. We are going to see a very highly competitive environment develop.
>
> Now is the time for that unity. Now is the time for the spokespeople to talk the same thing. There is nothing wrong with each institution having its own goals—got to—but we ought to all be going in the same direction.[1]

It was Bill Bell's opinion that the cost of health care was a great tragedy. He said, "We can't afford to do everything for everybody, but the real tragedy is we have not been able to start talking about what the priorities are and how to relate what we do to the quality of life. We are still throwing many dollars, much manpower, and much effort trying to solve all these problems without recognizing the effect on the quality of life." He went on to assert that this gets back to leadership. "You have 10 agencies in the Health Center and their institutional egos are such that each one

Attorney Bill Bell of Tulsa headed the Board of Trustees of the Oklahoma Medical Research Foundation. (OMRF)

of them thinks they're going to be the number one boy. You can't have that." He continued:

> The leadership comes from the hands-on people, the people in each institution who make the day-to-day decisions. But you also have to have understanding in the governor's office of the importance of this health sciences center. You are going to have to have the Oklahoma City leadership get involved; then bring in the key people out of Tulsa, Ardmore, Muskogee and Ponca City who are interested in health services to be the catalyst to move this thing forward.
>
> So it's a mixture of two things. The trustees can't make the day to-day decisions. But there has to be philosoph-

ical understanding among the major constituent groups here that they are going to be able to work together. That takes some decisions from the top guidance groups to say it is going to happen.

During the Dennis years, things were done. Decisions were made. There was discussion and a coming together and we haven't seen that for a while. Centers like the Oklahoma Health Center do not survive without lay leadership. They [lay leaders] cannot develop them and then walk away, saying, "They're big boys now; they can run their own shops." Great universities are not developed and run by faculties. Great universities are developed by leadership—usually a small group of trustees or regents is involved. The future of this health sciences center is going to be based on this kind of lay leadership.

I'm very concerned because the Oklahoma Health Sciences Foundation is slipping away. The Oklahoma City leadership is going to have to play a hands-on role. They are going to have to force the people who make the day-to-day decisions back into meetings which are on a first-level basis. When you are talking about parking and those types of problems, you are down to a "marching and chowder society."

We may have no choice but that the [Oklahoma Health Sciences] Foundation will come to an end one of these days. In my view, somewhere down the line, someone will have to pick up this [responsibility] again. It may be a governor who can put an advisory board together, with trustees from all of these [OHC] groups who have the power to be an umbrella board, officially or unofficially. It may be recognition by O.U. and the groups out here that they need this kind of umbrella board. Right now, each of these institutions wants to go its own way—that's human nature. But I hope we don't go through what I consider the tragedy of having to go some years without *any* type of board.[2]

Dean Bill Brown of the College of Dentistry concurred with Bell's thinking:

The public is asking more questions; they want to participate in the decision-making on their own health care. I'm absolutely supportive of that. I'm a person who is provided health care by others, too, and I bloody well want to participate in the decision-making: how often I go, what's going to be done, the whole bit. I think we should pull the public in with us more and more.

The cost of health care is almost obscene, it's so bad. We've got to do a better job. There are others out there, putting dental offices in shopping centers; corporate groups setting up chains [of dental offices] around the country. They're doing it at less cost and, with their hours the same as the shopping centers, making it more convenient for the people. They are trying to look after the people.

I don't disagree with Bill Bell at all. I'm not sure whether it should be a super-board, but I would welcome bringing the public into the health professions more and more.[3]

Frank Rees, whose firm had completed over 300 health care projects and was working in the Texas Medical Center in 1984, had the opportunity to compare the Oklahoma Health Center with similar campuses throughout the United States and in other parts of the world. After working with three major institutions in the OHC, it was his opinion that:

All of those buildings are fine pieces of architecture by themselves. I do not think they relate to each other in a manner that is successful and I'm glad we have the space between them. As it fills in, we may find that we will grow up and have one firm assigned to be at least an executive architect, reviewing the work of others. Eventually it will have a continuum and be a series of buildings that provides for efficient transportation of patients, materials, communication and utilities between the buildings we already have. The major opportunity was missed when the parking blanket idea was vetoed; we lost that continuum. The open spaces we have give us a second chance to have a great medical center some day.

The current Oklahoma Health Center shows its best face at night when it has a unified lighting system. That is because it is still in the awakening stage as a medical center. Even my Aunt Myrtle looks a lot better at 9 o'-clock in the morning when she has her "face" on and is starting to work than she does at 7:15 when she is just getting up and still has her hair in rollers. The OHC still has its hair in rollers. It's half way there.

If you think about the eventual development of the Oklahoma Health Center, you have to be very excited about the guaranteed future, even though there have been major disappointments. The wide open spaces that resulted from the early planning and from Mercy Hospital leaving to go out north will turn out to be a blessing. There is a fine residential neighborhood on the north side of the Medical Center that's on its way back as a beautiful place to live. The Harrison-Walnut area is in the process of renewal and if it continues in the direction it is going, will be a well-developed area that will complement the Health Center and join it to downtown. The major vehicular circulation system, the Central Expressway, is going to provide the Health Center with convenient contact with the north and the south.[4]

Former University of Oklahoma President Paul Sharp summed up the two decades between 1964 and 1984:

The Oklahoma Health Center turned out surprisingly

(University of Oklahoma)

well, given all the turmoil, stress, tension, misunderstandings, political rivalries and the "confusion of tongues" that accompanied it all. Today, you see the essentials of providing this state with a major center for health care, for health professional education, for health research—all of the things which Dr. Dennis is credited with having dreamed about. Of course, others contributed to that dream. There were lots of planners who enriched the result.

I think everybody who contributed to it ought to feel a certain sense of satisfaction. Here is a major health science center built with relatively limited resources. And that's a great achievement! Anybody can build magnificently with unlimited resources but it takes a great deal of effort, energy and imagination to build where resources are limited. That's what Oklahoma has done.[5]

NOTES

Introduction

[1]Interview, G. Rainey Williams, M.D., October 13, 1983, (Oklahoma Health Sciences Foundation Collection hereafter cited as OHSFC.)
[2]Interview, William L. Parry, M.D., January 19, 1984, OHSFC.
[3]Raymond E. Brady, ed., *The 1968 Sooner Medic*, Student Council, University of Oklahoma School of Medicine, p. 10.
[4]Donald B. Halverstadt, M.D., Interim Provost, OUHSC, Agency Heads Meeting, Oklahoma Health Center, November 28, 1979; Interview, C.G. Gunn, M.D., March 2, 1983, OHSFC.

Chapter 1

[1]Interview, James L. Dennis, M.D., February 26, 1983, OHSFC.
[2]Interview, Malcom E. Phelps, M.D., April 21, 1983, OHSFC.
[3]Interview, Robert S. Ellis, M.D., April 19, 1983, OHSFC.
[4]Interview, Dennis, February 26, 1983, OHSFC.
[5]Interview, George L. Cross, Ph.D., March 8, 1983, OHSFC.
[6]Interview, Dennis, February 26, 1983, OHSFC.
[7]Interview, Cross, March 8, 1983, OHSFC.
[8]Interview, Mark R. Johnson, M.D., March 16, 1983, OHSFC.
[9]Interview, Dennis, February 26, 1983, OHSFC.
[10]The Carnegie Commission on the Future of Higher Education, *Higher Education and the Nation's Health: Policies for Medical and Dental Education, A Special Report and Recommendations*, New York, McGraw Hill, October, 1970, p. 18; Mark S. Blumberg, *Trends and Projections of Physicians in the United States 1967-2002*, Berkeley, California, Carnegie Commission on Higher Education, 1971, p. 11.

Chapter 2

[1]Interview, E. T. Dunlap, Ed.D., January 19, 1983, OHSFC.
[2]*Ibid.*
[3]*Ibid.*
[4]*Ibid.*
[5]National Commission on Community Health Services, *Health Is a Community Affair*, Harvard University Press,1966; Interview, Jack Boyd, February 4, 1983, OHSFC.
[6]Interview, Mark Johnson, March 16, 1983, OHSFC.
[7]Interview, Louis Jolyon West, M.D., October 28, 1982, OHSFC.
[8]Interview, Stewart Wolf, M.D., June 27, 1983, OHSFC.
[9]Interview, Lloyd E. Rader, August 19, 1983, OHSFC.
[10]Interview, Mark Johnson, March 16, 1983, OHSFC.
[11]Interview, John Schilling, M.D., November 6, 1982, OHSFC.
[12]Interview, Parry, January 19, 1984, OHSFC.
[13]Interview, Mark Allen Everett, M.D., April 22, 1983, OHSFC.
[14]Interview, Schilling, November 6, 1982, OHSFC.
[15]Interview, Dunlap, January 19, 1983, OHSFC.
[16]Interview, Raymond Crews, February 23, 1984, OHSFC.
[17]Interview, Schilling, November 6, 1982, OHSFC.

Chapter 3

[1]Mark R. Everett, *Medical Education in Oklahoma*, Norman, University of Oklahoma Press, 1980, pp. 131, 148.
[2]Interview, E.W. Young, M.D., March 23, 1983, OHSFC.
[3]Interview, James A. Merrill, M.D., September 16, 1983, OHSFC.
[4]Interview, Jenell Hubbard, R.N., March 1, 1983, OHSFC.
[5]*Ibid.*
[6]Interview, Crews, February 23, 1984, OHSFC.
[7]Interview, William W. Schottstaedt, M.D., March 27, 1983, OHSFC.

[8]Interview, Dennis, February 26, 1983, OHSFC; Interview, Schilling, November 6, 1982, OHSFC.
[9]Interview, Dale Groom, M.D., March 29, 1983, OHSFC.

Chapter 4

[1]Interview, Dennis, February 26, 1983, OHSFC.
[2]Interview, Joseph M. White, M.D., April 29, 1983, OHSFC.
[3]Interview, Dennis, February 26, 1983, OHSFC.
[4]Interview, Bill J. Blair, January 12, 1983, OHSFC.
[5]Interview, Crews, February 23, 1984, OHSFC.
[6]Interview, Blair, January 12, 1983, OHSFC; Interview, David Benham, April 21, 1983, OHSFC.
[7]Interview, Dennis, February 26, 1983, OHSFC; L.J. West, C. M. Pierce, & W.D. Thomas, "Lysergic acid diethylamide: Its Effects on a Male Asiatic Elephant," *Science*, Volume 138, 1962, pp. 1100-1103.

Chapter 5

[1]Interview, Dennis, February 26, 1983, OHSFC.
[2]*Ibid.*
[3]Interview, Lester Gorsline, October 29, 1982, OHSFC.
[4]Interview, Mark Johnson, March 16, 1983, OHSFC; Interview, William Campbell, December 1, 1982, OHSFC.
[5]Interview, Mark Johnson, March 16, 1983, OHSFC.
[6]Interview, Roger Bennett, November 5, 1982, OHSFC.
[7]*Ibid.*
[8]Interview, Dennis, February 26, 1983, OHSFC.
[9]*Ibid.*

Chapter 6

[1]Oklahoma State Regents for Higher Education (hereafter cited as OSRHE), "Medical Education in Oklahoma", June, 1965.
[2]Interview, Joseph White, April 29, 1983, OHSFC.
[3]Interview, Dennis, February 26, 1983, OHSFC.
[4]Interview, Dunlap, January 19, 1983, OHSFC.
[5]Interview, Dennis, February 26, 1983, OHSFC.
[6]OSRHE, "Medical Education in Oklahoma", 1965.
[7]*Ibid.*
[8]*Ibid.*
[9]*Ibid.*
[10]*Ibid.*; Interview, Mark Johnson, March 16, 1983, OHSFC.
[11]OSRHE, "Medical Education in Oklahoma", 1965.
[12]*Ibid.*
[13]*Ibid.*
[14]*Ibid.*
[15]*Ibid.*
[16]Interview, Robert C. Terrill, June 29, 1983, OHSFC.
[17]OSRHE, "Medical Education in Oklahoma", 1965.
[18]*Ibid.*; Interview, Jack Boyd, February 4, 1983, OHSFC.

Chapter 7

[1]Interview, Joseph White, M.D., April 29, 1983, OHSFC.
[2]John Samuel Ezell, *Innovations in Energy: The Story of Kerr McGee*, Norman, University of Oklahoma Press, 1979, p. 182.
[3]Interview, Dennis, February 26, 1983, OHSFC.
[4]Interview, Paul Strasbaugh, December 29, 1982, OHSFC.
[5]Interview, Gloria Bremkamp, February 11, 1983, OHSFC.
[6]Interview, Dennis, February 26, 1983, OHSFC.
[7]*Ibid.*
[8]Interview, Dean A. McGee, July 23, 1983, OHSFC.

[9]Interview, Henry Bellmon, October 13, 1983, OHSFC.
[10]Interview, Dennis, February 26, 1983, OHSFC.
[11]Interview, Cross, March 8, 1983, OHSFC.
[12]Interview, Dennis, February 26, 1983, OHSFC.
[13]"Proposed 'Umbrella' Foundation for the Oklahoma Health Center," July, 1965 Archives of the Oklahoma Health Sciences Foundation, Inc. (hereafter cited as OHSF).
[14]Articles of Incorporation, December 15, 1965, OHSF.
[15]Ibid.
[16]Ibid.

Chapter 8

[1]Interview, Dennis, February 26, 1983, OHSFC; "The Oklahoma Health Center Development Plan—1968", OHSF.
[2]"RESEARCH A Continuing Challenge For A Better Tomorrow," Report of the Oklahoma Medical Research Foundation, 1966; Mark R. Everett, *Pioneering For Research: Origin of the Oklahoma Medical Research Foundation*, University of Oklahoma Medical Center, 1966.
[3]Interview, Gene White, January 14, 1983, OHSFC; O.B. Faulk, C.N. Tyson, and J.M. Thomas, *The McMan: The Lives of Robert M. McFarlin and James A. Chapman*, Oklahoma Heritage Association, 1977.
[4]Interview, B. Connor Johnson, Ph.D., December 22, 1982, OHSFC.
[5]Interview, Dan Macer, December 14, 1982, OHSFC.
[6]Interview, Walter H. Whitcomb, M.D., July 25, 1983, OHSFC.
[7]Interview, Ted Clemens, M.D., February 15, 1983, OHSFC.
[8]Interview, Kirk Mosley, M.D., May 18, 1983, OHSFC.
[9]Interview, LeRoy Carpenter, M.D., May 11, 1983, OHSFC.
[10]Peggy Quinn Wright and Odie B. Faulk, *Coletta: A Sister of Mercy*, Oklahoma Heritage Association, 1981, pp. 96-111.
[11]Interview, Boyd Shook, M.D., August 23, 1982, OHSFC.
[12]Interview, Joyce Swingle, April 19, 1983, OHSFC.
[13]Interview, Goldie McCall, June 1, 1983, OHSFC.
[14]Interview, Charlotte DeCair, June 3, 1983, OHSFC.
[15]Interview, Carpenter, May 11, 1983, OHSFC.
[16]Interview, DeCair, June 3, 1983, OHSFC.
[17]Ibid.
[18]Interview, Richard A. Clay, M.D., September 20, 1984, OHSFC.
[19]Oklahoma City Urban Renewal Authority, "Urban Renewal: The First Dozen Years," p. 1, OHSF.
[20]Interview, James B. White, January 6, 1983, OHSFC.
[21]Interview, Dennis, February 26, 1983, OHSFC.
[22]Ibid.
[23]Daily Oklahoman, March 3, 1966.
[24]Ibid.

Chapter 9

[1]Minutes, Executive Committee, May 6, 1966, OHSF.
[2]Ibid.
[3]Minutes, Operations Committee, May 27, 1966, OHSF.
[4]Oklahoma City Times, November 3, 1966.
[5]Articles of Incorporation, OHSF; Interview, Albert M. Donnell, April 30, 1983, OHSFC.
[6]Minutes, Operations Committee, July 13, 1966, OHSF.
[7]Interview, Lawrence Lackey, June 15, 1983, OHSFC.
[8]Interview, Bennett, November 5, 1982, OHSFC.
[9]Interview, Gorsline, October 29, 1982, OHSFC.
[10]Minutes, Operations Committee, June 22, 1966, OHSF.
[11]Minutes, Operations Committee, June 29, 1966, OHSF.
[12]Interview, H. Dean Chrislip, December 8, 1982, OHSFC.
[13]Oklahoma City Times, November 3, 1966.

Chapter 10

[1]Interview, Thomas C. Points, M.D., Ph.D., May 24, 1983, OHSFC.
[2]Interview, Dennis, July 10, 1983, OHSFC.
[3]Interview, Points, May 24, 1983, OHSFC; *Daily Oklahoman*, July 21, 1966.
[4]Interview, Dennis, February 26, 1983, OHSFC.
[5]Interview, John Day Williams, May 18, 1983, OHSFC.

[6]Thomas C. Points, M.D., Ph.D., *The Wakita Story*, The University of Oklahoma School of Medicine, pp. 20, 21.
[7]Interview, Points, May 24, 1983, OHSFC.
[8]Interview, Roger Lienke, M.D., April 5, 1983, OHSFC.
[9]Interview, Gorsline, October 29, 1982, OHSFC.
[10]Interview, Lienke, April 5, 1983, OHSFC.
[11]Interview, John Day Williams, May 18, 1983, OHSFC.
[12]Interview, Points, May 24, 1983, OHSFC.
[13]Ibid.
[14]Interview, Thomas N. Lynn, M.D., February 7, 1983, OHSFC.
[15]Interview, John Day Williams, May 18, 1983, OHSFC.
[16]Archives, Oklahoma State Board of Medical Examiners.
[17]Interview, Terrill, June 29, 1983, OHSFC.

Chapter 11

[1]*Daily Oklahoman*, January 13, 1967.
[2]Interview, Nancy Davies, September 27, 1983, OHSFC; Interview, Philip Smith, Sc.D., May 31, 1983, OHSFC.
[3]Archives, Oklahoma Publishing Company; Interview, Dennis, February 26, 1983, OHSFC.
[4]Interview, Frank B.Cox, Jr., D.D.S., June 3, 1983, OHSFC.
[5]Interview, Frank D. Lyons, April 22, 1983, OHSFC.
[6]Interview, Monty C. Murphy, March 7, 1983, OHSFC.
[7]Ibid.
[8]Daily Oklahoman, July 16, 1968, July 23, 1968.
[9]Interview, Bryce Baggett, January 26, 1983, OHSFC.

Chapter 12

[1]The Carnegie Commission on the Future of Higher Education, *Higher Education and the Nation's Health*.
[2]Daily Oklahoman, July 26, 1967.
[3]Interview, Frances I. Waddle, R.N., March 9, 1983, OHSFC.
[4]Interview, Phillip P. Chandler, Ph.D., September 6, 1983.
[5]Interview, Waddle, March 9, 1983, OHSFC.
[6]Archives, OHSF.
[7]Interview, Robert G. Hirschi, D.D.S., February 21, 1983, OHSFC; Interview, Frosty Troy, October 19, 1983, OHSFC.
[8]Interview, William E. Brown, D.D.S., August 25, 1983, OHFSC.
[9]Interview, John Bruhn, Ph.D., March 28, 1983, OHSFC.
[10]Interview, Lienke, April 5, 1983, OHSFC; *Daily Oklahoman*, December 10, 1966, August 8, 1968.

Chapter 13

[1]Interview, Wolf, June 27, 1983, OHSFC.
[2]Interview, James L. Dennis, M. D., July 10, 1983, OHSFC.
[3]Lester Gorsline Associates—Lawrence Lackey and Associates, "The Oklahoma Health Center Development Plan 1968", OHSF.
[4]Ibid.
[5]Interview, Arthur Tuttle, January 11, 1983, OHSFC.
[6]Interview, Gunn, March 2, 1983, OHSFC.
[7]Gorsline and Lackey, "The Oklahoma Health Center Development Plan 1968", OHSF.
[8]Ibid.
[9]Ibid.
[10]Interview, Campbell, December 1, 1982, OHSFC.
[11]Interview, Gorsline, October 29, 1982, OHSFC.
[12]Oklahoma Journal, February 4, 1968.

Chapter 14

[1]Oklahoma City Times, March 21, 1967.
[2]Interview, Baggett, January 26, 1983, OHSFC.
[3]Interview, Dunlap, January 19, 1983, OHSFC.
[4]Daily Oklahoman, April 7, 1967.
[5]Interview, Dunlap, January 19, 1983, OHSFC.
[6]Daily Oklahoman, July 31, 1967.
[7]Interview, Dunlap, January 19, 1983; Interview, Bremkamp, February 11, 1983, OHSFC.

[8]Interview, William P. Willis, April 10, 1984, OHSFC.
[9]Archives, OHSF; Interview, Dennis, February 26, 1983, OHSFC.
[10]*Daily Oklahoman*, November 16, 19, 22, 23, 25, 27, 29, December 3, 1968; *Sunday Oklahoman*, November 17, 24, December 8, 1968; *Oklahoma City Times*, November 15, 18, 19, 20, 21, 22, 25, 26, 27, 30, 1968.
[11]Archives, OHSF.
[12]*Daily Oklahoman*, December 11, 1968.
[13]Interview, Bremkamp, February 11, 1983, OHSFC.
[14]*Daily Oklahoman*, February 10, 1969.
[15]Oklahoma City Chamber of Commerce Report, "Developing a Vital Community Asset: Hospital Modernization and Expansion, June 19, 1969, OHSF.
[16]*Ibid.*
[17]*Ibid.*
[18]*Daily Oklahoman*, October 9, 1969.
[19]Interview, Strasbaugh, December 29, 1982, OHSFC.
[20]Oklahoma City Chamber of Commerce, Report II, "Developing a Vital Community Asset: Hospital Modernization and Expansion," December, 1969, OHSF.
[21]Interview, Clemens, February 15, 1983, OHSFC.
[22]Oklahoma City Chamber of Commerce, Report II, "Developing a Vital Community Asset: Hospital Modernization and Expansion," December, 1969, OHSF.

Chapter 15

[1]*Daily Oklahoman*, August 3, 1967.
[2]*Oklahoma Journal*, October 18, 1967.
[3]*Daily Oklahoman*, June 4, 1968.
[4]Interview, C.G. Gunn, M.D., March 2, 1983, OHSFC.
[5]Interview, W. David Steen, Ph.D., March 24, 1983, OHSFC.
[6]Archives, OHSF.
[7]*Daily Oklahoman*, January 28, 1970.
[8]Interview, Charles Wagner, June 24, 1983, OHSFC.
[9]Interview, James W. Woods, Ph.D., June 24, 1983, OHSFC.
[10]Interview, L. Vernon Scott, Sc.D., August 22, 1983, OHSFC.
[11]Interview, Tuttle, January 11, 1983, OHSFC.
[12]Interview, Everett, April 22, 1983, OHSFC.
[13]*Ibid.*
[14]*Daily Oklahoman*, June 19, 1970.

Chapter 16

[1]*Daily Oklahoman*, July 25, 1968.
[2]*The Denver Post*, October 13, 1968.
[3]*Oklahoma City Times*, August 5, 6, 7, 8, 1969.
[4]American Hospital Association, *Hospitals: Guide Issue*, 1968, Journal of the American Hospital Association, Chicago, Illinois.
[5]Interview, Albert M. Donnell, April 30, 1983, OHSFC.
[6]Archives, OHSF.
[7]Interview, Donnell, April 30, 1983, OHSFC.

Chapter 17

[1]*Tulsa Tribune*, December 18, 1967.
[2]*Ibid.*
[3]Interview, Richard D. Stansberry, M.D., June 8, 1983, OHSFC.
[4]The Study Committee on Medical Education, Tulsa County Medical Society (Hereafter cited as TCMS), "Medical Education in Tulsa County," November, 1981.
[5]*Oklahoma Journal*, December 27, 1967.
[6]Interview, Dennis, February 26, 1983.
[7]TCMS, "Medical Education in Tulsa County," November, 1981.
[8]Research Division, Oklahoma City Chamber of Commerce.
[9]*Oklahoma City Times*, January 28, 1969.
[10]TCMS, "Medical Education in Tulsa County," November, 1981.

Chapter 18

[1]Interview, Davies, September 27, 1983, OHSFC.
[2]*Oklahoma City Times*, May 24, 1967.

[3]Interview, Joseph White, August 29, 1983, OHSFC.
[4]Interview, Dale Groom, M.D., March 29, 1983, OHSFC.
[5]Interview, Leonard P. Eliel, M.D., November 4, 1982, OHSFC.
[6]Interview, Dennis, February 26, 1983, OHSFC.
[7]Interview, Eliel, November 4, 1982, OHSFC.
[8]Interview, Oscar Parsons, Ph.D., April 20, 1983, OHSFC.
[9]Interview, Joseph White, August 29, 1983, OHSFC.
[10]Interview, Edward N. Brandt, Jr., M.D., Ph.D., August 4, 1983, OHSFC.
[11]Interview, Joseph White, August 29, 1983; Interview, Dennis, February 26, 1983, OHSFC.
[12]Interview, Wolf, June 27, 1983, OHSFC.
[13]*Ibid.*
[14]*Oklahoma City Times*, September 18, 1969.
[15]*Oklahoma City Times*, September 30, 1969.

Chapter 19

[1]*Sunday Oklahoman*, August 3, 1969.
[2]*Ibid.*
[3]*Oklahoma City Times*, September 30, 1969.
[4]*Ibid.*
[5]*Daily Oklahoman*, September 30, 1969.
[6]*Daily Oklahoman*, January 28, 1970.

Chapter 20

[1]Interview, Shook, August 23, 1982, OHSFC.
[2]*Oklahoma City Times*, November 27, 1969.
[3]*Ibid.*
[4]Interview, Coletta, September 7, 1982, OHSFC; Wright and Faulk, *Coletta: A Sister of Mercy*, p. 137.
[5]Interview, Swingle, April 19, 1983, OHSFC.
[6]Interview, Charles L. Bennett, October 25, 1983, OHSFC.
[7]*Oklahoma Journal*, January 14, 1970.
[8]Interview, Shook, August 23, 1982, OHSFC.
[9]*Daily Oklahoman*, February 12, 1970.
[10]*Daily Oklahoman*, February 18, 25, 1970.
[11]*Oklahoma City Times*, March 2, 1970.
[12]Interview, W.Turner Bynam, M. D., April 25, 1983, OHSFC.
[13]Interview, Charles Bennett, October 25, 1983, OHSFC.
[14]*Daily Oklahoman*, May 15, 1970.
[15]*Oklahoma City Times*, March 5, 1970.
[16]Minutes, Board of Trustees, OHSF, June 24, 1969, OHSF.
[17]*Ibid.*
[18]Interview, Dennis, February 26, 1983, OHSFC.

Chapter 21

[1]Interview, J. Herbert Hollomon, Ph.D., June 29, 1983, OHSFC.
[2]*Ibid.*
[3]Gordon A. Christenson, *The Future of the University*, University of Oklahoma Press, 1969.
[4]Interview, Hollomon, June 29, 1983, OHSFC.
[5]*Ibid.*
[6]Interview, Mark Johnson, March 16, 1983, OHSFC.
[7]Interview, Hollomon, June 29, 1983, OHSFC.
[8]Interview, Dennis, February 26, 1983, OHSFC.
[9]*Oklahoma Journal*, May 26, 1970.
[10]*The Oklahoma Daily*, Norman, Oklahoma, October 16, 1968; Interview, Dennis, February 26, 1983, OHSFC.
[11]Interview, Ben Heller, M. D., October 30, 1982, OHSFC.
[12]. Interview, Campbell, December 1, 1982, OHSFC.
[13]. Interview, Hollomon, June 29, 1983, OHSFC.
[14]*Ibid.*
[15]*Oklahoma Journal*, June 15, 1970.
[16]*Oklahoma City Times*, June 23, 1970.
[17]Minutes, O.U. Board of Regents, June 24, 1970.
[18]Interview, Hollomon, June 29, 1983, OHSFC.
[19]*Ibid.*; Interview, Dennis, July 10, 1983, OHSFC.
[20]Interview, Reece McGee, January 21, 1983, OHSFC.

[21]*Oklahoma City Times*, June 25, 1970; Interview, Davies, September 27, 1983, OHSFC.

[22]*Oklahoma City Times*, June 25, 1970.

[23]Minutes, O.U. Board of Regents, June 24, 1970.

[24]*Daily Oklahoman*, June 27, 1970.

[25]Interview, Davies, September 27, 1983, OHSFC.

[26]*Daily Oklahoman*, June 27, 1970.

[27]*Oklahoma Journal*, July 7, 1970; Interview, Dennis, February 26, 1983, OHSFC.

[28]Interview, Dunlap, January 19, 1983, OHSFC.

[29]Interview, Dennis, February 26, 1983, OHSFC.

[30]Interview, Davies, September 27, 1983, OHSFC.

[31]Interview, Dennis, February 26, 1983, OHSFC.

[32]Interview, Mark Johnson, March 16, 1983, OHSFC; Interview, Wolf, June 27, 1983, OHSFC.

[33]Interview, James A. Merrill, M.D., September 16, 1983, OHSFC.

[34]Interview, Gordon Deckert, M.D., May 3, 1983, OHSFC.

[35]Minutes, O.U. Board of Regents, July 23, 1970.

[36]Interview, Campbell, December 1, 1982, OHSFC.

[37]*Oklahoma City Times*, July 8, 1970; *Oklahoma Journal*, July 8, 1970; *Daily Oklahoman*, July 8, 1970.

[38]Interview, Dennis, February 26, 1983, OHSFC.

[39]Interview, Tuttle, January 11, 1983, OHSFC.

[40]Interview, Eliel, November 4, 1982, OHSFC.

Chapter 22

[1]*Daily Oklahoman*, November 26, December 5, 1970; Minutes, O.U. Board of Regents, December 3, 1970.

[2]Interview, Terrill, June 29, 1983, OHSFC.

[3]Interview, Eliel, November 4, 1982, OHSFC.

[4]Interview, Dunlap, January 19, 1983, OHSFC.

[5]*Sunday Oklahoman*, January 24, 1971.

[6]*Ibid.*

[7]Interview, Paul Sharp, Ph.D., January 20, 1983, OHSFC.

[8]*Daily Oklahoman*, August 21, 1971.

[9]Interview, Sharp, January 20, 1983, OHSFC.

[10]Interview, Larry Brawner, February 16, 1983, OHSFC.

[11]Interview, Willis, April 10, 1984, OHSFC.

[12]*Daily Oklahoman*, December 7, 1971.

[13]Interview, Eliel, November 4, 1982, OHSFC.

[14]Interview, Sharp, January 20, 1983, OHSFC.

[15]Interview, Cox, June 3, 1983, OHSFC.

[16]*Daily Oklahoman*, March 6, 1972.

[17]Interview, Hamilton, February 3, 1984, OHSFC.

[18]Interview, Terrill, June 29, 1983, OHSFC.

[19]Interview, Rainey Williams, October 13, 1983, OHSFC.

[20]*Oklahoma Journal*, April 19, 1972.

[21]Robert E. L. Richardson and John W. Sturges, "Study of the University of Oklahoma Health Sciences Center," February, 1973, OHSF.

[22]Interview, Jeptha Dalston, Ph.D., July 7, 1983, OHSFC.

[23]Interview, Terrill, June 29, 1983, OHSFC.

[24]Interview, Dalston, July 7, 1983, OHSFC.

[25]Interview, Deckert, May 3, 1983, OHSFC.

Chapter 23

[1]Interview, Brawner, February 16, 1983, OHSFC.

[2]Interview, Sharp, January 20, 1983, OHSFC.

[3]Interview, Eliel, November 4, 1982, OHSFC.

[4]Richardson and Sturges, "Study of the University of Oklahoma Health Sciences Center"; Interview, Thomas E. Acers, M.D., January 27, 1983, OHSFC.

[5]Interview, Terrill, June 29, 1983, OHSFC.

[6]Richardson and Sturges, "Study of the University of Oklahoma Health Sciences Center"; Interview, Senator John McCune, January 11, 1983, OHSFC.

[7]Richardson and Sturges, "Study of the University of Oklahoma Health Sciences Center"; Interview, Dalston, July 7, 1983, OHSFC.

[8]Richardson and Sturges, "Study of the University of Oklahoma Health Sciences Center"; Interview, Sharp, January 20, 1983, OHSFC.

[9]Interview, Winston Howard, May 12, 1983; Richardson and Sturges,

"A Study of the University of Oklahoma Health Sciences Center"; Interview, Sharp, January 20, 1983, OHSFC.

[10]Richardson and Sturges, "A Study of the University of Oklahoma Health Sciences Center."

[11]Interview, Eliel, November 4, 1982, OHSFC.

[12]Interview, Dalston, July 7, 1983, OHSFC.

[13]Interview, Robert E. Lee Richardson, June 7, 1983, OHSFC.

[14]Interview, Brawner, February 16, 1983, OHSFC.

Chapter 24

[1]Interview, Sharp. January 20, 1983, OHSFC.

[2]Minutes, O.U. Board of Regents, October 18, 1972.

[3]Interview, Eliel, November 4, 1982, OHSFC.

[4]Interview, Sharp, January 20, 1983, OHSFC.

[5]Herman Smith Associates, "Interim Report: Concerning Immediate and Long Range Recommendations for Financing, Management, Governance, Planning and Physical Development of the University of Oklahoma Hospitals," March 9, 1973, OHSF; Interview, Sharp, January 20, 1983, OHSFC.

[6]Smith Associates, "Interim Report," OHSF.

[7]Interview, Terrill, June 29, 1983, OHSFC.

[8]Smith Associates, "Interim Report," OHSF.

[9]*Ibid.*

[10]Interview, Sharp, January 20, 1983, OHSFC.

[11]Smith Associates, "Interim Report," OHSF.

[12]Interview, Dalston, July 7, 1983, OHSFC.

[13]Interview, Brawner, February 16, 1983, OHSFC.

[14]Oklahoma Department of Human Services, "Fiscal Year 1983 Statistical Report," DHS Publication No. 83-58, OHSF; Interview, McCune, January 11, 1983, OHSF.

[15]Smith Associates, "Interim Report," OHSF.

[16]Interview, West, October 28, 1982, OHSFC.

[17]Interview, Schilling, November 6, 1982, OHSFC.

[18]Interview, Sharp, January 20, 1983, OHSFC.

[19]Smith Associates, "Interim Report," OHSF.

[20]Interview, Sharp, January 20, 1983, OHSFC.

[21]Smith Associates, "Interim Report", OHSF.

[22]Oklahoma City Chamber of Commerce, "Position Paper on the University of Oklahoma Health Sciences Center (O.U. Medical Center), April, 1973, OHSF.

Chapter 25

[1]Interview, James A. Killackey, May 6, 1983, OHSFC.

[2]Interview, Tom Tucker, August 18, 1983, OHSFC.

[3]Interview, Davies, September 27, 1983, OHSFC.

[4]Interview, John Day Williams, May 18, 1983, OHSFC.

[5]Interview, Points, May 24, 1983, OHSFC.

[6]Interview, Sharp, January 20, 1983, OHSFC.

Chapter 26

[1]Interview, Dunlap, January 19, 1983, OHSFC.

[2]Interview, Rader, August 19, 1983, OHSFC.

[3]*Ibid.*

[4]*Daily Oklahoman*, April 26, 1973.

[5]*Daily Oklahoman*, April 18, 1973; Interview, Dunlap, January 19, 1983, OHSFC.

[6]Interview, Eliel, November 4, 1982, OHSFC.

[7]Interview, Dalston, July 7, 1983, OHSFC.

[8]Interview, Rader, August 19, 1983, OHSFC.

[9]Interview, Hubbard, March 1, 1983, OHSFC.

[10]*Daily Oklahoman*, May 24, 1973.

[11]Interview, Campbell, December 1, 1982, OHSFC.

[12]Interview, Tuttle, January 11, 1983, OHSFC.

[13]Interview, Troy, October 19, 1983, OHSFC.

[14]Interview, Halverstadt, November 14, 1983, OHSFC.

[15]*Daily Oklahoman*, February 2, 1974.

[16]Interview, Dean McGee, July 23, 1983, OHSFC.

Chapter 27

[1]*The National Observer*, January 25, 1971.
[2]*The Evening Star*, Washington, D.C., February 23, 1971; *The Washington Post*, February 23, 24, 1971.
[3]Archives, OHSF.
[4]Interview, Dan Macer, December 14, 1982, OHSFC.
[5]Interview, Rader, August 19, 1983, OHSFC.
[6]*Ibid.*
[7]Interview, Robert Douglass, September 1, 1983, OHSFC.
[8]Interview, Macer, September 1, 1983, OHSFC.
[9]Interview, Douglass, September 1, 1983, OHSFC.
[10]Interview, Rader, August 19, 1983, OHSFC.
[11]Interview, Macer, December 14, 1982, OHSFC.
[12]Interview, Douglass, September 1, 1983, OHSFC.
[13]Archives, Oklahoma City Chamber of Commerce.
[14]*Oklahoma Journal*, July 16, 1974.
[15]Interview, Scott, August 22, 1983; Interview, Tuttle, January 11, 1983, OHSFC.
[16]Interview, Douglass, September 1, 1983, OHSFC.
[17]Interview, Macer, December 14, 1982, OHSFC.
[18]*Oklahoma Journal*, July 16, 1974.
[19]Robert Douglass Associates, "Federal-State Sharing in the Oklahoma Health Center: Sharing Program Development Plan," 1975, OHSF.
[20]*Ibid.*
[21]*Sunday Oklahoman*, May 25, 1975.
[22]Oklahoma City Chamber of Commerce, Report II, "Developing a Vital Community Asset: Hospital Modernization and Expansion," December, 1969; *The Miami Herald*, Miami, Florida, May 9, 1975.
[23]*Oklahoma City Times*, October 9, 1974.
[24]*Daily Oklahoman*, February 14, 1975.
[25]*Sunday Oklahoman*, February 23, 1975.

Chapter 28

[1]Interview, William Stanhope, January 11, 1983, OHSFC.
[2]Interviews, Keith Wright, University of Oklahoma and Larry Hayes, State Regents for Higher Education, October 5, 1983.
[3]Interview, Mark Johnson, March 16, 1983, OHSFC.
[4]*Oklahoma Journal*, February 4, 1971.
[5]Interview, Steen, March 24, 1983, OHSFC.
[6]*Daily Oklahoman*, February 15, 1971.
[7]*Daily Oklahoman*, August 27, September 10, 1971.
[8]Interview, Philip Smith, May 31, 1983, OHSFC.
[9]Interview, Steen, March 24, 1983, OHSFC.
[10]Interview, Schottstaedt, March 27, 1983, OHSFC.
[11]Interview, Sharp, January 20, 1983, OHSFC.
[12]Interview, Schottstaedt, March 27, 1983, OHSFC.
[13]Interview, Philip Smith, May 31, 1983, OHSFC.
[14]Interview, Eliel, November 4, 1982, OHSFC.
[15]Interview, Schottstaedt, March 27, 1983, OHSFC.
[16]Interview, Sharp, January 20, 1983, OHSFC.
[17]*Oklahoma Journal*, September 26, 1974.
[18]Interview, Lynn, February 7, 1983, OHSFC.
[19]*Daily Oklahoman*, November 15, 1974.
[20]*Ibid.*
[21]Interview, William S. Banowsky, Ph.D., April 16, 1984, OHSFC.
[22]Interview, Gloria Smith, Ph.D., February 15, 1983, OHSFC.

Chapter 29

[1]*Daily Oklahoman*, January 29, 1973.
[2]*Ibid.*
[3]Interview, Hamilton, February 3, 1984, OHSFC.
[4]*Daily Oklahoman*, April 1, 1974.
[5]*Oklahoma Journal*, May 7, 1974.
[6]*Sunday Oklahoman*, May 26, 1974.
[7]*Daily Oklahoman*, May 24, 1974.
[8]*Daily Oklahoman*, June 6, 1974.
[9]Interview, William Brown, August 25, 1983, OHSFC.
[10]Interview, Rainey Williams, October 13, 1983, OHSFC.

[11]*Daily Oklahoman*, June 12, 1974.
[12]Interview, Rainey Williams, October 13, 1983, OHSFC.
[13]Interview, Lynn, February 7, 1983, OHSFC.
[14]Interview, Halverstadt, November 14, 1983, OHSFC; *Daily Oklahoman*, June 14, 1974.
[15]Interview, James A. Merrill, M.D., September 16, 1983, OHSFC.
[16]Interview, Halverstadt, November 14, 1983, OHSFC.
[17]*Daily Oklahoman*, June 19, 1974.
[18]Interview, Killackey, May 6, 1983, OHSFC.
[19]Interview, Audrey Clonce, November 1, 1983, OHSFC.
[20]*Daily Oklahoman*, July 12, 1974; Interview, Dalston, July 7, 1983, OHSFC.
[21]*Oklahoma Journal*, July 16, 1974; *Daily Oklahoman*, July 23, 1974.
[22]Interview, Harry Neer, October 27, 1983, OHSFC.
[23]*Daily Oklahoman*, August 9, 1974.
[24]*Daily Oklahoman*, December 16, 1974.
[25]*Daily Oklahoman*, January 10, 1975; Interview, Greggory Harmon, August 30, 1982, OHSFC.
[26]Interview, Donnell, April 30, 1983, OHSFC; *Oklahoma Journal*, February 22, 1975.
[27]*Daily Oklahoman*, February 18, March 21, 1975.
[28]*Daily Oklahoman*, June 6, 1975
[29]Interview, William G. Thurman, M.D., May 18, 1983, OHSFC.
[30]interview, Deckert, May 3, 1983, OHSFC.
[31]Interview, Thurman, May 18, 1983; Interview, Sharp, January 20, 1983, OHSFC.
[32]*Daily Oklahoman*, May 13, 26, 1975; Interview, Dalston, July 7, 1983, OHSFC.
[33]Interview, Sharp, January 20, 1983, OHSFC.
[34]Interview, Troy, October 19, 1983, OHSFC.
[35]Interview, Bruce Perry, August 8, 1983, OHSFC.

Chapter 30

[1]*Daily Oklahoman*, April 22, 1971.
[2]*Ibid.*
[3]*Ibid.*
[4]Interview, Eliel, November 4, 1982, OHSFC.
[5]*Daily Oklahoman*, September 8, 1971.
[6]Interview, Larry Rember, March 22, 1983, OHSFC.
[7]Interview, Eliel, November 4, 1982, OHSFC.
[8]Iterview, Sharp, January 20, 1983, OHSFC.
[9]Interview, Lynn, February 7, 1983, OHSFC.
[10]Interview, John A. Voorhees, D.O., October 12, 1983, OHSFC.
[11]TCMS, "Medical Education in Tulsa County", November, 1981.
[12]*Daily Oklahoman*, October 27, 1971.
[13]*Oklahoma City Times*, November 10, 1971.
[14]*Oklahoma City Times*, December 13, 1971.
[15]*The National Observer*, December 11, 1971; Interview, Wagner, June 24, 1983, OHSFC.
[16]TCMS, "Medical Education in Tulsa County", November, 1981.
[17]Interview, Dunlap, January 19, 1983, OHSFC.
[18]Interview, Willis, April 10, 1984, OHSFC.
[19]TCMS, "Medical Education in Tulsa County", November, 1981.
[20]Interview, Hamilton, February 3, 1984, OHSFC; *Daily Oklahoman*, February 2, 1972.
[21]Robert C. Hardy, "Health Maintenance Organization Study Project", Oklahoma Regional Medical Program, February 28-October 20, 1972, OHSF.
[22]Interview, Rainey Williams, October 13, 1983, OHSFC.
[23]Interview, Dennis, February 26, 1983, OHSFC.
[24]Robert C. Hardy, "How Many Physicians Does Oklahoma Need?", Oklahoma Health Sciences Foundation, June, 1973, OHSF.
[25]Interview, Sharp, January 20, 1983, OHSFC; Hardy, "How Many Physicians Does Oklahoma Need?"
[26]Interview, Schilling, November 6, 1982, OHSFC.
[27]Minutes, OHSF Executive Committee, July 6, 1973, OHSF.
[28]Interview, Dunlap, January 19, 1983, OHSFC.
[29]Interview, Hamilton, February 3, 1984, OHSFC.
[30]Interview, William A. Bell, March 21, 1983, OHSFC.
[31]Interview, Richardson, June 7, 1983, OHSFC.
[32]Interview, Troy, October 19, 1983, OHSFC.
[33]Robert C. Hardy, "The Need for More Dentists in Oklahoma", Oklahoma Health Sciences Foundation, March, 1974, OHSF.

[34]*Daily Oklahoman*, July 20, 1974; Interview, Lynn, February 7, 1983, OHSFC.
[35]*Daily Oklahoman*, April 27, 1975.
[36]*Daily Oklahoman*, April 30, 1975.

Chapter 31

[1]Archives, OHSF; Interview, Macer, December 14, 1982, OHSFC.
[2]Interview, Tuttle, January 11, 1983, OHSFC.
[3]*Oklahoma Journal*, April 17, 1971; Interview, Tuttle, January 11, 1983, OHSFC.
[4]*Ibid*.
[5]*Daily Oklahoman*, May 15, 1971.
[6]*Daily Oklahoman*, February 8, 1972; Interview, Reece McGee, January 21, 1983, OHSFC; *Sunday Oklahoman*, February 13, 1972; Interview, Harvey Everest, January 13, 1983, OHSFC.
[7]Archives, OHSF.
[8]Interview, James Tolbert III, May 5, 1983, OHSFC.
[9]*Daily Oklahoman*, August 16, 1972.
[10]Interview, Tolbert, May 5, 1983, OHSFC.
[11]Interview, Mayor Patience Latting, November 30, 1983, OHSFC.
[12]Interview, William Brown, August 25, 1983, OHSFC.
[13]*Ibid*.
[14]Interview, Steen, March 24, 1983, OHSFC.
[15]Interview, Schottstaedt, March 27, 1983, OHSFC.
[16]*Daily Oklahoman*, November 1, 1973.
[17]Interview, Don H. O'Donoghue, M.D., February 4, 1983, OHSFC.
[18]*Daily Oklahoman*, January 22, 1974.
[19]Interview, Dalston, July 7, 1983, OHSFC.
[20]*Daily Oklahoman*, March 21, 24, 1975.

Chapter 32

[1]*Daily Oklahoman*, September 7, 1970
[2]*Daily Oklahoman*, September 24, 25, October 6, 1970.
[3]Interview, Jack W. Shrode, October 21, 1983, OHSFC.
[4]Interview, Clemens, February 15, 1983, OHSFC.
[5]Interview, Harry Neer, October 27, 1983, OHSFC.
[6]*Daily Oklahoman*, August 11, 1973.
[7]*Daily Oklahoman*, August 7, 1974.
[8]Interview, Tuttle, January 11, 1983, OHSFC.
[9]*Daily Oklahoman*, November 30, December 2, 1974.
[10]Interview, Neer, October 27, 1983, OHSFC.

Chapter 33

[1]Minutes, OHSF Executive Committee, July 6, 1973, OHSF.
[2]Archives, Community Council of Greater Oklahoma City.
[3]*Daily Oklahoman*, September 13, 1973.
[4]Interview, Clay, September 20, 1984, OHSFC.
[5]Interview, Tullos Coston, M.D., August 19, 1983, OHSFC.
[6]Interview, Clay, September 20, 1984; Interview, Dean McGee, July 23, 1983, OHSFC.
[7]Minutes, OHSF Executive Committee, February 11, 1974, OHSF.
[8]Interview, Coston, August 19, 1983, OHSFC.
[9]Interview, Acers, January 27, 1983, OHSFC.
[10]Interview, Rees, January 10, 1984, OHSFC.
[11]Interview, Coston, August 19, 1983, OHSFC.
[12]Interview, Acers, January 27, 1983, OHSFC.

Chapter 34

[1]Interview, Troy, October 19, 1983, OHSFC.
[2]Interview, Rader, August 19, 1983, OHSFC.
[3]Interview, Perry, August 8, 1983, OHSFC.
[4]Interview, Michael T. McEwen, July 22, 1982, OHSFC.
[5]*Oklahoma*, Official Publication of the Oklahoma City Chamber of Commerce, July 21, 1977.
[6]Interview, Perry, August 8, 1983, OHSFC.
[7]Interview, Governor George Nigh, December 19, 1983, OHSFC.
[8]Interview, Perry, August 8, 1983; Interview, Willis, April 10, 1984, OHSFC.

[9]Interview, Representative Hannah D. Atkins, August 17, 1983; Interview, Representative Cleta Deatherage, January 4, 1984, OHSFC.
[10]Interview, Perry, August 8, 1983, OHSFC.
[11]Interview, Tucker, August 18, 1983, OHSFC.
[12]*Ibid*.
[13]Interview, Deatherage, January 4, 1984, OHSFC.
[14]Interview, Dee A. Replogle, September 20, 1983, OHSFC.
[15]Interview, David Walters, December 16, 1982. OHSFC.
[16]Interview, Deatherage, January 4, 1984, OHSFC.
[17]Interview, Walters, December 16, 1982, OHSFC.
[18]Interview, McEwen, July 22, 1982, OHSFC.
[19]Interview, Everett, April 22, 1983, OHSFC.
[20]Interview, Troy, October 19, 1983, OHSFC.
[21]Interview, Deatherage, January 4, 1984, OHSFC.
[22]Interview, Willis, April 10, 1984, OHSFC.
[23]Interview, Rader, August 19, 1983, OHSFC.
[24]Interview, Tucker, August 18, 1983, OHSFC.
[25]Interview, Nigh, December 19, 1983, OHSFC.

Chapter 35

[1]Interview, Douglass, September 1, 1983, OHSFC.
[2]Letter to Dan Macer from Stanton L. Young, September 19, 1974, OHSF.
[3]Interview, Douglass, September 1, 1983, OHSFC.
[4]Letter to Dr. Paul Sharp from Chancellor E. T. Dunlap, April 19, 1977, OHSF.
[5]Interview, Douglass, September 1, 1983, OHSFC.
[6]Minutes, Human Services Mini-Cabinet, April 25, 1977, OHSF.
[7]Interview, Douglass, September 1, 1983, OHSFC.
[8]Interview, John Chase, M.D., November 5, 1982, OHSFC.
[9]Interview, Macer, December 14, 1982, OHSFC.
[10]Interview, Douglass, September 1, 1983, OHSFC.
[11]Interview, Macer, December 14, 1982, OHSFC.
[12]Interview, Douglass, September 1, 1983, OHSFC.
[13]Interview, Macer, December 14, 1982, OHSFC.
[14]Interview, Douglass, September 1, 1983, OHSFC.

Chapter 36

[1]Interview, Thurman, May 18, 1983, OHSFC.
[2]Interview, Harris D. "Pete" Riley, M.D., September 15, 1983, OHSFC.
[3]Interview, Thurman, May 18, 1983, OHSFC.
[4]Interview, James F. Hammarsten, M.D., April 19, 1984, OHSFC.
[5]Interview, Woods, June 24, 1983, OHSFC.
[6]Interview, Walters, December 16, 1982, OHSFC.
[7]Interview, Stanhope, January 10, 1983, OHSFC.
[8]Interview, Rodney Ice, Ph.D., November 8, 1983, OHSFC.
[9]*Ibid*.
[10]Interview, Clayton Rich, M.D., June 15, 1982.
[11]Interview, Charles McCall, M.D., June 10, 1984.
[12]Interview, William E. Brown, June 11, 1982.
[13]Interview, Gloria Smith, June 11, 1982.
[14]Interview, Philip Smith, June 11, 1982
[15]Interview, Nigh, December 19, 1983, OHSFC; Interview, Richard Shough, Ph.D., June 8, 1982.
[16]Interview, Peter Levin, Ph.D., June 8, 1982.
[17]Interview, Ralph Daniels, Ph.D., June 10, 1982.
[18]*Daily Oklahoman*, July 22, 1982; Interview, Banowsky, April 16, 1984, OHSFC.
[19]Interview, Wayne Beal, August 4, 1982, OHSFC.
[20]Interview, Jeanie Taller Marshall, January 26, 1983, OHSFC.
[21]Interview, Gale Adams, PH.D., February 1, 1983, OHSFC.

Chapter 37

[1]Interview, Dean McGee, July 23, 1983; Interview, Clay, September 20, 1984, OHSFC.
[2]Interview, Clay, September 20, 1984, OHSFC.
[3]Interview, John W. "Jack" Records, M.D., October 27, 1983, OHSFC.
[4]Interview, Neer, October 27, 1983, OHSFC.
[5]Interview, Ellis, April 19, 1983, OHSFC.

[6]Robert L. Nichols, Michael T. McEwen and Karen V. Waddell, "Project OMC: A Three-Year Plan Commencing October 1, 1978", OHSF.

[7]Interview, Records, October 27, 1983, OHSFC.

Chapter 38

[1]Gruen Associates, Inc., "Central City Plan—Oklahoma City", prepared for the Oklahoma City Urban Renewal Authority, February, 1975.

[2]Interview, Harvey Everest, January 13, 1983, OHSFC.

[3]Interview, Sharp, January 20, 1983, OHSFC.

[4]Interview, Murphy, March 7, 1983, OHSFC.

[5]Interview, Julia Brown, August 25, 1983, OHSFC.

[6]Ibid.

[7]Interview, Murphy, March 7, 1983, OHSFC.

[8]Ibid.

[9]"Conciliation Agreement between the Oklahoma Department of Transportation (ODOT) and the U.S. Department of Transportation (USDOT)"—In the Matter of: Kay Ahaus vs Oklahoma Department of Transportation, Complaint No. 78-530, Revised 10-12-79, OHSF.

[10]Interview, Julia Brown, August 25, 1983, OHSFC.

[11]Ibid.

[12]The American City Corporation, "Development Program and Strategy for the Harrison-Walnut Neighborhood, Oklahoma City, Oklahoma", December, 1981, OHSF.

[13]Interview, Cox, June 3, 1983, OHSFC.

Chapter 39

[1]U.S. Department of Health and Human Services, "Report of the Graduate Medical Education National Advisory Committee,"September 30, 1980.

[2]TCMS, "Medical Education in Tulsa County," November 1981, OHSF; Interview, Spears, March 3, 1983, OHSFC.

[3]Interview, Spears, March 3, 1983, OHSFC.

[4]Harry Schwartz, "The Shortage of Patients," Private Practice, Volume 13, Number 10, October, 1981; U. S. Bureau of the Census, Statistical Abstract of the United States: 1982-83, (103d Edition), Washington, D.C., 1982, p.109.

Chapter 40

[1]Interview, William E. Brown, August 25, 1983, OHSFC.

[2]Interview, Scott, August 22, 1983, OHSFC.

[3]Interview, John R. "Jack" Sokatch, Ph.D., March 2,1983, OHSFC.

[4]Interview, Gloria Smith, February 25, 1983, OHSFC.

[5]Interview, Walter Whitcomb, M.D., July 25, 1983, OHSFC.

[6]Archives, Oklahoma City Chamber of Commerce.

[7]Saturday Oklahoman and Times, January 7, 1984

Chapter 41

[1]Business Week, August 2, 1982.

[2]Wall Street Journal, April 12, 1984.

[3]Interview, Bellmon, October 13, 1983, OHSFC; Interview, Troy, October 19, 1983, OHSFC.

[4]Interview, Bellmon, October 13, 1983, OHSFC.

[5]Data provided by David L. Branson, OTH Finance, December 28, 1983; Oklahoma City Times, February 11, 1983.

[6]Interview, Tucker, August 18, 1983, OHSFC.

[7]Branson, OTH Finance, December 28, 1983.

[8]Interview, Troy, October 19, 1983, OHSFC; Oklahoma Observer, June 25, 1983.

[9]Interview, Deckert, May 3, 1983, OHSFC.

[10]Interview, Deatherage, January 4, 1984, OHSFC.

[11]Interview, Robert Fulton, April 3, 1984, OHSFC.

[12]Interview, Murphy, March 7, 1983, OHSFC.

[13]Interview, Julia Brown, November 22, 1983, OHSFC.

[14]Interview, Ice, November 8, 1983, OHSFC.

[15]Interview, Barton Boyle, August 16, 1983, OHSFC.

[16]Interview, Halverstadt, November 14, 1983, OHSFC.

[17]Oklahoma City Times, November 30, 1983.

Chapter 42

[1]Interview, Clayton Rich, M.D., January 23, 1984, OHSFC.

[2]Interview, Charles McCall, M.D., January 26, 1984, OHSFC.

[3]Interview, Rader, November ll, 1983, OHSFC.

[4]Daily Oklahoman, January 31, February 10, 1984.

[5]Interview, Deatherage, January 4, 1984, OHSFC.

[6]Ernst and Whinney, "Operations Appraisal of Department of Human Services, Oklahoma Teaching Hospitals (OTH)," December, 1983, OHSF.

[7]Interview, John Byrne, May 21, 1984.

[8]Daily Oklahoman/Times, May 15, 1984.

[9]Interview, Fulton, April 3, 1984, OHSFC; Interview, David Walters, May 14, 1984.

[10]Interview, Everett, April 22, 1983, May 8, 1984.

[11]Daily Oklahoman/Times, April 17, 19, 1984.

[12]Interview, Banowsky, April 16, 1984, OHSFC.

[13]Interview, Willis, April 10, 1984, OHSFC.

Chapter 43

[1]Interview, Lynn, February 7, 1983, OHSFC.

[2]C.S. Lewis, Jr., M.D., Hugh D. Tidler and Mary Piscitello, "Medical Manpower in Oklahoma in the Decade of the Eighties", The Journal of the Oklahoma State Medical Association, April, 1983, Volume 76, pp. 94-101.

[3]TCMS, "Medical Education in Tulsa County", November, 1981, OHSF.

[4]Interview, David Bickham, February 2, 1984, OHSFC.

[5]Wall Street Journal, March 13, 1984; Daily Oklahoman/Times, March 26, 1984.

[6]Interview, Bickham, February 2, 1984, OHSFC.

[7]Interview, Rainey Williams, October 13, 1983, OHSFC.

[8]Interview, McCall, January 26, 1984, OHSFC.

[9]Interview, Merrill, September 16, 1983, OHSFC.

[10]Ibid.

[11]Interview, Everett, April 22, 1983, OHSFC.

[12]Interview, Ralph Morgan, April 15, 1983, OHSFC.

[13]Interview, Merrill, September 16, 1983, OHSFC.

[14]Interview, Willis, April 10, 1984, OHSFC.

[15]Interview, Donnell, April 30, 1983, OHSFC.

[16]Interview, Donald Phelps, March 13, 1984.

[17]Interview, Troy, October 19, 1983, OHSFC.

[18]Physician Manpower Training Commission, "Overview of the Physician Manpower Training Commission Program and Related Accomplishments", November 1, 1983.

[19]Archives, Physician Manpower Training Commission.

[20]Interview, William S. Banowsky, Ph. D., April 16, 1984, OHSFC.

[21]Interview, Morgan, April 15, 1983, OHSFC.

Chapter 44

[1]Interview, Chrislip, December 8, 1982, OHSFC.

[2]Interview, Bellmon, October 13, 1983, OHSFC.

[3]Interview, Cleve Rodgers, May 16, 1984.

[4]Sunday Oklahoman, July 17, 1983; Saturday Oklahoman and Times, May 12, 1984.

[5]Daily Oklahoman, January 18, 1984.

[6]Sunday Oklahoman, April 24, 1983.

[7]Interview, Lynn, February 7, 1983, OHSFC.

[8]Business Week, July 25, 1983.

[9]Daily Oklahoman, December 6, 1983; Sunday Oklahoman, March 4, 1984.

[10]Daily Oklahoman, May 25, 1983.

[11]Interview, Latting, November 30, 1983, OHSFC.

[12]Interview, Banowsky, April 16, 1984, OHSFC.

[13]Interview, James L. Henry, March 9, 1983, OHSFC.

[14]Interview, Steen, March 24, 1983, OHSFC.

[15]Interview, Dennis McGrath, May 18, 1984; Interview, Neer, October 27, 1983, OHSFC.
[16]*Daily Oklahoman*, October 20, 1983.
[17]*Daily Oklahoman/Times*, July 16, 1984.
[18]*Business Week*, March 5, 1984, *Daily Oklahoman*, April 3, 1984.
[19]Interview, Wayne Coventon, May 16, 1984, OHSFC.
[20]*Daily Oklahoman/Times*, April 24, 1984.
[21]Interview, Records, October 27, 1983, OHSFC.
[22]*Daily Oklahoman/Times*, May 24, 1984.
[23]Interview, Donnell, April 30, 1983, OHSFC.
[24]*Business Week*, July 25, 1983.

Chapter 45

[1]Interview, Donald L. Graves, M.D., August 4, 1984, OHSFC.
[2]Interview, Stanhope, January 10, 1983, OHSFC.
[3]Interview, Dan Fox, P.A., May 8, 1984, OHSFC.
[4]*Ibid.*
[5]Interview, Shook, August 23, 1982, OHSFC.
[6]Interview, West, October 28, 1982, OHSFC.
[7]Edward N. Brandt, Jr., M.D., Assistant Secretary for Health, U. S. Department of Health and Human Services, "Should Health Care Costs Be Lower—Or Higher?" Presented to the combined Oklahoma Health Sciences Foundation - Oklahoma City Chamber of Commerce luncheon, August 4, 1983, OHSF.
[8]Interview, Rainey Williams, October 13, 1983, OHSFC.
[9]Interview, Charles McCall, January 26, 1984, OHSFC.

[10]Interview, Christian Ramsey, M.D., January 26, 1984; Interview, Walters, December 16, 1982, OHSFC.
[11]Interview, William E. Brown, August 25, 1983, OHSFC.
[12]Interview, Lorraine Singer, R.N., January 9, 1984, OHSFC.
[13]Interview, Waddle, March 9, 1983, OHSFC.
[14]Interview, Peter Levin, Sc. D., December 13, 1983, OHSFC.
[15]Interview, Lee Holder, Ph.D., May 3, 1984, OHSFC.
[16]Interview, H. Richard Shough, Ph.D., June 1, 1984, OHSFC.
[17]Interview, Rich, January 23, 1984, OHSFC.
[18]Interview, Banowsky, April 16, 1984, OHSFC.
[19]Interview, Reagan Bradford, Ph.D., M.D., December 28, 1983, OHSFC.
[20]Interview, Thurman, May 18, 1983, OHSFC.
[21]Interview, Dean McGee, July 23, 1983, OHSFC.
[22]Interview, Acers, January 27, 1983, OHSFC.
[23]Interview, Whitcomb, July 25, 1983, OHSFC.
[24]Interview, Joan Leavitt, M.D., September 26, 1983, OHSFC.
[25]Interview, Coventon, May 16, 1984, OHSFC.
[26]Interview, Stanton L. Young, June 6, 1984, OHSFC.
[27]Interview, Dean McGee, July 23, 1983, OHSFC.

Chapter 46

[1]Interview, Neer, October 27, 1983, OHSFC.
[2]Interview, Bell, March 21, 1983, OHSFC.
[3]Interview, William E. Brown, August 25, 1983, OHSFC.
[4]Interview, Rees, January 10, 1984, OHSFC.
[5]Interview, Sharp, January 20, 1983, OHSFC.

BIBLIOGRAPHY

Interviews

Oklahoma Health Sciences Foundation Collection

Acers, Thomas E., M..D., January 27, 1983, Oklahoma City
Adams, Gale, Ph.D., February 1, 1983, Oklahoma City
Atkins, Hannah D., August 17, 1983, Oklahoma City
Baggett, Bryce, January 26, 1983, Oklahoma City
Banowsky, William S., Ph.D., April 16, 1984, Oklahoma City
Beal, Wayne, August 4, 1982, Oklahoma City
Bell, William A., March 21, 1983, Oklahoma City
Bellmon, Henry, October 13, 1983, Edmond, Oklahoma
Benham, David, April 21, 1983, Oklahoma City, Telephone
Bennett, Charles L., October 25, 1983, Colorado Springs, Colorado, Telephone
Bennett, Roger, November 5, 1982, Seattle, Washington
Bickham, David, February 2, 1984, Oklahoma City
Blair, Bill J., January 12, 1983, Oklahoma City
Boyd, Jack, February 4, 1983, Oklahoma City
Boyle, Barton, August 16, 1983, Oklahoma City
Bradford, Reagan, Ph.D., M.D., December 28, 1983, Oklahoma City
Brandt, Edward N., Jr., M.D., Ph.D., August 4, 1983, Oklahoma City
Brawner, Larry, February 16, 1983, Oklahoma City
Bremkamp, Gloria, February 11, 1983, Oklahoma City
Brown, Julia, August 25, 1983, Oklahoma City
Brown, William E., D.D.S., August 25, 1983, Oklahoma City
Bruhn, John, Ph.D., March 28, 1983, Galveston, Texas
Bynam, W. Turner, M.D., April 25, 1983, Oklahoma City
Byrne, John, May 21, 1984, Oklahoma City
Campbell, William, December 1, 1982, Oklahoma City
Carpenter, LeRoy, M.D., May 11, 1983, Oklahoma City
Chandler, Phillip P., Ph.D., September 6, 1983, Oklahoma City, Telephone
Chase, John, M.D., November 5, 1982, Seattle, Washington
Chrislip, H. Dean, December 8, 1982, Oklahoma City
Clay, Richard A., M.D., September 20, 1984, Oklahoma City
Clemens, Ted, M.D., February 15, 1983, Oklahoma City
Clonce, Audrey, November 1, 1983, Arkansas, Telephone
Coletta, Sister Mary, September 7, 1982, Oklahoma City
Coston, Tullos, M.D., August 19, 1983, Oklahoma City
Coventon, Wayne, May 16, 1984, Oklahoma City
Cox, Frank B., Jr., D.D.S., June 3, 1983, Oklahoma City
Crews, Raymond, February 23, 1984, Norman, Oklahoma
Cross, George L., Ph.D., March 8, 1983, Norman, Oklahoma
Dalston, Jeptha, Ph.D., July 7, 1983, Ann Arbor, Michigan; August 5, 1983, Oklahoma City
Daniels, Ralph, Ph.D., June 10, 1982, Oklahoma City
Davies, Nancy, September 27, 1983, Enid, Oklahoma
Deatherage, Cleta, January 4, 1984, Oklahoma City
DeCair, Charlotte, June 3, 1983, Oklahoma City
Deckert, Gordon H., M.D., May 3, 1983, Oklahoma City
Dennis, James L., M.D., February 26, 1983, Little Rock, Ark.; July 10, 1983, Little Rock, Arkansas
Donnell, Albert M., April 30, 1983, Duncan, Oklahoma
Douglass, Robert, September 1, 1983, Oklahoma City
Dunlap, E.T., Ed. D., January 19, 1983, February , 1, 1983, March 1, 1983, Oklahoma City
Eliel, Leonard, M.D., November 4, 1982, Tacoma, Washington
Ellis, Robert S., M.D., April 19, 1983, Oklahoma City

Everest, Harvey, January 13, 1983, Oklahoma City
Everett, Mark Allen, M.D., April 22, 1983, Oklahoma City
Fox, Dan, May 8, 1984, Oklahoma City
Fulton, Robert, April 3, 1984, Oklahoma City
Gorsline, Lester, October 29, 1982, Half Moon Bay, California
Graves, Donald L., M.D., August 4, 1984, Wakita, Oklahoma
Groom, Dale, M.D., March 29, 1983, Rockport, Texas
Gunn, C.G., M.D., March 2, 1983, Oklahoma City
Halverstadt, Donald B., M.D., November 14, 1983, Oklahoma City
Hamilton, James, February 3, 1984, Poteau, Oklahoma
Hammarsten, James F., M.D., April 14, 1984, Boise, Idaho, Telephone
Harmon, Greggory, August 30, 1982, Oklahoma City
Hayes, Larry, October 5, 1983, Oklahoma City, Telephone
Heller, Ben, M.D., October 30, 1982, Carmel by the Sea, California
Henry, James L., March 9, 1983, Oklahoma City
Hirschi, Robert G., D.D.S., February 21, 1983, Oklahoma City
Holder, Lee, Ph.D., May 3, 1984, Oklahoma City
Hollomon, J. Herbert, Ph.D., June 29, 1983, Brookline, Massachusetts
Howard, Winston, May 12, 1983, Oklahoma City, Telephone
Hubbard, Jenell, R.N., March 1, 1983, Oklahoma City
Ice, Rodney, Ph.D., November 8, 1983, Edmond, Oklahoma
Johnson, B. Connor, Ph.D., December 22, 1982, Oklahoma City
Johnson, Mark R., M.D., March 16, 1983, Oklahoma City
Killackey, James A., May 6, 1983, Oklahoma City
Lackey, Lawrence, June 15, 1983, San Rafael, California, Telephone
Latting, Patience, November 30, 1983, Oklahoma City
Leavitt, Joan, M.D., September 26, 1983, Oklahoma City
Levin, Peter, Ph.D., June 8, 1982, December 13, 1983, Oklahoma City
Lienke, Roger, M.D., April 5, 1983, Oklahoma City
Lynn, Thomas A., M.D., February 7, 1983, Oklahoma City
Lyons, Frank, April 22, 1983, Oklahoma City
Macer, Dan, December 14, 1982, Oklahoma City
Marshall, Jeanie Taller, January 26, 1983, Oklahoma City
Merrill, James A., M.D., September 16, 1983, Oklahoma City
Morgan, Ralph, April 15, 1983, Oklahoma City
Mosley, Kirk, M.D., May 18, 1983, Enid, Oklahoma
Murphy, Monty C., March 7, 1983, Oklahoma City
McCall, Charles, M.D., January 26, 1984, Oklahoma City
McCall, Goldie, June 1, 1983, Oklahoma City
McCune, John, January 11, 1983, Oklahoma City
McEwen, Michael T., July 22, 1982, Oklahoma City
McGee, Dean A., July 23, 1983, Oklahoma City
McGee, Reece, January 21, 1983, Yukon, Oklahoma
McGrath, Dennis, May 18, 1984, Oklahoma City, Telephone
Neer, Harry, October 27, 1983, Oklahoma City
Nigh, George, December 19, 1983, Oklahoma City
O'Donoghue, Don H., M.D., February 4, 1983, Oklahoma City
Parry, William L., M.D., January 9, 1984, Oklahoma City
Parsons, Oscar, Ph.D., April 20, 1983, Oklahoma City
Perry, Bruce, August 8, 1983, Oklahoma City
Peter, Claribel, July 22, 1983, Oklahoma City

Phelps, Donald, March 13, 1984, Waurika, Oklahoma, Telephone
Phelps, Malcom E., M.D., April 21, 1983, El Reno, Oklahoma, Telephone
Rader, Lloyd E., August 19, 1983, November 11, 1983, Oklahoma City
Ramsey, Christian, M.D., January 26, 1984, Oklahoma City
Records, John W., M.D., October 27, 1983, Oklahoma City
Rees, Frank, January 10, 1984, Oklahoma City
Rember, Larry, March 22, 1983, Oklahoma City
Replogle, Dee A., September 20, 1983, Oklahoma City
Rich, Clayton, M.D., January 23, 1984, Oklahoma City
Richardson, Robert E. Lee, June 7, 1983, Norman, Oklahoma
Riley, Harris D., M. D., September 15, 1983, Oklahoma City
Rogers, Cleve, May 16, 1984, Oklahoma City
Schilling, John A., M.D., November 6, 1982, Seattle, Washington
Schottstaedt, William W., M.D., March 27, 1983, Galveston, Texas
Scott, Vernon L., Sc.D., August 22, 1983, Oklahoma City
Sharp, Paul, Ph.D., January 20, 1983, January 24, 1983, Norman, Oklahoma
Shrode, Jack W., October 21, 1983, Lake Tenkiller, Oklahoma
Shook, Boyd, M.D., August 23, 1982, Oklahoma City
Shough, Richard, Ph.D., June 8, 1982, June 1, 1984, Oklahoma City
Singer, Lorraine, R.N., January 9, 1984, Oklahoma City
Smith, Gloria, Ph.D., February 15, 1983, Oklahoma City
Smith, Philip, Sc.D., May 31, 1983, Oklahoma City
Sokatch, John R., Ph.D., March 2, 1983, Oklahoma City
Spears, Jack, March 3, 1983, Tulsa, Oklahoma
Stanhope, William, January 11, 1983, Oklahoma City
Stansberry, Richard D., M.D., June 8, 1983, Oklahoma City
Steen, W. David, Ph.D., March 24, 1983, Oklahoma City
Strasbaugh, Paul, December 29, 1982, Oklahoma City
Swingle, Joyce, April 19, 1983, Oklahoma City
Terrill, Robert C., June 29, 1983, Newton, Massachusetts
Thurman, William G., M.D., May 18, 1983, Oklahoma City
Tolbert, James, III, May 5, 1983, Oklahoma City
Troy, Frosty, October 19, 1983, Oklahoma City
Tucker, Tom, August 18, 1983, January 11, 1984, Oklahoma City
Tuttle, Arthur, January 11, 1983, Oklahoma City
Voohees, John A., D.O., October 12, 1983, Oklahoma City
Waddle, Frances I., R.N., March 9, 1983, Oklahoma City
Wagner, Charles, June 24, 1983, Bethesda, Maryland
Walters, David, December 16, 1982, January 18, 1984, Oklahoma City
West, Louis Jolyon, M.D., October 28, 1982, Los Angeles, California
Whitcomb, Walter H., M.D., July 25, 1983, Oklahoma City
White, Gene, January 14, 1983, Oklahoma City
White, James B., January 6, 1983, Oklahoma City
White, Joseph M., M.D., April 29, 1983, Dallas, Texas
Williams, G. Rainey, M.D., October 13, 1983, Oklahoma City
Williams, John Day, May 18, 1983, Wakita, Oklahoma
Willis, William P., April 10, 1984, Oklahoma City
Wolf, Stewart George, M.D., June 27, 1983, Totts Gap, Pennsylvania
Woods, James W., Ph.D., June 24, 1983, Bethesda, Maryland
Wright, Keith, October 5, 1983, Oklahoma City, Telephone
Young, E. W., M.D., March 23, 1983, Oklahoma City
Young, Stanton L., June 6, 1984, Oklahoma City

Newspapers
Daily Oklahoman, Oklahoma City, Oklahoma
Oklahoma City Times, Oklahoma City, Oklahoma
Oklahoma Journal, Midwest City, Oklahoma
Sunday Oklahoman, Oklahoma City, Oklahoma
Washington Post, Washington, D.C.
Evening Star, Washington, D.C.
Miami Herald, Miami, Florida
Wall Street Journal, New York, N.Y.
Oklahoma Observer, Oklahoma City, Oklahoma
Denver Post, Denver, Colorado
Oklahoma Daily, Norman, Oklahoma
National Observer, Washington, D. C.
Tulsa Tribune, Tulsa, Oklahoma
Saturday Oklahoman and Times, Oklahoma City
Daily Oklahoman/Times, Oklahoma City

Published Materials
American Hospital Association. *Hospitals—Guide Issue* 1968. Journal of the American Hospital Association, Chicago, Illinois.
Brady, Raymond E., Editor. *The 1968 Sooner Medic*. Oklahoma City: Student Council, University of Oklahoma School of Medicine.
Blumberg, Mark S. *Trends and Projections of Physicians in the United States, 1967-2002*. Berkeley, California.
Carnegie Commission on Higher Education, 1971.
Business Week. New York, N.Y. August 2, 1982, July 25, 1983, March 5, 1984.
Carnegie Commission on the Future of Higher Education. *Higher Education and the Nation's Health; Policies for Medical and Dental Education, A Special Report and Recommendations*. New York: McGraw Hill, October, 1970.
Christenson, Gordon A. *The Future of the University*. Norman: The University of Oklahoma Press, 1969.
Douglass, Robert, Associates. "Federal-State Sharing in the Oklahoma Health Center—Sharing Program Development Plan" 1975.
Everett, Mark R. *Medical Education in Oklahoma*, 2 vols. 1900-1931 and 1932-1964 Norman: University of Oklahoma Press, 1972 and 1980.
_____. *Pioneering for Research: Origin of the Oklahoma Medical Research Foundation* Oklahoma City: University of Oklahoma Medical Center, 1966
Ezell, John Samuel. *Innovations in Energy, The Story of Kerr McGee*. Norman: University of Oklahoma Press, 1979
Gorsline, Lester, Associates—Lackey, Lawrence, and Associates. *The Oklahoma Health Center Development Plan, 1968*.
Gruen Associates, Inc. *Central City Plan: Oklahoma City*. Oklahoma City Urban Renewal Authority, February, 1975.
Lewis, C.S., Jr., M.D., Tidler, Hugh D. and Piscitello, Mary. "Medical Manpower in Oklahoma in the Decade of the Eighties," *The Journal of the Oklahoma Medical Association*, April 1983, Vol. 76.
National Commission on Community Health Services. *Health is a Community Affair*. Cambridge: Harvard University Press, 1966.
Oklahoma Regents for Higher Education. "Medical Education in Oklahoma" June, 1965.
Oklahoma Medical Research Foundation. "Research. A Continuing Challenge for a Better Tomorrow," 1966.
Oklahoma City Chamber of Commerce. "Developing a Vital Community Asset: Hospital Modernization and Expansion," Report I—June 19, 1969. Report II—December, 1969.
_____. "Position Paper on the University of Oklahoma Health Sciences Center (O.U. Medical Center) April, 1973.
_____. *OKLAHOMA*. Official publication of the Oklahoma City Chamber of Commerce, July 21, 1977.

Oklahoma Department of Human Services. "Fiscal Year 1983 Statistical Report." DHS Publication No. 83-58.

Points, Thomas C., M.D., Ph.D. *The Wakita Story*. Oklahoma City: University of Oklahoma School of Medicine.

Schwartz, Harry. "The Shortage of Patients," *Private Practice*, Vol. 13, No. 10, October, 1981.

Tulsa County Medical Society. Study Commission on Medical Education. "Medical Education in Tulsa County." November, 1981.

Tyson, C.N., Thomas, J.H., and Faulk, O.B. *The McMan: The Lives of Robert M. McFarlin and James A. Chapman*. Oklahoma City: Oklahoma Heritage Association, 1977.

U.S. Department of Health and Human Services. "Report of the Graduate Medical Education National Advisory Committee" GMENAC). September 30, 1980.

U.S. Bureau of the Census. *Statistical Abstract of the United States: 1982-83*. 103d Edition. Washington, D.C. 1982 West, L.J., Pierce, C.M. and Thomas, W.D. "Lysergic acid Diethlamide: Its Effects on a Male Asiatic Elephant." *Science*, Vol. 138, 1962.

Wright, Peggy Quinn and Faulk, Odie B. *Coletta: A Sister of Mercy*. Oklahoma City: Oklahoma Heritage Association, 1981.

Other Materials

American City Corporation. "Development Program and Strategy for the Harrison-Walnut Neighborhood, Oklahoma City, Oklahoma." Columbia, Maryland: December, 1981.

Brandt, Edward N., Jr., M.D., Ph.D. "Should Health Care Costs Be Lower— Or Higher?" Address to combined meeting of the Oklahoma Health Sciences Foundation and the Oklahoma City Chamber of Commerce, Oklahoma City, August 4, 1983.

Boren, Governor David. Human Services Mini-Cabinet. Minutes, April 25, 1977.

Dunlap, E.T., Ed. D. Letter to Dr. Paul Sharp, April 19, 1977.

Ernst and Whinney. "Operations Appraisal of Department of Human Services, Oklahoma Teaching Hospitals (OTH)." December, 1983.

Hardy, Robert C. "Health Maintenance Organization Study." Oklahoma Regional Medical Program, February 28-October 20, 1972.

_____. "How Many Physicians Does Oklahoma Need?" Oklahoma Health Sciences Foundation, June, 1973.

_____. "The Need For More Dentists In Oklahoma." Oklahoma Health Sciences Foundation, March, 1974.

Nichols, Robert L., McEwen, Michael T. and Waddell, Karen V. "Project OMC: A Three Year Plan Commencing October 1, 1978.

Oklahoma City Urban Renewal Authority. "Urban Renewal: The First Dozen Years" 1974.

Oklahoma Department of Transportation. "Conciliation Agreement between the Oklahoma Department of Transportation (ODOT) and the U.S. Department of Transportation (USDOT)"—In the Matter of: Kay Ahaus vs Oklahoma Department of Transportation, Complaint No. 78-530, Revised October 12, 1979.

Oklahoma Health Sciences Foundation. "Proposed 'Umbrella' Foundation for the Oklahoma Health Center, July, 1965. Articles of Incorporation, December 15, 1965. Minutes, Board of Trustees, 1966-1984. Minutes, Executive Committee, 1966-1984. Minutes, Operations Committee, 1966 1973.

Oklahoma State Board of Medical Examiners. Physician Statistics.

Oklahoma Teaching Hospitals. Financial data provided by David L. Branson.

University of Oklahoma Board of Regents. Minutes.

Physician Manpower Training Commission, State of Oklahoma. "Overview of the Physician Manpower Training Commission and Related Accomplishments" November 1, 1983.

Richardson, Robert E. Lee and Sturges, John W. "Study of the University of Oklahoma Health Sciences Center," February, 1973.

Smith, Herman, Associates. "Interim Report: Concerning Immediate and Long Range Recommendations for Financing, Management, Governance, Planning and Physical Development of the University of Oklahoma Hospitals," March 9, 1973.

Young, Stanton L. Letter to Dan Macer, September 19, 1974.

INDEX